# Multitarget - Multisensor Tracking: Applications and Advances

# Volume II

For a complete listing of the *Artech House Radar Library*,
turn to the back of this book . . .

# Multitarget - Multisensor Tracking: Applications and Advances

# Volume II

## Yaakov Bar-Shalom
### Editor

Artech House
Boston • London

**Library of Congress Cataloging-in-Publication Data**
(Revised for Vol. 2)

Multitarget-multisensor tracking.
    "This book is an outgrowth of the series of short courses titled Multitarget-multisensor
tracking: advanced applications, held at UCLA Extension"–Pref., v. 1.
    Includes bibliographical references and index.
    Contents: [1] Advanced applications–v. 2. Applications and advances.  1.Tracking
radar.  2. Radar–Data processing.  I. Bar-Shalom, Yaakov.  II. University of California,
Los Angeles.  University Extension.
TK6580.M85 1989   621.3848          89-27459
ISBN 0-89006-377-X (v. 1)
ISBN 0-89006-517-9  (v. 2)


**British Library Cataloguing in Publication Data**

Multitarget-multisensor tracking: applications and advances.
    I. Bar-Shalom, Yaakov, 1941-
    621.3848


ISBN  0-89006-517-9


© 1992   ARTECH HOUSE, INC.
685 Canton Street
Norwood, MA 02062

**International Standard Book Number: 0-89006-517-9**
**Library of Congress Catalog Card Number: 89-27459**

10   9    8    7    6    5    4    3    2    1

# CONTENTS

# *PREFACE*

This volume, a follow-up to a 1990 book with a similar title, contains several chapters based on new topics offered in the ongoing series of short courses entitled "Multitarget-Multisensor Tracking and Surveillance" held at UCLA Extension, as well as other relevant contributions by leading national and international experts in the field. The editor is indebted to the contributors for their patience in going through several revisions following editorial and technical reviews. The reviewers' comments definitely have helped to clarify certain points as well as to make the contributions more relevant to practicing engineers and scientists.

We hope to have succeeded in presenting a compilation of the latest techniques that will prove to be useful for those involved in designing future advanced systems for tracking, surveillance, and navigation (and, possibly, some other areas as well that we did not anticipate, such as the emerging application of data association to contour estimation in image processing).

The number of contributions is also a reflection of the fact that the field continues to evolve and, in the opinion of this writer and several colleagues, is still in need of further advances. Very large scale problems (with hundreds of targets) at one time were believed to be close to trivial, but now some of them appear closer to impossible unless very simple algorithms are used, in which case the performance might not be adequate. The issue of performance evaluation is still far from being solved, even though some recent progress in that area is reported in this volume.

The editor would like to express his continued appreciation for the long-standing support from ONR—in particular, to James G. Smith and, for more recent support, to Dr. R. Madan.

Recent events have shown the value of systems capable of accurate target tracking, whether they involve a precision guided weapon aimed at a stationary target or the simultaneous tracking of a number of moving targets. It is the belief of this writer that, although existing systems have shown remarkable capability, there is room— as well as need—to further the technology of tracking to take advantage of the recently developed algorithmic capabilities while continuing the development of algorithms with enhanced capabilities. This can be summarized by the following paraphrase: *Keep on tracking!*

# INTRODUCTION

One area in which modern tracking technology has begun to make an impact is *air traffic control* (ATC). Most of the current ATC tracking systems are still using 1960s-vintage $\alpha$-$\beta$ filters [1]. When I was asked "How can one improve the performance of $\alpha$-$\beta$ filters in clutter?" the only answer I could come up with was, "Replace them!" The ATC tracking problem is a challenging one. With civilian aircraft turn rates of up to 3°/s and radar scan periods of 10s, such a target can finish a 90-degree turn in three scans, and very few of the existing schemes among the many in the literature (even adaptive ones with maneuver detection) can track such a target with good accuracy. This brings up one of the main reasons why ATC people are so reluctant to use filtered target state estimates: during such turns the unfiltered measurements are more accurate than the filtered position estimates! Thus, when accurate estimates are the most critical (as during a maneuver), they cannot be tolerated to be less accurate than raw measurements.

The first two chapters deal with ATC problems in two new, advanced systems being developed in Europe. Both are based on the *multiple model* (MM) adaptive estimation approach, which is based on the fact that the behavior of a target cannot be characterized at all times by a single model, but a finite number of models can adequately describe its behavior in different regimes. In practice, a small number (two to four) of such models can be used to succesfully describe the various behavior regimes of an aircraft in an ATC environment. However, such targets undergo "switching" from one regime to another in a manner that is not completely predictable. Although static (i.e., nonswitching) MM estimation algorithms have been known since the mid 1960s, practical algorithms for the switching case have become available only recently.

A unified tutorial presentation on the topic of MM estimation—static *versus* dynamic and the various algorithms for the dynamic case (the optimal one, which is not feasible due to exponentially increasing requirements in time; suboptimal ones with fixed requirements)—can be found in [2]. The most notable advance in this area is the *interacting multiple model* (IMM) algorithm [5, 6], which has requirements that are linear in the number of models, yet performs as well as the generalized pseudo Bayesian algorithm of order 2, which has requirements that are quadratic in the number of models. Although static MM algorithms have been adapted heuristically for use in dynamic (i.e., switching) environments [6], they are less desirable than the IMM algorithm; their cost is the same but they lack the ability to incorporate the modeling of the regime switches and have to rely on an artificial finite memory.

Another advantage of the IMM is its modularity. It can be set up using as its building blocks Kalman filters (KF) or extended Kalman filters (EKF) to account for nonlinearities in the motion equation (e.g., for coordinated turns and in the measurement equation for range-azimuth-elevation observations), or probabilistic data association filters (PDAF) based on KF or EKF, if data association (due to false alarms or neighboring targets) is a significant problem. The combination of the MM approach with the PDAF method is discussed in [1].

The IMM design parameters are

1. The set of models for the various regimes and their structure.
2. The process noise intensities for the various models, including the nonmaneuvering model with low-level process noise and the maneuvering model(s) with certain higher noise levels determined by the assumed maneuverability of the targets.
3. The jump probabilities (usually Markov) between the models from the selected set. These probabilities are chosen according to the designer's beliefs about the frequency of the regime switches and can be subsequently adjusted based on Monte Carlo simulation results.

**Outline of the Contents of This Volume**

The first four chapters deal with various applications of the IMM, some of them in combination with the *probabilistic data association filter* (PDAF), sometimes erroneously designated as the probability data association filter.

The first chapter, written by P. Vacher, I. Barret, and M. Gauvrit, describes the Hadamard advanced tracking project developed for the French ATC system. The algorithms used in that project had to meet certain accuracy requirements and the MM approach was found to satisfy these requirements. The tracking was developed with the assumption of reliable data association from the transponder information. The authors discuss their rationale for the selection of the IMM configuration for the estimator and the set of models for the targets' various behavior regimes: nearly constant velocity, left turn, and right turn. They also share their positive experience in using the Ada programming language for the implementation.

The second chapter, written by H.A.P. Blom, R.A. Hogendoorn, and B.A. van Doorn, deals with a somewhat more complex tracking problem for a multisensor ATC system developed in the Netherlands in which data association is not assumed to be available, but part of the tracking algorithm instead. This system also carries out in real time systematic error estimation across the sensors. (The static version—radar registration—was discussed in [2, Ch. 5]). The algorithm used, JUMPDIF (diffusion-based models driven by continuous-time white noise that undergo jumps from one model to another), which is a generalized IMM/PDAF, is shown to be an adequate Bayesian tracker: it provides a reliable indication of the accuracy of the state estimate and it can be implemented on existing hardware.

Chapter 3, written by F. Dufour and M. Mariton, discusses an application similar to those discussed in the previous chapters, except that in this case two passive, *infrared* (IR) sensors provide the observations. In this application, two sensors are necessary to ensure the observability of the target states and false alarms cannot be neglected. The algorithm is the IMM, with PDAFs used as building blocks for each of the models. The choice of the Markov chain transition probabilities between the models is discussed in detail.

Chapter 4, written by Y. Bar-Shalom, K.C. Chang, and H.A.P. Blom, deals with the problem of a target that "splits"—a platform that launches a weapon or a target that breaks up. (For example, a dud Scud that can pose a major problem for an intercept system that does not have an algorithm ready to handle such an occurrence.) The algorithm presented, which is an IMM combined with a coupled version of the joint PDAF, provides a relatively simple solution to this problem with fixed computational requirements. The results are illustrated using the software MULTIDAT [4].

I once was asked how to track with an imaging sensor two targets whose trajectories cross in the sensor's field of view, causing overlapping of their images. The solution to the problem is presented in Chapter 5, written by H.M. Shertukde and Y. Bar-Shalom. First, the statistical characterization of the measurements obtained by an IR sensor is derived in terms of the pixel size, target intensity pattern, and video noise intensity. The achievable subpixel accuracies from single-frame centroid measurements and the correlation of two consecutive frames (target displacement) are quantified with simple, closed-form expressions. We also show that the displacement measurement noise is autocorrelated and that suitable modeling of this improves the performance of the tracking filter. Following this, a coupled version of the JPDA [2] is used to track targets whose images overlap in the sensor's focal plane.

In Chapter 6, F. Daum describes a systems approach to *multitarget tracking* (MTT) and points out some aspects that have not been sufficiently considered in the literature, such as sensor resolution, radar waveform design, and uniform versus nonuniform sampling policy. Sensor resolution can be a more important issue than data association. Nonuniform patterns are possible with phased-array radars and some IR sensors. The optimization of measurement patterns is discussed and illustrated and a procedure to find a performance bound on an MTT algorithm is presented. Although this technique still requires simulations, more recent work points in the direction of obtaining *Cramér-Rao lower bound* (CRLB) type results (i.e., results obtained without recourse to simulations). This was prompted by the comment of a noted expert* on MTT that there is no CRLB-type result for the MTT problem.

An important step forward in performance evaluation is reported in Chapter 7, where S. Mori, K.C. Chang, and C.Y. Chong present new results in off-line performance analysis and quantify the effect of misassociations on estimation performance. Simple and reliable closed-form expressions that relate performance to environmental parameters are presented, as are tools for predicting track purity (an important measure of quality of a tracker).

In Chapter 8, S.S. Blackman considers the tracking of multiple targets with a phased-array radar, characterized primarily by the agility with which its beam is pointed. The problem considered is a tracking system in an environment with many low-observable, closely spaced, and highly maneuverable targets. System evaluation and design are discussed. The agile beam allows (and necessitates) real-time allocation of the radar resources between search and update illumination. A survey of tracking and association techniques is given and the coordinate choice options are discussed together with the role of a radar in a multisensor suite.

Chapter 9, written by J. Dezert, presents a novel use of the PDA technique for autonomous vehicle navigation using landmarks, a viable and less-expensive alternative to map storage and image correlation. A special feature of the algorithm presented is that the PDA is augmented to utilize uncertain landmark classification information. Uncertainties can be modeled in a Bayesian or in a Shaferian manner.

In Chapter 10, R. Popoli takes up the issue of sensor resource allocation from a pragmatic point of view, using both utility theory and fuzzy decision approaches. Several architectures for the sensor management are discussed. Examples are given that illustrate the benefits of sensor management.

The application of fuzzy decision theory using triangular norms to problems with uncertainty that cannot be characterized in a probabilistic manner is presented in Chapter 11 by R. Yannone and P.P. Bonissone. The implementation of a system based on this approach for attribute fusion and situation assessment is described for *electronic warfare* (EW) and surveillance systems.

## REFERENCES

[1]   Y. Bar-Shalom and T.E. Fortmann, *Tracking and Data Association,* Academic Press, Boston, 1988.

[2]   Y. Bar-Shalom, "Multitarget-Multisensor Tracking: Principles and Techniques," Short Course Notes, 1989.

*Unfortunately, this expert was unable to contribute to the present volume. We hope a contribution on tracking in very large scale systems will appear in a future volume. Rather regrettably, several other contributions could not be included in this volume due to institutional constraints of the organizations with whom the authors are affiliated.

[3]     Y. Bar-Shalom (ed.), *Multitarget-Multisensor Tracking: Advanced Applications,* Vol. 1, Artech House, Norwood, MA, 1990.

[4]     Y. Bar-Shalom, *MULTIDAT—MULTImodel Data Association for Tracking,* Version 4.0 Interactive Software, 1991.

[5]     H.A.P. Blom, "An Efficient Filter for Abruptly Changing Systems," *Proc. 23rd IEEE Conference on Decision and Control,* pp. 656–658, 1984.

[6]     H.A.P. Blom and Y. Bar-Shalom, "The Interacting Multiple Model Algorithm for Systems with Markovian Switching Coefficients," *IEEE Trans. on Auto. Control,* Vol. AC-33, August 1988, pp. 780–783.

[7]     C.T. Leondes (ed.), *Advances in Aerospace Systems Dynamics and Control Systems,* Part 1, Academic Press, Boston, 1989.

# Chapter 1
# DESIGN OF A TRACKING ALGORITHM FOR AN ADVANCED ATC SYSTEM

## P. Vacher, I. Barret, M. Gauvrit

### CERT-DERA, Toulouse, France

## 1.1 INTRODUCTION

The rapid growth of civil air traffic and the anticipation of future growth pose the need for more accurate traffic control systems to preserve passenger security. To this end, the quality of radar measurements was remarkably improved with monopulse technology. In this context, it also was necessary to refine tracking procedures. In the framework of the Hadamard project of the French civil administration, advanced tracking methods were investigated at CERT (Centre d'Etudes et de Recherches de Toulouse).

The next section describes the characteristics of Hadamard project and especially the tracking accuracy requirements. The following section deals with the aircraft motion modeling and shows that stringent speed estimation can be obtained only with multiple model algorithms. The third section is devoted to the presentation of a multimodel representation of trajectories and the description of an algorithm that proved quite suited to this problem, the *interacting multiple model* (IMM) algorithm. Finally, the last section presents Monte Carlo performance comparisons of several IMM configurations leading to the selection of a procedure for the future French ATC system.

## 1.2 THE HADAMARD PROJECT

This project was a five-year study initiated in 1985 by the French civil aviation administration (DGAC). The first aim was to develop tracking techniques that take better advantage of the improved measurements of a new generation of monopulse radars. The ultimate result would augment traffic security while reducing separation minima between aircraft down to 5 nautical miles. The other goal of the project was to evaluate the adequacy of Ada programming language for an ATC system and, more especially, the real-time aspects of the language. In this section, the overall features of this ATC system will be presented. Then the requirements concerning the tracking accuracy will be described.

### 1.2.1 Characteristics of the New ATC System

The purpose of the tracking function of an ATC system is to update track elements (position, velocity, flight level, *et cetera*) for each airplane by utilizing the information transmitted by radar stations. This information consists of various data: the airplane's relative position (bearing and range), its flight level, an identification number, and so forth.

Preprocessing is then performed locally by radar stations to determine the association between measurements and tracks. Unlike military tracking systems, this association here is easier because of the widespread use of transponders that enable reliable identification with a rate of success better than 95%. The association quality can be affected sometimes by phenomena such as "fruit" (interfering asynchronous transponder replies due to other interrogations) and "garble" (transponder replies overlapping in time). But it is greatly improved with monopulse technique due to improved target bearing determination and reduced interrogation rate. With the emergence of mode S, fruit and especially garble will be eliminated because each aircraft will be assigned an identity code with which it is addressed during the interrogation. In this way, only the aircraft being interrogated will reply. The problems of track initiation and deletion also are solved using transponder message.

The radars currently used are classical secondary radars. In the coming decade, they will be replaced progressively by monopulse ones. But, for some time, both kinds of radars will coexist. So the new ATC system should be able to process equally the data from both generations of sensors.

Currently a track is updated locally at each radar. The monoradar tracks related to one airplane are merged, in a second stage, to yield a single multiradar track. This track is generally obtained by the selection of the best quality monoradar track. The disadvantage of such processing is that it does not use the full potential of multiradar information. In particular, maneuver detection does not benefit of the faster measurement rate of a multiple radar surveillance system.

The Hadamard tracking system is based on a single, centralized track maintenance for each aircraft. This track is updated by measurements obtained from several radars (an average of four). The procedure thus allows more accurate estimation of airplane trajectories.

One possible objection to this approach is eventual misalignment and bias errors between radars that could deteriorate the global estimation. In the Hadamard system, these biases are evaluated and corrected by an independent mechanism to preserve the accuracy of track reconstitution.

The algorithms introduced in the sequel deal with two-dimensional tracking in the horizontal plane (actually, in a plane tangential to the earth surface). The altitude is processed by a separate procedure, based on the corresponding data of the transponder message. In this first analysis, the available measurements for the estimation process are the aircraft's relative position (range and bearing). Soon, primary doppler stations will provide radial velocity measurements. In the long term (1995), the mode S transponder will also transmit airborne information: vertical speed, turning rate, aircraft roll angle, heading, and eventually an on-board computed position.

### 1.2.2   Tracking Accuracy Requirements

These requirements concern only the systems to be developed for near-term applications. So, only position measurement and eventually radial velocity information would be used. Nevertheless, the methods developed in the framework of the project should also be able to operate on mode S data with minor modifications.

The Hadamard ATC system is designed to track three types of flying objects: airplanes, helicopters, and balloons (meteorological and dirigible). Airplanes or helicopters carrying out military missions or moving on the ground on taxiways or runways are excluded. The characteristics of these objects are listed in Table 1.1.

**Table 1.1**
Tracked Objects Characteristics

| Object Type | Airplanes | Helicopters | Balloons |
|---|---|---|---|
| Height range | 0–75,000 ft | 0–20,000 ft | 0–127,000 ft |
| Speed range: | | | |
|   Horizontal | 0–1,200 knots | 0–300 knots | 0–100 knots |
|   Vertical | 0–20,000 ft/min | 0–3,000 ft/min | |
| Maximum accelerations: | | | |
|   Transversal | 2 g | 2 g | 0.1 g |
|   Longitudinal | 1 g | 1 g | 0.1 g |

The average number of objects to be tracked simultaneously will be 2000 with a maximum of 3000. The algorithms described in the sequel are designed especially for aircraft tracking although they can be used for helicopters and balloons as well.

The sensors used in Hadamard project are classical secondary radars and new monopulse radars, which are being set up on the French territory. The total number of sensors the system should be able to take into account will be about fifty. Table 1.2 describes the performances of these sensors.

**Table 1.2**
Sensor Specifications

| Radar Type | Classical Secondary | Monopulse Secondary |
|---|---|---|
| Measurement accuracy: | | |
|   Range | 0.12 nmi | 0.06 nmi |
|   Bearing | 0.14° | 0.07° |
| Rotation period | 10 s | 4 s/8 s |
| Maximum range | 180 nmi | 200 nmi |
| Measurement timing accuracy | 0.5 s | 0.01 s |
| Mean radars overlapping | | |
|   Below FL 250 | 4 | |
|   Above FL 250 | 6 | |

The most important aspects of tracking accuracy for air traffic control are

- A precise estimation of aircraft kinematic elements during the constant velocity flight phases that are the most frequent in air traffic control. The requirements are particularly stringent for the estimation of the aircraft speed vector, which is the basis for collision prevention.
- A rapid detection of maneuvers so that traffic controllers can check as soon as possible if their orders are effectively followed by the pilots. A maneuver indicator is thus needed to provide this information. It must be reliable; that is, not too sensitive to false alarms so as not to alert the controller unduly.
- A computational load compatible with the performances of current computers.

On a quantitative standpoint, the performance specifications are summed up in Table 1.3. These requirements concern only a track being updated by at least *three radars*. In this table, the specifications for constant velocity phases (first row) are described by two values: the *accuracy,* which is equal to the mean value over these flight phases of the root mean square of the filter errors; and the *stability,* which is the greatest absolute variation about this mean value. The aim of these specifications is to deliver steady estimates to the controller. The maneuver indicator sensitivity is the minimum value of the turn rate that should be detected by the tracking procedure.

**Table 1.3**
Tracking Accuracy Requirements

|  | *Accuracy/Stability* |
|---|---|
| Constant velocity track (0): |  |
|   Position | 0.2 nmi/0.2 nmi |
|   Speed | 10 knots/7 knots |
|   Heading (1) | 1.5°/1° |
|   Heading (2) | 3°/2° |
| Maneuver detection: |  |
|   Maneuver indicator sensitivity | 1.5°/s |
|   Maximum delay for maneuver detection | 20 s |
| Maximum estimation bias during maneuvers: |  |
|   Heading | 60° |
|   Position | 1 nmi |
| Initiation phase duration | 20 s |

Note: (0) is for a constant velocity track for at least one minute.
      (1) is for a 300 knot track.
      (2) is for a 150 knot track.

## 1.3   AIRCRAFT MOTION MODELING

The tracking techniques developed in the sequel are based on accurate modeling of every flight phase. This choice was guided by the analysis of conventional tracking methods utilizing a single, global model. In this case, a compromise is made on estimation accuracy between the constant velocity and the maneuver phases. We can infer intuitively that precise modeling of every flight phase will lead to more accurate results, especially in velocity estimation.

The aim of the next subsection is to quantify the influence of modeling on the estimation of uniform motions. Concerning maneuvering phases, several state representations were also analyzed and the resulting choice is presented in the following subsection.

### 1.3.1   Modeling Influence on Estimation Quality

Let us consider an airplane traveling at a constant velocity. The state vector of a model matching with this motion comprises, for instance, the coordinates in a Cartesian frame of aircraft position and velocity $X = (x, y, v_x, v_y)^T$. A constant acceleration model $X = (x, y, v_x, v_y, a_x, a_y)^T$ also can yield a correct restitution of aircraft cinematic elements by estimating a null acceleration. Whereas the potential advantage of this model is that it can account for acceleration phases as well, the estimation errors will be greater during constant velocity phases. This degradation is evaluated in the following paragraphs.

We shall subsequently consider two Kalman filters, one ($F_v$) operating on a constant velocity model, the other ($F_a$) based on the constant acceleration model. We also assume that the system dynamic equation is noise free.

The observation equation is identical for both filters, given by

$$z = h(X) + w \qquad (1.1)$$

where $w$ is the measurement noise. This equation is nonlinear since the measurement vector comprises the range $\rho$ and the bearing $\theta$. It then can be written as

$$\begin{pmatrix} \rho \\ \theta \end{pmatrix} = \begin{pmatrix} \sqrt{(x - x_{\text{rad}})^2 + (y - y_{\text{rad}})^2} \\ \arctan\left(\dfrac{x - x_{\text{rad}}}{y - y_{\text{rad}}}\right) \end{pmatrix} + w \qquad (1.2)$$

where the radar location is ($x_{\text{rad}}$, $y_{\text{rad}}$). The extended Kalman filter requires linearization of $h(X)$ about the position prediction that yields the Jacobian

$$H = \begin{pmatrix} \sin\hat{\theta} & \cos\hat{\theta} \\ \dfrac{\cos\hat{\theta}}{\hat{\rho}} & \dfrac{-\sin\hat{\theta}}{\hat{\rho}} \end{pmatrix} \qquad (1.3)$$

The Kalman filter covariance at time $t_k$ then is given by

$$P_{k/k}^{-1} = W_k + \Phi^T(t_0, t_k)P_{0/0}\Phi(t_0, t_k) \qquad (1.4)$$

where $\Phi$ is the transition matrix related to the filter dynamic equation (constant velocity or constant acceleration) and $W_k$ the observability gramian, the expression of which is given by

$$W_k = \sum_{l=1}^{k} \Phi^T(t_l, t_k)H_l^T R_l^{-1}H_l\Phi(t_l, t_k) \qquad (1.5)$$

The matrix $H_l$ is the linearization of the measurement equation about the state prediction at time $t_l$. In this matrix, only the coefficients related to position derivatives are nonzero and equal to those of eq. (1.3). The matrix $R_l$ is the measurement noise covariance. When the number of measurements $k$ is sufficiently large, the initial covariance $P_{0/0}$ influence on $P_{k/k}$ in (1.4) can be neglected. Hence, the covariance is approximately the inverse of observability gramian.

In this study, we further assume that a single radar is tracking the aircraft and that its trajectory is *radial to the radar station* to separate the effects of range and bearing measurements. With these hypotheses, it is possible to perform a symbolic computation of the variance of the down-range and cross-range components of position and speed for filters $F_v$ and $F_a$.

The measurement linearization of the *down-range components* is independent of the range prediction (top row in (1.3)). The ratio between the position variance of filter $F_a$ ($\sigma_p^2(F_a)$) and filter $F_v$ ($\sigma_p^2(F_v)$) tends toward 9/4 as the number of measurement $k$ increases. The ratio correspondent to velocity variances ($\sigma_v^2(F_a)$ and $\sigma_v^2(F_v)$) converges to 16. Thus,

$$\frac{\sigma_p^2(F_a)}{\sigma_p^2(F_v)} \to \frac{9}{4} \qquad\qquad \frac{\sigma_y^2(F_a)}{\sigma_v^2(F_v)} \to 16 \qquad\qquad\qquad (1.6)$$

Then, on the down-range axis, the use of the acceleration model induces a degradation much greater on velocity estimation than on position.

The linearization of $h(X)$ of the *cross-range components* is function of range prediction. We can show that the ratios between position and velocity variances of the two filters are dependent only on the ratio $r$ between the final range and the initial range of the trajectory. This is depicted in Figure 1.1, which reveals that the deterioration is worse when the aircraft flies away from the radar station. The speed degradation, which lies between 4 and 28, is also much more important here than the position degradation, which varies from 1 to 4.

In both cases, the utilization of a higher-order model leads to a deterioration that can be acceptable on position estimation (from 1 to 4 on the variance), but is much more severe for the determination of speed (from 4 to 28). Because the requirements are relatively stringent on the estimation of aircraft velocity vector used to prevent collision, this analysis clearly indicates that we should not use a higher-order model for trajectory reconstitution during constant velocity flight phases.

### 1.3.2   Aircraft Maneuver Modeling

To obtain as accurate as possible an estimation during maneuvers, a precise representation of this motion was investigated. Moreover, civil aircraft evolutions generally are well defined: longitudinal accelerations are rare and small (magnitude order of 0.1 g) and direction changes are carried out at a roughly constant turn rate. Closed-form but nonlinear equations can be easily derived to represent such maneuvers.

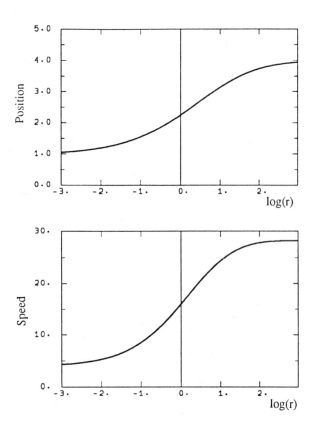

**Figure 1.1** Estimation error increase in a high-order model (cross-range components).

Several models were analyzed by running an extended Kalman filter on different trajectories (swift turn, slow turn, straight trajectories with several radar scanning periods):

$$X^T = (x, y, v_x, v_y, \omega) \tag{1.7}$$

$$X^T = (x, y, v_x, v_y, a_t) \tag{1.8}$$

$$X^T = (x, y, v, \psi, \omega) \tag{1.9}$$

where $v$ is the speed, $\psi$ is the heading angle, $\omega = \dot{\psi}$ is the turn rate, and $a_t$ the aircraft transversal acceleration.

Nonlinearity problems were encountered in all cases, especially during the initialization phases. In incorporating this maneuver filter in a multimodel algorithm, it is very crucial to find a formulation very robust to equation nonlinearities because, as we will show later, maneuver models are constantly being initialized by such algorithms during the constant velocity phases.

Among the various representations tested, the following was retained:

$$X = \begin{pmatrix} x \\ y \\ v_x \\ v_y \\ \omega \end{pmatrix} \tag{1.10}$$

The corresponding state equations in discrete time can be written as

$$t_{k-1} \to t_k \tag{1.11}$$

$$\begin{pmatrix} x \\ y \\ v_x \\ v_y \\ \omega \end{pmatrix} \to \begin{pmatrix} x + C_1(\omega)v_x + C_2(\omega)v_y \\ y - C_2(\omega)v_x + C_1(\omega)v_y \\ C_3(\omega)v_x + C_4(\omega)v_y \\ -C_4(\omega)v_x + C_3(\omega)v_y \\ \omega \end{pmatrix}$$

where the coefficients are given by

$$\begin{aligned} C_1(\omega) &= \frac{\sin\omega\Delta t}{\omega} \qquad C_2(\omega) = \frac{1 - \cos\omega\Delta t}{\omega} \\ C_3(\omega) &= \cos\omega\Delta t \qquad C_4(\omega) = \sin\omega\Delta t \end{aligned} \tag{1.12}$$

and $\Delta t = t_k - t_{k-1}$ is the sampling period. The linearization problems were solved by using a second-order extended Kalman filter [4], which tremendously improves the filter robustness and accuracy at the cost of a moderate increase of computational load due to the particular structure of the equations involved. This also is one of the simplest state representations directly derived from the conventional constant-velocity model. Furthermore, these equations are linear with respect to all components except the turn rate $\omega$. This model is also quite appropriate for civil air traffic control, where the heading variations are characterized by the turn rate (for instance, the standard turn rate is 3°/s). To account for eventual longitudinal accelerations, a fictitious state noise is added to the longitudinal combinations of position and velocity components. This noise covariance is equal to

$$Q_a = \sigma_a^2 \begin{pmatrix} \Delta t^4/4 & \Delta t^3/2 \\ \Delta t^3/2 & \Delta t^2 \end{pmatrix} \tag{1.13}$$

where $\sigma_a$ is the standard deviation of the expected accelerations.

As the specification requirements are less severe for maneuver tracking, approximate models could be considered as well. The choice of linear representations removes the aforementioned nonlinearity difficulties. The computational load also is greatly reduced but the speed estimation is severely deteriorated. The other two candidates are the constant acceleration model $X = (x, y, v_x, v_y, a_x, a_y)^T$ and the constant velocity model $X = (x, y, v_x, v_y)^T$. Because both models are approximations of actual aircraft motion, a fictitious state noise is introduced to account for mismodeling. In the constant acceleration model, this state noise affects only the combination of acceleration components longitudinal to the velocity to allow the rotation of the acceleration vector during a maneuver. In the constant velocity model, the usual constant acceleration disturbance is considered with a standard deviation high enough to represent current aircraft maneuvers ($\sigma_a = 1$ g).

In Chapter 3 of [5], we can find estimation results depicting the performance of several models for different simulated trajectories (swift turn, slow turn, constant velocity trajectory). The effects of nonlinearity on estimation accuracy also are demonstrated.

## 1.4 TRACKING ALGORITHM

The approach we are going to deal with is a multiple-model formulation of the aircraft trajectory in which the jumps between models occur according to a Markov chain. First, the framework of this formulation will be detailed. Then follows the description of an estimation algorithm that proved to be very efficient, the *interacting multiple model* algorithm.

### 1.4.1 Multiple Model Formulation of Aircraft Trajectory

This formulation was developed by H. Blom [10], who based it on the assumption that the system equations are governed by a Markov chain. The state of this chain $m_k$ represents the mode of flight of the aircraft during the time interval $[t_{k-1}, t_k]$, which is assumed to be among the $n$ possible modes of the set $M$:

$$M = \{m^1, \ldots, m^n\} \tag{1.14}$$

This set consists, for example, of a constant velocity model $V$ and a unique maneuver model $T$ based on the state (1.10) ($M = \{V, T\}$). Another solution that will be analyzed later chooses $M = \{V, \text{RT}, \text{LT}\}$ where RT and LT are right turn and left turn models. The process $m_k$ is characterized by its *a priori* transition probabilities:

$$p(m_k = m^i / m_{k-1} = m^j) = p_{i/j} \tag{1.15}$$

which constitute the transition matrix Π. These are design parameters for the algorithm.

The system equation between $t_{k-1}$ and $t_k$ are then dependent on $m_{k-1}$ and $m_k$ according to

$$X_k = \mathcal{F}(X_{k-1}, m_{k-1}, m_k) + \mathcal{G}(m_{k-1}, m_k)v_{k-1} \qquad (1.16)$$

$$z_k = \mathcal{H}(X_k, m_k) + w_k \qquad (1.17)$$

The characteristics of the state noise $v_{k-1}$ may depend on the models $m_{k-1}$, $m_k$, and those of the measurement disturbance $w_k$ also may depend on $m_k$. Both $m_{k-1}$ and $m_k$ appear in the dynamic eq. (1.16) to reflect the effect of model switching on the system state $X$. For instance, the transition from a constant velocity model to a right-turn model ($m_{k-1} = V$, $m_k = $ RT) results in a jump on the turn rate component of $X$ from a zero value to a positive one. This formulation is a very effective and mathematically sound manner of modeling processes with abrupt changes. Reference [10] is recommended for further comments.

Actually, the discrete time dynamic eq. (1.16) models a constant time process, and the switch from $m_{k-1}$ to $m_k$ can occur at any time between $t_{k-1}$ and $t_k$. A mathematically more correct approach would be a continuous time modeling of the evolution of both system state $X(t)$ and model $m(t)$, such as developed in [10, 13, 17]. In the sequel of this section, several assumptions will be made to simplify the estimation algorithms and thus decrease the computational load.

First, we assume that the transitions of aircraft accelerations or turn rates are short compared to the radar scanning period, so that they can be modeled by step functions with random amplitude. In civil traffic tracking, this assumption turned out to be valid but, if the real-world transitions were more progressive compared to the sampling period, a transition model should be included in the set $M$ to account for acceleration variations. This would result in an increase of algorithm complexity. Nevertheless, an advantage of this option would be to allow transitions between several nonzero values of aircraft acceleration.

The second hypothesis concerns the time of jump from $m_{k-1}$ to $m_k$, which we suppose to occur just after the last measurement update at a time denoted $t_{k-1}^+$. Under this assumption, the state eq. (1.16) can be decomposed into two phases: one reflecting the jump on the state vector $X_{k-1}$ at time $t_{k-1}^+$ and the second is the state evolution between $t_{k-1}^+$ and $t_k$ under the model $m_k$. The effect of the model switch on state $X$ is described by

$$X_{k-1}^+ = \mathcal{F}_j(X_{k-1}, m_{k-1}, m_k) + \mathcal{G}_j(m_{k-1}, m_k)v_{j_{k-1}} \qquad (1.18)$$

while the evolution up to time $t_k$ can be written

$$X_k = \mathcal{F}_e(X_{k-1}^+, m_k) + \mathcal{G}_e(m_k)v_{e_{k-1}} \qquad (1.19)$$

For the transition between identical models ($m_{k-1} = m_k = m^i$), eq. (1.18) obviously is the identity function. The switch from a maneuver model to the constant velocity model $V$ is obtained immediately by setting the turn rate component of $X$ to zero. In the transition from model $V$ to a maneuver model ($T$, RT, or LT), the jump $v_j$ of the turn rate is modeled by a random variable with a Gaussian distribution $\mathcal{N}(\mu_\omega, \sigma_\omega^2)$. It follows that the function $\mathcal{F}_j$, in this case, is equal to the identity function, and $\mathcal{G}_j$ is a vector the components of which are null except the last one equal to unity.

The state eq. (1.19) between $t_{k-1}^+$ and $t_k$ is the constant velocity state equation when $m_k = V$ or a maneuver state equation otherwise (eq. (1.11), for instance).

Instead of $t_{k-1}^+$, the time $t_j$ of the jump, in fact, could be fixed at any moment in the interval $[t_{k-1}, t_k]$. This would result in a three-stage decomposition of (1.16):

1. Evolution from $t_{k-1}$ to $t_j$ under the model $m_{k-1}$,
2. State transition from model $m_{k-1}$ to model $m_k$,
3. Evolution from $t_j$ to $t_k$ under model $m_k$.

This decomposition introduces added complexity to estimation procedures with no significant improvement on the accuracy of the result.

As several radar stations are involved in the tracking process, the time interval $\Delta t$ between measurements is not constant. Consequently, the transition matrix $\Pi$ between models is dependent on $\Delta t$. This is done by discretization of a continuous time Markov process [14], resulting in

$$\Pi(\Delta t) = \exp(Q\Delta t) \tag{1.20}$$

where the coefficients $q_{i/j}$ of the matrix $Q$ satisfy $\Sigma_{i=1}^n q_{i/j} = 0$, $q_{j/j} < 0$, and $q_{i/j} \geqslant 0$ for $i \neq j$.

These coefficients can be determined by using the following equality:

$$q_{j/j} = -\frac{1}{\overline{T}_j} \tag{1.21}$$

where $\overline{T}_j$ is the mean time of stay of the Markov process $m(t)$ on the model $m^j$. This gives a convenient indication for the choice of the diagonal terms of $Q$. Concerning the other elements, we can consider the coefficients $a_{i/j}$ defined for $i \neq j$ by

$$q_{i/j} = \frac{a_{i/j}}{\overline{T}_j} \tag{1.22}$$

They verify $\Sigma_{i \neq j} a_{i/j} = 1$ and represent the distribution of the jumps from model $m^j$ to the other models of the set $M$. For example, in the case where $M = \{V, RT, LT\}$, the distribution of jumps with RT as the origin model could be 90% to model $V$ and 10% to model LT leading to $a_{V/RT} = 0.9$ and $a_{LT/RT} = 0.1$.

In multimodel systems such as those described in (1.16–1.17), the purpose of estimation algorithms is to yield an estimation of both state $X_k$ and model $m_k$ given the sequence of measurements

$$Z_k = \{z_1, \ldots, z_k\} \tag{1.23}$$

There is a theoretical solution that consists of considering all the model sequences $S_k = \{m_1, \ldots, m_k\}$. For each sequence $S_k$, a Kalman filter produces a state estimate $\hat{X}_{k/Z_k, S_k}$ and an *a posteriori* probability $p(S_k/Z_k)$ can be computed. The global state estimate then is a weighted sum of the estimates $\hat{X}_{k/Z_k, S_k}$ by the probabilities $p(S_k/Z_k)$. Because the number of sequences $S_k$ increases exponentially, this method is not applicable. To limit this mushrooming, two types of approximations can be performed: *sequence pruning* or *sequence merging.*

In the *pruning* process, only a limited number of model sequences among the $n^k$ possible are considered. In the literature, we find two algorithms based on this principle:

- The *detection and estimation algorithm* (DEA) [19], where the least likely sequences are eliminated in a first stage. Then, only a maximum fixed number of sequences is retained (the most probable ones).
- The *random sampling algorithm* (RSA) [2], which is based on a Monte Carlo technique and performs a random generation of the sequences.

In the *merging* methods, several sequences ending with the same fixed-length subsequence are merged into a single sequence. From a mathematical standpoint, this operation corresponds to the approximation of a Gaussian density mixture by a Gaussian density. Two algorithms utilize this principle:

- The *generalized pseudo Bayes* algorithm of order $r$ (GPB$r$), where $r - 1$ is the length of subsequences on which the merging process is performed. It was first introduced by Ackerson and Fu [1] and rarely is presented in its most general form. It requires a bank of $n^r$ Kalman filters.
- The interacting multiple model algorithm by Blom [8], which requires $n$ Kalman filters.

Various experiments showed that pruning methods are inferior and less efficient than merging procedures [20, 6, 5]. Among the GPB family, only GPB2 and GBP1 are in practical use. GBP1 has roughly the same computational load as the IMM ($n$ Kalman filters); but, in addition to the merging process, an approximation is performed [5] that introduces a marked degradation compared to the IMM. GBP2 is theoretically more precise than the IMM but, in practical situations, the differences between these algorithms are negligible [12, 6]. Moreover, GPB2 proved less robust to system mismodeling. So, the IMM algorithm, which will be presented briefly in the next section, provides the best trade-off between estimation performance and computational load.

### 1.4.2 The Interacting Multiple Model Algorithm

Only the basic principles of the IMM algorithm will be addressed in this section. The details and demonstrations can be found in [9, 12, 5].

As depicted in Figure 1.2, the IMM consists of a recursive update for each model $m_k$ of the state density $p(x_k/Z_k, m_k)$ and the model *a posteriori* probability $p(m_k/Z_k)$. The state densities are supposed to be Gaussian. So, like a Kalman filter, this procedure updates both the state estimates $\hat{X}_{k/Z_k, m_k}$ and their associated covariance matrices $P_{k/Z_k, m_k}$. The global state reconstruction $\hat{X}_{k/k} = \hat{X}_{k/Z_k}$ is obtained simply as a weighted sum of the model-conditioned estimates.

As shown in Figure 1.2, a recursion of the IMM between times $t_{k-1}$ and $t_k$ can be divided into two stages:

- An *interaction stage* at time $t_{k-1}$ to account for eventual model switches.
- An *updating stage* dealing with the time and measurement updates of the models estimates and covariances.

The *interaction stage* itself is a succession of two stages:

- The *extension stage,* where every elementary sequence $m_{k-1}$ is extended into two-step sequences $S_k = \{m_{k-1}, m_k\}$ and the pertinent probabilities and state densities are computed

$$p(X_{k-1}/Z_{k-1}, m_{k-1}) \Rightarrow p(X_{k-1}^+/Z_{k-1}, m_{k-1}, m_k)$$
$$p(m_{k-1}/Z_{k-1}) \Rightarrow p(m_{k-1}, m_k/Z_{k-1})$$

  The state density moments can easily be obtained by using the jump relations (1.18) that, in this case, are linear. The probabilities of the sequences $S_k$ derive directly from the transition probabilities $\Pi$.

- The *merging stage,* where sequences $S_k$ ending with the same model $m_k$ are merged into a single one-step sequence $m_k$. This corresponds to the operations

$$p(X_{k-1}^+/Z_{k-1}, m_{k-1}, m_k) \Rightarrow p(X_{k-1}^+/Z_{k-1}, m_k)$$
$$p(m_{k-1}, m_k/Z_{k-1}) \Rightarrow p(m_k/Z_{k-1})$$

The merged models probabilities are nothing more than the marginal probabilities of the extension probabilities. The state merging phase, which is the cornerstone of the algorithm, deserves more explanation. An approximation is needed to

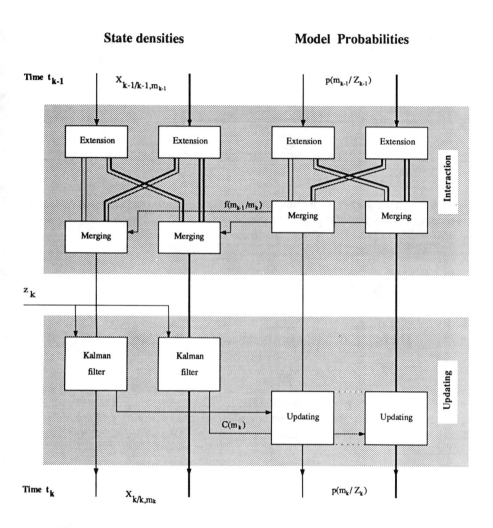

**Figure 1.2** The IMM algorithm.

obtain Gaussian distributions for the densities $p(X^+_{k-1}/Z_{k-1}, m_k)$ concerning state merging. This approximation corresponds to the relation

$$p(X^+_{k-1}/Z_{k-1}, m_k) \overset{N}{\approx} \sum_{m_{k-1} \in M} p(X^+_{k-1}/Z_{k-1}, m_{k-1}, m_k) p(m_{k-1}/Z_{k-1}, m_k) \qquad (1.24)$$

where the symbol $\overset{N}{\approx}$ means that a Gaussian approximation of the Gaussian mixture on the right-hand side of the equation is performed. When linear systems are

---

involved (1.16 and 1.17), this is the only approximation of the algorithm, compared to the optimal solution. The first- and second-order moments of the densities $p(X_{k-1}^+/Z_{k-1}, m_k)$ result from properties of the conditional expectation:

$$\hat{X}_{k-1/Z_{k-1},m_k}^+ = E^{m_{k-1}}(\hat{X}_{k-1/Z_{k-1},m_{k-1},m_k}^+)$$

$$P_{k-1/Z_{k-1},m_k}^+ = \text{var}^{m_{k-1}}(\hat{X}_{k-1/Z_{k-1},m_{k-1},m_k}^+) + E^{m_{k-1}}(P_{k-1/Z_{k-1},m_{k-1},m_k}^+)$$

where the symbols $E^{m_{k-1}}$ and $\text{var}^{m_{k-1}}$ are the expectation and the covariance with respect to the conditional fusing probability $f(m_{k-1}/m_k) = p(m_{k-1}/Z_{k-1}, m_k)$ on models $m_{k-1}$.

The IMM last stage is a time and measurement update identical to classical Bayesian multiple-model algorithms, which were introduced by Magill [16] and further developed in [18, 15]. It corresponds to

$$p(X_{k-1}^+/Z_{k-1}, m_k) \Rightarrow p(X_k/Z_k, m_k)$$

$$p(m_k/Z_{k-1}) \Rightarrow p(m_k/Z_k)$$

The state densities update is performed by a bank of $n$ Kalman filters based on (1.19) and (1.17). The probabilities update is derived from Bayes's rule according to

$$p(m_k/Z_k) = C\, p(z_k/Z_{k-1}, m_k) p(m_k/Z_{k-1}) \tag{1.25}$$

where $C$ is a normalization constant. The likelihood function $c(m_k) = p(z_k/Z_{k-1}, m_k)$ is provided by the Kalman filter operating on the model $m_k$ and is equal to the density of the predicted measurement computed for the value of the last measurement $z_k$.

## 1.5   EVALUATION OF THE IMM FOR AIR TRAFFIC SIMULATIONS

In this section, several configurations of the IMM algorithm are presented and analyzed on different simulated trajectories. The results discussed and depicted are the root mean square errors in position, speed, and heading estimation. They were obtained from 30 Monte Carlo runs.

A first group of algorithms whose maneuver models are based on an exact modeling eq. (1.11) will be examined. They then will be compared to IMM mechanization using an approximate maneuver model. Finally, the selection of an appropriate method for air traffic control will be addressed.

The set of trajectories used in this evaluation consists of a single turn at a constant speed and occurring at time $t_M = 3$ min. This turn is followed by another constant-velocity phase. Two sharply different monoradar trajectories were simulated.

Their characteristics are listed in Table 1.4. The maneuver durations are intentionally long compared to actual ones to allow the study of algorithm convergence during such phases.

**Table 1.4**
Test Trajectories

| Trajectory | Radar Type and Period | Aircraft-Radar Range | Aircraft Speed | Turn Rate | Turn Duration |
|---|---|---|---|---|---|
| T1 | monopulse 4 s | 110 nmi | 150 knots | 1°/s | 2 min |
| T2 | classical 10 s | 40 nmi | 300 knots | 3°/s | 1.5 min |

Trajectory T2 is a relatively rapid turn and involves a low-scan rate radar. This induces strong nonlinearities on the state evolution between two sampling times. Trajectory T1 is more representative of typical cruise flight maneuvers.

### 1.5.1 Algorithms Based on Exact Maneuver Modeling

Three IMM algorithms are evaluated with simulations on trajectories T1 and T2:

1. Algorithm A1 is a *two-model* algorithm $M = \{V, T\}$; that is, a constant-velocity and constant-turn rate model. The filter operating on the latter model is a *second-order extended* Kalman filter. The jump modeling characteristics given in Section 1.4.1 are then tuned for both left and right turn ($\mu_\omega = 0°/s$, $\sigma_\omega = 1.8°/s$).

2. Algorithm A2 uses three models $M = \{V, \text{RT}, \text{LT}\}$. The state estimation for the right-turn and left-turn models utilizes *first-order extended* filters. The results here are based on the values $\mu_\omega = \pm 3°/s$, $\sigma_\omega = 1.5°/s$ but the case where $\mu_\omega = \pm 1.5°/s$ also was analyzed.

3. Algorithm A3, too, is a three-model mechanization but the turn rate is not estimated ($\sigma_\omega = 0$). This results in a four-component state for the maneuver models and, hence, a decrease in computational load. Moreover, eq. (1.11) in this case is linear and thus standard Kalman filters are used. The quantity $\mu_\omega$ was fixed at $\pm 3°/s$ to encompass all possible value of $\omega$.

The transition matrices of these algorithms are computed on the basis of a mean time of stay of 1000 s for model $V$ and 100 s for maneuvers models according to (1.21).

Concerning trajectory T2 (Figure 1.3), algorithm A3, which is perfectly adapted for this kind of trajectory, represents the best that could be done, especially speed estimation. Comparison between A1 and A2 reveals similar performances

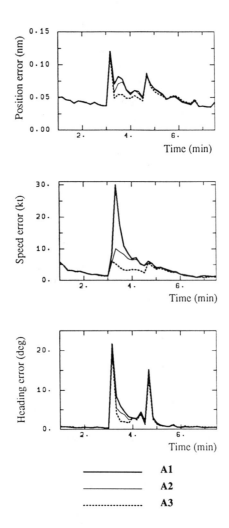

**Figure 1.3** Algorithm comparison on trajectory T2, exact maneuver model.

except for the speed estimation of A1, which exhibits much greater errors during the few seconds following the beginning of the turn.

It is also noteworthy to mention the general behavior of these error curves (especially those for the heading), which are quite typical of IMM algorithms. The peaks at the start and end of a maneuver are caused by the delay of model probabilities in switching from one model to another. After this switching, the slower decrease on the errors corresponds to the convergence of the maneuver filter (improvement of turn rate estimation).

The order of classification of these three procedures is reversed on trajectory T1 (Figure 1.4). In this situation, algorithm A1 outperforms the two others. The value $\omega = \pm 3°/s$ in the maneuver models of algorithm A3 leads to a coarse heading estimation. Concerning A2, if the value $\mu_\omega$ had been set to $\pm 1.5°/s$, it would yield results similar to A1 on trajectory T1. On the other hand, speed and position estimation would be deeply degraded on trajectory T2 because the first-order extended Kalman filters involved in A2 are not able to correctly process the nonlinearities of this simulation.

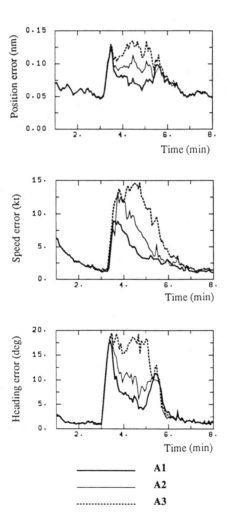

**Figure 1.4** Algorithm comparison on trajectory T1, exact maneuver model.

The analysis of the evolution of the models probabilities is quite relevant for the underlying mechanisms of these different IMM configurations. The geometry of trajectory T2 as well as the high value of its associated turn rate allow an easy distinction between the various flight phases. Thus, the corresponding probabilities, in this case, are quite close to one. This is not true for trajectory T1 because Figure 1.5 shows that the probability of model $T$ of algorithm A1 is about 0.8 during the turn. Moreover, the maneuver models of algorithms A2 and A3 are not quite fit for small values of $\omega$. Hence, distinction between models $V$ and RT of algorithm A2 during

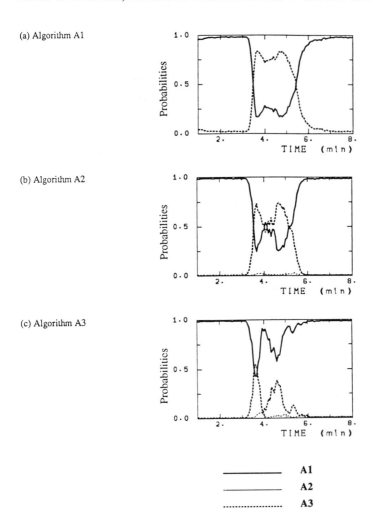

**Figure 1.5** Evolution of the model probabilities, trajectory T1.

the turn is rather fuzzy. The value $\omega = \pm 3°/s$, with which algorithm A3 models are designed, is quite inadequate for such trajectories. This is why model $V$ is the most probable, as it corresponds to the zero value of $\omega$. In this specific situation, the global estimation during the maneuver is really a combination of models $V$ and RT estimates.

Among the configurations presented in this section, the two-model algorithm A1 seems to represent the best trade-off. It produces the best results on slow-turn trajectories. For trajectories with rapid maneuvers, a degradation of speed estimation can be observed for half a minute after the maneuver starts. Nevertheless, these high turn-rate trajectories are not frequent in civil air traffic.

An additional disadvantage of the three model algorithms relates to the tracking of longitudinally accelerated aircraft motion. No maneuver model of these algorithms is tuned for such maneuvers because the expectation of the jump on $\omega$ is set to a nonzero value. A fourth model consequently must be incorporated to account for this situation, leading to an increase in computational load. The maneuver model of algorithm A1, which is able to estimate a zero value for $\omega$, can be modified to process longitudinally accelerated phases as well. This option will be studied in the next subsection.

### 1.5.2 Algorithms Based on Approximate Maneuver Modeling

Because tracking requirements are less severe during maneuvers, we can contemplate utilizing approximate maneuver models. In this section, the following two-model algorithms are analyzed:

4. Algorithm A4, which is identical to algorithm A1 except that a fictitious state noise is added in the maneuver model to account for longitudinal accelerations. This approach is preferred to an exact modeling of both constant turn rate and constant longitudinal acceleration motions for a variety of reasons. First, such a model would introduce considerable added complexity and non-linearity. Second, longitudinal accelerations are rare and small in civil air traffic. The state noise is tuned for acceleration levels up to 0.2 g. Comparison of Figures 1.6 and 1.7 with Figures 1.3 and 1.4 reveals that parameter estimation during uniform motions is not influenced by this additional noise. In maneuver phases, minor degradations can be observed on position (0.010 nmi) and heading (0.5°) reconstructions, whereas speed estimation, of course, is markedly affected (6–8 knots).

5. Algorithm A5, which includes a constant acceleration model with a fictitious state noise as discussed in Section 1.3.

6. Algorithm A6 consisting of two constant velocity models, one of which includes a state noise large enough to account for aircraft maneuvers (see Section 1.3).

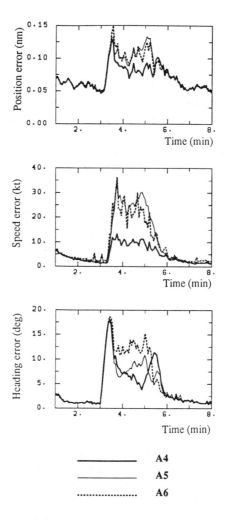

**Figure 1.6** Algorithm comparison on trajectory T1, approximate maneuver model.

The results of Figures 1.6 and 1.7 call for several remarks. Estimation performance during the constant-velocity phases is not affected much by the choice of the maneuver model. Heading and especially speed estimation are affected significantly during maneuvers. Algorithm A5 with a constant acceleration model produces considerable error in the speed estimation of trajectory T2. For this simulation, it is also worth mentioning that errors of algorithm A6 during the turn propagate for some time on the ensuing straight motion.

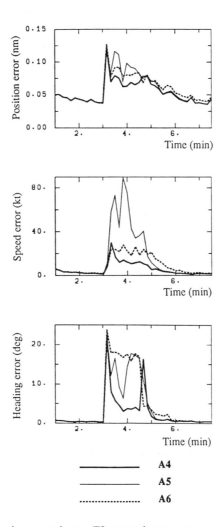

**Figure 1.7** Algorithm comparison on trajectory T2, approximate maneuver model.

These three algorithms also were tested on a simulation that can be considered a worst case situation, as far as civil traffic control is concerned. This trajectory, depicted in Figure 1.8, is a hippodrome (racetrack) trajectory carried out by aircraft waiting for landing clearance at a busy airport. The simulation involves a single monopulse radar with a scanning period of 4 s and the aircraft-radar range evolves between 30 and 40 nmi. Table 1.5 details the different phases of this trajectory.

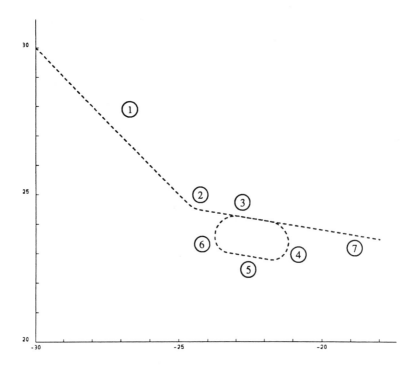

**Figure 1.8** Hippodrome trajectory, radar location: (0.,0.).

**Table 1.5**
Hippodrome Trajectory Phases

| Phases | 1 | 2 | 3 | 4 | 5 | 6 | 7 |
|---|---|---|---|---|---|---|---|
| Duration (s) | 180 | 12 | 60 | 60 | 60 | 60 | 120 |
| Turn rate (°/s) | 0 | −3 | 0 | 3 | 0 | 3 | 0 |
| Longitudinal acceleration (m/s²) | 0 | 0 | 0 | −0.5 | 0 | 0.5 | 0 |
| Speed (knots) | 150 | 150 | 150 | — | 92 | — | 150 |
| Heading (°) | 135 | — | 99 | — | 279 | — | 99 |

This simulation is an extreme case for four reasons:

1. The airplane is tracked by only one radar whereas an average of four (see Table 1.2) should be involved.
2. This trajectory includes three maneuvers with a high heading rate (3°/s) interspersed with short constant-velocity legs.
3. The first turn, when the aircraft gets aligned on the hippodrome axis, is very short (12 s) and includes only three measurements.

4. A speed variation occurs during the U-turns that is supposed to model a strong wind component (30 knots) along the hippodrome axis.

The results of the three algorithms, depicted in Figure 1.9, show no divergence in spite of great errors on speed estimation of algorithm A5 (constant acceleration model). The initial short turn of the trajectory does not compromise the stability of the algorithms, although the heading estimation of algorithm A4 (exact turn model) is affected a little more than the other two. But, apart from this, algorithm A4 is by far the most accurate.

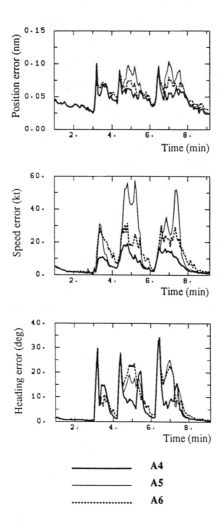

**Figure 1.9** Hippodrome trajectory results.

### 1.5.3 Algorithm Selection for Hadamard Tracking System

In Section 1.4 several algorithms were presented, based on the hypothesis that the jumps between models are governed by a Markov chain. Among these methods, various results in the literature prove that the IMM is the best compromise between estimation accuracy and computational load. In [5], the GPB2 algorithm, which is the IMM's best competitor, also was tested on air traffic simulations. In monoradar trajectories (trajectory T2, for instance), a little improvement of speed estimation could be observed (1 knot) but, on the other hand, the stability of heading estimation was markedly degraded. Because of these estimation results, the GPB2 algorithm was abandoned in favor of the IMM, which requires only $n$ Kalman filters instead of $n^2$ for GPB2.

A possible criticism of IMM relates to this bank of filters. Most of the time of civilian flights is spent in constant-velocity phases, where a single, simple Kalman filter would be sufficient. Thus, with the aim of reducing the processing time of IMM, other multiple model techniques were worked out and analyzed in [5]. The principles of these methods are similar to those developed by Bar-Shalom and Birmiwal in [3]: a unique filter is run at each time and the switches between the different models are monitored by statistical detection tests [7, 21]. But, contrary to the study [3] where the maneuvers were represented by an approximate model (constant acceleration), the procedure analyzed in [5] uses the exact-turn model eq. (1.11). Compared to IMM (algorithm A4), this method turned out to be less reliable and very sensitive to parameter tuning: it required the precise estimation of the maneuver start instant $t_M$, which implies data storage of past estimates. More accurate and stable estimations were delivered during uniform motions. Nevertheless, errors were much greater during maneuvers, and maneuver detection itself was delayed more than with the IMM. So, despite shorter computational time, this technique was rejected because of its complexity, its lack of reliability and precision during maneuvers, and its greater storage requirements.

The advantage for the IMM of concurrently running several filters during straight trajectories is that it *automatically* adapts to disturbance by an implicit adjustment of the *a posteriori* models probabilities to place more importance on the maneuver model (see [5]). A single Kalman filter would need to introduce a state noise, with the attendant and crucial problem of choosing the noise covariance.

In the previous sections, various configurations of the IMM algorithm were studied. Their computational loads also are interesting to examine. Processing times are listed in Table 1.6, where algorithm A4 time was used as the basis. These figures are only an indication because the implementation of such methods has not been optimized for faster computation. No precise results are available for A3, which was obtained using A2 mechanization. It is also worth mentioning that the use of a second-order Kalman filter in A4 instead of a first-order extended one resulted only in an extra 10% processing time.

**Table 1.6**
IMM Algorithms Computation Time

| Algorithm | A1 or A4 | A2 | A5 | A6 |
|---|---|---|---|---|
| Computation time | 1 | 1.75 | 0.75 | 0.45 |

Judging from the performance analysis of the preceding sections and the processing capacity requirements of the different procedures, algorithm A4 (i.e., the two model IMM based on an exact modeling of aircraft turn and a state noise modeling of longitudinal accelerations) seems the best suited for this problem. Nevertheless, if estimation errors of algorithm A6 (the constant-velocity maneuver model) are judged acceptable, it could be considered a second candidate due to its smaller computational complexity.

Algorithm A4 was integrated in the test bed of the civil aviation administration research center and put through an exhaustive series of evaluation simulations, representative of various present and future air traffic situations. The tracking accuracy requirements (Table 1.3) proved easy to fulfill. Tables 1.7 and 1.8 summarize the algorithm performance for multiradar trajectories (three monopulse radars). Maneuver detection delays are about 10 s for a 3°/s turn and 20 s for a 1°/s turn.

**Table 1.7**
Estimation Errors for Uniform-Motion Multiple-Radar Trajectories

| Error Standard Deviations | Position (nmi) | Speed (knot) | Heading (°) |
|---|---|---|---|
| Aircraft speed: | | | |
| 150 knot | 0.020 | 0.60 | 0.6 |
| 300 knot | 0.025 | 0.65 | 0.3 |

**Table 1.8**
Estimation Errors After the Start of the Turn for Multiple-Radar Trajectories
(aircraft speed: 300 knots)

| Error Standard Deviations | | Position (nmi) | Speed (knot) | Heading (°) |
|---|---|---|---|---|
| Turn rate: | maximum | 0.11 | 8 | 12 |
| 1°/s | after 30 s | 0.045 | 7 | 4 |
| Turn rate: | maximum | 0.13 | 13 | 20 |
| 3°/s | after 30 s | 0.040 | 7 | 5 |

## 1.6 CONCLUSION

The French future ATC system issued from the Hadamard project will incorporate several innovative features. A first aspect concerns the use of a new generation of monopulse radars that provide more accurate measurements and also allows improved plot-to-track association. A specific characteristic of the tracking system also is the maintenance of a unique multiradar track for each aircraft, thus deriving a maximum advantage from the sensor information, especially for maneuver detection. But the two most original features are the utilization of Ada programming language to implement the entire ATC system and a sophisticated tracking technique, the IMM algorithm.

The specifics of Ada profoundly modified programming philosophy and proved to be quite attractive even at an advanced research stage. It allowed the development of general interest and easily reusable software components such as generic packages on linear algebra operations, Kalman filtering, and Monte Carlo simulations. Object-oriented programming and use of abstract data types permit a high-level implementation of algorithms directly from functional diagrams such as Figure 1.2. One consequence is an easier mechanization of different configurations of an algorithm and also much greater reliability, which could not be obtained with a conventional language such as Fortran. Finally, Ada portability was remarkably appreciated when the algorithm was transferred to the Hadamard project.

Concerning the tracking algorithm, the IMM procedure was established on a solid theoretical basis and proved to be quite appropriate for this maneuvering aircraft tracking problem. Moreover, an exact but nonlinear modeling of maneuvers also significantly enhances estimation accuracy. Future investigation will be devoted to the integration of mode S data, which is expected to yield better maneuver detection and model switching.

## REFERENCES

[1]  Guy A. Ackerson and K.S. Fu, "On State Estimation in Switching Environments," *IEEE Trans. on Automatic Control,* Vol. Ac-15, No. 1, February 1970, pp. 10–17.

[2]  Hajime Akashi and Hiromitsu Kumamoto, "Random Sampling Approach to State Estimation in Switching Environments," *Automatica,* Vol. 13, 1977, pp. 429–434.

[3]  Y. Bar-Shalom and K. Birmiwal, "Variable Dimension Filter for Maneuvering Target Tracking," *IEEE Trans. on Aerospace and Electronic Systems,* Vol. AES-18, No. 5, September 1982, pp. 621–629.

[4]  Yaakov Bar-Shalom and Thomas E. Fortmann, *Tracking and Data Association,* Mathematics in Science and Engineering, Vol. 179, Academic Press, Boston, 1988.

[5]  Isabelle Barret, "Synthèse d'algorithmes de poursuite multiradars d'avions civils manœuvrants," thèse de doctorat, Ecole Nationale Supérieure de l'Aéronautique et de l'Espace, 1990.

[6]  Isabelle Barret and Pierre Vacher, "Poursuite de cibles manœuvrantes par des algorithmes markoviens hybrides," *Douzième Colloque GRETSI sur le Traitement du Signal et des Images,* Juans-les-Pins, France, 1989, pp. 189–192.

[7] Michèle Basseville, "Detecting Changes in Signals and Systems—A Survey," *Automatica,* Vol. 24, No. 3, 1988, pp. 309–326.

[8] Henk A.P. Blom, "Detection-Filter Representations for Markov Jump Diffusions," Tech. Rep. NLR TR 82019 U, National Aerospace Laboratory, Amsterdam, the Netherlands, March 1982.

[9] Henk A.P. Blom, "Markov Jump-Diffusion Models and Decision-Making-Free Filtering," A. Bensoussan and J.L. Lions (eds.), *Analysis and Optimization of Systems,* chapter Part 1, Springer-Verlag, 1984, pp. 568–580.

[10] Henk A.P. Blom, "An Efficient Decision-Making-Free Filter for Processes with Abrupt Changes," *IFAC Symp. on Identification and System Parameter Estimation,* York, United Kingdom, July 1985.

[11] Henk A.P. Blom, "Bayesian Estimation for Decision-Directed Stochastic Control," Tech. Rep. NLR TP 90039 U, National Aerospace Laboratory, Amsterdam, the Netherlands, March 1990.

[12] Henk A.P. Blom and Yaakov Bar-Shalom, "The Interacting Multiple Model Algorithm for Systems with Markovian Switching Coefficients," *IEEE Trans. on Automatic Control,* Vol. AC-33, No. 8, August 1988, pp. 780–783.

[13] Yang Chun, P. Bertrand, and M. Mariton, "Analyse des performances d'un filtre de détection de ruptures markoviennes." Symp. AIPAC, Nancy, July 1989.

[14] D.R. Cox and H.D. Miller, *The Theory of Stochastic Processes,* Science Paperbacks, Chapman and Hall, London, 1978.

[15] D.G. Lainiotis, "Partitioning: A Unifying Framework for Adaptive Systems," *Proc. IEEE,* Vol. 64, No. 8, 1976, pp. 1126–1143.

[16] D.T. Magill, "Optimal Adaptive Estimation of Sampled Stochastic Processes," *IEEE Trans. on Automatic Control,* Vol. AC-10, No. 4, October 1965, pp. 434–439.

[17] Michel Mariton, "Les Systèmes linéaires à sauts markoviens," thèse de docteur es sciences physiques, Université de Paris-Sud, 1986.

[18] Raman K. Mehra, "Approaches to Adaptive Filtering," *IEEE Trans. on Automatic Control,* Vol. AC-17, October 1972, pp. 693–698.

[19] J.K. Tugnait and A.H. Haddad, "A Detection-Estimation Scheme for State Estimation in Switching Environments," *Automatica,* Vol. 15, 1979, pp. 477–481.

[20] Jitendra K. Tugnait, "Detection and Estimation for Abruptly Changing Systems," *Automatica,* Vol. 18, No. 5, 1982, pp. 607–625.

[21] Alan S. Willsky, "Detection of Abrupt Changes in Dynamic Systems," M. Basseville and A. Benveniste, (eds.), *Detection of Abrupt Changes in Signals and Dynamical Systems,* Springer-Verlag, Paris, March 1984, pp. 27–49.

# Chapter 2
# DESIGN OF A MULTISENSOR TRACKING SYSTEM FOR ADVANCED AIR TRAFFIC CONTROL

**Henk A.P. Blom, René A. Hogendoorn, and Bas A. van Doorn\***

**National Aerospace Laboratory NLR, Amsterdam, The Netherlands**

## 2.1 INTRODUCTION

In an *air traffic control* (ATC) system the radar tracking system forms a critical link between the radar extractors and the air traffic controller. Part of the control loop, the tracking system has a considerable impact on the operational quality of an ATC system. Therefore, there is an increasing need for a tracking system that makes optimal use of all available sensor outputs and the best available tracking techniques. In view of this need, during recent years an extensive study on tracking aircraft for ATC has been done at NLR. The objective was to develop a multisensor tracking system that would provide far better aircraft state information (tracks) than at present.

The desired improvements are *more accurate* state estimates and *additional* state information. The first means better track continuity and better estimates of position, velocity, and acceleration. By additional state information, we mean information on

- Probability of track types, such as aircraft or false tracks.
- Probability of the mode of flight, such as straight flight or turning flight,
- Reliable indication of the accuracy of the state estimates.

---

*The authors would like to thank Paul C. de Kraker from the Dutch Organization of Civil Aviation (RLD) for his invaluable support to the JUMPDIF project.

Providing more accurate state and additional information to an ATC system seems particularly important in view of the growing need of air traffic controller–friendly systems for planning, conflict alert, and conflict resolution. These systems can be made more friendly only if they are provided with more complete state information. This can be done by improved sensors, extractor systems, tracking systems, and aircraft transponder systems (e.g., providing aircraft-derived state information). As new sensor, extraction, and transponder systems already have the full attention of the ATC community (e.g., [1]) the desired design concentrates on improvement in the tracking system, with the requirement that measurements, by using new types of transponders, sensors, or extractors, easily be incorporated into the new tracking set-up.

To reach these objectives, the theoretically well-known Bayesian approach was used in this study. The elaboration of the approach started shortly after the invention of the Kalman filter, and it has led to a steadily growing number of (approximate) Bayesian methods [2–5]. The result of this tracking study is a Bayesian multisensor multitarget tracking system, which is practically implementable and already yields high-quality tracks from measurements of a single primary surveillance radar system with a conventional extractor [6, 7].

This chapter gives an overview of the design and the performance of this tracking system. In Section 2.2, we present the main modules of the tracking system. Next, in Section 2.3, we look at the module that executes the track maintenance, most critical for ATC. The track maintenance module consists of a combination of those approximate Bayesian methods that proved to most efficiently handle the main problems of track maintenance: the interacting multiple model algorithm (IMM) for filtering in the presence of sudden mode switchings, *extended Kalman filtering* (EKF) for nonlinear dynamics, and *probabilistic data association* (PDA) for handling ambiguities in the association of measurements. In Section 2.4, we describe the systematic error estimation method developed. To allow for true multisensor tracking, all relevant systematic sensor errors are corrected in a dynamic way. To that end, there is one EKF-like module to estimate all systematic errors. The key to this solution is a particular transformation that decouples systematic error estimation from track maintenance. In Section 2.5, we outline the performance of this tracker for measurements from a single primary en-route surveillance radar and compare it with other trackers. Comparisons of the IMM/EKF/PDA-based tracking with $\alpha$-$\beta$ tracking, a (single-mode) EKF/PDA-based tracking, and an adaptive $\alpha$-$\beta$-$\gamma$ tracking show the superiority of the IMM/EKF/PDA approach for ATC surveillance. In Section 2.6, we draw a number of conclusions.

## 2.2 MULTISENSOR TRACKING MODULES

The task of a multisensor tracker is to provide estimates (tracks) of the state of aircraft in the ATC surveillance area. This area is covered by multiple sensors, possibly of different types. To perform this task, we developed a modular system consisting of the following subsystems:

- Coordinate transformation,
- Track maintenance (continuation),
- Track deletion,
- Measurement memorization,
- Track formation (initiation),
- Track merging,
- Systematic error estimation,
- Aircraft track selection,
- Synchronization.

In this section we give a short outline of these subsystems.

### 2.2.1 Coordinate Transformation

A prerequisite for multisensor tracking is to handle the registration problem [8–10]. To that end, first, all measurements are corrected for relevant systematic errors: sensor location errors, direction bias, range bias, range gain bias (if a range measurement is $1 + \Delta_g$ times the true range, we call $\Delta_g$ the range gain bias), and the offset between geometric height (distance from earth model's surface) and flight level (atmospheric pressure transformed to geometric height according to some standard atmospheric model). Following this, the measurements are transformed into a fixed-reference coordinate system.

### 2.2.2 Track Maintenance (Continuation)

Because track maintenance plays a crucial role in ATC, we use a centralized architecture; that is, one track maintenance module receives all measurements immediately after coordinate transformation. This module propagates the tracks to the next measurement time through an IMM/EKF approach and updates the tracks according to an appropriate PDA approach with all available measurements. We devote the next section to an outline of the IMM/EKF/PDA methods used for track maintenance.

### 2.2.3 Track Deletion

If an aircraft leaves the surveillance area, it no longer can be seen by any sensor. Because the border of the surveillance area fluctuates randomly (due to atmospheric conditions, sensor malfunctioning, *et cetera*), such an exit occurs randomly. Therefore, after each update of a track with new measurements, a track deletion system checks both the accuracy and the consistency of that track. If one or both are out of bounds, the track is deleted. Obviously, this module also deletes any false track that might sneak into the track maintenance system.

### 2.2.4   Measurement Memorization

For each sensor we store all measurements from the most recent five scans in a so-called plot memory. Moreover, for each (nondeleted) track-sensor pair, we memorize which have been the *nearest neighbor PDA* (NNPDA) measurements [11].

### 2.2.5   Track Formation (Initiation)

Our track formation system has a distributed architecture [12], in the sense that each site has its own track initiation module. Each such module is responsible for aircraft that enter the surveillance area through the area of the corresponding site. The input to such a module consists of all measurements in the corresponding "plot memory" that are not memorized as NNPDA measurements. Each initiated track is immediately handed over to the track maintenance system. With this set-up, our track continuator can work in combination with any track formation system. But, as a track can be continued only after it has been initiated, we think that a high-performance track continuator should cooperate with a high-performance track initiation system. Because the latter may be obtained by a *multiple hypotheses tracking* (MHT) approach, we developed a retrospective [13] version of MHT-based track formation [14].

### 2.2.6   Track Merging

Due to split measurements of aircraft flying in tight formation, which occasionally are seen apart, tracks may be generated that are essentially the same. To reduce the workload of the tracking system, these tracks are combined into a single track by a track-merging module.

### 2.2.7   Systematic Error Estimation

For the estimation of constant systematic errors effective methods exist [12, 15, 16]. Unfortunately, some systematic errors of radar systems may undergo sudden changes. For instance, if during technical maintenance we switch to another measurement extraction system, the result may be an abrupt change of range bias and range gain bias. To that end, we developed an algorithm to estimate the systematic errors in a dynamic way [17]. A description of this algorithm is given in Section 2.4. We simply use the most recent NNPDA measurements as input to this algorithm.

### 2.2.8 Aircraft Track Selection

The task of this module is only postprocessing. Throughout the design of the advanced tracker we implicitly aimed at tracking all objects observed. Hence, at the output of the track maintenance module we have both aircraft tracks and nonaircraft tracks (tracks from fixed objects, sidelobe plots, reflection plots, highway traffic, and so forth). As such, the aircraft track-selection module chooses from that output the tracks that may be from aircraft and presents them at the output of our multisensor-multitarget tracking system. This aircraft track-selection module has the option of using geographic information (e.g., aeronautical information and locations of highways and radar reflection planes).

### 2.2.9 Synchronization

This module organizes a proper timing of task execution with the reception of measurements and the provision of desired tracking output.

### 2.3 BAYESIAN TRACK CONTINUATION

In this section, we outline the principles that underlie the track maintenance system. Once a track has been initiated, the track maintenance system has to continue that track as long as it is observed by at least one sensor. In our design, all measurements received by the track maintenance system are adequately corrected for systematic sensor errors. Hence, our multisensor track-continuation problem is reduced to a "single-sensor" track-continuation problem, where the updating pattern is sequential across the sensors. While performing, track continuation has to cope with several uncertainties, of which the following four cause the major complications:

- Nonlinear aircraft dynamics during a turn,
- The association of measurements with existing tracks,
- Gaussian-mixture-type measurement noise (outlier measurement),
- Sudden starts and stops of maneuvers (mode switching).

To develop a high-quality track continuator we adopted the Bayesian approach. It consists of building appropriate stochastic models; developing the exact filter solution from the theory of Bayesian estimation for Markov processes; and finally, introducing efficient numerical approximations of the exact solution. By following these three steps, several approximate Bayesian methods were developed for each of the subproblems of tracking. The various approximate Bayesian methods show a trade-off between computational load and performance, depending on the particular application [18–22].

To cope with the first subproblem, the well-known extended Kalman method of linearization along the predicted path is adopted as a good compromise [2]. Of the various approximate methods to cope with the second subproblem, a *multiple-model probabilistic data association* (MMPDA) method [5, 23] is judged to be the best compromise to update an aircraft track from new observations (a PDA method efficiently updates a track from all measurements, rather than from one likely measurement). Moreover, the PDA approach allows us to include an efficient solution to the third subproblem.

For the fourth subproblem, the existing methods were judged insufficient to meet the objectives of the study. Therefore, the desired results have been developed as part of the NLR study. They consist of modeling aircraft behavior as a hybrid-state Markov process and developing an efficient approximation of the Bayesian estimation equations [24]. Without going into the mathematical details of these methods, it is quite well possible to explain how they apply to sudden aircraft maneuvers.

An aircraft trajectory, as seen by ATC, can be subdivided into distinct segments, corresponding to modes of flight, such as constant acceleration, bank angle, or flight-path angle. Switching from one mode to another is controlled by the pilot. An appropriate model for the switching between modes is a finite-state (semi-)Markov process. An aircraft is then modeled as having a hybrid state; consisting of a Euclidean-valued (diffusive) state component and a discrete-valued state component. The discrete state models the mode of flight. The diffuse state models the horizontal position, ground speed, course, and, for some modes, bank angle, flight-path angle, and transversal acceleration. The evolution in time of the discrete state (i.e., switching between modes) and the diffusive state is determined by the physical relations between the state components, the jump-type changes of the control commands of the pilot, and disturbances caused by both the pilot and the wind. In this model, switching from one mode to another mode generally causes a simultaneous random jump in bank angle, flight-path angle, and acceleration. The combination of discrete and diffusive states in a maneuvering trajectory model causes the associated tracking problem to fall within the class of so-called hybrid-state estimation problems. Filtering algorithms for hybrid-state estimation in general consist of a bank of Kalman filters and some algorithm to organize the cooperation between the individual Kalman filters. The better such cooperation is organized, the fewer Kalman filters are necessary to perform close to the exact Bayesian solution. The study of this type of problems led to a better way of organizing the cooperation between Kalman filters; viz., the interacting multiple model algorithm [25–27].

The IMM algorithm (Figure 2.1) has one Kalman filter for each of the $N$ possible mode values. Efficient cooperation between the Kalman filters is realized by an interaction between the estimates $\hat{X}_\theta$ (representing the conditional mean and covariance given mode $\theta$ is in effect) for the different modes at the beginning of each filter

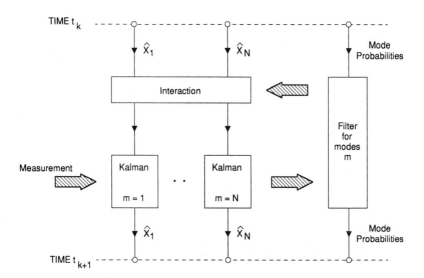

**Figure 2.1** One cycle of the IMM algorithm (N modes). $\hat{X}_i$ represents the conditional expectation and covariance given mode $i$ is effective. The mode probabilities represent the conditional probability that each of the $N$ modes is effective.

cycle. The interaction is determined by the conditional probabilities of switching between modes. For problems like tracking, the IMM interaction is so effective, that the IMM algorithm performs almost like the exact Bayesian filter [26–27]. Moreover, the IMM requires a far lower computational power than other, recently developed, high-performance algorithms for tracking maneuvering aircraft [27–29].

The last step is to assemble a complete track-maintenance module from the three selected suboptimal Bayesian methods:

- The EKF to deal with the nonlinear aircraft dynamics during turns,
- The PDA approach to deal with unassociated measurements and Gaussian-mixture errors,
- The IMM algorithm to deal with sudden maneuvers.

Figure 2.2 shows the complete track maintenance set-up. Due to the generality of the Bayesian approach, each of the three approximate methods in Figure 2.2 is efficient for a large family of causal stochastic models. As such, the Bayesian tracking set-up of Figure 2.2 can be parametrized adequately for a large family of track continuation problems. Therefore, it is possible to incorporate the measurements of a large variety of sensors into its set-up. The price of this generality is that a large number of parameters have to be set properly. Experience, however, showed that most of these parameters are not very critical.

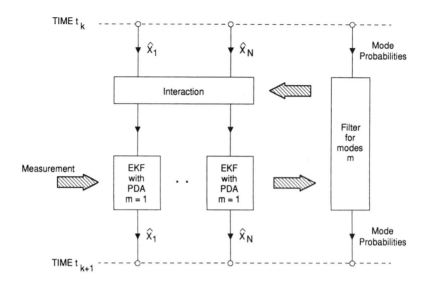

**Figure 2.2** One cycle of the Bayesian track continuator ($N$ modes). $\hat{X}_i$ represents the conditional expectation and covariance given mode $i$ is effective. The mode probabilities represent the conditional probability that each of the $N$ modes is effective.

## 2.4 SYSTEMATIC ERROR ESTIMATION

A prerequisite for multisensor tracking is to handle the registration problem. Following [30] there are both micro- and macro-type registration problems. Micro-type problems (errors) are due to the systematic errors that differ for each object. Macro-type problems (errors) are due to the systematic errors that differ for each sensor. For ATC radar systems, the micro-type errors are aircraft transponder delay and offset between flight level and geometric height. The macro-type errors are radar location error, direction bias, range bias, range-gain bias, and sampling time error.

Because micro-type errors differ for each object, their estimation and correction actually is a problem of track maintenance. An effective way to handle such errors in an ATC environment is to extend the aircraft state components with transponder delay and geometric height and to extend the track maintenance equations in an appropriate way [17, 31]. For simplicity, in this chapter we assume that there are no micro-type errors (no transponder delay and no offset between geometric height and flight level).

The simplest approach to the estimation of macro-type errors is to assume that they are constant in time. Under this assumption, their estimation can be done off-line (e.g., [17]), prior to tuning a multisensor tracking system. Unfortunately, macro errors may change abruptly in time due to technical maintenance or the influence of a changing wind direction on the mechanics of a radar antenna. This requires dynamic estimation of these macro errors, on-line with the maintenance of tracks.

The problem with dynamic estimation of macro-type errors is that, in theory, their filter equations are coupled to the track maintenance equations for the individual tracks. Hence, to keep things manageable, in Appendix B of this chapter we develop an approach to decouple filter equations for macro-error estimation from the track maintenance filter equations. The result is a second-order Kalman filter to estimate the sampling time error and a newly developed EKF-like filter to estimate all other macro errors. We give a detailed description of the latter EKF-like filter in the remainder of this section.

We consider a situation of $\kappa$ surveillance radars, from each of which the systematic error estimator receives the NNPDA measurements $y_{i,t}$, $i = 1, \ldots, \kappa$. Each such measurement consists of direction $\psi_t$ and range $\rho_i$:

$$y_{i,t} = [y_{i,\psi,t} y_{i,\rho,t}]^T \tag{2.1}$$

with direction component $y_{i,\psi,t}$ and range component $y_{i,\rho,t}$ of an object at the (2-D) geographic position:

$$s_t = [s_{x,t} s_{y,t}]^T \tag{2.2}$$

at a measurement frequency $\varphi_i$. For each track, the systematic error estimation module receives the NNPDA measurements of all radars. These measurements are used in the dynamic estimation of the macro errors of the radars (radar location errors $\Delta_{i,x,t}$ and $\Delta_{i,y,t}$, direction bias $\Delta_{i,\psi,t}$, range bias $\Delta_{i,\rho,t}$, and range-gain bias $\Delta_{i,g,t}$):

$$\Delta_{i,t} = [\Delta_{i,x,t} \Delta_{i,y,t} \Delta_{i,\rho,t} \Delta_{i,g,t} \Delta_{i,\psi,t}]^T \tag{2.3}$$

$$y_{i,t} = \begin{bmatrix} n_{i,\psi,t} \\ n_{i,\rho,t} \end{bmatrix} + \tag{2.4}$$

$$\begin{bmatrix} \arctan[(s_{y,t} - r_{i,y} - \Delta_{i,y,t})/(s_{x,t} - r_{i,x} - \Delta_{i,x,t})] + \Delta_{i,\psi,t} \\ (1 + \Delta_{i,g,t})[(s_{x,t} - r_{i,x} - \Delta_{i,x,t})^2 + (s_{y,t} - r_{i,y} - \Delta_{i,y,t})^2 + z_{i,t}^2]^{1/2} + \Delta_{i,\rho,t} \end{bmatrix}$$

where $(r_{i,x}, r_{i,y})$ is the specified geographic radar location; $z_{i,t}$ is the difference in height between the object and the $i$th radar location; and $\{n_{i,\ldots,t}\}$ are independent sequences of independent and identically distributed Gaussian variables of zero expectation and covariances $\sigma_{i,\psi}^2$ and $\sigma_{i,\rho}^2$.

Due to changing wind direction or technical maintenance, the systematic errors may vary in time. Hence, we assume the following linear Gaussian system as an appropriate dynamic error model:

$$\Delta_t = a\Delta_{t-1} + (I - a)E\{\Delta_0\} + w_t \tag{2.5}$$

with $\Delta_0$ the initial error ($\Delta_t$ at $t = 0$), $a = \text{diag}\{a_1, \ldots, a_\kappa\}$, $a_i = \text{diag}\{a_{i,x}, a_{i,y}, a_{i,\psi},$ $a_{i,\rho}, a_{i,g}\}$, $w_t = \text{col}\{w_{1,t}, \ldots, w_{5\kappa,t}\}$, and $\{w_{i,t}\}$, $i = 1 \ldots 5\kappa$, are independent sequences of Gaussian variables of zero expectation, so that the covariance of $\{w_t\}$ satisfies

$$\text{cov}\{w_t\} = \text{cov}\{\Delta_0\} - a\,\text{cov}\{\Delta_0\}a^T \tag{2.6}$$

The setting of the parameters $E\{\Delta_0\}$ and $\text{cov}\{\Delta_0\}$ follows from off-line systematic error evaluations [8, 17].

We assume that for each object there is a filter to estimate the object state from the measurements. Then, for the measurements of all $\kappa$ radars on the interval $(t - 1, t]$ we arrived at the following EKF-like equations (see Appendix B).

The prediction equations are

$$\overline{\Delta}_t = E\{\Delta_0\} + a[\hat{\Delta}_{t-1} - E\{\Delta_0\}] \tag{2.7}$$

$$\overline{P}_{\Delta,t} = \text{cov}\{\Delta_0\} + a[\hat{P}_{\Delta,t-1} - \text{cov}\{\Delta_0\}]a^T \tag{2.8}$$

The measurement update equations are

$$\hat{\Delta}_t \approx \overline{\Delta}_t + \overline{P}_{\Delta,t}\left[\sum_{i=1}^{\kappa} \sum_{u_i \in (t-1,t]} v_{i,u_i}\right] \tag{2.9}$$

$$\hat{P}_{\Delta,t} \approx \overline{P}_{\Delta,t} - \overline{P}_{\Delta,t}\left[\sum_{i=1}^{\kappa} \sum_{u_i \in (t-1,t]} V_{i,u_i}\right]\overline{P}_{\Delta,t}^T \tag{2.10}$$

with $u_i$ running through the sample times of the $i$th radar, and

$$v_{i,t} = [F_{l,i,t}F_{\Delta,i,t} - \overline{F}_t]^T E_{i,t}^{-1} F_{l,i,t}(y_{i,t} - \overline{y}_{i,t}) \tag{2.11}$$

$$V_{i,t} = [F_{l,i,t}F_{\Delta,i,t} - \overline{F}_t]^T E_{i,t}^{-1}[F_{l,i,t}F_{\Delta,i,t} - \overline{F}_t] \tag{2.12}$$

$$\overline{F}_t = \left[\sum_{i=1}^{\kappa} \varphi_i S_{i,t}^{-1}\right]^{-1} \sum_{i=1}^{\kappa} [\varphi_i S_{i,t}^{-1} F_{l,i,t}F_{\Delta,i,t}] \tag{2.13}$$

$$S_{i,t} = F_{l,i,t}R_i F_{l,i,t}^T \tag{2.14}$$

$$E_{i,t} = S_{i,t} + \overline{P}_{s,t} \tag{2.15}$$

where $\overline{P}_{s,t}$ is the predicted covariance of the geometric horizontal position of the object, and

$$R_i = \text{diag}\{\sigma_{i,\psi}^2, \sigma_{i,\rho}^2\} \tag{2.16}$$

$$\bar{y}_{i,t} = \left[ \frac{\bar{\psi}_{i,t} + \overline{\Delta}_{i,\psi,t}}{(1 + \overline{\Delta}_{i,g,t})\bar{\rho}_{i,t} + \overline{\Delta}_{i,\rho,t}} \right] \tag{2.17}$$

$$F_{\Delta,i,t} = \{[F_{\Delta,i,t}]_1 \cdots [F_{\Delta,i,t}]_i \cdots [F_{\Delta,i,t}]_\kappa\} \tag{2.18}$$

$$[F_{\Delta,i,t}]_j = 0, \quad \text{if } j \neq i \tag{2.19}$$

$$[F_{\Delta,i,t}]_i = \left[ \begin{array}{ccc} \cos\bar{\psi}_{i,t}/\bar{d}_{i,t} & -\sin\bar{\psi}_{i,t}/\bar{d}_{i,t} & 1\ 0\ 0 \\ -(1 + \overline{\Delta}_{i,g,t})\cos\bar{\psi}_{i,t} & -(1 + \overline{\Delta}_{i,g,t})\sin\bar{\psi}_{i,t} & 0\ 1\ \bar{\rho}_{i,t} \end{array} \right] \tag{2.20}$$

$$F_{l,i,t} = \left[ \begin{array}{cc} -\bar{d}_{i,t}/2\ \cos(\bar{\psi}_{i,t}) & \bar{\rho}_{i,t}/2(1 + \overline{\Delta}_{i,g,t})\bar{d}_{i,t}\ \cos(\bar{\psi}_{i,t}) \\ \bar{d}_{i,t}/2\ \sin(\bar{\psi}_{i,t}) & \bar{\rho}_{i,t}/2(1 + \overline{\Delta}_{i,g,t})\bar{d}_{i,t}\ \sin(\bar{\psi}_{i,t}) \end{array} \right] \tag{2.21}$$

$$\bar{d}_{i,t} = [(\bar{s}_{x,t} - r_{i,x} - \overline{\Delta}_{i,x,t})^2 + (\bar{s}_{y,t} - r_{i,y} - \overline{\Delta}_{i,y,t})^2]^{1/2} \tag{2.22}$$

$$\bar{\rho}_{i,t} = (\bar{d}_{i,t}^2 + \bar{z}_{i,t}^2)^{1/2} \tag{2.23}$$

$$\bar{\psi}_{i,t} = \operatorname{arctg}[(\bar{s}_{y,t} - r_{i,y} - \overline{\Delta}_{i,y,t})/(\bar{s}_{x,t} - r_{i,x} - \overline{\Delta}_{i,x,t})] \tag{2.24}$$

## 2.5  EVALUATION OF THE TRACKING PERFORMANCE

In this section, we describe the track maintenance performance of a prototype implementation of the tracker. This prototype is called *jump-diffusion* (JUMPDIF) tracking. For track maintenance, its underlying model incorporates four ($N = 4$) horizontal modes of flight (straight flight at constant ground speed, straight flight at changing ground speed, right turn, and left turn) and two ($N = 2$) vertical modes of flight (level flight and climb or descent). The horizontal diffusion state components are 2-D position, ground speed, course, and transversal acceleration. The vertical diffuse state components are flight level and rate of climb or descent. For completeness, in Appendix A, we give a detailed specification of the algorithm in horizontal direction for primary radar data input, provided by a conventional extractor (moving target indicator). This algorithm has been further extended to incorporate additional information provided by new type extractors, such as radial velocity and azimuth extension (azimuth size of object). For secondary radar data input this algorithm has been further extended to incorporate ID information (from a squawking aircraft transponder) and to estimate aircraft state components in the vertical direction. These extensions are not specified, as they do not lead to another type of equation.

The performance evaluation is based on both Monte-Carlo-simulated measurements and measurements of actual traffic. These data sets are selected so that they present a wide range of difficulty to a tracker. Some typical JUMPDIF tracking results, on data from a single, primary radar with a conventional extractor are given in Figures 2.3–2.6. In addition, some typical flight level estimation results, on data

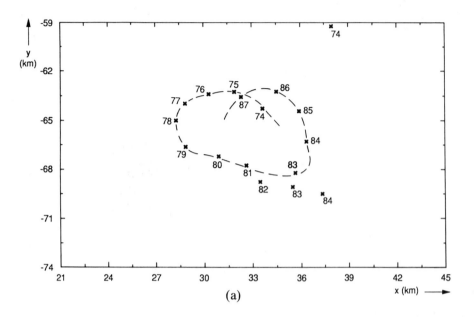

(a)

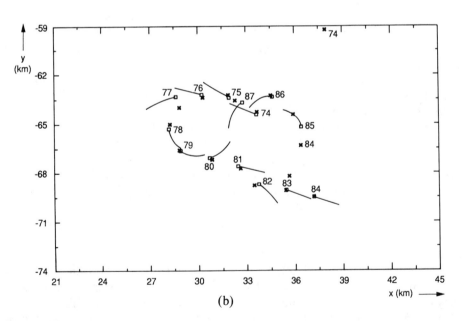

(b)

**Figure 2.3** A "1 g" maneuver with nasty false measurements ($x$ = measurement, # = scan number): (a) hand-reconstructed path; (b) the JUMPDIF track.

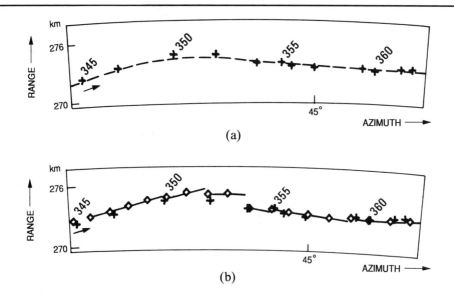

**Figure 2.4** A tangential flight with a change of course ($x$ = measurement, # = scan number): (a) hand-reconstructed path; (b) the JUMPDIF track.

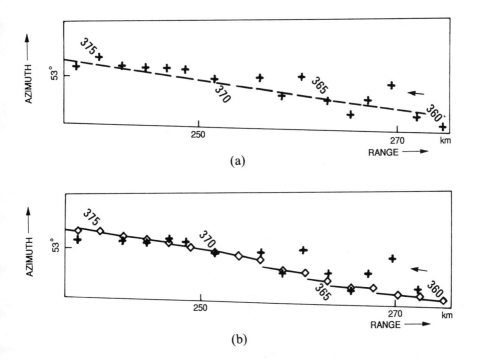

**Figure 2.5** A radial flight ($x$ = measurement, # = scan number): (a) hand-reconstructed path; (b) the JUMPDIF track.

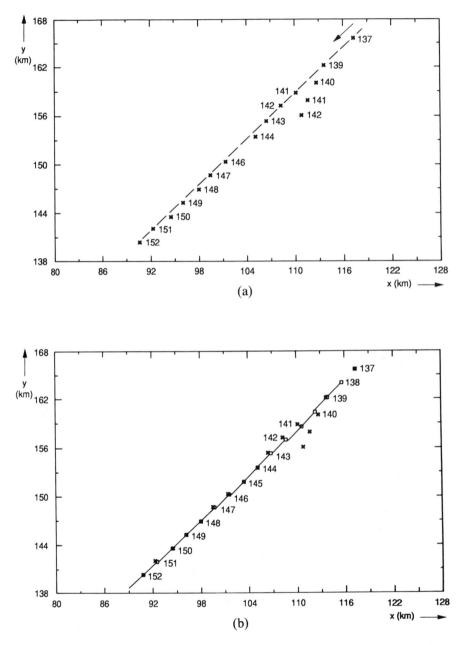

**Figure 2.6** False plots during straight flight ($x$ = measurement, # = scan number): (a) hand-reconstructed path; (b) the JUMPDIF track.

from a single secondary radar, are given in Figure 2.7. The main results of this evaluation are that JUMPDIF provides

- Very accurate state estimates during constant mode of flight,
- Very fast response on and convergence after a change of mode,
- Estimates of its own accuracy that are consistent with the actual errors.

Next, based on [32], we discuss the performance of JUMPDIF compared to a tracker that consists of a (single-mode) EKF in combination with PDA. Although this, too, is a Bayesian tracker, it lacks an adequate solution to switching maneuvers. Using the previously mentioned data sets, the comparison showed that JUMPDIF responds far better on sudden maneuvers and, at the same time, is far less sensitive to bad measurement conditions. The observed differences are even larger than the differences reported for comparisons between Kalman filtering and IMM filtering in simpler situations of sudden mode switchings [26]. These results indicate that JUMPDIF realizes an effective cooperation between the IMM, the EKF, and the PDA methods.

For practical applications, of course, it is more interesting to compare JUMPDIF with operational trackers. The operational trackers we used for this comparison were an $\alpha$-$\beta$ tracker and an adaptive $\alpha$-$\beta$-$\gamma$ tracker, where the indication "adaptive" for the $\alpha$-$\beta$-$\gamma$ refers to its ability to detect and follow turns (the $\gamma$ applies to the transversal acceleration during a turn). The particular $\alpha$-$\beta$ and adaptive $\alpha$-$\beta$-$\gamma$ trackers used have been operational for the main en-route radar systems in the Netherlands, respectively, before and after 1985. Some typical examples of position and speed comparisons between the adaptive $\alpha$-$\beta$-$\gamma$ tracker and JUMPDIF are given in Figures 2.8 (a and b) (actual data is from the "Leerdam" primary radar system).

The result of the comparison is that JUMPDIF performs best, the adaptive $\alpha$-$\beta$-$\gamma$ tracker scores second, the (single-mode) EKF/PDA scores third, and the $\alpha$-$\beta$ tracker scores last. Moreover, the differences between the first and the last trackers are very large: RMS errors and track drop rates differ *one to two orders of magnitude.* The (single-mode) EKF/PDA performs significantly better than the $\alpha$-$\beta$ tracker; that is, far less sensitivity to outlier and false measurements, better convergence during a turn, and smaller RMS speed errors. The adaptive $\alpha$-$\beta$-$\gamma$ tracker shows significant improvement over the (single-mode) EKF/PDA; that is, far smaller RMS state errors during uniform motion and far better convergence after starting or stopping a turn. JUMPDIF performs significantly better than the adaptive $\alpha$-$\beta$-$\gamma$ tracker:

- Far less sensitivity to outliers and false measurements,
- Faster convergence after starting or stopping a maneuver,
- Far smaller RMS speed errors (up to an order of magnitude),
- More stable behavior during "strange" maneuvers (accelerated turn, S-turn, expedite turn, noncircular turn, *et cetera*).

These comparisons show that JUMPDIF provides ATC far better information than even an advanced design like the adaptive $\alpha$-$\beta$-$\gamma$ tracker.

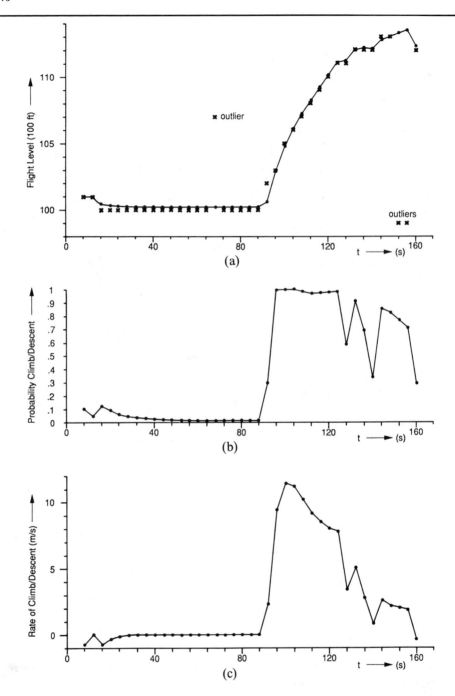

**Figure 2.7** Typical example of JUMPDIF height tracking results. Outlier measurements have no influence, and there is a quick response to a change from flight level to climb: (a) measured (**x**) and estimated (-●-) flight level; (b) climb or descent probability; (c) estimated rate of climb.

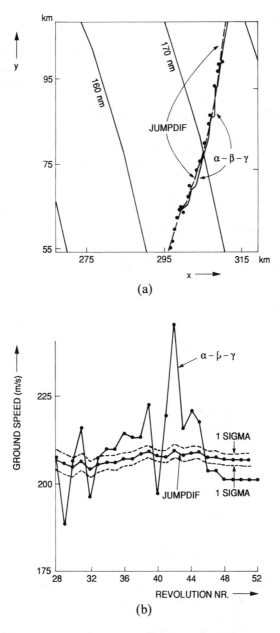

(a)

(b)

**Figure 2.8** Typical $\alpha$-$\beta$-$\gamma$ and JUMPDIF results on an en-route flight: (a) measurements (●) and track positions (—); (b) estimated ground speeds.

## 2.6  SUMMARY AND CONCLUSIONS

A description is given of the design and capabilities of a multisensor tracking system for advanced ATC. This system consists of several modules, of which track maintenance plays the most important role. We outlined the underlying principles of the Bayesian track continuator. It is assembled from the most-efficient approximate Bayesian methods, such as extended Kalman filtering. Probabilistic data association and the interacting multiple model algorithm. The last was developed as a part of the tracking study reported here. A prototype of this multifaceted Bayesian track-maintenance system, called JUMPDIF, was implemented, and its performance was evaluated and compared with that of other trackers. JUMPDIF performed better than other trackers or, more specifically, it showed a far better response to sudden maneuvers and a far lower sensitivity to measurement errors. Also, when measurement conditions deteriorate, the performance degrades far more slowly than the performance of other trackers. Although the computational load of JUMPDIF is rather high (two orders of magnitude compared to $\alpha$-$\beta$ tracking), we can run a multisensor version in real time on available computer systems [33].

The overall conclusion of the study is that an adequate Bayesian approach to the problem of tracking aircraft for ATC resulted in a sophisticated tracker design that can be implemented on available hardware. A prototype version showed excellent behavior and the ability to provide an advanced ATC system with additional state information, such as mode of flight probabilities and a reliable indication of its own accuracy.

## APPENDIX 2.A:   JUMPDIF TRACK MAINTENANCE EQUATIONS IN THE HORIZONTAL DIRECTION

Between two successive measurement moments, $t$ and $t + \tau$, one cycle of the track maintenance module of JUMPDIF consists of four steps:

- Interaction step of generalized IMM,
- EKF time extrapolation equations,
- PDA-based measurement update equations,
- Output calculations.

These steps are carried out in horizontal and vertical directions, respectively. In this appendix we give a detailed description of all models and algorithms to apply the four steps in a horizontal direction on data from a primary surveillance radar with a conventional MTI extractor system.

At the beginning of a cycle at moment $t$, the following horizontal state estimates are available. Probability of mode $\theta$:

$$\hat{P}_{t,\theta} \triangleq \text{Prob}\{\theta_t = \theta \,|\, \mathcal{Y}_t\} \tag{2.A1}$$

State expectation and covariance conditioned on mode $\theta$:

$$\hat{x}_{t,\theta} \triangleq \mathrm{E}\{x_t | \theta_t = \theta, \mathcal{Y}_t\} \tag{2.A2}$$

$$\hat{R}_{t,\theta} \triangleq \mathrm{cov}\{x_t | \theta_t = \theta, \mathcal{Y}_t\} \tag{2.A3}$$

with the past and present measurements:

$$\mathcal{Y}_t = \{y_s; s \leq t\} \tag{2.A4}$$

the state vector ($x$, $y$-position, ground speed, course, transversal acceleration):

$$x_t = \mathrm{Col}\{x_{x,t}, x_{y,t}, x_{v,t}, x_{\phi,t}, x_{a,t}\} \tag{2.A5}$$

the mode being one of four options

$$\theta \in \mathbf{M} = \{\text{uniform, left turn, right turn, speed change}\} \tag{2.A6}$$

where *uniform* is short for straight flight at a constant ground speed and *speed change* is short for a straight flight with changing ground speed.

## 2.A1 Interaction Step of Generalized IMM

This step involves the following parameters, inputs, and outputs:
Parameters:

$\tau$ (sampling period)

$\tau_\theta$,     $\theta \in \mathbf{M}$ (mean sojourn times)

$\pi_{\theta\eta}$,     $\theta \neq \eta \in \mathbf{M}$ (transition probabilities)

$\sigma_{a_1}$,     $\sigma_{a_2}$,     $\sigma_{v_1}$,     $\sigma_{v_2}$ (standard deviations)

Inputs:

$\hat{P}_{t,\theta}$,     $\theta \in \mathbf{M}$ (mode probabilities)

$\hat{x}_{t,\theta}$,     $\theta \in \mathbf{M}$ ($n$-vector means of given modes)

$\hat{R}_{t,\theta}$,     $\theta \in \mathbf{M}$ (covariances of given modes)

Outputs:

$$\bar{P}_{t+\tau,\theta}$$

$$\hat{x}_{t+,\theta}$$

$$\hat{R}_{t+,\theta}, \qquad \theta \in \mathbf{M}$$

The processing during this step consists of evaluating the interaction equations of a continuous-discrete IMM algorithm [24, pp. 106–109]. The underlying model consists of discrete-time measurements of a hybrid-state stochastic differential equation, so that the underlying model for the interaction equations is

$$\text{Prob}\{\theta_{t+\tau} = \theta\} = \sum_{\eta} \Pi_{\theta\eta}(\tau)\,\text{Prob}\{\theta_t = \eta\} \tag{2.A7}$$

$$x_{t+} \overset{\Delta}{=} \lim_{s\downarrow t+} x_s = C_{x,\theta\eta}x_t + C_{c,\theta\eta} + C_{u,\theta\eta}u_{t+\tau} \tag{2.A8}$$

where $\theta$ and $\eta$ are short for $\theta_{t+\tau}$ and $\theta_t$, respectively;

$$\Pi_{\theta\eta}(\tau) \overset{\Delta}{=} \text{Prob}\{\theta_{t+\tau} = \theta \mid \theta_t = \eta\} \tag{2.A9}$$

and $\{u_{t_i}\}$ is a sequence of independent standard Gaussian variables.
For JUMPDIF, the following type of parametrization is used:

$$\Pi_{\theta\eta}(\tau) = \begin{cases} \exp\left(-\tau/\tau_\theta\right), & \text{if } \eta = \theta \\ \pi_{\theta\eta}[1 - \Pi_{\theta\theta}(\tau)], & \text{if } \eta \neq \theta \end{cases} \tag{2.A10}$$

with

$$\pi_{\theta\theta} = 0 \text{ and } \sum_{\eta\in\mathbf{M}} \pi_{\theta\eta} = 1 \tag{2.A11}$$

$$C_{x,\theta\eta} = [1\ 1\ 1\ 1\ c_{x,\theta\eta}]^T \tag{2.A12}$$

$$C_{c,\theta\eta} = [0\ 0\ 0\ 0\ c_{c,\theta\eta}]^T \tag{2.A13}$$

$$C_{u,\theta\eta} = [0\ 0\ c_{v,\theta\eta}\ 0\ c_{u,\theta\eta}]^T \tag{2.A14}$$

$$C_{c,\theta\eta} = \begin{cases} -\sigma_{a_1}, & \text{if } \eta \neq \theta = \text{left turn} \\ \sigma_{a_1}, & \text{if } \eta \neq \theta = \text{right turn} \\ 0, & \text{otherwise} \end{cases} \tag{2.A15}$$

$$c_{x,\theta\eta} = \begin{cases} 0, & \text{if } \eta \neq \theta = \text{uniform or left or right turn} \\ 1, & \text{otherwise} \end{cases} \tag{2.A16}$$

$$c_{u,\theta\eta} = \begin{cases} \sigma_{a_2}, & \text{if } \eta \neq \theta = \text{left or right turn} \\ 0, & \text{otherwise} \end{cases} \tag{2.A17}$$

$$c_{v,\theta\eta} = \begin{cases} \sigma_{v_1}, & \text{if } \theta = \text{speed change}, & \eta = \text{uniform} \\ \sigma_{v_2}, & \text{if } \theta = \text{speed change}, & \eta = \text{left or right turn} \\ 0, & \text{otherwise} \end{cases} \tag{2.A18}$$

Substitution of this model in the interaction equations of the generalized IMM [26] yields the equations to be evaluated during step A1.

Starting with the $N$ weights $\hat{P}_{t,\theta}$, the $N$ means $\hat{x}_{t,\theta}$ and the $N$ associated covariances $\hat{R}_{t,\theta}$, we compute the mixed initial condition for the filter matched to $\theta_{t+\tau} = \theta$, according to the following equations:

$$\overline{P}_{t+\tau,\theta} = \sum_{\eta \in M} \Pi_{\theta\eta}(\tau)\hat{P}_{t,\eta} \tag{2.A19}$$

if $\overline{P}_{t+\tau,\theta} = 0$ prune hypothesis $\theta_{t+\tau} = \theta$, otherwise

$$\hat{x}_{t+,\theta} = \sum_{\eta \in M} \Pi_{\theta\eta}(\tau)\hat{P}_{t,\eta}\hat{\mathcal{X}}_{t+,\theta\eta}/\overline{P}_{t+\tau,\theta} \tag{2.A20}$$

$$\hat{R}_{t+,\theta} = \sum_{\eta \in M} \Pi_{\theta\eta}(\tau)\hat{P}_{t,\eta}(\hat{\mathcal{R}}_{t+,\theta\eta} + (\hat{\mathcal{X}}_{t+,\theta\eta} - \hat{x}_{t+,\theta})(\cdots)^T]/\overline{P}_{t+\tau,\theta} \tag{2.A21}$$

with the values of $\hat{\mathcal{X}}$ and $\hat{\mathcal{R}}$ defined by

$$\hat{\mathcal{X}}_{t+,\theta\eta} = C_{c,\theta\eta} + [I + C_{x,\theta\eta}]\hat{x}_{t,\eta} \tag{2.A22}$$

$$\hat{\mathcal{R}}_{t+,\theta\eta} = [I + C_{x,\theta\eta}]\hat{R}_{t,\eta}[I + C_{x,\theta\eta}]^T + C_{u,\theta\eta}C_{u,\theta\eta}^T \tag{2.A23}$$

## 2.A2   EKF Time Extrapolation Equations

This step involves the following parameters, inputs, and outputs:
Parameters:

$\tau$ (sampling period)

$\sigma_{v_3}$ (standard deviation)

Inputs:

$$\overline{P}_{t+\tau,\theta}$$

$$\hat{x}_{t^+,\theta}$$

$$\hat{R}_{t^+,\theta}, \qquad \theta \in \mathbf{M}$$

Outputs:

$$\overline{P}_{t+\tau,\theta}$$

$$\overline{x}_{t+\tau,\theta}$$

$$\overline{R}_{t+\tau,\theta}, \qquad \theta \in \mathbf{M}$$

The processing during this step consists of evaluating $N$ EKF time extrapolation equations, one for each of the $N$ modes [24, pp. 106–109]. The underlying model for this step is the following stochastic differential equation on $(t, t + \tau)$:

$$dx_s = a(x_s)\, ds + b(\theta_s)\, dw_s \qquad (2.\text{A}24)$$

with $\{w_s\}$ a standard Brownian motion and

$$a(x) = [x_v \cos x_\phi \; x_v \sin x_\phi \; 0 \; x_a/x_v \; 0]^T, \qquad (2.\text{A}25)$$

$$b(\theta) = \begin{cases} [0\;0\;\;\sigma_{v_3}\;0\;0]^T, & \text{if } \theta \neq \text{Uniform}, \\ [0\;0\;\;0\;\;0\;0]^T, & \text{else.} \end{cases} \qquad (2.\text{A}26)$$

To place (2.A24) within a discrete-time EKF framework, we need an appropriate discrete-time approximation and linearization. As such, we first introduce a refined Euler-Cauchy scheme for the drift term and an implicit scheme for the diffusion term.

$$x_{t+\tau} \cong A(x_t, \tau) + b(\theta_{t+\tau})\,[w_{t+\tau} - w_t], \qquad (2.\text{A}27)$$

with: $\qquad A(x, \tau) \triangleq x + \tau\, a(\mathbf{x}(x)), \qquad (2.\text{A}28)$

$$\mathbf{x}(x) \triangleq x + \tfrac{1}{2}\tau\, a(x). \qquad (2.\text{A}29)$$

Subsequent linearization of $A(x, \tau)$ around $\hat{x}$ yields

$$A(x, \tau) \cong A'(\hat{x}, \tau)\,[x - \hat{x}], \qquad (2.\text{A}30)$$

with: $\qquad A'_{ij}(\hat{x}, \tau) \triangleq \dfrac{\partial A_i}{\partial x_j}(\hat{x}, \tau). \qquad (2.\text{A}31)$

Substitution of the latter model into EKF time extrapolation equations, yields for each $\theta \in \mathbf{M}$, the equations to be evaluated during step 2:

$$\overline{x}_{t+\tau,\theta} \approx A(\hat{x}_{t^+,\theta}, \tau) \tag{2.A32}$$

$$\overline{R}_{t+\tau,\theta} \approx A'(\hat{x}_{t^+,\theta}, \tau)\hat{R}_{t^+,\theta}A'(\hat{x}_{t^+,\theta}, \tau)^T + b(\theta, \tau)b(\theta, \tau)^T \tag{2.A33}$$

## 2.A3  PDA-Based Measurement Update Equations

This step involves the following parameters, inputs, and outputs:
Parameters:

$p_{\text{det}}$ (detection probability)

$p_{\text{out}}$ (outlier probability)

$c_{\text{out}}$ (outlier deviation factor)

$\sigma_\rho$, $\sigma_\varphi$ (standard deviations)

$\lambda$ (false plot density)

$q$ (constant in eq. (2.A53))

Inputs:

$Y_{t+\tau}$ (measurements)

$\overline{P}_{t+\tau,\theta}$

$\overline{x}_{t+\tau,\theta}$

$\overline{R}_{t+\tau,\theta}, \qquad \theta \in \mathbf{M}$

Outputs:

$\hat{P}_{t+\tau,\theta}, \qquad \theta \in \mathbf{M}$ (mode probabilities)

$\hat{x}_{t+\tau,\theta}, \qquad \theta \in \mathbf{M}$ ($n$-vector means given modes)

$\hat{R}_{t+\tau,\theta}, \qquad \theta \in \mathbf{M}$ (covariance given modes)

The processing during this step consists of evaluating a modified version of multiple model PDA equations [23]. The modification consists of an incorporation of a model for outlier measurements. In short, we specify the measurement update equations only in primary radar measurements. Moreover, if it is clear from the context, we suppress the time index $t + \tau$.

The first step is to apply an appropriate gating mechanism, which reduces the number of interesting measurements, say $\{y_{t+\tau}^1, \ldots, y_{t+\tau}^K\} \subset Y_{t+\tau}$, of which at most one satisfies the observation equation:

$$y^j = h(x) + g(x, \chi)n, \qquad j \in [1, K] \tag{2.A34}$$

with $n$ a standard Gaussian vector, and $\chi$ a 0–1 valued random variable with parameter $p_{out} = \text{Prob}\{\chi = 1\}$ (both $\{n_{t_i}\}$ and $\{\chi_{t_i}\}$ are i.i.d. sequences). All other values of $y^j$ are assumed to be homogeneously distributed false measurements. The model underlying this step covers range-azimuth measurements $(y_\rho^j, y_\varphi^j)$:

$$h_\rho(x) = [(x_x^2 + x_y^2)^{1/2}\ 0\ 0\ 0\ 0]^T \tag{2.A35}$$

$$h_\varphi(x) = [0\ \arctan(x_x/x_y)\ 0\ 0\ 0]^T \tag{2.A36}$$

whereas the following parametrization of $g$ is used:

$$g_\rho(x, \chi) = (1 + \chi c_{out}) \cdot [1\ 0\ ]^T \tag{2.A37}$$

$$g_\varphi(x, \chi) = (1 + \chi c_{out}) \cdot [0\ \max\{\sigma_\varphi, \sigma_\rho/(x_x^2 + x_y^2)^{1/2}\}]^T \tag{2.A38}$$

To linearize the model around a nominal state, $x'$, we introduce the following transformation:

$$f(y^j) = [y_\rho^j \cos y_\varphi^j\ \ y_\rho^j \sin y_\varphi^j] \tag{2.A39}$$

which allows us to approximate the measurement equation of $x$ by a linear equation:

$$f(y^j) \approx Hx + F(x')g(x', \chi)n \tag{2.A40}$$

with

$$F_{ik}(x') = \frac{\partial f_i}{\partial y_k^j} [h(x')] \tag{2.A41}$$

$$H = [1\ 1\ 0\ 0\ 0]^T \tag{2.A42}$$

To derive the equations to update the state estimates with the $K$ measurements, we next consider the following hypothesis weights:

$$\beta_\theta^0 \triangleq \text{Prob}\{\text{no plot is correct} | \mathcal{Y}, \theta\} \tag{2.A43}$$

$$\beta_\theta^j \triangleq \text{Prob}\{y^j \text{ is correct, } \chi = 0 | \mathcal{Y}, \theta\} \tag{2.A44}$$

$$\beta_\theta^{-j} \triangleq \text{Prob}\{y^j \text{ is correct, } \chi = 1 | \mathcal{Y}, \theta\}, \qquad j \in [1, K] \tag{2.A45}$$

In case there is no more than one track and no outlier measurements ($p_{\text{out}} = 0$), the evaluation of these weights in the MMPDA situation is well known [23]. To incorporate our outlier measurement model we combine this MMPDA approach with the GPB1 (generalized pseudo-Bayes, type 1 [27, 34]) approach of Athans and Chang. The eventual result of this is the following modified MMPDA weight evaluation:

$$\beta_\theta^0 \approx 2\pi\lambda'(1 - p_{\text{det}})p_{\text{det}}^{-1}/c_\theta \tag{2.A46}$$

$$\beta_\theta^j \approx (1 - p_{\text{out}})|E_\theta|^{-1/2} \exp\{-\tfrac{1}{2}v_\theta^{jT}E_\theta^{-1}v_\theta^j\}/c_\theta \tag{2.A47}$$

$$\beta_\theta^{-j} \approx p_{\text{out},\theta}|E_{\text{out},\theta}|^{-1/2} \exp\{-\tfrac{1}{2}v^{jT_\theta}E_{\text{out},\theta}^{-1}v_\theta^j\}/c_\theta \tag{2.A48}$$

with $\lambda'$ equal to $\lambda$ in the case of a single track, and

$$c_\theta \text{ so that } \sum_{j=-K}^{K} \beta_\theta^j = 1 \tag{2.A49}$$

$$v_\theta^j = f(y^j) - H\bar{x}_\theta \tag{2.A50}$$

$$E_\theta = H\bar{R}_\theta H^T + F(\bar{x}_\theta)g(\bar{x}_\theta, 0) \text{ diag}\{\sigma_\rho, \sigma_\varphi\}g(\bar{x}_\theta, 0)^T F(\bar{x}_\theta)^T \tag{2.A51}$$

$$E_{\text{out},\theta} = H\bar{R}_\theta H^T + F(\bar{x}_\theta)g(\bar{x}_\theta, 1) \text{ diag}\{\sigma_\rho, \sigma_\varphi\}g(\bar{x}_\theta, 1)^T F(\bar{x}_\theta)^T \tag{2.A52}$$

To incorporate multiple tracks into our modified MMPDA approach, without running into problems of permutational complexity or track coalescense [11], we make a worst case assumption about other tracks: the nearest track in the gate causes an increase of the local false plot density $\lambda'$ that is inversely proportional to the squared distance between the two tracks. This leads to the following equation for $\lambda'$:

$$\lambda' = \lambda + p_{\text{det}}/2\pi\min_i\{(\bar{x}_x - \bar{x}_x^i)^2 + (\bar{x}_y - \bar{x}_y^i)^2 + q^2|E_\theta|\} \tag{2.A53}$$

where $i$ runs across all other tracks within the gate, $q$ is a parameter, and $\bar{x}_x$ and $\bar{x}_y$ refer to the weighted average of the mode conditional predicted means, $\bar{x}_{x,\theta}$ and $\bar{x}_{y,\theta}$; $\theta \in \mathbf{M}$.

Having evaluated the $\beta$-weights for each plot, we finally arrive at the equations to update the state estimates from measurements:

$$\hat{P}_\theta \approx \bar{P}_\theta c_\theta/c \tag{2.A54}$$

$$\hat{x}_\theta \approx \overline{x}_\theta + K_{\theta,0} V_{\theta,0} + K_{\theta,1} V_{\theta,1} \tag{2.A55}$$

$$\hat{R}_\theta \approx \overline{R}_\theta - \left[ K_{\theta,0} \sum_{j=1}^{K} \beta_{j,\theta} + K_{\theta,1} \sum_{j=1}^{K} \beta_{-j,\theta} \right] H\overline{R}_\theta \tag{2.A56}$$

$$- [K_{\theta,0} V_{\theta,0} + K_{\theta,1} V_{\theta,1}][K_{\theta,0} V_{\theta,0} + K_{\theta,1} V_{\theta,1}]^T$$

$$+ K_{\theta,0} \sum_{j=1}^{K} [\beta_{j,\theta} \nu_\theta^j \nu_\theta^{jT}] K_{\theta,0} + K_{\theta,1} \sum_{j=1}^{K} [\beta_{-j,\theta} \nu_\theta^j \nu_\theta^{jT}] K_{\theta,1}$$

with

$$K_{\theta,0} = \overline{R}_\theta H^T E_\theta^{-1} \tag{2.A57}$$

$$K_{\theta,1} = \overline{R}_\theta H^T E_{\text{out},\theta}^{-1} \tag{2.A58}$$

$$V_{\theta,0} = \sum_{j=1}^{K} \beta_{j,\theta} \nu_\theta^j \tag{2.A59}$$

$$V_{\theta,1} = \sum_{j=1}^{K} \beta_{-j,\theta} \nu_\theta^j \tag{2.A60}$$

and $c$ so that $\sum_{\theta \in M} \hat{P}_\theta = 1$.

## 2.A4  Output Calculations

For output purpose only, this step calculates the weighted average of the state estimates for the different modes:

$$\hat{x}_{t+\tau} = \sum_{\theta \in M} \hat{P}_{t+\tau,\theta} \hat{x}_{t+\tau,\theta} \tag{2.A61}$$

$$\hat{R}_{t+\tau} = \sum_{\theta \in M} \hat{P}_{t+\tau,\theta} \{ \hat{R}_{t+\tau,\theta} + [\hat{x}_{t+\tau,\theta} - \hat{x}_{t+\tau}][\cdot \cdot \cdot]^T \} \tag{2.A62}$$

## APPENDIX 2.B:  JOINT TRACKING AND SENSORS' SYSTEMATIC ERROR ESTIMATION

In this appendix we develop an approach to the estimation of systematic sensor measurement errors jointly with multisensor tracking. We restrict our attention to systematic errors that are not observable in a single sensor situation. We consider a situation of $\kappa$ sensors, each of which makes partial observations of the state of an object during each scan. Each sensor has its own scan rate, $\varphi_i$, $i \in [1, \kappa]$.

Let $\{\Delta_t\}$ represent the systematic error process and let $\{s_t\}$ represent the observed output components of the object's state process $\{x_t\}$; that is, $s_t = h(x_t)$, where $h$ is *equal for all sensors*. Furthermore, we assume that a measurement $y_{i,t}$ of the $i$th sensor is $m$-dimensional and satisfies the following model:

$$y_{i,t} = f_i(\Delta_t, s_t) + g_i(\Delta_t, s_t)n_{i,t} \tag{2.B1}$$

with $\{n_{i,t}\}$ a sequence of i.i.d. standard Gaussian variable, whereas $\{n_{i,t}\}$, $\{\Delta_t\}$, and $\{s_t\}$ are independent.

As a starting point to recursive estimation we use the measurement update equations of an extended Kalman filter for the combined state

$$z_t^T = [\Delta_t^T s_t^T] \tag{2.B2}$$

with

$$\Delta_t^T \triangleq [\Delta_{1,t}^T \cdots \Delta_{\kappa,t}^T] \tag{2.B3}$$

The linearized observation equation reads

$$y_{i,t} - \bar{y}_{i,t} \approx F_{s,i,t}(s_t - \bar{s}_t) + F_{\Delta,i,t}(\Delta_t - \bar{\Delta}_t) + G_{i,t}n_{i,t} \tag{2.B4}$$

with

$$\bar{y}_{i,t} \triangleq f_i(\bar{\Delta}_t, \bar{s}_t) \tag{2.B5}$$

$$G_{i,t} \triangleq g_i(\bar{\Delta}_t, \bar{s}_t) \tag{2.B6}$$

$$(F_{s,i,t})_{jk} \triangleq \frac{\partial f_{ij}}{\partial s_k}(\bar{z}_t) \tag{2.B7}$$

$$F_{\Delta,i,t} = [0 \cdots 0 \, F_{\Delta_{i,t}} \, 0 \cdots 0] \tag{2.B8}$$

$$(F_{\Delta_{i,t}})_{jk} \triangleq \frac{\partial f_{ij}}{\partial \Delta_{i_k}}(\bar{z}_t) \tag{2.B9}$$

Next we introduce the C.1 assumption: $F_{s,i,t}^T F_{s,i,t}$ is invertible for every $(i,t)$. Under C.1, the linearized observation equation transforms to

$$v_{i,t} \approx F_{l,i,t}F_{\Delta,i,t}(\Delta_t - \bar{\Delta}_t) + (s_t - \bar{s}_t) + F_{l,i,t}G_{i,t}n_{i,t} \tag{2.B10}$$

58

with

$$\nu_{i,t} \triangleq F_{l,i,t}(y_{i,t} - \overline{y}_{i,t}) \tag{2.B11}$$

and $F_{l,i,t}$ the left-inverse of $F_{s,i,t}$ [35, p. 138];

$$F_{l,i,t} \triangleq (F_{s,i,t}^T F_{s,i,t})^{-1} F_{s,i,t}^T \tag{2.B12}$$

## 2.B1  Extended Kalman Filter

Let $\overline{z}_t$ and $\overline{P}_t$ denote the predicted conditional mean and covariance of $z_t$. The extended Kalman measurement update equations we consider are

$$\hat{z}_t = \overline{z}_t + K_{i,t}E_{i,t}^{-1}\nu_{i,t} \tag{2.B13}$$
$$\hat{P}_t = \overline{P}_t - K_{i,t}E_{i,t}^{-1}K_{i,t}^T \tag{2.B14}$$
$$K_{i,t} = \overline{P}_t F_{i,t}^T \tag{2.B15}$$

with

$$F_{i,t} \triangleq [F_{l,i,t} F_{\Delta,i,t} I] \tag{2.B16}$$
$$E_{i,t} \triangleq F_{l,i,t}G_{i,t}G_{i,t}^T F_{l,i,t}^T + F_{i,t}\overline{P}_t F_{i,t}^T \tag{2.B17}$$

Let $(\overline{\Delta}_t, \overline{s}_t)$, $(\overline{P}_{\Delta,t}, \overline{P}_{s,t})$, and $\overline{P}_{\Delta s,t}$ denote the predicted conditional means, conditional covariances, and conditional cross-covariance of $(\Delta_t, s_t)$. With this, the preceding equations can be written as

$$\hat{\Delta}_t = \overline{\Delta}_t + K_{\Delta,i,t}E_{i,t}^{-1}\nu_{i,t} \tag{2.B18}$$
$$\hat{P}_{\Delta,t} = \overline{P}_{\Delta,t} - K_{\Delta,i,t}E_{i,t}^{-1}K_{\Delta,i,t}^T \tag{2.B19}$$
$$K_{\Delta,i,t} = \overline{P}_{\Delta,t}F_{\Delta,i,t}^T F_{l,i,t}^T + \overline{P}_{\Delta s,t} \tag{2.B20}$$
$$\hat{s}_t = \overline{s}_t + K_{s,i,t}E_{i,t}^{-1}\nu_{i,t} \tag{2.B21}$$
$$\hat{P}_{s,t} = \overline{P}_{s,t} - K_{s,i,t}E_{i,t}^{-1}K_{s,i,t}^T \tag{2.B22}$$
$$K_{s,i,t} = \overline{P}_{s,t} + \overline{P}_{s\Delta,t}F_{\Delta,i,t}^T F_{l,i,t}^T \tag{2.B23}$$
$$E_{i,t} = [F_{l,i,t}G_{i,t}G_{i,t}^T F_{l,i,t}^T + \overline{P}_{s,t} + F_{l,i,t}F_{\Delta,i,t}\overline{P}_{\Delta,t}F_{\Delta,i,t}^T F_{l,i,t}^T \tag{2.B24}$$
$$+ \overline{P}_{s\Delta,t}F_{\Delta,i,t}^T F_{l,i,t}^T + F_{l,i,t}F_{\Delta,i,t}\overline{P}_{\Delta s,t}]$$

The appearance of the cross-covariance $\overline{P}_{\Delta s,t}$ in these equations makes them too complex for direct numerical implementation. Hence, we like to introduce an effective approximation of that cross-covariance. To develop such an approximation, we first consider the single-sensor situation.

## 2.B2  The Single-Sensor Situation

By assumption, the systematic errors are not observable in the single-sensor case ($\kappa = 1$), which means

$$E[\nu_t(\Delta_t - \overline{\Delta}_t)^T | \mathcal{Y}_{t-}] \approx 0 \tag{2.B25}$$

Substitution of (2.B10) and evaluation yields

$$E[(s_t - \overline{s}_t)(\Delta_t - \overline{\Delta}_t)^T | \mathcal{Y}_{t-}] \approx -E[F_{l,t}F_{\Delta,t}(\Delta_t - \overline{\Delta}_t)(\Delta_t - \overline{\Delta}_t)^T | \mathcal{Y}_{t-}] \tag{2.B26}$$

Hence,

$$\overline{P}_{s\Delta,t} \approx -F_{l,t}F_{\Delta,t}\overline{P}_{\Delta,t} \tag{2.B27}$$

Substituting this into (2.B20), (2.B23), and (2.B24) yields

$$K_{\Delta,t} \approx 0, \tag{2.B28}$$
$$K_{s,t} \approx \overline{P}_{s,t} - F_{l,t}F_{\Delta,t}\overline{P}_{\Delta,t}F_{\Delta,t}^T F_{l,t}^t \tag{2.B29}$$
$$E_t \approx F_{l,t}G_tG_t^T F_{l,t}^T + \overline{P}_{s,t} - F_{l,t}F_{\Delta,t}\overline{P}_{\Delta,t}F_{\Delta,t}^T F_{l,t}^T \tag{2.B30}$$

Notice that $K_{\Delta,t} \approx 0$ corresponds with the assumption that the systematic errors are not observable in the single-sensor case.

## 2.B3  The Multisensor Situation

If *there are $\kappa$ sensors,* the systematic errors may be partly observable. Hence, we propose the following approximation

$$E\left[\sum_{i=1}^{\kappa} \varphi_i S_{i,t}^{-1}\nu_{i,t}(\Delta_t - \overline{\Delta}_t)^T | \mathcal{Y}_{t-}\right] \approx 0 \tag{2.B31}$$

where the index $i$ refers to the $i$th sensor, and $S_{i,t}$ is

$$S_{i,t} \triangleq F_{l,i,t} G_{i,t} G_{i,t}^T F_{l,i,t}^T \tag{2.B32}$$

Substitution of (2B.10) and subsequent evaluation yields

$$\mathrm{E}\left[\sum_{i=1}^{\kappa} \varphi_i S_{i,t}^{-1}(s_t - \bar{s}_t)(\Delta_t - \bar{\Delta}_t)^T | \mathcal{Y}_{t-}\right]$$

$$\approx -\mathrm{E}\left[\sum_{i=1}^{\kappa} \varphi_i S_{i,t}^{-1} F_{l,i,t} F_{\Delta,i,t}(\Delta_t - \bar{\Delta}_t)(\Delta_t - \bar{\Delta}_t)^T | \mathcal{Y}_{t-}\right] \tag{2.B33}$$

which implies

$$\sum_{i=1}^{\kappa} \varphi_i S_{i,t}^{-1} \bar{P}_{s\Delta,t} \approx - \sum_{i=1}^{\kappa} \varphi_i S_{i,t}^{-1} F_{l,i,t} F_{\Delta,i,t} \bar{P}_{\Delta,t} \tag{2.B34}$$

Hence,

$$\bar{P}_{s\Delta,t} \approx -\bar{F}_t \bar{P}_{\Delta,t} \tag{2.B35}$$

with

$$\bar{F}_t \triangleq \left(\sum_{i=1}^{\kappa} \varphi_i S_{i,t}^{-1}\right)^{-1} \sum_{i=1}^{\kappa} (\varphi_i S_{i,t}^{-1} F_{l,i,t} F_{\Delta,i,t}) \tag{2.B36}$$

Substituting (2.B35) into the extended Kalman measurement update equations (2.B20), (2.B23), and (2.B24) yields

$$K_{\Delta,i,t} \approx \bar{P}_{\Delta,t}[F_{l,i,t} F_{\Delta,i,t} - \bar{F}_t]^T \tag{2.B37}$$

$$K_{s,i,t} \approx \bar{P}_{s,t} - \bar{F}_t \bar{P}_{\Delta,t} F_{\Delta,i,t}^T F_{l,i,t}^T \tag{2.B38}$$

$$E_{i,t} \approx S_{i,t} + \bar{P}_{s,t} + F_{l,i,t} F_{\Delta,i,t} \bar{P}_{\Delta,t} F_{\Delta,i,t}^T F_{l,i,t}^T \tag{2.B39}$$

$$- \bar{F}_t \bar{P}_{\Delta,t} F_{\Delta,i,t}^T F_{l,i,t}^T - F_{l,i,t} F_{\Delta,i,t} \bar{P}_{\Delta,t} \bar{F}_t^T$$

## 2.B4    Systematic Error Estimation After Convergence

Our next step is to evaluate (2.B18) through 2.B39) under the assumption that the systematic error estimates converge to accurate values. Hence, it is reasonable to make assumption C.2: $\|F_{l,i,t}F_{\Delta,i,t}\overline{P}_{\Delta,t}F_{\Delta,i,t}^{T}F_{l,i,t}^{T}\| \ll \epsilon_{\min}(\overline{P}_{s,t})$, for every $(i,t)$, with $\| \ \|$ denoting the $L_2$-norm and $\epsilon_{\min}(P)$ denoting the smallest singular value of $P$.

If C.2 is satisfied, (2.B21) through (2.B23) and (2.B38) and (2.B39) simplify to

$$\hat{s}_t \approx \overline{s}_t + \overline{P}_{s,t}E_{i,t}^{-1}\nu_{i,t} \tag{2.B40}$$

$$\hat{P}_{s,t} \approx \overline{P}_{s,t} - \overline{P}_{s,t}E_{i,t}^{-1}\overline{P}_{s,t}^{T} \tag{2.B41}$$

$$E_{i,t} \approx S_{i,t} + \overline{P}_{s,t} \tag{2.B42}$$

The meaning of (2.B40) through (2.B42) is that the influence of systematic error estimation on state estimation is restricted to the influence of the predicted systematic error estimate $\{\overline{\Delta}_t\}$ on the innovation process $\{\nu_{i,t}\}$ and the matrix process $\{F_{s,t}\}$.

To evaluate the systematic error estimation equations, we substitute (2.B37) into (2.B18) and (2.B19), which yields

$$\hat{\Delta}_t = \overline{\Delta}_t + \overline{P}_{\Delta,t}\upsilon_{i,t} \tag{2.B43}$$

$$\hat{P}_{\Delta,t} = \overline{P}_{\Delta,t} - \overline{P}_{\Delta,t}V_{i,t}\overline{P}_{\Delta,t}^{T} \tag{2.B44}$$

with

$$\upsilon_{i,t} \overset{\Delta}{=} [F_{l,i,t}F_{\Delta,i,t} - \overline{F}_t]^{T}E_{i,t}^{-1}\nu_{i,t} \tag{2.B45}$$

$$V_{i,t} \overset{\Delta}{=} [F_{l,i,t}F_{\Delta,i,t} - \overline{F}_t]^{T}E_{i,t}^{-1}[F_{l,i,t}F_{\Delta,i,t} - \overline{F}_t] \tag{2.B46}$$

Under the assumption that $\Delta_{t+u} \approx \Delta_t$, for $u \in [0, \tau]$, this yields

$$\hat{\Delta}_{t+\tau} \approx \overline{\Delta}_t + \sum_{i=1}^{\kappa} \sum_{u_i \in [0,\tau]} \overline{P}_{\Delta,t+u_i}\upsilon_{i,t+u_i} \tag{2.B47}$$

$$\hat{P}_{\Delta,t+\tau} \approx \overline{P}_{\Delta,t} - \sum_{i=1}^{\kappa} \sum_{u_i \in [0,\tau]} \overline{P}_{\Delta,t+u_i}V_{i,t+u_i}\overline{P}_{\Delta,t+u_i}^{T} \tag{2.B48}$$

Together with C.2, this implies

$$\hat{\Delta}_{t+\tau} \approx \overline{\Delta}_t + \overline{P}_{\Delta,t}\left[\sum_{i=1}^{\kappa} \sum_{u_i \in [0,\tau]} \upsilon_{i,t+u_i}\right] \tag{2.B49}$$

$$\hat{P}_{\Delta,t+\tau} \approx \overline{P}_{\Delta,t} - \overline{P}_{\Delta,t}\left[\sum_{i=1}^{\kappa} \sum_{u_i \in [0,\tau]} V_{i,t+u_i}\right]\overline{P}_{\Delta,t}^{T} \tag{2.B50}$$

# REFERENCES

[1] FEATS Group, "Description of the Concept for the Future Air Traffic Management System in the European Region," Rep. ICAO-EUR-DOC-004, European Office of the ICAO, June 1989.

[2] A.H. Jazwinski, *Stochastic Processes and Filtering Theory*, Academic Press, New York, 1970.

[3] A. Farina and F.A. Studer, *Radar Data Processing*, Vol. 1, *Introduction and Tracking*, Research Studies Press, 1985.

[4] S.S. Blackman, *Multiple Target Tracking with Radar Applications*, Artech Book Company, London, 1986.

[5] Y. Bar-Shalom and T.E. Fortmann, *Tracking and Data Association*, Academic Press, Boston, 1988.

[6] H.A.P. Blom, "A Sophisticated Tracking Algorithm for ATC Surveillance Radar Data," *Proc. Intn'l Conf. on Radar 1984*, Paris, 1984, pp. 393–398.

[7] H.A.P. Blom, R.A. Hogendoorn, and F.J. van Schaik, "Bayesian Multi-Sensor Tracking for Advanced Air Traffic Control Systems," A. Benoit (ed.), *Aircraft Trajectories, Computation, Prediction, Control*, Vol. 2, AGARDograph 301, paper 34, 1990.

[8] W. Fischer, C. Muehe, and A. Cameron, "Registration Errors in a Netted Air Surveillance System," MIT Lincoln Labs, Tech. Note 40, 1980.

[9] W.G. Bath, "Association of Multisite Radar Data in the Presence of Large Navigation and Sensor Alignment Errors," *Proc. Int. Radar Conf.*, IEE, London, 1982, pp. 169–173.

[10] M.P. Dana, "Multiple Sensor Registration: A Prerequisite for Multisensor Tracking," Y. Bar-Shalom (ed.), *Multitarget-Multisensor Tracking: Advanced Applications*, Artech House, Norwood, MA, 1990, pp. 155–185 (Chapter 5).

[11] R.J. Fitzgerald, "Development of Practical PDA Logic for Multitarget Tracking by Microprocessor," Y. Bar-Shalom (ed.), *Multitarget-Multisensor Tracking: Advanced Applications*, Artech House, Norwood, MA, 1990, pp. 1–23 (Chapter 1).

[12] A. Farina and F.A. Studer, *Radar Data Processing*, Vol. 2, *Advanced Topics and Applications*, Research Studies Press/Wiley, New York, 1986.

[13] R.J. Prengaman, R.E. Thurber, and W.G. Bath, "A Retrospective Detection Algorithm for Extraction of Weak Targets in Clutter and Interference Environments," Proc. Radar-82, IEE Conf. Publ. 216, London, 1982, pp. 341–345.

[14] R.A. Hogendoorn and H.A.P. Blom, "Bayesian Track Initiation by Time-Reversion of Trajectory Models," Proc. IEEE Int. Conf. on Control and Applications, April 1989, Jerusalem, paper WA-1-5.

[15] R. Giordano, A. Farina, and S. Pardini, "Algorithms for the Compensation of Errors of Disalignment in Multiradar Systems," *Rivista Technica Selenia*, Vol. 7, 1980, pp. 14–19.

[16] P. Van der Kraan, "Aircraft Trajectory Reconstitution on the Basis of Multi-Radar Plot Information," A. Benoit (ed.), *Aircraft Trajectories, Computation, Prediction, Control*, Vol. 2, AGAR-Dograph 301, paper 33, 1990.

[17] H.A.P. Blom, B.A. van Doorn, R.A. Hogendoorn, and W.H.L. Neven, "Organisation and Registration of Data for Multi-Sensor Jump-Diffusion Tracking," NLR Report, TR 91301, 1991.

[18] C.Y. Chong, S. Mori, E. Tse, and R.P. Wishner, "Distributed Hypothesis Formation in Distributed Sensor Networks," Rep. TR 1015-1, Advanced Decision Systems, Mountain View, 1982.

[19] K.R. Pattipati and N.R. Sandell, Jr., "A Unified View of State Estimation in Switching Environments," Proc. 1983 American Control Conf., June 1983, pp. 458–465.

[20] C.B. Chang and J.A. Tabaczynski, "Application of State Estimation to Target Tracking," *IEEE Trans. on Automatic Control*, Vol. AC-29, 1984, pp. 98–109.

[21] T. Kurien and M.E. Liggins, "Report to Target Assignment in Multisensor Multitarget Tracking," Proc. '88 IEEE Conf. on Decision and Control, 1988, pp. 2484–2488.

[22]  Y. Bar-Shalom, "Recursive Tracking Algorithms: From the Kalman Filter to Intelligent Trackers for Cluttered Environment," Proc. IEEE Int. Conf. on Control and Applications (ICCON89), Jerusalem, April 1989, paper RA-1-3.

[23]  M. Gauvrit, "Bayesian Adaptive Filtering for Tracking with Measurements of Uncertain Origin," *Automatica,* Vol. 20, 1984, pp. 217–224.

[24]  H.A.P. Blom, "Bayesian Estimation for Decision-Directed Stochastic Control," Ph.D. thesis, Delft University of Technology, May 1990.

[25]  H.A.P. Blom, "An Efficient Filter for Abruptly Changing Systems," *Proc. 23rd IEEE Conf. on Decision and Control,* 1984, pp. 656–658.

[26]  H.A.P. Blom, "An Efficient Decision-Making-Free Filter for Processes with Abrupt Changes," *Proc. 7th IFAC Symp. Identification and System Parameter Estimation,* York, United Kingdom, 1985, pp. 631–636.

[27]  H.A.P. Blom and Y. Bar-Shalom, "The Interacting Multiple Model Algorithm for Systems with Markovian Switching Coefficients," *IEEE Trans. on Automatic Control,* Vol. AC-33, 1988, pp. 780–783.

[28]  P. Bogler, "Tracking a Maneuvering Target Using Input Estimation," *IEEE Trans. on Aerospace and Electronic Systems,* Vol. AES-23, 1987, pp. 298–310.

[29]  Y. Bar-Shalom, K.C. Chang, and H.A.P. Blom, "Tracking a Maneuvering Target Using Input Estimation versus the Interacting Multiple Model Algorithm," *IEEE Trans. on Aerospace and Electronic Systems,* Vol. AES-25, 1989, pp. 296–300.

[30]  R.C. Luo and M.G. Kay, "Multisensor Integration and Fusion in Intelligent Systems," *IEEE Trans. on Systems, Man and Cybernetics,* Vol. 19, 1989, pp. 901–931.

[31]  J.L. Gertz, "Multisensor Surveillance for Improved Aircraft Tracking," *Lincoln Laboratory J.,* Vol. 2, 1989, pp. 381–396.

[32]  H.A.P. Blom, "Comparison of a Jump Diffusion Tracker with a Kalman Tracker, An Evaluation with Emphasis on Air Traffic Control," Report NLR TR 83063, National Aerospace Laboratory NLR, Amsterdam, The Netherlands, 1983.

[33]  J.F. Gerlofs, "Technical Feasibility of the Multi-Radar Jump-Diffusion Tracker," NLR Memo. IR-86-030L, National Aerospace Laboratory NLR, Amsterdam, The Netherlands, 1986.

[34]  J.K. Tugnait, "Detection and Estimation for Abruptly Changing Systems," *Automatica,* Vol. 18, 1982, pp. 607–615.

[35]  G. Strang, *Linear Algebra and Its Applications,* Academic Press, New York, 1980.

# Chapter 3
# PASSIVE SENSOR DATA FUSION AND MANEUVERING TARGET TRACKING

## Francois Dufour

*Dept. de Physique Appliquée, Ecole Normale Supérieure, Cachan, France*

## Michel Mariton*

*MATRA MS2i, Laboratoire de Traitement des Images et du Signal, St Quentin en Yvelines Cedex, France*

## 3.1 INTRODUCTION

The case of maneuvering targets is a well-established topic in the tracking literature. Many solutions have been proposed using variable dimension filters [3], adaptive process noise [15], and multiple model techniques [10, 12]. The recent monograph [4] provides an in-depth review of these and other related techniques (see also [6] for a radar-oriented perspective).

A promising approach is the interacting multiple models algorithm originally proposed by Blom [7]. This algorithm is based on a hybrid system description of the maneuver scenarios, where the occurrence of maneuvers is explicitly included in the kinematic equations through regime jumps: to the usual state variable $x_k \in \mathbf{R}^n$ (position, speed, *et cetera*), a discrete regime variable $c_k \in \{1, 2, \ldots, M\}$ is appended with

---

*While working on this chapter, we benefited from stimulating discussions with Professor D.D. Sworder (University of California at San Diego) during his stay at MATRA, supported by NATO under Grant No. 890885. We also thank Professor Y. Bar-Shalom (University of Connecticut) for his help in improving the final version of the chapter. Address correspondence to this author. Research supported by DRET (DGA, Paris) under Grant 89/357 and by NATO under Grant No. 890885.

---

$r_t = 1$ corresponding to a no-maneuver situation, and $c_k = 2$ to $M$ corresponding to different maneuvering hypothesis. The transitions of the regime variable are modeled with a Markov chain. A large body of results from hybrid systems research supports the design of tracking applications, both in continuous-time [20, 17] and discrete-time [9, 11, 18], and, if needed, non-Markovian transitions could be taken into account [9, 16]. Compared to other multiple model approaches the main advantage of hybrid system–based solutions is that they are not subject to the so-called "obliviousness to detection" difficulty: the *a priori* jump probabilities used in the regime dynamics make hybrid algorithms alert to regime changes whereas classical solutions are biased toward the no-maneuver hypothesis after long quiescent periods.

The potential of the IMM solution has now been thoroughly investigated and confirmed through simulations [8], and it is available as part of the MULTIDAT software [4]. In the presence of clutter, the IMM has to be complemented to take into account the uncertainty of the measurements' origin. Houles and Bar-Shalom [14] showed that the probabilistic data association is an efficient solution for this aspect.

Existing applications of the IMM algorithm have emphasized radars (active sensors), like in [7] or [2, 22] for civil aircraft. The passive sensor was first considered in [14] where the azimuth and elevation measured by an *infrared search and track* (IRST) sensor were fused with the range and azimuth measured by a radar.

The contribution of this chapter is twofold. First, a novel application of the IMM algorithm is studied where passive only sensors (two IR sensors) are fused to track a target maneuvering in three dimensions. Second, more accurate models of target motion are proposed to improve performance. When general models are used to describe the maneuvering periods, we show that the IMM behavior is unsatisfactory, in that the innovations associated to the different models do not discriminate between the corresponding target maneuvering regimes. The tuning of the Markov chain transition matrix, that is, the *a priori* information, is then crucial to obtaining the correct ordering of the *a posteriori* regime probabilities. We will show that a more satisfactory behavior of the IMM algorithm is obtained by carefully selecting the target motion models in the different regimes.

The rest of the chapter is organized as follows. Section 3.2 describes the application and discusses passive fusion concepts for 3-D tracking. Section 3.3 reviews the IMM and PDA equations, and Section 3.4 focuses on the modeling issue. Simulation results are reported in Section 3.5 together with recommendations on the selection of models.

## 3.2 THE APPLICATION: PASSIVE SENSOR DATA FUSION

The emergence of passive sensors like IRST and *forward looking infrared* (FLIR) had a significant impact on the design of weapons systems that traditionally depended on radars. The fusion of IR and *electromagnetic* (EM) sensors make the system less susceptible to target countermeasures and destruction of one sensor by a preemptive strike. Also the physical measurements of IR and EM sensors nicely complement each other: a surveillance radar delivers range and azimuth but elevation usually is not available because of a broad elevation beam or multipath reflections; on the other hand, the azimuth and elevation measurements of a passive sensor do not allow an instantaneous range determination. Also the quality of the azimuth and elevation delivered by an IR sensor can improve the angular information provided by the radar.

Passive sensors clearly will play a role in applications where radars traditionally have been employed as stand-alone sensors, but it is also clear that an efficient integration of these new sensors requires dedicated data fusion algorithms. This chapter reports on parts of recent efforts in this direction and considers the, *a priori* more difficult, problem of data fusion from passive sensors only.

When the passive sensor platform is allowed to move freely, it is possible to recover range observability by selecting an appropriate path for the platform (this solution has been investigated in sonar in [13]). In other applications (e.g., a command and control system for air defense) the sensor platforms have very slow mobility compared to the target dynamics, and this solution is not feasible. A solution then is to use several passive sensors and fuse their information in some way to estimate the range.

To be more specific, consider the situation depicted in Figure 3.1. Each infrared sensor measures two angles, azimuth and elevation; and two main architectures and

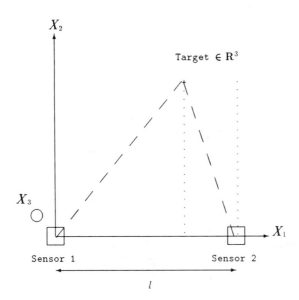

**Figure 3.1** Geometry of the scenario.

algorithmic solutions are possible to perform fusion. First, a tracking algorithm can be implemented at the sensor level (locally) to produce tracks of concatenated angles. The azimuth and elevation track files then are passed to a central fusion node where the range is estimated to generate 3-D target estimates. This is called *track fusion*. Second, the raw angle measurements can be passed to the fusion node where they are directly fed into a 3-D tracking filter. This is called *detection fusion*. Figure 3.2 summarizes the two architectures.

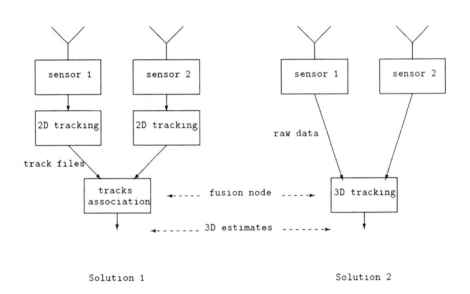

**Figure 3.2** Two fusion system architectures.

The choice between these two solutions has many system implications and depends on the specifics of the application; therefore, it will not be discussed in detail here. However, the two solutions can be compared on a general basis. True, the first solution has lower bandwidth requirements for the communication from sensor nodes to the fusion node: the 2-D filtering of raw data eliminates most false alarms before transmission whereas the complete set of measurements (including false alarms) is transmitted with the second solution. On the other hand, the prefiltering of the first solution degrades performance even if the common-process noise correction is taken into account [5, 19]. This degradation is most significant when hard target maneuvers are present. The tracking of multiple targets with the second solution, though possible, is made cumbersome by the many combinations involved in the data association step. A possible recommendation therefore is to use the two solutions in a complementary fashion, with the first solution associated to a surveillance mode, covering a large area, tracking multiple targets with slow dynamics and measurement rates; and the second solution associated to a track-and-fire mode, the sensors focused on a narrow field-of-view centered on a single target with high dynamics and measurement rates. In the sequel we present a detection fusion design (second solution). The target is maneuvering and uses countermeasures that generate a localized clutter (false alarms).

## 3.3   A HYBRID MODEL BASED ALGORITHM: THE IMMPDA FILTER

In this section we introduce the algorithm coupling the IMM tracker, to account for maneuvers, and the PDA processing of multiple detections.

### 3.3.1   Hybrid Systems

The target is modeled by a hybrid system

$$x_{k+1} = A(c_k)x_k + v_k \qquad (3.1)$$

where $x_k \in \mathbf{R}^n$ is the usual state (e.g., position and velocity) and $c_k \in \{1, 2, \ldots, M\}$ is the target regime (e.g., $c_k = 1$ when the target moves at constant speed, and $c_k = 2$ when the target accelerates). As it will be the case later, $n$ also may depend on $c_k$. The process $v_k$ is a zero-mean white Gaussian noise with known covariance $R^v(c_k)$. We also need nonlinear state models such as

$$x_{k+1} = g(c_k, x_k) + v_k \qquad (3.2)$$

The jumps of $c_k$ are described by a Markov chain:

$$\pi_{ij} = P\{c_{k+1} = j \mid c_k = i\} \qquad (3.3)$$

or in vector form:

$$p_{k+1} = \Pi' p_k \qquad (3.4)$$

with $p_k = [P\{c_k = 1\}, \ldots, P\{c_k = M\}]'$ and $\Pi = (\pi_{ij})_{i,j=1,M}$.

The measurements $y_k \in \mathbf{R}^{n'}$ are a nonlinear function of the state

$$y_k = h(x_k) + w_k \qquad (3.5)$$

where $w_k$ is a zero-mean white Gaussian noise with known covariance $R^w$. We can include regime-dependent measurements in a hybrid filter [17] but this will not be needed here. For our application, the nonlinearity $h$ converts Cartesian target coordinates to azimuth and elevation angles as shown later.

### 3.3.2 Hybrid Filters

The contribution of this chapter is not the IMMPDA filter itself but rather the discussion of the role of new and more accurate target models and the introduction of a new application to passive sensors fusion. The reader therefore is referred to [4, 8, 14] for a comprehensive presentation of this filter, and the algorithm is recalled here without proof.

Hybrid filters essentially are infinite-dimensional filters, and consequently, approximations are needed to arrive at implementable near-optimal solutions. The IMM concept is based on a single approximation (a sum of Gaussian variables is replaced by a single Gaussian variable), and it belongs to the class of merging suboptimal hybrid filters. In this class it was shown, both through simulation [8] and analysis [2, 22], that the IMM compares favorably to its closest competitor, the *generalized pseudo-Bayes algorithm* (GPBA) of order 2 [1]. Roughly speaking, the IMM provides the performance of the GPBA2 with much fewer computational requirements. The other class of suboptimal hybrid filters is based on pruning unlikely regime sequences [21], but [2, 22] show that pruning may lose the track by eliminating valid sequences when a maneuver occurs.

The PDA concept is an efficient way to handle data origin uncertainty where measurements are first validated through gating and then weighted according to the likelihood of their origin. It has been favorably compared to its competitors, including nearest neighbors and multiple hypothesis techniques [4]. In the following paragraphs we detail the IMMPDA Filter equations.

#### 3.3.2.1 Notations

We consider the $k$th time step. At the end of step $k - 1$, $\hat{x}_{k-1|k-1}(j)$, the associated error covariance $R^x_{k-1|k-1}(j)$ and the *a posteriori* probabilities $P\{c_{k-1} = j \mid Z_{k-1}\}$ for each regime $c_k = j, j = 1, \ldots, M$ have been computed based on the cumulative data $Z_{k-1}$ as defined later.

The first function is to expand the regime Markovian transitions to compute $M$ estimates and the associated covariances ($\hat{x}^+_{k-1|k-1}(j)$ and $R^{x+}_{k-1|k-1}(j)$). These variables serve as inputs to $M$ probabilistic data association filters running in parallel to perform state extrapolations and updates ($\hat{x}_{k|k}(j)$ and $R^x_{k|k}(j)$). The innovations ($\tilde{z}_k(j)$) finally are fed to the regime probabilities update function. The output of step $k$ thus is $\hat{x}_{k|k}(j)$, $R^x_{k|k}(j)$, and $P\{c_k = j \mid Z_k\}$ for $j = 1, \ldots, M$.

We shall use the following notations:

- $(\vec{a}_1, \vec{a}_2, \ldots, \vec{a}_n)$ the canonical basis of $\mathbf{R}^n$.
- $m_k$ is the number of measurements validated at time $k$ (according to the validation technique presented in Section 3.3.2.6).
- $Z_k$ is the set of measurements validated at time $k$, $Z_k = \{z^1_k, \ldots, z^{m_k}_k\}$ where $z^j_k$ is the $j$th validated measurement at instant $k$.

- $Z_k = \{Z_1, \ldots, Z_k\}$
- $\hat{x}_{k-1|k-1}(i) = E\{x_{k-1} | Z_{k-1}, c_{k-1} = i\}$
- $\hat{x}^+_{k-1|k-1}(j) = E\{x_{k-1} | Z_{k-1}, c_k = j\}$
- $\hat{x}_{k|k-1}(i) = E\{x_k | Z_{k-1}, c_k = i\}$
- $R^x_{k-1|k-1}(i) = E\{[x_{k-1} - \hat{x}_{k-1|k-1}(i)][x_{k-1} - \hat{x}_{k-1|k-1}(i)]' | Z_{k-1}, c_{k-1} = i\}$
- $R^{x+}_{k-1|k-1}(i) = E\{[x_{k-1} - \hat{x}^+_{k-1|k-1}(i)][x_{k-1} - \hat{x}^+_{k-1|k-1}(i)]' | Z_{k-1}, c_k = i\}$
- $R^x_{k|k-1}(i) = E\{[x_k - \hat{x}_{k|k-1}(i)][x_k - \hat{x}_{k|k-1}(i)]' | Z_{k-1}, c_k = i\}$
- $p_{k-1|k-1}(i) = P\{c_{k-1} = i | Z_{k-1}\}$
- $p_{k|k-1}(i) = P\{c_k = i | Z_{k-1}\}$
- $\hat{y}_{k|k-1}(i) = E\{y_k | Z_{k-1}, c_k = i\}$
- $\hat{y}_{k|k-1} = E\{y_k | Z_{k-1}\}$
- $R^y_{k|k-1}(i) = E\{[y_k - \hat{y}_{k|k-1}(i)][y_k - \hat{y}_{k|k-1}(i)]' | Z_{k-1}, c_k = i\}$
- $R^{xy}_{k|k-1}(i) = E\{[x_k - \hat{x}_{k|k-1}(i)][y_k - \hat{y}_{k|k-1}(i)]' | Z_{k-1}, c_k = i\}$
- The event $\theta^0_k(i)$ is defined as "no validated measurement corresponds to the target for model $i$."
- The event $\theta^l_k(i)$ is defined as "$z^l_k$ is the correct target measurement at instant $k$ for model $i$."
- $\beta^l_k(i) = P\{\theta^l_k(i) | Z_k\}, 0 \le l \le m_k$ are the probabilities of the preceding events.
- $P_d$ is the probability of detecting the target.
- $P_g$ is the probability (at $g$ sigma) of validating a target measurement within the gate.
- $V_{O_k}(i)$ is the volume of the validation region at time $k$ for model $i$.
- $\hat{x}^l_{k|k}(i) = E\{x_k | \theta^l_k(i), Z_k, c_k = i\}$
- $R^l_{k|k}(i) = E\{[x_k - \hat{x}^l_{k|k}(i)][x_k - \hat{x}^l_{k|k}(i)]' | \theta^l_k(i), Z_k, c_k = i\}$
- $\tilde{z}^l_k(i) = z^l_k - \hat{y}_{k|k-1}(i)$

### 3.3.2.2 Regime Probabilities Extrapolation

$$p_{k|k-1}(i) = \sum_{l=1}^{M} \pi_{li} p_{k-1|k-1}(l) \tag{3.6}$$

### 3.3.2.3 State and Covariance Expansion

$$\hat{x}^+_{k-1|k-1}(i) = \sum_{l=1}^{M} \pi_{li} \frac{p_{k-1|k-1}(l)}{p_{k|k-1}(i)} \hat{x}_{k-1|k-1}(l) \tag{3.7}$$

$$R^{x+}_{k-1|k-1}(i) = \sum_{l=1}^{M} \pi_{li} \frac{p_{k-1|k-1}(l)}{p_{k|k-1}(i)} \{R^x_{k-1|k-1}(l)$$
$$+ [\hat{x}_{k-1|k-1}(l) - \hat{x}^+_{k-1|k-1}(i)][\hat{x}_{k-1|k-1}(l) - \hat{x}^+_{k-1|k-1}(i)]'\} \tag{3.8}$$

### 3.3.2.4 State and Covariance Extrapolation

When the state model is linear, we get the usual Kalman equations:

$$\hat{x}_{k|k-1}(i) = A(i)\hat{x}_{k-1|k-1}^{+} \tag{3.9}$$

$$R_{k|k-1}^{x}(i) = A(c_k = i)R_{k-1|k-1}^{x+}(i)A'(c_k = i) + R^v \tag{3.10}$$

However, we also use nonlinear state models and the nonlinearity $x_k = g(c_{k-1}, x_{k-1}) + v_k$ must then be linearized near $\hat{x}_{k-1|k-1}^{+}(i)$. With $(\partial^2 g^l(i)/\partial x^2)$ the Hessian of the $l$th component of $g(i, x)$ and $(\partial g(i)/\partial x)$ the Jacobian of $g(i, x)$ computed at $\hat{x}_{k-1|k-1}^{+}(i)$, we obtain

$$\hat{x}_{k|k-1}(i) = g[i, \hat{x}_{k-1|k-1}^{+}(i)] + \frac{1}{2}\sum_{l=1}^{n} Tr\left\{\left[\frac{\partial^2 g^l(i)}{\partial x^2}\right] R_{k-1|k-1}^{x+}(i)\right\}\vec{a}_l \tag{3.11}$$

$$R_{k|k-1}^{x}(i) = R^v + \left[\frac{\partial g(i)}{\partial x}\right] R_{k-1|k-1}^{x+}(i)\left[\frac{\partial g(i)}{\partial x}\right]^t$$

$$+ \frac{1}{2}\sum_{l=1}^{n}\sum_{p=1}^{n} Tr\left\{\left[\frac{\partial^2 g^l(i)}{\partial x^2}\right] R_{k-1|k-1}^{x+}(i)\left[\frac{\partial^2 g^p(i)}{\partial x^2}\right] R_{k-1|k-1}^{x}(i)\right\}\vec{a}_l(\vec{a}_p)^t \tag{3.12}$$

### 3.3.2.5 Measurement Linearization

With $(\partial^2 h^l/\partial x^2)$ the Hessian of the $l$th component of $h$ and $(\partial h/\partial x)$ the Jacobian of $h$ (computed at $\hat{x}_{k|k-1}(i)$), we obtain

$$\hat{y}_{k|k-1}(i) = h[\hat{x}_{k|k-1}(i)] + \frac{1}{2}\sum_{l=1}^{n'} Tr\left[\left(\frac{\partial^2 h^l}{\partial x^2}\right) R_{k|k-1}^{x}(i)\right]\vec{a}_l \tag{3.13}$$

$$R_{k|k-1}^{xy}(i) = R_{k|k-1}^{x}\left(\frac{\partial h}{\partial x}\right)^t \tag{3.14}$$

$$R_{k|k-1}^{y}(i) = R^w + \left(\frac{\partial h}{\partial x}\right) R_{k|k-1}^{x}(i)\left(\frac{\partial h}{\partial x}\right)^t$$

$$+ \frac{1}{2}\sum_{l=1}^{n'}\sum_{p=1}^{n'} Tr\left[\left(\frac{\partial^2 h^l}{\partial x^2}\right) R_{k|k-1}^{x}(i)\left(\frac{\partial^2 h^p}{\partial x^2}\right) R_{k|k-1}^{x}(i)\right]\vec{a}_l(\vec{a}_p)^t \tag{3.15}$$

### 3.3.2.6 Measurement Validation

The measurement $z_k^l$ is validated if and only if

$$(z_k^l - \hat{y}_{k|k-1})'(R_{k|k-1}^{y})^{-1}(z_k^l - \hat{y}_{k|k-1}) < g \tag{3.16}$$

where $R^y_{k|k-1}$ stands for the largest among the model conditioned innovation covariances ($R^y_{k|k-1} = R^y_{k|k-1}(i_0)$ so that $\det[R^y_{k|k-1}(i_0)] \geq \det[R^y_{k|k-1}(i)]$ for any $i = 1, \ldots, M$) and

$$P_g = 1 - (1 + g^2)\, e^{-g^2/2} \tag{3.17}$$

For our application where the dimension of the measurement is $n' = 2$, the volume of this validation region is $V_{O_k} = \dfrac{\pi^2}{2}\sqrt{\det(R^y_{k|k-1})}\, g^2$ at instant $k$.

### 3.3.2.7 Association Probabilities

We use the parametric PDA and assume Poissonian false alarms with known rate $\lambda$ $\left(\text{there are } m^F = m \text{ false alarms with probability } P\{m^F = m\} = e^{-\lambda V_{O_k}}\dfrac{(\lambda V_{O_k})^m}{m!}\right)$ so that

$$\beta^j_k(i) = \frac{a^j_k(i)}{b_k(i) + \sum_{l=1}^{m_k} a^l_k(i)} \tag{3.18}$$

for $1 \leq j \leq m_k$, and

$$\beta^0_k(i) = \frac{b_k(i)}{b_k(i) + \sum_{l=1}^{m_k} a^l_k(i)} \tag{3.19}$$

where

$$a^j_k(i) = e^{-1/2\{[z^j_k - \hat{y}_{k|k-1}(i)]'[R^y_{k|k-1}(i)]^{-1}[z^j_k - \hat{y}_{k|k-1}(i)]\}} \tag{3.20}$$

$$b_k(i) = \lambda\sqrt{\det[2\pi R^y_{k|k-1}(i)]}\,\frac{1 - P_d P_g}{P_d} \tag{3.21}$$

### 3.3.2.8 Update for Measurement 1

For an observation $z^j_k$ we have

$$x^j_{k|k}(i) = \hat{x}_{k|k-1}(i) + R^{xy}_{k|k-1}(i)[R^y_{k|k-1}(i)]^{-1}\tilde{z}^j_k(i) \tag{3.22}$$

$$R^j_{k|k}(i) = R^x_{k|k-1}(i) - R^{xy}_{k|k-1}(i)[R^y_{k|k-1}(i)]^{-1}R^{yx}_{k|k-1}(i) \tag{3.23}$$

Because $R_{k|k}^l(i)$ does not depend on $l$, it is denoted $R_{k|k}^*(i)$ in the sequel. In the absence of validated measurements, the update step is skipped:

$$\hat{x}_{k|k}^0(i) = \hat{x}_{k|k-1}(i) \tag{3.24}$$

$$R_{k|k}^0(i) = R_{k|k-1}^x(i) \tag{3.25}$$

### 3.3.2.9 PDA Fusion

$$\hat{x}_{k|k}(i) = \sum_{l=0}^{mk} \beta_k^l(i)\hat{x}_{k|k}^l(i) \tag{3.26}$$

$$R_{k|k}^x(i) = \beta_k^0(i)R_{k|k-1}^x(i) + [1 - \beta_k^0(i)]R_{k|k}^*(i)$$

$$+ R_{k|k-1}^{xy}(i)[R_{k|k-1}^y(i)]^{-1} \left\{ \sum_{l=1}^{mk} \beta_k^l(i)\tilde{z}_k^l(i)[\tilde{z}_k^l(i)]' \right. \tag{3.27}$$

$$\left. - \tilde{z}_k(i)[\tilde{z}_k(i)]' \right\} \{R_{k|k-1}^{xy}(i)[R_{k|k-1}^y(i]^{-1}\}'$$

where $\tilde{z}_k(i) = \sum_{l=1}^{m_k} \beta_k^l(i)\tilde{z}_k^l(i)$.

### 3.3.2.10 Regime Probabilities Update

$$p_{k|k}(i) = \frac{1}{\alpha} \left\{ \sum_{p=1}^{m_k} V_{O_k}^{1-m_k} P_g^{-1} \gamma_k^p(m_k) \mathcal{N}[z_k^p(i); 0, R_{k|k-1}^y(i)] \right.$$

$$\left. + V_{O_k}(i)^{-m_k} \gamma_k^0(m_k) \right\} p_{k|k-1}(i) \tag{3.28}$$

where $\mathcal{N}(x; \bar{x}, R)$ is a Gaussian law with mean $\bar{x}$ and variance $R$, and

$$\gamma_k^p(m_k) = \frac{P_d P_g}{P_d P_g m_k + (1 - P_d P_g)\lambda V_{O_k}} \tag{3.29}$$

$$\gamma_k^0(m_k) = \frac{(1 - P_d P_g)\lambda V_{O_k}}{P_d P_g m_k + (1 - P_d P_g)\lambda V_{O_k}} \tag{3.30}$$

($\alpha$ is the normalization constant).

## 3.4 TARGET MOTION MODELS

As any model-based algorithm the IMM algorithm cannot perform better than the models on which it relies. In this section we introduce three different sets of models to describe target maneuver scenarios. Each of these sets demonstrates different dynamic behavior and performance of the algorithm.

### 3.4.1 First Set of Models

We start with the set of models most often used in the multiple models tracking literature. Target motion is described with three models ($M = 3$):

- Model 1.1. For flight segments with constant speed, a state vector of order 6 ($n = 6$) is used:

$$x = [X_1, X_2, X_3, \dot{X}_1, \dot{X}_2, \dot{X}_3]^t \tag{3.31}$$

and the discrete time dynamics matrix

$$A = \begin{bmatrix} 1 & 0 & 0 & T & 0 & 0 \\ 0 & 1 & 0 & 0 & T & 0 \\ 0 & 0 & 1 & 0 & 0 & T \\ 0 & 0 & 0 & 1 & 0 & 0 \\ 0 & 0 & 0 & 0 & 1 & 0 \\ 0 & 0 & 0 & 0 & 0 & 1 \end{bmatrix} \tag{3.32}$$

For the process noise covariance matrix we take

$$R^v = \begin{bmatrix} \frac{1}{4}T^4 & 0 & 0 & \frac{1}{2}T^3 & 0 & 0 \\ 0 & \frac{1}{4}T^4 & 0 & 0 & \frac{1}{2}T^3 & 0 \\ 0 & 0 & \frac{1}{4}T^4 & 0 & 0 & \frac{1}{2}T^3 \\ \frac{1}{2}T^3 & 0 & 0 & T^2 & 0 & 0 \\ 0 & \frac{1}{2}T^3 & 0 & 0 & T^2 & 0 \\ 0 & 0 & \frac{1}{2}T^3 & 0 & 0 & T^2 \end{bmatrix} \sigma_v^2 \tag{3.33}$$

Note that this model describes flight segments with constant *averaged* speed, as opposed to a sample pathwise constant speed.
- Model 1.2. For flight segments where the target maneuvers, a state vector of order 8 ($n = 8$) is considered:

$$x = [X_1, X_2, X_3, \dot{X}_1, \dot{X}_2, \dot{X}_3, \ddot{X}_1, \ddot{X}_2]^t \tag{3.34}$$

and the discrete time dynamics matrix

$$
A = \begin{bmatrix}
1 & 0 & 0 & T & 0 & 0 & \frac{1}{2}T^2 & 0 \\
0 & 1 & 0 & 0 & T & 0 & 0 & \frac{1}{2}T^2 \\
0 & 0 & 1 & 0 & 0 & T & 0 & 0 \\
0 & 0 & 0 & 1 & 0 & 0 & T & 0 \\
0 & 0 & 0 & 0 & 1 & 0 & 0 & T \\
0 & 0 & 0 & 0 & 0 & 1 & 0 & 0 \\
0 & 0 & 0 & 0 & 0 & 0 & 1 & 0 \\
0 & 0 & 0 & 0 & 0 & 0 & 0 & 1
\end{bmatrix}
\tag{3.35}
$$

The process noise covariance matrix is taken as

$$
R^v = \begin{bmatrix}
\frac{1}{4}T^4 & 0 & 0 & \frac{1}{2}T^3 & 0 & 0 & \frac{1}{2}T^2 & 0 \\
0 & \frac{1}{4}T^4 & 0 & 0 & \frac{1}{2}T^3 & 0 & 0 & \frac{1}{2}T^2 \\
0 & 0 & \frac{1}{4}T^4 & 0 & 0 & \frac{1}{2}T^3 & 0 & 0 \\
\frac{1}{2}T^3 & 0 & 0 & T^2 & 0 & 0 & T & 0 \\
0 & \frac{1}{2}T^3 & 0 & 0 & T^2 & 0 & 0 & T \\
0 & 0 & \frac{1}{2}T^3 & 0 & 0 & T^2 & 0 & 0 \\
\frac{1}{2}T^2 & 0 & 0 & T & 0 & 0 & 1 & 0 \\
0 & \frac{1}{2}T^2 & 0 & 0 & T & 0 & 0 & 1
\end{bmatrix} \sigma_v^2
\tag{3.36}
$$

With this model we consider maneuvers in the $X_1 X_2$ plane for a flight at nearly constant altitude (in later simulations the target will fly at a constant $X_3$). Of course, we also could have considered vertical maneuvers by increasing the state vector with a vertical acceleration term.

- Model 1.3. A third model is used, with the same variables as the second model but a larger $\sigma_v$. This was first suggested in [14] to account for the transitions between constant speed segments (described by Model 1.1) and turns (described by Model 1.2).

### 3.4.2 Second Set of Models

Again three models are used.

- Model 2.1. For flight segments with constant average speed, Model 1.1 again is selected.
- Model 2.2. For turns, the exact kinematics of a turn with a constant angular rate $\omega$ are used. This leads to a state vector in $\mathbf{R}^6$ with

$$
x = [X_1, X_2, X_3 \, \dot{X}_1, \dot{X}_2, \dot{X}_3]^t
\tag{3.37}
$$

In continuous time, we have

$$\begin{cases} \ddot{X}_1 = -\dot{X}_2\omega \\ \ddot{X}_2 = \dot{X}_1\omega \\ \ddot{X}_3 = 0 \end{cases} \tag{3.38}$$

and a continuous-time dynamics matrix

$$F = \begin{bmatrix} O_3 & | & I_3 \\ O_3 & | & B \end{bmatrix} \tag{3.39}$$

where $O_n$ is the null matrix and $I_n$ the identity matrix of dimension $n \times n$, with

$$B = \begin{pmatrix} 0 & -\omega & 0 \\ \omega & 0 & 0 \\ 0 & 0 & 0 \end{pmatrix} \tag{3.40}$$

We can show by recurrence that

$$F^n = \begin{bmatrix} O_3 & | & B^{n-1} \\ O_3 & | & B^n \end{bmatrix} \tag{3.41}$$

so that for a sampling period $T = 1$ we obtain the discrete-time dynamics matrix

$$A = e^F = \begin{bmatrix} 1 & 0 & 0 & \dfrac{\sin(\omega)}{\omega} & \dfrac{\cos(\omega)-1}{\omega} & 0 \\ 0 & 1 & 0 & \dfrac{1-\cos(\omega)}{\omega} & \dfrac{\sin(\omega)}{\omega} & 0 \\ 0 & 0 & 1 & 0 & 0 & 1 \\ 0 & 0 & 0 & \cos(\omega) & -\sin(\omega) & 0 \\ 0 & 0 & 0 & \sin(\omega) & \cos(\omega) & 0 \\ 0 & 0 & 0 & 0 & 0 & 1 \end{bmatrix} \tag{3.42}$$

For the covariance of the process noise we take

$$R^v = \begin{bmatrix} \frac{1}{4}T^4 & 0 & 0 & \frac{1}{2}T^3 & 0 & 0 \\ 0 & \frac{1}{4}T^4 & 0 & 0 & \frac{1}{2}T^3 & 0 \\ 0 & 0 & \frac{1}{4}T^4 & 0 & 0 & \frac{1}{2}T^3 \\ \frac{1}{2}T^3 & 0 & 0 & T^2 & 0 & 0 \\ 0 & \frac{1}{2}T^3 & 0 & 0 & T^2 & 0 \\ 0 & 0 & \frac{1}{2}T^3 & 0 & 0 & T^2 \end{bmatrix} \sigma_v^2 \tag{3.43}$$

- Model 2.3. For $\omega > 0$, Model 2.2 describes a counterclockwise turn, and Model 2.3 is its natural counterpart for a clockwise turn.

Obviously Models 2.2 and 2.3 assume that the turn rate of the target is known. This generally is the case for a civilian aircraft [2, 22] because its maneuvers are constrained by flight rules, especially when approaching an airport. For a military aircraft this assumption is less natural, but it often has been reported that pilots in combat or attack situations tend to fly on the limit of their flight envelope, so that taking as a known $\omega$ the maximum $g$ turning rate is not unrealistic.

### 3.4.3 Third Set of Models

Finally, we consider the generalization of Model 2.2 to the case where $\omega$ is not known. Because we then have to estimate $\omega$, only two models are needed and $\hat{\omega}$ will take positive (or negative) values for the turn described by Model 2.2 (or Model 2.3) in the previous solution.

- Model 3.1. For flight segments with constant speed, a model similar to Model 1.1 again is selected, but the noise input is modified. Whereas in Model 1.1 we described speed as *constant on the average* here we consider a *constant* speed. This leads to a covariance matrix as

$$
R^v = \begin{bmatrix} 1 & 0 & 0 & 0 & 0 & 0 \\ 0 & 1 & 0 & 0 & 0 & 0 \\ 0 & 0 & 1 & 0 & 0 & 0 \\ 0 & 0 & 0 & 0 & 0 & 0 \\ 0 & 0 & 0 & 0 & 0 & 0 \\ 0 & 0 & 0 & 0 & 0 & 0 \end{bmatrix} \sigma_v^2 \tag{3.44}
$$

The use of this model leads to less volatile estimates of speed when the target is not maneuvering.
- Model 3.2. We include the rotation rate $\omega$ in the state vector

$$
x = (X_1, X_2, X_3, \dot{X}_1, \dot{X}_2, \dot{X}_3, \omega)^t \tag{3.45}
$$

The continuous-time kinematics of the turn can then be written exactly

$$
\dot{x}_t = f(x_t) \tag{3.46}
$$

with

$$
f(x_t) = (\dot{X}_1, \dot{X}_2, \dot{X}_3, -\omega \dot{X}_2, \omega \dot{X}_1, 0, 0)^t \tag{3.47}
$$

The sampled version of this equation is

$$x_{k+1} = [e^{TL_f}(\text{Id})]_{x_k} \qquad (3.48)$$

with Id the identity of $\mathbf{R}^7$ and $L_f$ the Lie derivative with respect to $f(L_f(\text{Id})_x = f(x)$ and $L_f \circ L_f(\text{Id})_x = (J_f)_x \cdot f(x)$ where $(J_f)_x$ is the Jacobian of $f$ computed at $x$). Up to a second order in $T$ we get

$$x_{k+1} = g(x_k) \qquad (3.49)$$

for

$$g(x) = \begin{bmatrix} X_1 + T\dot{X}_1 - \dfrac{T^2}{2} \dot{X}_2 \omega \\[2mm] X_2 + T\dot{X}_2 + \dfrac{T^2}{2} \dot{X}_1 \omega \\[2mm] X_3 + T\dot{X}_3 \\[2mm] \dot{X}_1 - T\dot{X}_2\omega - \dfrac{T^2}{2} \dot{X}_1 \omega^2 \\[2mm] \dot{X}_2 + T\dot{X}_1\omega - \dfrac{T^2}{2} \dot{X}_2 \omega^2 \\[2mm] \dot{X}_3 \\[2mm] \omega \end{bmatrix} \qquad (3.50)$$

For the noise covariance, we consider the constant speed for Model 3.1 and noisy sample path for $\omega$:

$$R^v = \begin{bmatrix} \sigma_v^2 & 0 & 0 & 0 & 0 & 0 & 0 \\ 0 & \sigma_v^2 & 0 & 0 & 0 & 0 & 0 \\ 0 & 0 & \sigma_v^2 & 0 & 0 & 0 & 0 \\ 0 & 0 & 0 & 0 & 0 & 0 & 0 \\ 0 & 0 & 0 & 0 & 0 & 0 & 0 \\ 0 & 0 & 0 & 0 & 0 & 0 & 0 \\ 0 & 0 & 0 & 0 & 0 & 0 & \sigma_\omega^2 \end{bmatrix} \qquad (3.51)$$

## 3.5  SIMULATION RESULTS

Two infrared sensors are located along the $x_1$ axis with sensor 1 at $x_1 = 0$ and sensor 2 at $x_1 = l = 10{,}000$ m. The sampling rate is $T = 1$ s. Using the detection fusion architecture, the azimuth and elevation angles, $a_i$ and $e_i$, measured by sensor $i$ are transmitted to the fusion node, where the measurement vector $(a_1, e_1, a_2\ e_2)^t$ is formed at each time step. The observation equation is then of the form (3.5) with

$$h(x) = \begin{bmatrix} \arctan\left(\dfrac{X_2}{X_1}\right) \\[2ex] \arctan\left(\dfrac{X_3}{\sqrt{X_1^2 + X_2^2}}\right) \\[2ex] \arctan\left[\dfrac{X_2}{(X_1 - l)}\right] \\[2ex] \arctan\left[\dfrac{X_3}{\sqrt{(X_1 - l)^2 + X_2^2}}\right] \end{bmatrix} \qquad (3.52)$$

We assume that the raw angle errors are independent and the measurement noise $w_t$ has a diagonal covariance $R^w = I_4\sigma_w^2$. The false alarms are generated from a Gaussian distribution with $\sigma = 3$ mrad centered on the true target position. False alarms are uniformly distributed in the horizontal plane, and the average delay between false alarms also is a random variable with uniform distribution over [0 s, 15 s].

The different algorithms were tested using the same trajectory. As shown in Figure 3.3 the target makes three circular turns with rectilinear segments connecting them. The speed is kept constant throughout (= 300 m/s). The target starts at $t = 0$ s at $X_1 = 10{,}000$ m, $X_2 = 15{,}000$ m, $X_3 = 200$ m with $\dot{X}_1 = -300$ m/s, $\dot{X}_2 = 0, \dot{X}_3 = 0$. The segments are defined as follows:

- First Segment. Rectilinear flight till the plane $X_1 = 3{,}000$ m (from $t = 0$ s to $t = 23$ s).
- Second Segment. Circular turn for $-3$ rad with acceleration 70 m/s$^2$ (from $t = 23$ s to $t = 36$ s).
- Third Segment. Rectilinear flight till the plane $X_1 = 9{,}000$ m (from $t = 36$ s to $t = 60$ s).
- Fourth Segment. Circular turn for $+3$ rad with acceleration 70 m/s$^2$ (from $t = 60$ s to $t = 73$ s).
- Fifth Segment. Rectilinear flight till the plane $X_1 = 3{,}000$ m (from $t = 73$ s to $t = 90$ s).
- Sixth Segment. Circular turn for $+3$ rad with acceleration 70 m/s$^2$ (from $t = 90$ s to $t = 103$ s).
- Seventh Segment. Rectilinear flight till final time $t = 147$ s (from $t = 103$ s to $t = 147$ s).

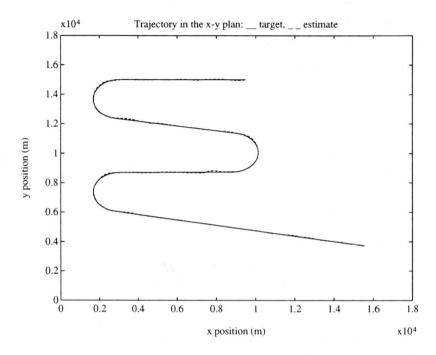

**Figure 3.3** The true and estimated trajectories (the estimate is that of the second IMM).

### 3.5.1 Parameter Values

The following values have been chosen for the model parameters:

- First set of models.

  Model 1.1. $\sigma_v = 5 \text{ m/s}^2$ and $\sigma_w = 0.004$ rad

  Model 1.2. $\sigma_v = 7.5 \text{ m/s}^2$ and $\sigma_w = 0.004$ rad

  Model 1.3. $\sigma_v = 40 \text{ m/s}^2$ and $\sigma_w = 0.004$ rad

  with

$$\Pi = \begin{bmatrix} 0.7 & 0 & 0.3 \\ 0 & 0.8 & 0.2 \\ 0.2 & 0.25 & 0.55 \end{bmatrix} \tag{3.53}$$

$$\lambda = 0.00035 \text{ (rad)}^{-2} \tag{3.54}$$

$$g = 4 \qquad P_d = 1 \tag{3.55}$$

- Second set of models.

  Model 2.1. $\sigma_v = \sqrt{500}$ m/s$^2$ and $\sigma_w = 0.003$ rad

  Model 2.2. $\sigma_v = \sqrt{500}$ m/s$^2$ and $\sigma_w = 0.003$ rad

  Model 2.3. $\sigma_v = \sqrt{500}$ m/s$^2$ and $\sigma_w = 0.003$ rad

  with

$$\Pi = \begin{bmatrix} 0.98 & 0.01 & 0.01 \\ 0.2 & 0.795 & 0.05 \\ 0.2 & 0.05 & 0.795 \end{bmatrix} \tag{3.56}$$

$$\lambda = 0.00035 \ (\text{rad})^{-2} \tag{3.57}$$

$$g = 4 \qquad P_d = 1 \qquad \omega = 0.3 \ \text{rad/s} \tag{3.58}$$

- Third set of models.

  Model 3.1. $\sigma_v = \sqrt{250}$ m and $\sigma_w = 0.003$ rad

  Model 3.2. $\sigma_v = \sqrt{250}$ m, $\sigma_\omega = 0.05$ rad/s and $\sigma_w = 0.003$ rad

  with

$$\Pi = \begin{bmatrix} 0.9 & 0.1 \\ 0.005 & 0.995 \end{bmatrix} \tag{3.59}$$

$$\lambda = 0.00035 \ (\text{rad})^{-2} \tag{3.60}$$

$$g = 4 \qquad P_d = 1 \tag{3.61}$$

We assume no prior knowledge of $\omega$, and its estimate initially is set to zero.

### 3.5.2 Single Model Reference

For comparison purposes, we also designed a single-model Kalman tracker. The model was chosen as Model 1.1 with $\sigma_v = \sqrt{500}$ m/s$^2$ and $\sigma_w = 0.003$ rad and

$$\lambda = 0.00035 \ (\text{rad})^{-2} \tag{3.62}$$

$$g = 4 \qquad P_d = 1 \tag{3.63}$$

### 3.5.3 Performance Analysis

The three IMMPDA algorithms associated to the three sets of models presented were simulated. Their performance and behavior are compared here. For the purpose of these simulations, all state estimates were initialized with the true target state.

### 3.5.3.1   First Algorithm

The probabilities of the three regimes are plotted in Figure 3.4. The correct regime has the largest probability during each segment and the turns are quickly detected. The expected role of Model 1.3 is apparent from Figure 3.5, where the regime probabilities have been enlarged for the onset of the sixth segment maneuver. We see that the probability of regime 3 rises at the start of the turn and then gives way to a dominant probability of being in regime 2. Once the turn is completed regime 1 takes over again.

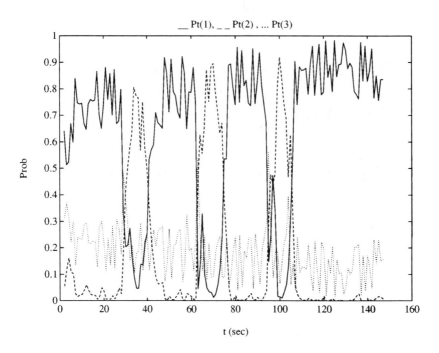

**Figure 3.4** Regime probabilities for the first IMM.

The corresponding error on the location of the target is plotted in Figure 3.6. Natural transients are observed at the onset of maneuvers and the error remains acceptable. However, as we can see from Figure 3.7, the error is not significantly reduced compared to that obtainable by using the single-model filter. Both curves show peak errors around 160 m. To understand this phenomenon, the errors associated with the three regimes are plotted on Figure 3.8: we find that these errors are comparable for the three regimes both in quiescent and maneuvering segments. This is contrary to the natural behavior of the IMM dynamics, where we would expect to

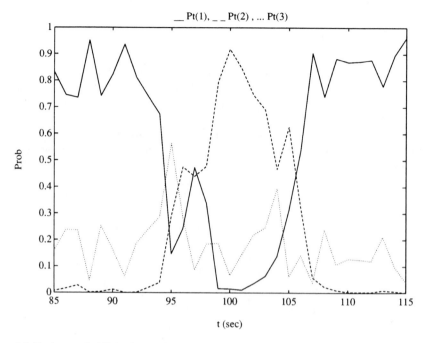

**Figure 3.5** Regime probabilities for the first IMM; zoom in for the start of a turn.

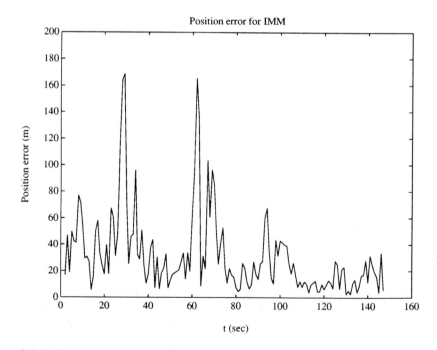

**Figure 3.6** Position error with the first IMM filter.

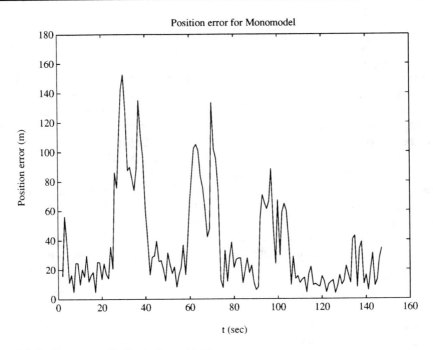

**Figure 3.7** Position error with the single-model filter.

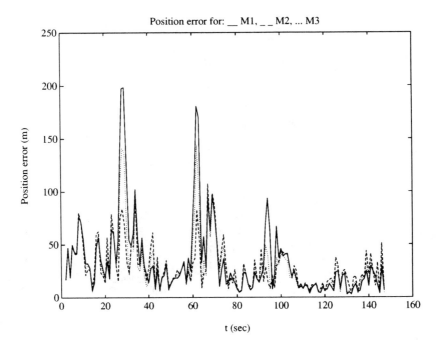

**Figure 3.8** Model errors for the first IMM.

have the smallest errors for regime 1 (or regime 2) during rectilinear segments (or maneuvering segments). The explanation is that the Models 1.1, 1.2, and 1.3 are not discriminating enough: although Model 1.1 works better during rectilinear flight, it does so only marginally; and Models 1.2 and 1.3 also do quite a good job. It appears that Model 1.1 is quite able to track the target when it maneuvers. Also the state expansion step mixes the regime-conditioned estimates in a way that helps the filters based on the "wrong" models to come back on track. The tuning of the regime-transition matrix (i.e., *a priori* information) then is important to recover the correct ordering of the regime probabilities, as shown on Figure 3.4, because the *a posteriori* information conveyed by the innovations conditioned on regime hypothesis do not have enough contrast. Also, note that the primary objective of the tracker is to reduce uncertainty on the kinematics of the target and a correct ordering of the model probabilities is not an objective *per se* but only a means to improve tracking performance. In this respect the comparison between Figures 3.6 and 3.7 is disappointing.

### 3.5.3.2    Second Algorithm

The goal of the second set of models is to improve the preceding results by more carefully modeling the maneuvers. The three probabilities displayed on Figure 3.9

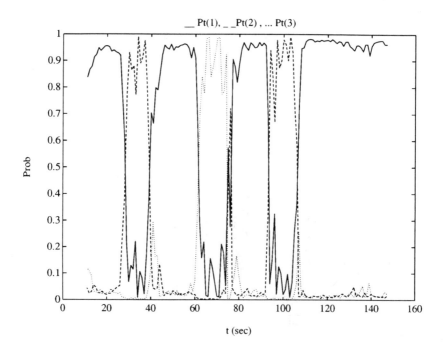

**Figure 3.9** Regime probabilities for the second IMM.

show that the regimes are correctly ordered, and we see on Figure 3.10 that the dynamics of these probabilities are now significantly driven by the *a posteriori* information contained in the innovations: the errors of Model 2.1 are smallest during rectilinear flight and larger than that of Model 2.2 (or 2.3) during counterclockwise (or clockwise) turns. Due to this more satisfactory behavior of the IMM internal dynamics, tracking performance improves as seen on Figure 3.11, where the peak errors at the onset of the first maneuver are reduced to 100 m (compared to 160 m with the first version of the algorithm).

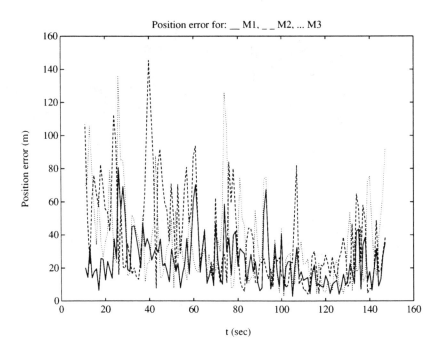

**Figure 3.10** Model errors for the second IMM.

### 3.5.3.3  Third Algorithm

The second algorithm provides a satisfactory performance and a natural behavior of the IMM dynamics. However, it depends on the hypothesis that the turning rate is known. For situations where this assumption is too unrealistic, we can use the third set of models, where the turning rate is estimated through nonlinear state dynamics. The probabilities are shown in Figure 3.12, and again a correct ordering is obtained. Because of the delay in estimating $\omega$ at the onset of a maneuver, this solution pro-

88

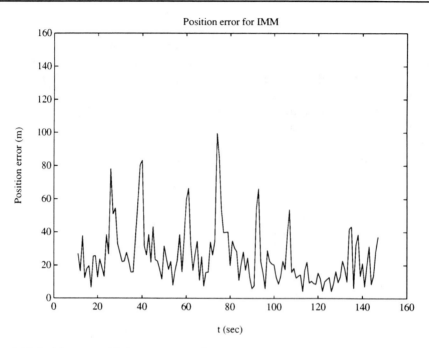

**Figure 3.11** Position error with the second IMM filter.

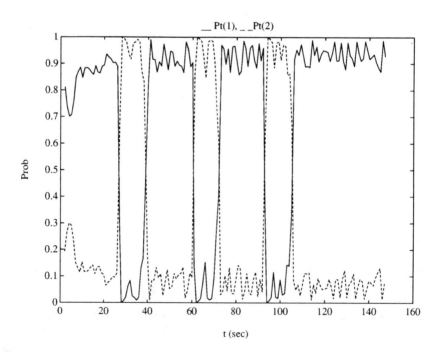

**Figure 3.12** Regime probabilities for the third IMM.

duces rather large peaks as seen on Figure 3.13. However, once the $\omega$ estimate has converged, a very good tracking performance is obtained during turns.

We finally modified this third algorithm by using a different transition rates matrix

$$\Pi = \begin{bmatrix} 0.7 & 0.3 \\ 0.3 & 0.7 \end{bmatrix} \tag{3.64}$$

With larger off-diagonal entries this matrix favors regime transitions and results in much more volatile sample paths of the probabilities (see Figure 3.14). This shows the possibility of a different behavior of the IMM algorithm where no single regime is allowed to rise significantly above the others. This could be called *regime mixing*. It provides the best performance as shown on Figure 3.15, where the occurrence of maneuvers is now hardly noticeable (the peak error is around 60 m, compared to 160 m with the single model filter, and only slightly above the errors caused by noise and false alarms during quiescent segments). We believe that this kind of mixing should play an important role in future applications of the IMM technique, in particular because it opens the way to treat the maneuvers of military aircraft by

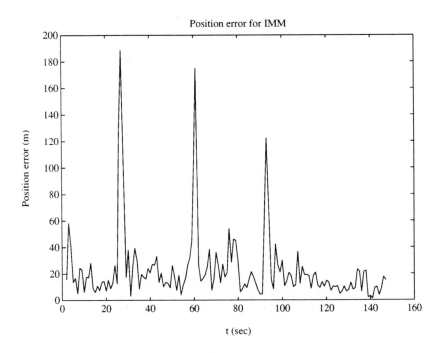

Figure 3.13 Position error with the third IMM filter.

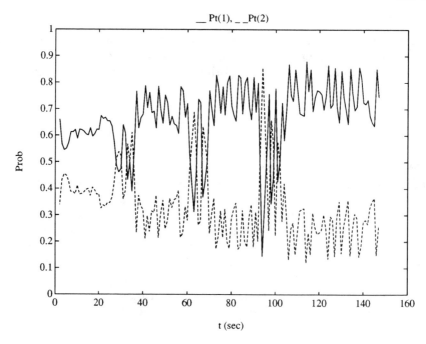

**Figure 3.14** Regime probabilities for the modified third IMM.

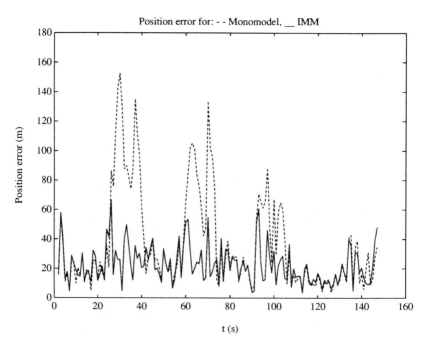

**Figure 3.15** Position error with the modified third IMM filter and the single-model filter.

weighting models associated to maximum g turns and rectilinear flights: a 3 g turn would then be tracked by probabilistically mixing a tracker with a 7 g model and a tracker with a constant-speed model.

## 3.6 SUMMARY AND CONCLUSION

We studied a passive sensor fusion system where a single target maneuvering in clutter was tracked by fusing the angles-only measurements in a 3-D filter. Good tracking performance was achieved without active sensors even in the presence of extreme maneuvers.

Regarding the multiple model concept, we have analyzed the hybrid system-based IMM algorithm and in particular the necessity of accurate models. There appears to be a kind of equivalence between the complexity of a single model in the IMM bank and the number of models to be included in that bank; for example, our third modeling includes a nonlinear model (Model 3.2) and thus introduces additional complexity, however, it saves a filter with respect to our second modeling, where two linear models (Models 2.2 and 2.3) were needed for positive and negative turns. More detailed complexity and performance analysis will be required to understand this alternative.

## REFERENCES

[1]   G.A. Ackerson and K.S. Fu, "On State Estimation in Switching Environments,"*IEEE Trans. on Automatic Control,* Vol. AC-15, February 1970, pp. 10–17.

[2]   I. Barret and P. Vacher, "Poursuite de cibles manoeuvrantes par des algorithmes markoviens hybrides," *Actes du 8ème Colloque GRETSI,* Juan-les-Pins, France, June 1989.

[3]   Y. Bar-Shalom and K. Birmiwal, "Variable Dimension Filter for Maneuvering Target Tracking," *IEEE Trans. on Aerospace and Electronics Systems,* Vol. AES-18, September 1982, pp. 621–629.

[4]   Y. Bar-Shalom and T.E. Fortmann, *Tracking and Data Association,* Academic Press, New York, 1988.

[5]   Y. Bar-Shalom, "Comments on 'Comparison of Two-Sensor Tracking Methods Based on State Vector Fusion and Measurement Fusion,'" *IEEE Trans. on Aerospace and Electronics Systems,* Vol. AES-24, July 1988, pp. 456–457.

[6]   S.S. Blackman, *Multiple Target Tracking with Radar Applications,* Artech House, Dedham, MA, 1986.

[7]   H.A.P. Blom, "A Sophisticated Tracking Algorithm for ATC Surveillance Data," Proc. Int. Radar Conf., Paris, France, May 1984.

[8]   H.A.P. Blom and Y. Bar-Shalom, "The Interacting Multiple Model Algorithm for Systems with Markovian Switching Coefficients," *IEEE Trans. on Automatic Control,* Vol. AC-33, August 1988, pp. 780–783.

[9]   L. Campo, P. Mookerjee, and Y. Bar-Shalom, "State Estimation for Systems with Sojourn Time Dependent Markov Model Switching," *IEEE Trans. on Automatic Control,* Vol. AC-36, Feb. 1991, pp. 238–243.

[10]   C.B. Chang and M. Athans, "State Estimation for Discrete Systems with Switching Parameters," *IEEE Trans. on Aerospace and Electronics Systems,* Vol. AES-14, May 1978, pp. 418–425.

[11]   H.J. Chizeck, A.S. Willsky, and D.A. Castanon, "Discrete Time Markovian Jump Linear Quadratic Optimal Control," *Int. J. Control,* Vol. 43, pp. 213–231.

[12]   M. Gauvrit, "Bayesian Adaptive Filter for Tracking with Measurements of Uncertain Origin," *Automatica,* Vol. 20, 1984, pp. 217–224.

[13]   S.E. Hammel, P.T. Liu, E.J. Hilliard, and K.F. Gong, "Optimal Observer Motion for Localization with Bearing Measurements," *Computers and Mathematics with Applications,* Vol. 18, 1989, pp. 171–180.

[14]   A. Houles and Y. Bar-Shalom, "Multisensor Tracking of a Maneuvering Target in Clutter," *IEEE Trans. on Aerospace and Electronics Systems,* Vol. AES-25, March 1989, pp. 176–188.

[15]   A. Jazwinski, "Adaptive Filtering," *Atuomatica,* Vol. 5, 1969, pp. 475–485.

[16]   M. Mariton, "On Systems with Non-Markovian Regime Changes," *IEEE Trans. on Automatic Control,* Vol. AC-34, March 1989, pp. 346–349.

[17]   M. Mariton, *Jump Linear Systems in Automatic Control,* M. Dekker Inc., New York, 1990.

[18]   M. Millnert, "Identification and Control of Systems Subject to Abrupt Changes," Ph.D. dissertation, Linkoping University, Sweden, 1982.

[19]   J.A. Roecker, and C.D. McGillem, "Comparison of Two-Sensor Tracking Methods Based on State Vector Fusion and Measurement Fusion," *IEEE Trans. on Aerospace and Electronics Systems,* Vol. AES-24, July 1988, pp. 447–449.

[20]   D.D. Sworder, "Control of Systems Subject to Sudden Changes in Character," *Proc. IEEE,* Vol. 64, 1976, pp. 1219–1225.

[21]   J.K. Tugnait, "Detection and Estimation of Abruptly Changing Systems," *Automatica,* Vol. 18, 1982, pp. 607–615.

[22]   P. Vacher, I. Barret, and M. Gauvrit, "Design of a Tracking Algorithm for an Advanced ATC System," Chapter 1 of this book.

# Chapter 4
# *TRACKING SPLITTING TARGETS IN CLUTTER BY USING AN INTERACTING MULTIPLE MODEL JOINT PROBABILISTIC DATA ASSOCIATION FILTER*

**Y. Bar-Shalom**
*University of Connecticut*

**K. C. Chang**
*Advanced Decision Systems, Mt. View, CA*

**H. A. P. Blom**
*National Aerospace Laboratory—NLR, Amsterdam, The Netherlands*

## 4.1  INTRODUCTION

The interacting multiple model algorithm [8, 11] has been shown to be a simple, very effective algorithm for estimating hybrid state systems. Such systems are described by a continuous-valued state component that evolves according to one out of a finite number of switching models (or "modes," the discrete state component). The mode switching takes place according to a Markov (or semi-Markov) chain with an appropriate transition matrix. The IMM algorithm has been shown to perform especially well in estimation of targets undergoing sudden maneuvers [9, 3].

Research supported by ONR Contract N00014-87-K-0057.

Tracking in clutter was discussed extensively in [14, 1, 4], the *probabilistic data association filter* (PDAF) and the *multiple hypothesis tracker* (MHT) suitable for tracking targets in clutter. The PDAF, which considers only the latest association events, has fixed computational requirements. The MHT, which considers all branching hypotheses (including new tracks), has growing computational requirements that have to be limited by various means. The different computational and memory requirements of these algorithms motivated interest in recursive algorithms, with *fixed requirements,* that can initiate tracks, maintain a track in the presence of maneuvers, and terminate tracks if warranted. Such algorithms, based on a combination of the IMM and the PDAF, have been successfully developed and presented [7, 13, 12, 4 Chapter 2].

This chapter combines the IMM and a *joint PDAF* (JPDAF) to yield a new algorithm that, in a cluttered environment, can track a target that "splits" into two targets; such as a platform target that launches another target or a formation of targets becoming resolved. Because the new algorithm evaluates the split-track probability, the approach also yields a solution to the problem of automatic detection of a splitting event. To illustrate the problem, see Figure 4.1 and 4.2 in Section 4.5. The key result, the estimated trajectory of a target that split into two targets, is depicted in Figure 4.3.

Section 4.2 formulates the approach to the problem. The family of models used to capture the splitting process is described in Section 4.3, together with the corresponding model-conditioned estimation algorithms. The interaction between these models, needed by the IMM algorithm, is discussed in Section 4.4. Section 4.5 presents simulation results with a sensor that is realistically modeled as having a limited resolution in addition to less than unity target detection probability and nonzero clutter density (or false alarms).

## 4.2   THE APPROACH

The approach to the track-splitting problem is formulated as a generalization of the previously described IMMPDAF algorithm for the problem of automatic track formation [4 Chapter 2]. This algorithm uses two models:

Model 1. Undetectable target ("no target"),

Model 2. True target moving with nearly constant velocity.

Model 2 assumes a certain nonzero target detection probability $P_D$ whereas Model 1 is the same type of moving target except that $P_D = 0$. The probability of each model is updated recursively.

Once a track is formed and its *true target probability* (TTP), which is the probability of Model 2, is high, it can go into "precision tracking"; that is, with the algorithm augmented for maneuvering target tracking as well. This can be accomplished by using two additional models [3, 5]:

Model 3. Motion with large acceleration increments,

Model 4. Nearly constant acceleration motion.

Other models also are explored in [10, 12]. Model 3 serves as a transient between Models 2 and 4, and in both these models the target has the same $P_D$ as in Model 2. Some additional situations of interest can be encountered. The track can be composed of a number of neighboring targets that will become resolved (or unresolved) as the formation gets closer to (or farther from) the sensor or if the formation is broken (or formed). Or a single target can serve as a platform from which another target can be launched (or approached). Both these situations lead to what can be called *target splitting* or *recombining*.

To incorporate the "splitting" into two targets, as well as their possible "recombining," into the IMMPDAF approach, two new models are added:

Model 5: "Just split" target,

Model 6: "Split target" (two targets).

These two models form a realistic representation of a track splitting into two in the case of limited-sensor resolution. Later in the chapter, we describe these new models (Section 4.3) and develop a tracking method (Section 4.4) that globally works as follows.

For the "just split" model, a tracking cycle starts with a single predicted state and ends up with two updated states (in the form of a double-dimensional vector). For the "split target" model, a tracking cycle starts with two predicted states that are updated with a coupled version of the JPDAF [2] to yield two updated states. The coupling is needed because the estimation errors of the two targets are correlated [6, 2].

As soon as the two targets separate sufficiently (their validation regions no longer overlap), they can be considered two independent tracks, leading to a straightforward reconfiguration of the tracking. The criterion for decoupling is presented later.

The IMMPDAF has been fully documented in [4, Chapter 2] and will not be repeated here. The present algorithm has the same structure except for the two additional models, 5 and 6, which are discussed in the next section. The interaction between these additional models is presented in Section 4.4.

## 4.3 THE MODELS FOR THE SPLITTING AND THEIR STATE ESTIMATION

### 4.3.1 The Transitions Between the Models

The Markov chain transition matrix between the six models described in the previous section consists of the elements

$$p_{ij} = P\{\text{Model } j \text{ in effect at time } k \,|\, \text{Model } i \text{ in effect at time } k - 1\} \quad (4.1)$$

Table 4.1 shows the nonzero probabilities (4.1) assumed for the present problem for $i, j = 1, \ldots, 6$. (the zero terms are omitted). These probabilities are the principal design parameters for the IMM algorithm, in addition to the selection of the set of models.

**Table 4.1**
The Assumed Model Transition Probabilities

|   | 1 | 2 | 3 | 4 | 5 | 6 |
|---|---|---|---|---|---|---|
| 1 | $p_{11}$ | $p_{12}$ | | | | |
| 2 | $p_{21}$ | $p_{22}$ | $p_{23}$ | | $p_{25}$ | |
| 3 | | $p_{32}$ | $p_{33}$ | $p_{34}$ | | |
| 4 | | | $p_{43}$ | $p_{44}$ | | |
| 5 | | | | | | $p_{56}$ |
| 6 | | $p_{62}$ | | | | $p_{66}$ |

The following list is an illustrative set of numerical values for the transition probabilities (these were the values used in the simulations presented in Section 4.5):

$p_{11} = 0.98$, target stays unobservable (or "false" or "dead")

$p_{12} = 1 - p_{11}$, target is "reborn" ("comes back to life")

$p_{21} = 0.02$, target becomes unobservable ("dies")

$p_{22} = 0.88$, target is observable and continues with a nearly constant velocity motion

$p_{23} = 0.05$, target has large acceleration increment (start of maneuver)

$p_{25} = 0.05$, target splits

$p_{32} = 0.33$, target returns to a nearly constant velocity

$p_{33} = 0.34$, target continues with a large acceleration increment

$p_{34} = 0.33$, target goes into nearly constant acceleration motion

$p_{44} = 0.9$, target stays in nearly constant acceleration motion

$p_{43} = 0.1$, target ends the nearly constant acceleration motion

$p_{56} = 1$, target splitting has been accomplished

$p_{66} = 0.97$, target continues being split (2 targets)

$p_{62} = 0.03$, split target becomes single target (recombination).

The splitting is assumed to occur from the nearly constant velocity motion, and the recombination goes to the same motion model. Different transitions might be possible if the corresponding terms in the transition matrix, which now are set to zero, are chosen appropriately.

### 4.3.2 The "Just Split" Model

This model starts with a single predicted measurement $\hat{z}(k\,|\,k-1)$. The number of validated measurements must be at least two. The set of validated measurements is partitioned into two subsets (clusters), to be associated with the two targets (that just split) as follows:

1. The measurement with the highest probability is associated with the first target; this will be the center of the first cluster.
2. The measurement with the second highest probability is associated with the second target; this will be the center of the second cluster.
3. If there are more than two measurements, they are associated to one of the clusters[1] by using a distance criterion.
4. The association probabilities are renormalized so that within each cluster they sum to unity. This implicitly assumes that both split targets have been detected (a reasonable assumption, because otherwise there is no reason to split).
5. The state vector corresponding to the "just split" model is formed by stacking the state vectors of the two targets.

The $2n_x$-dimensional stacked vector of the states of the two targets ($n_x$ denotes the dimension of the target state $x$) is formed for the "just split" (indicated by superscript $J$) model as

$$x^J(k) = \begin{bmatrix} x_1^J(k) \\ x_2^J(k) \end{bmatrix} \qquad (4.2)$$

[1]Note that the two subsets of measurements have no element in common.

where $x_t$ is the state of target $t$, $t = 1, 2$. This is updated as follows:

$$\hat{x}^J(k|k) = \hat{x}^J(k|k - 1) + W^J(k)\nu^J(k) \tag{4.3}$$

where

$$\hat{x}^J(k|k - 1) = \begin{bmatrix} \hat{x}_1^J(k|k - 1) \\ \hat{x}_2^J(k|k - 1) \end{bmatrix} \tag{4.4}$$

$$\hat{x}_1^J(k|k - 1) = \hat{x}_2^J(k|k - 1) \tag{4.5}$$

That is, we assume that the two just split targets have the same predicted state, which follows from the interaction between the models, discussed in the next section. The $2n_z$-dimensional innovation ($n_z$ denotes the dimension of the measurement) is

$$\nu^J(k) = \begin{bmatrix} \sum_{i \in I_1} \beta_{i,1}^J(k) \nu_i^J(k) \\ \sum_{i \in I_2} \beta_{i,2}^J(k) \nu_i^J(k) \end{bmatrix} \tag{4.6}$$

where $\beta_{i,t}(k)$ is the renormalized probability of measurement $z_i(k)$ belonging to target $t$ according to step 4. The innovations are calculated with respect to the (common) predicted measurement:

$$\nu_i^J(k) = z_i(k) - \hat{z}^J(k|k - 1) \tag{4.7}$$

The set $I_t$ represents the cluster of $m_t(k)$ measurements associated with target $t$ according to steps 1–3.

The gain is

$$W^J(k) = \begin{bmatrix} W_1^J(k) & 0 \\ 0 & W_2^J(k) \end{bmatrix} \tag{4.8}$$

where

$$W_j^J(k) = W(k) \quad j = 1, 2 \tag{4.9}$$

that is, the stacked matrix of the (standard) gains from the PDAF.

The covariance associated with the prediction (4.4) is

$$P^J(k|k-1) = \begin{bmatrix} P^J_{11}(k|k-1) & P^J_{12}(k|k-1) \\ P^J_{21}(k|k-1) & P^J_{22}(k|k-1) \end{bmatrix} \tag{4.10}$$

where

$$P^J_{ij}(k|k-1) = P(k|k-1) \quad i,j = 1,2 \tag{4.11}$$

The updated ($2n_x \times 2n_x$-dimensional) covariance corresponding to (4.3), is obtained as follows: The blocks on the diagonal follow from separate standard PDAF updates[2] with the corresponding innovation clusters; the off-diagonal block (with $H(k)$ denoting the measurement matrix of one target) is

$$P^J_{12}(k|k) = [I - W(k)H(k)]P^J_{12}(k|k-1)[I - W(k)H(k)]' \tag{4.12}$$

This term reflects the correlation between the new estimates of the two targets due to their past common history.

As indicated in step 4, we assume that both targets are detected at the time a split is considered. The likelihood function of the "just split" model at $k$, denoted as the event $M^J(k)$, then is the product of two mixtures of $n_z$-dimensional Gaussians as follows:

$$\Lambda[M^J(k)] = \prod_{t=1}^{2} \sum_{i \in I_t} \frac{1}{m_t(k)} N[z_i(k); \hat{z}(k|k-1), S(k)]V^{-[m_t(k)-1]} \tag{4.13}$$

where $S(k)$ is the innovation covariance, $V$ is the validation region volume, and $m_t(k)$ is the number of measurements in cluster $t$.

### 4.3.3 The "Split" Model

This model, which has a $2n_x$-dimensional state, as discussed before, is handled, with a JPDAF. This "stacked" state vector of the split model is denoted as $x^S$.

In [1] the JPDA is described under the assumption that, conditioned on the past, the target states are *independently distributed*. Consequently, the joint associ-

---

[2]Note that at $k$ we can use separate PDAFs because each target utilizes a separate subset of measurements, as indicated at the beginning of this subsection.

ation is then followed by *decoupled* filtering of the targets' states. However, for targets that "share" measurements (in the sense of the JPDA) for several sampling times, a dependence of their estimation errors ensues, and this can be taken into account [6], obviously at the cost of some extra computation. The resulting algorithm is called a *JPDA coupled filter* (JPDACF) [2]; the filtering is done in a *coupled* manner for the targets with "common" measurements, yielding a covariance matrix with off-diagonal blocks that reflect the correlation between the targets' state estimation errors.

The conditional probability for a joint association event becomes (for the non-parametric JPDA [1])

$$P\{\theta(k)|Z^k\} = \frac{1}{c} \phi! V^{-\phi} f_{t_{j_1}, t_{j_2}}[z_j(k), j: \tau_j = 1] \prod_{t=1}^{2} (P_D^t)^{\delta_t}(1 - P_D^t)^{1-\delta_t} \qquad (4.14)$$

where $\phi$ is the number of measurements in the validation region of volume $V$ deemed false in event $\theta$; $f_{t_{j_1}, t_{j_2}}$ is the joint pdf of the measurements of the targets under consideration; $t_{j_1}$ is the target to which $z_{j_1}(k)$ is associated in event $\theta$; $\tau_j$ is the target association indicator for measurement $j$ in the event $\theta$; $P_D^t$ is the detection probability of target $t$; the binary variable $\delta_t$ is the detection indicator for target $t$ (equal to unity if target $t$ is assumed detected in event $\theta$).

The joint probabilities are not "boiled down" to the marginal association probabilities for use in decoupled PDA filters. Instead, these joint probabilities are used directly in a *coupled filter.*

Denoting the stacked vector of the predicted states of the two targets under consideration as

$$\hat{x}^S(k|k-1) = \begin{bmatrix} \hat{x}_1^S(k|k-1) \\ \hat{x}_2^S(k|k-1) \end{bmatrix} \qquad (4.15)$$

with the associated covariance matrix

$$P^S(k|k-1) = \begin{bmatrix} P_{11}^S(k|k-1) & P_{12}^S(k|k-1) \\ P_{21}^S(k|k-1) & P_{22}^S(k|k-1) \end{bmatrix} \qquad (4.16)$$

where $\hat{x}_t^S$ and $P_{tt}^S$ correspond to target $t$, $P_{t_1 t_2}^S$ is the cross-covariance between targets $t_1$ and $t_2$.

The updated state with the coupled filtering is

$$\hat{x}^S(k|k) = \hat{x}^S(k|k-1) + W^S(k)\nu^S(k) \qquad (4.17)$$

where

$$v^S(k) \triangleq \sum_\theta P\{\theta(k) \mid Z^k\} v^S(k, \theta) \tag{4.18}$$

$$v^S(k, \theta) \triangleq z^S(k, \theta) - \hat{z}^S(k \mid k - 1) \tag{4.19}$$

$$z^S(k, \theta) = \begin{bmatrix} z_{j_1(\theta)}(k) \\ z_{j_2(\theta)}(k) \end{bmatrix} \tag{4.20}$$

and $j_t(\theta)$ is the index of the measurement associated with target $t$ in event $\theta$ at time $k$.

The filter gain in (4.17) is

$$W^S(k) = P^S(k \mid k - 1) H^S(k)'[H^S(k) P^S(k \mid k - 1) H^S(k)' + R^S(k)]^{-1} \tag{4.21}$$

where

$$H^S(k) = \begin{bmatrix} H(k) & 0 \\ 0 & H(k) \end{bmatrix} \tag{4.22}$$

$$R^S(k) = \begin{bmatrix} R(k) & 0 \\ 0 & R(k) \end{bmatrix} \tag{4.23}$$

are the (block diagonal) measurement matrix and noise covariance matrix, respectively, for the two targets under consideration. The predicted stacked measurement vector for the "split" model is

$$\hat{z}^S(k \mid k - 1) = H^S(k) \hat{x}^S(k \mid k - 1) \tag{4.24}$$

The covariance associated with the updated state (4.17) is

$$P^S(k \mid k) = \beta_0(k) P^S(k \mid k - 1)$$
$$+ [1 - \beta_0(k)][I - W^S(k) H^S(k)] P^S(k \mid k - 1) \tag{4.25}$$
$$+ W^S(k) \left[ \sum_\theta P\{\theta(k)\} v^S(k, \theta) v^S(k, \theta)' - v^S(k) v^S(k)' \right] W^S(k)'$$

where

$$\beta_0(k) \triangleq P\{\theta_0(k) \mid Z^k\} \tag{4.26}$$

is the probability that none of the measurements at $k$ belong to either target (event $\theta_0$). The summations are over all the possible joint association events except $\theta_0$.

After the two targets separate so that they no longer have any common validated measurements, their state estimation can be carried out separately; that is, there is no "coupling" between them. The criterion for decoupling is that their validation regions no longer overlap. The "no overlap" test for the validation regions is

$$[\hat{z}_1^S(k|k-1) - \hat{z}_2^S(k|k-1)]'[S_1(k) + S_2(k)]^{-1}$$
$$\cdot [\hat{z}_1^S(k|k-1) - \hat{z}_2^S(k|k-1)] \geq c \qquad (4.27)$$

where $S_t(k)$ is the innovation covariance for target $t$. The constant $c$ can be chosen as the 99% percentile (i.e., 1% tail) of the $n_z$-degrees-of-freedom chi-square distribution.

## 4.4  THE INTERACTION BETWEEN THE MODELS

Because Models 5 and 6 (or, $J$ and $S$, respectively) have a double-dimensional state, the interaction (mixing of estimates at the beginning of the cycle) between the various filters in the IMM requires some additional specifications.

The initial estimate at the beginning of a cycle, for filter matched to Model $j$, is obtained from the interaction [8, 11, 4 Chapter 2]

$$\hat{x}^{0j}(k-1|k-1) = \sum_{i=1}^{r} \hat{x}^i(k) - 1|k-1)\mu_{i|j}(k-1|k-1) \qquad (4.28a)$$

$$P^{0j}(k-1|k-1) = \sum_{i=1}^{r} \{P^i(k-1|k-1) + [\hat{x}^i(k-1|k-1)$$
$$- \hat{x}^{0j}(k-1|k-1)][\hat{x}^i(k-1|k-1) \qquad (4.28b)$$
$$- \hat{x}^{0j}(k-1|k-1)]'\}\mu_{i|j}(k-1|k-1)$$

where $\hat{x}^i(k-1|k-1)$ is the Model $i$ conditioned estimate at the end of cycle $k-1$ (given that Model $i$ was in effect during this cycle), and the mixing (interaction) probabilities are

$$\mu_{i|j}(k-1|k-1) = \frac{1}{c_j} p_{ij}\mu_i(k-1) \qquad (4.29)$$

with $p_{ij}$ denoting the model transition probabilities and $\mu_i$ the updated model probabilities.

For $j = 5$ (the "just split" model, also denoted by $J$), the interaction equation (4.28a), in view of (4.4), (4.5), and Table 4.1, according to which only Model 2 can be a predecessor to Model 5, reduces to

$$\hat{x}_t^{05}(k-1|k-1) \triangleq \hat{x}_t^{0J}(k-1|k-1)$$
$$= \hat{x}^2(k-1|k-1) \qquad t = 1, 2 \tag{4.30}$$

where the notation of (4.2) is used for the components of the stacked state vector.

For $j = 6$ (the "split" model), we have the standard interaction equations (4.28), because its predecessors (Models 5 or 6) have the same dimension.

For Model $j = 2$ we cannot use (4.28) in its standard form, because Model 6, which has double dimension, can be a predecessor of Model 2 and, thus, enters into (4.28). Therefore the state of Model 6 ("split") will have to be modified. This can be done by premultiplying it with the matrix

$$I_2 \triangleq \tfrac{1}{2}[I \quad I] \tag{4.31}$$

where $I$ is the $n_x \times n_x$ identity matrix. In other words $I_2$ will average the states of the two targets when they "recombine." The corresponding covariance is $I_2 P_2 I_2'$. The other mixings are carried out in the standard manner [8, 11, 4 Chapter 2].

## 4.5 SIMULATION RESULTS

A target moving in a plane with initial state (in Cartesian coordinates $\xi$, $\eta$)

$$x = [\xi \; \dot{\xi} \; \ddot{\xi} \; \eta \; \dot{\eta} \; \ddot{\eta}] = [100 \; 20 \; 0 \; 100 \; 0 \; 0] \tag{4.32}$$

was tracked with a sampling period of 1 s for 20 periods. The equation of motion was a third-order kinematic model with piecewise constant random acceleration increments [1] modeled by a white process noise sequence with variance 0.01, independent among the two coordinates. At time $k = 8$ this target split into two; after the split the two targets' states evolved according to the same model but with mutually independent process noises; the new target exhibited an additional acceleration of $\ddot{\eta} = 1$ in the time interval [10, 13]. The trajectories of the two targets are depicted in Figure 4.1.

The state estimation was done with position $(\xi, \eta)$ measurements corrupted by additive noise with standard deviations of $\sqrt{R_{ii}} = 5$ for each coordinate, in the presence of false alarms with a spatial density $\lambda$. To be realistic, the sensor is modeled as having a limited resolution: the resolution cell is taken in each coordinate as $2\sqrt{R_{ii}}$. A realistic model is particularly important because the two targets will be very close

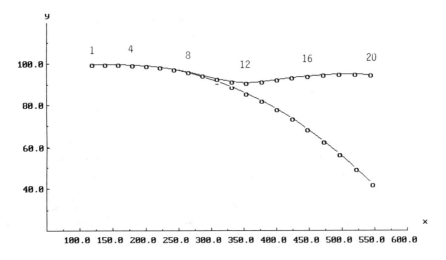

**Figure 4.1** Trajectories of the two targets (with sample time shown above the trajectory).

to each other at the beginning, and the algorithm will have to detect the existence of two targets. The detection probability of the targets was $P_D$. Figure 4.2 shows one realization of the measurements (one run) for $P_D = 0.99$, false alarm rate (per unit area in the measurement space) $\lambda = 10^{-4}$, and sensor resolution cell $C_r = 10 \times 10$

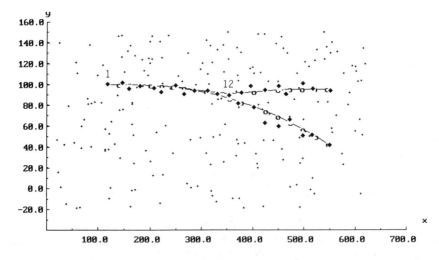

**Figure 4.2** Measurements from the two targets with a finite resolution sensor and clutter with 20 scans overlayed (o true position; ♦ true measurement, + clutter measurement).

(this corresponds to $P_{FA} = 10^{-2}$ per cell). Due to the sensor's limited resolution, the two targets yielded two detections only starting at scan 13, which is the first time when their separation in one coordinate exceeds the resolution.

Figure 4.3 presents one realization of the estimated trajectories[3] for this scenario. The display shows two targets from the moment that the probability of Model 6 (split target) becomes largest. As we can see, the resolution limitation causes the split to be "detected" only at $k = 16$, because the first time at which the sensor "sees" two targets is only at $k = 13$.

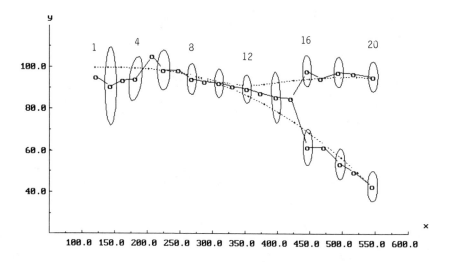

**Figure 4.3** Estimated trajectories (with the two targets after the split mode becomes dominant).

Figure 4.4 shows the evolution in time of the "split" model (6) probability for this realization. This probability is seen to rise rapidly, starting from $k = 13$, in a few periods to practically unity. The average of this probability over Monte Carlo runs is presented later.

Table 4.2 shows the results of 100 Monte Carlo runs in terms of the rate of successfully detecting the target split for various parameters. Two cases are presented: the finite resolution sensor, with resolution cell $C_r$ equal to two standard deviations of the measurement noise in each coordinate, and the perfect resolution case. Each case is evaluated for several values of the target detection probability $P_D$ and

---

[3]Initialization is assumed to have been done separately through; for example, the procedure of [4, Chapter 2]. At every scan, the measurements not associated with the existing tentative or confirmed tracks should be used to initialize new tracks. The simulations presented here do not include initialization.

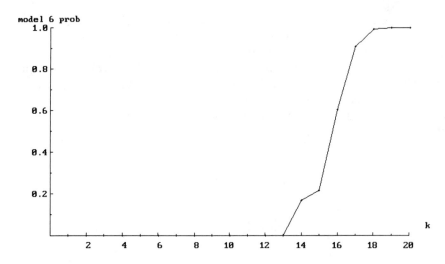

**Figure 4.4** Probability of the split model.

**Table 4.2**
Percentage of Runs Where the Target Split Was Detected Successfully

| | | Success Rate | |
|---|---|---|---|
| $P_D$ | $\lambda$ | $C_r = 10 \times 10$ | $C_r = 0 \times 0$ |
| .99 | $10^{-4}$ | 92% | 98% |
| .99 | $2.5 \cdot 10^{-4}$ | 82% | 95% |
| .99 | $5 \cdot 10^{-4}$ | 60% | 74% |
| .95 | $10^{-4}$ | 82% | 94% |
| .95 | $2.5 \cdot 10^{-4}$ | 77% | 91% |
| .95 | $5 \cdot 10^{-4}$ | 66% | 77% |
| .90 | $10^{-4}$ | 75% | 87% |
| .90 | $2.5 \cdot 10^{-4}$ | 72% | 83% |
| .90 | $5 \cdot 10^{-4}$ | 68% | 74% |

false alarm density $\lambda$. Success is declared if (1) the probability of the split model is dominant, and (2) the normalized state estimation error squared [1] for both targets is below 16. As we see from the table, the success rate with the limited resolution sensor is unavoidably lower than with an ideal perfect resolution sensor. If this algorithm does not detect the split, then initialization of the "new" target is necessary; this is what the multiple hypothesis tracker [1, 4 Chapter 3] does. Thus, the present algorithm has a good probability of being able to detect the split sooner and use the "mother" target's state to initialize the new target, rather than have a "cold start."

Figures 4.5–4.7 present the average probability of the split model (6) from 100 Monte Carlo runs. This average is over the cases in which the split has been detected successfully. The time it takes to detect the split is taken as the elapsed time from the first scan when the two targets are resolved by the sensor until the Model 6 proba-

(a)

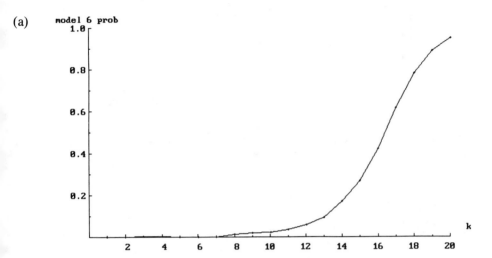

(b)

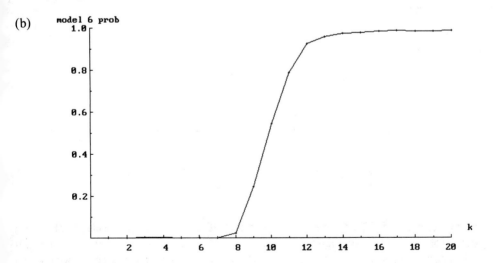

**Figure 4.5** Average probability of the split model (100 runs) for $P_D = 0.99$, $\lambda = 10^{-4}$: (a) $C_r = 10 \times 10$; (b) $C_r = 0 \times 0$.

(a)

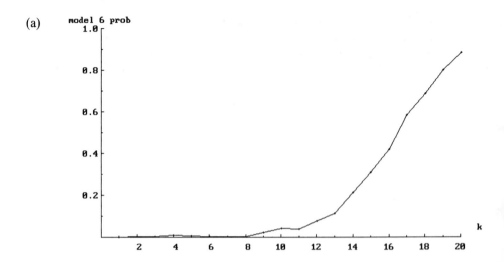

(b)

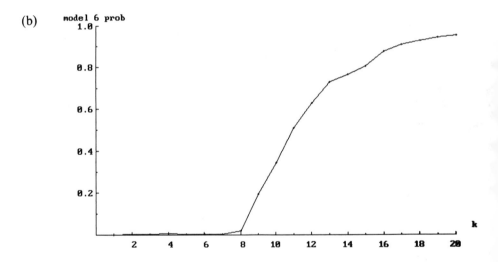

**Figure 4.6** Average probability of the split model (100 runs) for $P_D = 0.9$, $\lambda = 10^{-4}$: (a) $C_r = 10 \times 10$; (b) $C_r = 0 \times 0$.

bility exceeds 0.5. The figures show the effect of the resolution in delaying the split detection. As shown in Figure 4.5, for $P_D = 0.99$ and clutter density $\lambda = 10^{-4}$, it takes about five scans to detect the split in the limited resolution case, as opposed to three scans for the (ideal) perfect resolution case. Figure 4.6 shows how the lower value $P_D = 0.9$ delays this for the perfect resolution case by about one scan, but in

(a)

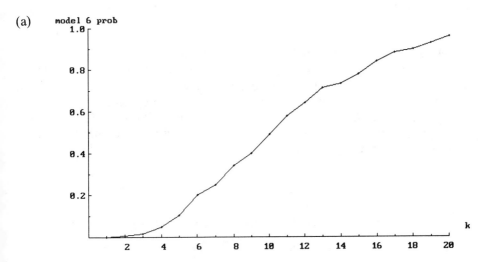

(b)

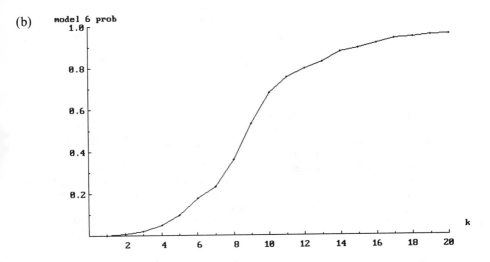

**Figure 4.7** Average probability of the split model (100 runs) for $P_D = 0.9$, $\lambda = 5 \cdot 10^{-4}$: (a) $C_r = 10 \times 10$; (b) $C_r = 0 \times 0$.

the limited resolution case it still takes five scans. Heavier clutter is seen in Figure 4.7 to cause an early rise in the split model probability, but then it takes longer to reach a high value. Also, in the heavier clutter, the difference between the limited and perfect resolution cases is quite small. These simulations were made with the interactive software [5].

## 4.6 CONCLUSION

The IMMJPDAF algorithm presented here can track a target that splits into two. This has been accomplished by using a set of models that include the "transformation" of the single target in track into two targets. The effectiveness of this algorithm has been evaluated for the realistic situation of less than unity detection probability, the presence of false alarms, and a finite resolution sensor. The algorithm has a good probability of being able to detect the split sooner than other algorithms and use the "mother" target's state to initialize the new target, rather than have a "cold start."

### REFERENCES

[1]   Y. Bar-Shalom and T.E. Fortmann, *Tracking and Data Association,* Academic Press, Orlando, FL, 1988.
[2]   Y. Bar-Shalom, "Multitarget-Multisensor Tracking: Principles and Techniques," Short Course Notes, 1989.
[3]   Y. Bar-Shalom, K.C. Chang, and H.A.P. Blom, "Tracking a Maneuvering Target Using the Input Estimation vs. the Interacting Multiple Model Algorithm," *IEEE Trans. on Aerospace and Electronic Systems,* Vol. AES-25, March 1989, pp. 296–300.
[4]   Y. Bar-Shalom (ed.), *Multitarget-Multisensor Tracking: Advanced Applications,* Artech House, Norwood, MA, 1990.
[5]   Y. Bar-Shalom, MULTIDAT—Multimodel Data Association Tracker (4.0), Interactive Software, 1991.
[6]   S. Blake and S.C. Watts, "A Multitarget Track-White-Scan Filter," Proc. IEE Radar 87 Conf., London, October 1987.
[7]   H.A.P. Blom, "A Sophisticated Tracking Algorithm for ATC Surveillance Data." Proc. Intn'l. Radar Conf., Paris, May 1984.
[8]   H.A.P. Blom, "An Efficient Filter for Abruptly Changing Systems," Proc. 23rd IEEE Conf. Decision and Control, Las Vegas, December 1984.
[9]   H.A.P. Blom, "An Efficient Decision-Making-Free Filter for Processes with Abrupt Changes," Proc. 7th IFAC Symp. Identification and System Parameter Estimation. York, U.K., July 1985.
[10]  H.A.P. Blom, "Overlooked Potential of Systems with Markovian Switching Coefficients," Proc. 25th IEEE Conf. Decision and Control, Athens, December 1986.
[11]  H.A.P. Blom and Y. Bar-Shalom, "The Interacting Multiple Model Algorithm for Systems with Markovian Switching Coefficients," *IEEE Trans. on Automatic Control,* Vol. AC-33, August 1988, pp. 780–783.
[12]  H.A.P. Blom, R.A. Hogendoorn, and F.J. van Schaik, "Bayesian Multisensor Tracking for Advanced Air Traffic Control Systems," A. Benoit, (ed.), *Aircraft Trajectories: Computation, Prediction and Control,* AGARDOgraph No. 301, 1990.
[13]  A. Houles and Y. Bar-Shalom, "Multisensor Tracking of a Maneuvering Target in Clutter," *IEEE Trans. on Aerospace and Electronics Systems,* Vol. AES-25, March 1989, pp. 176–189.
[14]  S.S. Blackman, *Multiple Target Tracking with Radar Applications,* Artech House, Norwood, MA, 1986.

# Chapter 5

# PRECISION TRACKING OF SMALL EXTENDED TARGETS WITH IMAGING SENSORS

*H. M. Shertukde*
*Electrical Engineering*
*Department*
*University of Hartford*

*Y. Bar-Shalom*
*Electrical and Systems*
*Engineering Department*
*University of Connecticut*

## 5.1 INTRODUCTION

In this chapter we first discuss the extraction of measurements for precision tracking of the centroid of an extended target from a forward looking infrared (FLIR) imaging sensor. A statistical characterization of the centroid of a frame as a noisy linear measurement of the centroid of the target is obtained. Over the past decade considerable research examined several methods of tracking using FLIR sensors. In [12–15] an extended Kalman filter was used to track with nonlinear measurements as the observed pixel intensities. This required an accurate model of the target intensity distribution parameters in the sensor's focal plane, and an adaptive scheme to estimate these parameters also was proposed. This approach is costly as it utilizes a 64-dimensional measurement vector for an $8 \times 8$ frame. Other work [16, 22] used linear measurements, centroid offset (displacement) measurement derived from the correlation of adjacent frames, but the measurement noise was assumed to be white

H.M. Shertukde's research was partially supported by faculty research release time from the University of Hartford, Connecticut. Y. Bar-Shalom's research was supported by the Office of Naval Research, under contract N00014-87-K-0057.
We thank Dr. L.C. Ng for his stimulating discussions and the original suggestion of the topic of this chapter.

[also 12, 14, 15] and its variance assumed to be known. We will show that the offset measurement noise is autocorrelated and the output of a moving average system driven by white noise. Next, simulations are given and quantitative conclusions are drawn about achievable subpixel tracking accuracy. State variable models are presented to track the target centroid with these measurements. The principal conclusion of this study is that the best performance is achieved from the filter that accounts for the autocorrelated measurement noise.

Finally, we discuss an algorithm for tracking crossing targets by using the centroid measurement and the centroid offset measurement of the distributed image formed by the targets, obtained from a FLIR sensor. Target images overlap when the lines of sight of the targets cross. The resulting centroid measurement of the distributed image is a single merged measurement, which can be modeled as a linear combination of the centroids of the individual targets under consideration. The overlapping images result in measurements "shared" over several sampling times and a dependence of the state estimation errors for the two targets, which has to be taken into account. The *joint probabilistic data association merged-measurement coupled filter* (JPDAMCF) is used for state estimation in a coupled manner for the targets with *common* measurements. Two filters are examined: one assuming the displacement noise is white and the other modeling it correctly as *autocorrelated*. The latter is shown to yield better performance. The simulation results presented validate the performance predictions of the proposed algorithm.

### Target Centroid and Target Offset Estimation (Section 5.2)

The accuracy of two target image centroid estimators ("center of mass" based on a single frame) and the target offset estimator (based on image correlation from two consecutive frames) are derived for a FLIR sensor. The previous methods of obtaining the accuracy of such sensors (needed for tracking and pointing algorithms) was either by "tuning" the algorithm [16] or running Monte Carlo results for a large number of images [22]. Comparison of the theoretical results obtained with Monte Carlo runs of noisy images confirms the analytical results.

### Tracking a Single Target (Section 5.3)

Based on the results shown, a precision tracking algorithm could estimate the target centroid with very good subpixel accuracy: standard deviation of about 0.1 pixel, which corresponds to approximately $\frac{1}{30}$ of the size of the target (assumed to extend over 10 pixels) or less. The centroid offset measurement requires more computation and a more complex state model for estimation than the direct centroid measurement, but it yields significantly better results if the filter accounts for the autocorrelated noise. Furthermore, the offset measurement is less sensitive to target obscuration and has greater potential for tracking crossing targets.

*Tracking Multiple Targets (Section 5.4)*

The proposed algorithm demonstrates the usefulness of the JPDAMCF for tracking crossing targets in combination with the models for the centroid and offset measurements described in Section 5.2. Even though the centroid offset measurement requires more computation and a more complex model for estimation, it yields significantly better results; 50% MSE, if the filter accounts for its colored measurement noise.

## 5.2  EXTRACTION OF MEASUREMENTS FROM AN IMAGING SENSOR

This section deals with two measurements pertaining to the centroid of a target obtained from a FLIR imaging sensor: the location of the centroid (center of mass based on a single frame), and the offset of the centroid (based on two consecutive frames). These measurements will be used in a precision tracking algorithm. The size of the target's image, which can be a missile exhaust plume or a jet engine exhaust, is assumed to cover around 10 pixels of the sensor's 64 pixels (i.e., an $8 \times 8$ array is assumed as in [14]). The effect of atmospheric jitter is not considered here—it is well documented in [14]. The current methods to obtain the accuracy of measurements from imaging sensors are either by "tuning" the tracking filters [16] or Monte Carlo runs of a large number of images [22]. In [7] the estimation of image motion parameters was discussed, based on "match points." Recursive estimation was used, but the measurement noise was assumed to be white and its variance assumed to be known. We provide explicit expressions that map the *video signal-to-noise ratio* (SNR) into the *centroid measurement noise statistics* needed by the tracking filters. A centroid location estimator was considered in [23]; however, unlike here, where pixel intensities are used, it was assumed that pixels are classified only into target or background.

The modeling of the image is presented in Subsection 5.2.1. The estimation of the location of the centroid of the target is the topic of Subsection 5.2.2. Closed-form expressions for the noise effects are presented and a simple numerical example illustrates the results. The estimation of the offset of the target centroid between two consecutive frames is considered in Subsection 5.2.3, and its accuracy is derived and illustrated with an example. The offset measurement noise is shown to be *autocorrelated.* We show that the offset measurement noise is the output of a moving average system driven by white noise. Subsection 5.2.4 applies these techniques to a Gaussian plume image, which is typical of a jet or missile. The simulation results confirm the theoretically derived statistical characterization of the measurement noises.

### 5.2.1  Modeling the Image

A two-dimensional array of

$$m = m_\xi \times m_\eta \tag{5.1}$$

pixels is considered, where each pixel is denoted by a single index $i = 1, \ldots, m$. The measured intensity of pixel $i$ is

$$I_i = s_i + n_i \tag{5.2}$$

where $s_i$ is the signal (target) intensity and $n_i$ is the noise intensity in pixel $i$. The image noise is modeled as independent and identically distributed with first and second moments given by

$$E[n_i] = 0 \tag{5.3}$$

$$E[n_i n_j] = \sigma^2 \delta_{ij} \tag{5.4}$$

The mean of the noise is assumed already to have been subtracted from the measured intensities.

The *total target-related intensity* is denoted as

$$s = \sum_{i=1}^{m} s_i \tag{5.5}$$

where the summation is over all the pixels (the limits of the summations will be omitted from now on). Denoting by $m_s$ the number of pixels covered by the target (termed the target *extent*), we can define the average target intensity over its extent as

$$\mu_s = \frac{s}{m_s} \tag{5.6}$$

The average target intensity over the entire frame is denoted as

$$\bar{s} = \frac{s}{m} \tag{5.7}$$

The *contrast* of the target image with respect to the frame will be defined as

$$\kappa = \Sigma(s_i - \bar{s})^2 = \Sigma s_i^2 - \frac{s^2}{m} \tag{5.8}$$

This quantity, which is the signal's "variance" (multiplied by $m$) will be shown later to play a key role in the accuracy of the target offset measurement obtained from correlating two consecutive frames.

Another important quantity needed later is the *frame SNR,* defined as

$$r = \frac{\Sigma s_i}{\text{rms}[\Sigma n_i]} = \frac{s}{\sqrt{m}\, \sigma} = \frac{m_s \mu_s}{\sqrt{m}\, \sigma} \tag{5.9}$$

Note that this differs from the *average pixel SNR* (over the target's "extent"):

$$r' = \frac{\mu_s}{\sigma} = r\frac{\sqrt{m}}{m_s} \tag{5.10}$$

The Cartesian coordinates of pixel $i$ will be denoted as $(\xi_i, \eta_i)$. Assuming the center of coordinates to be in the center of the frame, we have

$$\Sigma \xi_i = 0 \tag{5.11}$$

and, similarly, for $\eta_i$. The analysis presented later will be done for the $\xi$ coordinate; a similar analysis holds for the $\eta$ coordinate. For the sake of illustration and validation of the approximations to be made in the course of the derivations, the results at various stages will be evaluated numerically for an $8 \times 8$ array (i.e., $m = 64$).

*Numerical Example*

The target is assumed to cover $m_s = 10$ pixels with a constant intensity of $\mu_s = 6$; that is, a "flat" signal is considered. The total target intensity is then $s = 60$. With noise rms of $\sigma = 1$, what is the frame SNR, pixel SNR, and contrast of the target image over the entire frame? From eq. (5.9) the frame SNR is $r = 7.5$. From (5.10) the pixel SNR is $r' = 6$. The contrast of the target image over the entire frame, given by (5.8), is

$$\kappa = 303.75 \approx 300$$

### 5.2.2 Estimation of the Centroid

The estimate of the $\xi$-coordinate of the location of the centroid to be used, in pixel units, is the "center of mass":

$$\xi_c = \frac{\Sigma \xi_i I_i}{\Sigma I_i} \tag{5.12}$$

where $\xi_i$ is the $\xi$ coordinate of the center of pixel $i$ and the measured intensity $I_i$ corresponding to this pixel is given by (5.11). The two sources of error in (5.12) are

1. The image noise: the measured pixel intensities are noisy,
2. The image discretization: the pixels are of finite size and their intensities are assumed to be located in their centers, rather than their centroids (which are not available due to the sensor's resolution limitation).

The coefficient of variation $c_v$ of a random variable $x$ is defined as the ratio of its standard deviation to its mean:

$$c_v(x) \triangleq \frac{\sigma_x}{x} \tag{5.13}$$

We assume that

$$c_v(\Sigma I_i) = c_v[\Sigma(s_i + n_i)] = \frac{\sqrt{m}\,\sigma}{s} \ll 1 \tag{5.14}$$

where notations (5.3)–(5.5) have been used. In other words, the coefficient of the variation of the denominator of (5.12) is assumed "small," practically 0.15 or less. For the numerical example described in Subsection 5.2.1, it is 0.13.

With this assumption, derivations presented in Appendix A yield the measurement equation

$$\hat{\xi}_c = \xi_c + w_c \tag{5.15}$$

where the centroid measurement noise $w_c$ is zero-mean and, from (5.A21), has the variance

$$\sigma_c^2 = \xi_c^2 \frac{m\sigma^2}{s^2 + m\sigma^2} + \frac{\sigma^2 \Sigma \xi_i^2}{s^2 + m\sigma^2} + \frac{\Sigma s_i^2}{12s^2} \tag{5.16}$$

where the multiplicative factor $\xi_c$ is the actual centroid.

Using (5.8) and (5.9) this can be rewritten as

$$\sigma_c^2 = \xi_c^2 \frac{1}{r^2 + 1} + \frac{\Sigma \xi_i^2}{m(r^2 + 1)} + \frac{\kappa + s^2/m}{12s^2} \tag{5.17}$$

*Numerical Example*

For the numerical example described in Subsection 5.2.1, with $m = 64$, $r = 7.5$, $\kappa = 300$, and assuming $\xi_c = 1$, the variance (5.16), using (5.A8), is

$$\sigma_c^2 = (0.13)^2 + (0.3)^2 + (0.09)^2 \approx (0.34)^2 \tag{5.18}$$

that is, about one-third of a pixel rms value.

### 5.2.3 The Offset Measurement from Image Correlation

The correlation coefficient between two frames from times $k$ and $k - 1$ with displacement $\delta$ (along one axis) is

$$\hat{\rho}_\delta(k) = \frac{\Sigma[I_i(k) - \bar{I}(k)][i_{i_\delta}(k-1) - \bar{I}(k-1)]}{\{\Sigma[I_i(k) - \bar{I}(k)]^2 \Sigma[I_{i_\delta}(k-1) - \bar{I}(k-1)]^2\}^{1/2}} \qquad (5.19)$$

where $I_i(k)$ is the intensity of pixel $i$ at time $k$; $i_\delta$ is the index of the pixel in the image at $k - 1$ corresponding to pixel $i$ at $k$, when the image from $k - 1$ has been shifted by $\delta$ pixels along the axis under consideration ($\delta$ is an integer, with two axes the shifts form a two-dimensional array of integers). The summations are over only the overlying pixels, and the denominator is a normalizing factor. The average intensities $\bar{I}(k)$ and $\bar{I}(k - 1)$ also are based on only the overlying pixels.

Let the three highest image correlations (for displacement in one direction) be for the displacements $\delta - 1, \delta, \delta + 1$ with the peak in the center:

$$\hat{\rho}_{\delta-1} < \hat{\rho}_\delta > \hat{\rho}_{\delta+1} \qquad (5.20)$$

The maximum correlation, using a parabolic interpolation between these three points, is at location

$$\hat{d} = \delta + \frac{\alpha_1}{\alpha_2} \qquad (5.21)$$

where

$$\alpha_1 \triangleq \hat{\rho}_{\delta+1} - \hat{\rho}_{\delta-1} \qquad \alpha_2 \triangleq 2(2\hat{\rho}_\delta - \hat{\rho}_{\delta-1} - \hat{\rho}_{\delta+1}) \qquad (5.22)$$

The estimated location (5.21) of the peak correlation is the image offset measurement.

As shown in Appendix 5.B, the measurement (5.21) can be written as

$$\hat{d} = d + w_d \qquad (5.23)$$

where $d$ is the true offset (displacement) and the measurement noise $w_d$ is zero-mean with the variance given later. Furthermore, this measurement noise sequence is not white: the correlation coefficient magnitude between two such noises consecutive in time can be up to 0.5; if the separation is longer than one sampling period, however, they are uncorrelated. This is a consequence of the affect of the video noises in the two consecutive frames on its image correlation: the offsets from $k - 1$ to $k$ and from $k$ to $k + 1$ (see Figure 5.3) share half the noises (from time $k$).

The variance of the measurement noise in (5.23), from (5.B2), (5.B9), is given by the expression

$$\sigma_d^2 = \frac{2(2\kappa\sigma^2 + m\sigma^4)}{\kappa^2(\alpha_2^2 + 12\alpha_1^2)} \tag{5.24}$$

*Numerical Example*

For the numerical example of Subsection 5.2.1, with nominal values $\hat{\rho}_\delta = 0.8$, $\hat{\rho}_{\delta-1} = \hat{\rho}_{\delta+1} = 0.6$, we have $\sigma_d = 0.15$; that is, one-sixth of a pixel rms value.

These results show that we can obtain subpixel accuracy even from single measurements. Further improvement can be obtained by filtering these measurements, as will be shown in Section 5.3.


### 5.2.4   Application to a Gaussian Plume Target

Consider a target whose intensity in the sensor's focal plane is a Gaussian plume

$$S(\xi, \eta) = S_{max} \, e^{-1/2[(\xi-\xi_c)^2/a_\xi^2 + (\eta-\eta_c)^2/a_\eta^2]} \tag{5.25}$$

with the center at $(\xi_c, \eta_c)$, semiaxes $a_\xi$, $a_\eta$ ("footprint" assumed, for simplicity, to be oriented along the sensor's coordinates).

The intensity of pixel $i$ ($1 \le i \le 64$) due to the signal is

$$
\begin{aligned}
s_i &= \int_{\xi_i-1/2}^{\xi_i+1/2} \int_{\eta_i-1/2}^{\eta_i+1/2} S(\xi, \eta) \, d\xi \, d\eta \\
&= 2\pi \, S_{max} a_\xi a_\eta \left[ \Phi\left(\frac{\xi_i + 0.5 - \xi_c}{a_\xi}\right) - \Phi\left(\frac{\xi_i - 0.5 - \xi_c}{a_\xi}\right) \right] \\
&\quad \cdot \left[ \Phi\left(\frac{\eta_i + 0.5 - \eta_c}{a_\eta}\right) - \Phi\left(\frac{\eta_i - 0.5 - \eta_c}{a_\eta}\right) \right]
\end{aligned}
\tag{5.26}
$$

where

$$\xi_i = -4 + (i - 1)_8 + \frac{1}{2} \tag{5.27}$$

$$\eta_i = -4 + \overline{\left(\frac{i-1}{8}\right)} + \frac{1}{2} \tag{5.28}$$

$$(i)_n \underset{\Delta}{} i \text{ modulo } n \qquad (5.29)$$

$$(\cdot)^- \underset{\Delta}{} \text{ rounded down to nearest integer} \qquad (5.30)$$

$$\Phi(y) \underset{\Delta}{} \int_{-\infty}^{y} N(x; 0, 1) \, dx \qquad (5.31)$$

Next the quantities that determine the accuracy of the centroid and offset measurements are obtained.

Assuming that the target is entirely within the frame, the total target-related intensity (5.5) is

$$s = \Sigma s_i = S_{max} 2\pi a_\xi a_\eta \int_{-\infty}^{\infty} \int_{-\infty}^{\infty} \frac{1}{2\pi a_\xi a_\eta} e^{-1/2[\cdot]} \, d\xi \, d\eta$$

$$= S_{max} 2\pi a_\xi a_\eta \qquad (5.32)$$

where the exponent is the same as in (5.25).

The sum of the squares of the intensities, needed in (5.16), is obtained numerically by using (5.26), or we can use the following approximation:

$$\Sigma s_i^2 = S_{max}^2 2\pi \frac{a_\xi a_\eta}{2} \iint \frac{1}{2\pi \frac{a_\xi a_\eta}{2}} e^{-[\cdot]} \, d\xi \, d\eta = S_{max}^2 \pi a_\xi a_\eta \qquad (5.33)$$

With (5.32) and (5.33), the expression of the variance (5.16) of the centroid measurement is

$$\sigma_c^2 = \xi_c^2 \frac{m\sigma^2}{s^2 + m\sigma^2} + \frac{\sigma^2 \Sigma \xi_i^2}{s^2 + m\sigma^2} + \frac{\Sigma s_i^2}{12 s^2}$$

$$= \frac{\xi_c^2 m\sigma^2 + \sigma^2 \Sigma \xi_i^2}{(S_{max} 2\pi a_\xi a_\eta)^2 + m\sigma^2} + \frac{1}{48\pi a_\xi a_\eta} \qquad (5.34)$$

The "contrast" (5.8), using (5.7), is

$$\kappa = \Sigma(s_i - \bar{s})^2 = \Sigma s_i^2 - \frac{s^2}{m} = S_{max}^2 \pi a_\xi a_\eta \left[ 1 - \frac{4\pi a_\xi a_\eta}{m} \right] \qquad (5.35)$$

*Numerical Example*

Using the numerical values $a_\xi = 1.5$ and $a_\eta = 1$, we have

$$s = 3\pi S_{\max} \tag{5.36}$$

$$\Sigma s_i^2 = 1.5\pi S_{\max}^2 \tag{5.37}$$

With $m = 64$ and $\sigma = 1$, from (5.34) we have the variance of the centroid measurement:

$$\sigma_c^2 = \frac{\xi_c^2 64 + 336}{9\pi^2 S_{\max}^2 + 64} + \frac{1}{72\pi} = \frac{64\xi_c^2 + 336}{64 + 9\pi^2 S_{\max}^2} + (0.066)^2 \tag{5.38}$$

The contrast for these numbers and $S_{\max} = 10$ (i.e., a *peak* pixel SNR of 10), using (5.35), is

$$\kappa = 100\pi 1.5 \left[ 1 - \frac{6\pi}{64} \right] = 332 \tag{5.39}$$

To check the theoretical derivations, 100 Monte Carlo runs were made for a Gaussian plume image with these parameters. The image was centered at the origin; that is, $\xi_c = 0$. The theoretical calculation of the centroid measurement noise (5.38) in this case yields $\sigma_c = 0.195$. The rms values of the $x$ and $y$ measurement noises (from the 100 runs) were 0.188 and 0.171; that is, within less than 10% of the theoretical calculations. Because the 95% confidence region is 14% for a 100-run sample average [2], this validates the theoretical formulas derived here.

For the offset measurements, the average correlations were $\hat{\rho}_\delta = 0.85$, $\hat{\rho}_{\delta+1} \approx \hat{\rho}_{\delta-1} = 0.58$, which yield $\alpha_1 = 0$ and $\alpha_2 = 1.1$, and from (5.24) we obtain $\sigma_d = 0.104$. The 100-run averages for the two coordinates were 0.106 and 0.102, which validate (5.24).

The sample correlation coefficient between two consecutive offset measurement noises was obtained from 100 runs as $-0.52$. This also confirms the assertion presented in Subsection 5.2.3, and we can conclude that the actual correlation coefficient is $-0.5$.

## 5.3 PRECISION TARGET TRACKING OF THE IMAGE CENTROID

This section presents the state models to be used to estimate the target centroid by using the following measurements: the centroid measurement based on a single frame, and the centroid offset measurement based on two consecutive frames.

First, the estimation is presented assuming the offset measurement noise to be white. Then, the correlation of these noises is accounted for via an augmented state model. The simulation results presented in Subsection 5.3.3 indicate that the best estimation performance is obtained by accounting for the autocorrelated offset measurement noise. This can yield very good *subpixel* accuracy, in the range of 0.1 pixel rms error.

### 5.3.1  Filter with White Measurement Noise Model

Denoting the position of the image centroid at time $k$ in one of the coordinates as $x_1(k)$, the centroid measurement (5.15) is

$$z_1(k) = x_1(k) + w_c(k) \tag{5.40}$$

where the centroid measurement noise $w_c(k)$ is defined in (5.A20), and its variance, $\sigma_c^2$, is given in (5.16).

The displacement measurement (5.23) can be written as

$$z_2(k) = x_1(k) - x_1(k-1) + w_d(k) \tag{5.41}$$

where the displacement measurement noise is (see (5.B1))

$$w_d(k) \triangleq \hat{d}(k) \tag{5.42}$$

and its variance $\sigma_d^2$ is given in (5.24).

Assuming the displacement measurement noise to be white, the state equation for tracking a nearly constant velocity target using these measurements is

$$x(k+1) = \begin{bmatrix} x_1(k+1) \\ x_2(k+1) \\ x_3(k+1) \end{bmatrix}$$

$$= \begin{bmatrix} 1 & T & 0 \\ 0 & 1 & 0 \\ 1 & 0 & 0 \end{bmatrix} \begin{bmatrix} x_1(k) \\ x_2(k) \\ x_3(k) \end{bmatrix} + \begin{bmatrix} T^2/2 \\ T \\ 0 \end{bmatrix} v(k) \tag{5.43}$$

where the state consists of the current position, current velocity, and previous position; $T$ is the sampling period, and $v(k)$ is the zero mean, white motion process noise (acceleration), with variance $q$.

The measurement equation is

$$z(k) = \begin{bmatrix} 1 & 0 & 0 \\ 1 & 0 & -1 \end{bmatrix} x(k) + w(k) \tag{5.44}$$

The covariance of the measurement noise is

$$R = \text{diag}(\sigma_c^2, \sigma_d^2) \tag{5.45}$$

We can show that the correlation between the two noises is zero. This has been confirmed via a simulation that yielded a statistically insignificant correlation coefficient. The state estimation problem based on (5.43) and (5.44) can be solved by using the standard Kalman filter technique as in, for example, [2].

### 5.3.2  Filter with Autocorrelated Noise Model

The non-white measurement noise in the displacement observation can be incorporated into the state estimation as follows.

From the discussion of Subsection 5.2.3, it follows that

$$E[w_d(k)w_d(j)] = \begin{cases} \sigma_d^2 & k=j \\ \alpha\sigma_d^2 & |k-j| = 1 \\ 0 & |k-j| > 1 \end{cases} \tag{5.46}$$

where $\alpha = -0.5$. Such a noise is the output of the following (moving average) system driven by white noise:

$$w_d(k) = \beta_1 v_2(k) + \beta_2 v_2(k-1) \tag{5.47}$$

where $v_2(k)$ is a zero-mean white sequence with variance $\sigma_d^2$. The weighting coefficients in (5.46) are

$$\beta_1 = \tfrac{1}{2}(\sqrt{1+2\alpha} + \sqrt{1-2\alpha}) \qquad \beta_2 = \tfrac{1}{2}(\sqrt{1+2\alpha} - \sqrt{1-2\alpha}) \tag{5.48}$$

This type of autocorrelated noise is different from the usual (autoregressive) model [1] and requires state augmentation. The augmented state equation needed to incorporate the autocorrelated measurement noise model (5.47) is

$$
\begin{aligned}
x(k+1) &= \begin{bmatrix} x_1(k+1) \\ x_2(k+1) \\ x_3(k+1) \\ x_4(k+1) \end{bmatrix} \\[6pt]
&= Fx(k) + Gv(k) \\[6pt]
&= \begin{bmatrix} 1 & T & 0 & 0 \\ 0 & 1 & 0 & 0 \\ 1 & 0 & 0 & 0 \\ 0 & 0 & 0 & 0 \end{bmatrix} \begin{bmatrix} x_1(k) \\ x_2(k) \\ x_3(k) \\ x_4(k) \end{bmatrix} + \begin{bmatrix} T^2/2 & 0 \\ T & 0 \\ 0 & 0 \\ 0 & \beta_2 \end{bmatrix} \begin{bmatrix} v_1(k) \\ v_2(k) \end{bmatrix}
\end{aligned} \tag{5.49}
$$

Note that in (5.43) the state was a three-dimensional vector whereas in (5.49) the state is a four-dimensional vector. The measurement equation is

$$z(k) = Hx(k) + w(k) \qquad (5.50)$$

$$= \begin{bmatrix} 1 & 0 & 0 & 0 \\ 1 & 0 & -1 & 1 \end{bmatrix} \begin{bmatrix} x_1(k) \\ x_2(k) \\ x_3(k) \\ x_4(k) \end{bmatrix} + \begin{bmatrix} w_1(k) \\ w_2(k) \end{bmatrix}$$

where $v_1(k)$ is the motion process noise, $v_2(k)$ is the white noise input to the auto-correlated noise (5.47) in the displacement measurement with variance $\sigma_d^2$, $w_1(k)$ is the noise in the centroid measurement, and

$$w_2(k) \triangleq \beta_1 v_2(k) \qquad (5.51)$$

The measurement and process noise sequences are white but $v(k)$ and $w(k)$ are correlated. This is described as follows:

$$E[Gv(k)v(j)'G'] = GQG'\delta_{kj} = qGG'\delta_{kj} \qquad (5.52)$$

$$E[w(k)w(j)'] = R\delta_{kj} = \begin{bmatrix} \sigma_c^2 & 0 \\ 0 & \beta_1^2\sigma_d^2 \end{bmatrix} \delta_{kj} \qquad (5.53)$$

$$E[v(k)w(j)'] = U\delta_{kj} = \begin{bmatrix} 0 & 0 \\ 0 & \beta_1\sigma_d^2 \end{bmatrix} \delta_{kj} \qquad (5.54)$$

where the last equation indicates cross correlation between the two noise sequences; that is, it is not a standard filtering problem.

The technique described in [1, 18] can be used to obtain the state estimation filter. The plant equation is rewritten so that it has a *new process noise* uncorrelated with the measurement noise. Using an arbitrary matrix $T$, to be determined later, we can write

$$x(k + 1) = Fx(k) + Gv(k) + T[z(k) - Hx(k) - w(k)] \qquad (5.55)$$
$$= (F - TH)x(k) + Gv(k) - Tw(k) + Tz(k)$$

Denote the new transition matrix

$$F^* \triangleq F - TH \qquad (5.56)$$

new process noise

$$v^*(k) \triangleq Gv(k) - Tw(k) \qquad (5.57)$$

and new input

$$u^*(k) \triangleq Tz(k) \tag{5.58}$$

Then we can write the new state equation

$$x(k + 1) = F^*x(k) + v^*(k) + u^*(k) \tag{5.59}$$

Setting the cross correlation between the new process noise and the measurement noise to zero,

$$E[v^*(k)w(k)'] = 0 \tag{5.60}$$

yields

$$T = GUR^{-1} \tag{5.61}$$

The covariance of the new process noise can be shown to be

$$E[v^*(k)v^*(k)'] = Q - GUR^{-1}G' \triangleq Q^* \tag{5.62}$$

The state estimation problem based on (5.59) and (5.50) with the noise covariances given by (5.53), (5.60), and (5.62) now is standard and can be solved by using the standard Kalman filter technique.

### 5.3.3   Simulation Results

A target whose intensity in the sensor's focal plane is a Gaussian plume as given by (5.25) was considered for simulations. Target motion described by a second-order kinematic model with white noise acceleration with $q = (0.05)^2$ in each of the two coordinates was considered. The sampling period was $T = 1$ and the filters were initialized by using two-point differencing [2]. Using the following values of the parameters: $S_{max} = 10$, $a_\xi = 1.5$, $a_\eta = 1$ yields $\sigma_c = 0.195$, $\sigma_d = 0.104$, and the correlation coefficient $\alpha = -0.5$. The following filters were run:

- Case A, centroid measurements only. In this case the state equation is (5.43) without the third state component (which is needed only when displacement measurements also are available).
- Case B, centroid and displacement measurements, assuming the displacement measurement noise is white. The state equation is (5.43), and the measurement equation is (5.44).
- Case C, with centroid and displacement measurements, with the displacement measurement noise accounted for as colored according to (5.46) with $\alpha =$

−0.5. The state equation is then (5.59), and the measurement equation (5.50) with noise covariances according to (5.53), (5.60), and (5.62).

Table 5.1 summarizes the results in terms of achievable accuracies for the problem considered. Also, the average *normalized* state *estimation error squared* (NEES) from 100 runs is shown to be very close to its theoretical average (based on the chi-square distribution [2]), indicating that the filters are consistent; that is, their calculated variances match the actual errors. Clearly the filter design taking into consideration the autocorrelated displacement measurement noise yields by far the best performance.

**Table 5.1**
Position and Velocity Variances (in Steady State) for Each Coordinate and Filter Consistency Verification from 100 Runs

| Case | Position Variance | Velocity Variance | Average NEES | Expected NEES |
|------|-------------------|-------------------|--------------|---------------|
| A | 0.0194 | 0.0058 | 3.87 | 4 |
| B | 0.0138 | 0.0041 | 5.53 | 6 |
| C | 0.0071 | 0.0032 | 7.79 | 8 |

These results show that we can obtain very good subpixel accuracy in the range of 0.1 pixel rms error. Note that the target maneuvering index (ratio of the rms values of the effect of the process noise on the position in one sampling period and the effect of the measurement noise on the position) [2] is about 0.25. The process noise can be related as follows to the actual target acceleration. Assuming that a pixel corresponds to 1 m (target extent is about $3 \times 4$ pixels) and the actual sampling rate is $1/T_0 = 30\text{Hz}$, the process noise standard deviation corresponds to an acceleration $a$ given by

$$aT_0^2 = \sqrt{q}\, T^2 \qquad (5.63)$$

This yields for the assumed value of $q$ an acceleration of $a \approx 5$ g, which is quite significant.

For targets maneuvering less, we can use lower process noise $q$ in the filter, which results in even smaller estimation errors.

## 5.4  TRACKING CROSSING TARGETS WITH FLIR SENSORS

### 5.4.1  Background

In air or space defense, the problem of crossing targets with measurements obtained by a FLIR sensor is critical. In practice, the tracking is done based on a small image of a jet engine exhaust or a missile exhaust plume. As discussed in Section 5.2, the measurement errors emanate from sensor noise, optics, and the irregularity of the exhaust in addition to the atmospheric jitter. These errors are compounded in the case of two targets whose lines of sight from the sensor cross. The crossing lines of sight result in *ambiguity* in the offset measurements from the two targets over several sampling times. The overlap of the two images also generates a mixed (merged) target image with a centroid that can be assumed to be a linear combination of the centroids of the individual targets. In light of this, proper association of the measurements to targets can be difficult. Furthermore, this "sharing" of measurements over several sampling times also causes a dependence of the state estimation errors for the two targets. This aspect of the problem has been handled in the sonar tracking of multiple targets using the joint probabilistic data association filter technique as in [9, 2], further augmented with a measurement-merging model in [8]. An extension of the JPDAF, called the *joint probabilistic data association coupled filter algorithm* [6], which performs filtering in a coupled manner for targets with *common* measurements, is employed for state estimation. The merged measurement is accounted for by a model as in [8]. The resulting algorithm, which is the main result of this section, is the *joint probabilistic data association merged-measurement coupled filter* (JPDAMCF). Subsection 5.4.2 deals with the problem formulation. The state estimation algorithm for the two targets under consideration with overlapping images is presented in Subsection 5.4.3. Subsection 5.4.4 illustrates the procedure with simulation results.

### 5.4.2   Problem Formulation

*5.4.2.1   Modeling Assumptions*

We assume that two targets are moving with nearly constant velocities and their tracks already are established. The images of the two targets in the focal plane are Gaussian plumes with signal intensity distributions $S_j(\xi, \eta)\, j = 1, 2$. Following [10, 11, 17] we assume that the radiation source (jet exhaust) is not opaque, so that, when the lines of sight of the two targets from the sensor cross, the resultant intensity in each pixel of the two-dimensional array is approximately the addition of the two individual intensities.

The intensity measured in pixel $i$ (again single-argument pixel indexing is used for simplicity) is

$$I_i = s_{1i} + s_{2i} + \eta_i \qquad i = 1, \ldots, m \qquad (5.64)$$

where $s_{ji}$ is the signal (target) intensity of target $j, j = 1, 2$ in pixel $i$ and $n_i$ is the noise intensity in pixel $i$ after subtracting its mean; $m$ is the total number of pixels in the two-dimensional $m_\xi \times m_\eta$ array given by eq. (5.1). As in Section 5.2 the image noise is modeled as a set of independently and identically distributed random variables with first and second moments given by (5.3) and (5.4), respectively. The total target related intensity in the two-dimensional array is

$$s = \sum_{i=1}^{m} (s_{1i} + s_{2i}) \tag{5.65}$$

### 5.4.2.2 The Centroid of the Combined Image versus the Individual Target Centroids

The estimate of the $\xi$-coordinate of the location of the centroid of the combined image at time $k$, in pixel units (as in Subsection 5.2.2), is

$$\hat{\xi}_c = \frac{\sum \xi_i I_i}{\sum I_i} \tag{5.66}$$

where $\xi_i$ is the $\xi$ coordinate of the center of pixel $i$ and the measured intensity $I_i$ corresponding to this pixel is given by (5.64). The summations are over the entire frame. As shown in Appendix C, the estimated centroid (5.64) of the combined image relates to the centroids of the two targets according to the equation

$$\xi_c = \iota \xi_{c_1} + (1 - \iota)\xi_{c_2} + w_c \tag{5.67}$$

where $\xi_{c_i}$ is the true centroid of target $i$, $\iota$ is the *image-mixing parameter* discussed in Appendix C, and $w_c$ is the measurement noise that, as shown in (Subsection 5.2.2) is zero-mean, white, and with variance $\sigma_c^2$ given by (5.17). The image mixing parameter has to be estimated before the targets overlap; this also is discussed in Appendix C.

### 5.4.2.3 Evaluation of the Offset Measurement from the Image Correlation Matrix due to Two Targets

The correlation coefficient between two frames from times $k$ and $k - 1$ with displacement (offset) $\Delta$, similar to (5.19), is

$$\hat{\rho}_\Delta(k) = \frac{\sum [I_i(k) - \bar{I}(k)][I_{i_\Delta}(k - 1) - \bar{I}(k - 1)]}{\{\sum [I_i(k) - \bar{I}(k)]^2 \sum [I_{i_\Delta}(k - 1) - \bar{I}(k - 1)]^2\}^{1/2}} \tag{5.68}$$

where in this case

$$\Delta = [\delta_\xi \ \delta_\eta]' \tag{5.69}$$

and $I_i(k)$ is the intensity of pixel $i$ at time $k$ given by (5.64); $\Delta$ is a two-dimensional vector of integers, and all other evaluations are done in the same way as in (5.19) to obtain the value of the correlation coefficient.

Due to the existence of two targets in the image plane, the correlation function exhibits a *multimodal distribution*. Figures 5.1–5.3 show three consecutive sensor frames using some numerical values for the intensity distributions and the velocities for the two targets. The image of target 1 is moving with heading of 135° with a nearly constant speed of 1 pixel per sampling period and the image of target 2 is moving with heading of 27° with a nearly constant speed of 2 pixels per sampling period.

The image correlation matrix elements between frames at $k - 1$ and $k$ and between frames at $k$ and $k + 1$ are shown in Tables 5.2 and 5.3, respectively. The displacement measurements are obtained by using a parabolic interpolation for each peak with its neighbors. The resulting displacement measurements contain the additive zero-mean noise $w_d$ that is not white: the error in the observed displacement between frames $k - 1$ and $k$ and the error in the one between frames $k$ and $k + 1$ are correlated because both are affected by the noise in frame $k$. The autocorrelation function of $w_d(k)$ is given by eq. (5.46).

From Tables 5.2 and 5.3 it is clear that, based on the rule of eight nearest neighbors, two peaks correspond to the two targets. Although in this case there are no false peaks, we do not know which peak should be associated with which target to evaluate

**Table 5.2**
Image Correlation Coefficient Matrix Between Noisy Frames at $k - 1$ and $k$

| 0.52 | −0.07 | −0.15 | 0.42 | 0.13 | −0.16 | −0.03 | 0.19 |
|---|---|---|---|---|---|---|---|
| 0.13 | −0.20 | −0.16 | [0.72] | 0.51 | −0.05 | −0.25 | 0.12 |
| −0.20 | −0.24 | −0.16 | 0.23 | 0.38 | 0.00 | −0.32 | −0.27 |
| −0.18 | −0.26 | −0.12 | 0.00 | 0.02 | −0.18 | −0.23 | −0.17 |
| −0.12 | −0.18 | −0.06 | 0.09 | 0.07 | −0.07 | −0.21 | −0.09 |
| −0.10 | −0.08 | −0.04 | 0.17 | 0.46 | 0.29 | −0.06 | −0.10 |
| −0.19 | −0.19 | −0.08 | 0.07 | 0.42 | [0.55] | 0.28 | 0.05 |
| −0.27 | −0.18 | 0.26 | −0.04 | −0.05 | 0.01 | −0.21 | −0.26 |

**Table 5.3**
Image Correlation Coefficient Matrix Between Noisy Frames at $k$ and $k + 1$

| −0.10 | −0.32 | −0.26 | −0.19 | −0.04 | −0.08 | −0.17 | −0.16 |
|---|---|---|---|---|---|---|---|
| −0.32 | −0.28 | −0.29 | −0.15 | −0.09 | −0.13 | −0.36 | −0.31 |
| −0.12 | −0.22 | −0.22 | 0.10 | 0.41 | 0.21 | 0.17 | −0.28 |
| 0.21 | −0.08 | −0.03 | 0.09 | 0.32 | [0.45] | 0.15 | −0.19 |
| 0.03 | −0.14 | −0.09 | 0.35 | 0.36 | 0.26 | 0.04 | −0.17 |
| −0.17 | −0.22 | −0.10 | 0.24 | [0.48] | 0.17 | −0.20 | −0.15 |
| −0.30 | −0.32 | −0.20 | −0.09 | 0.18 | 0.10 | −0.29 | −0.40 |
| −0.25 | −0.28 | −0.27 | −0.17 | −0.11 | 0.01 | −0.15 | −0.22 |

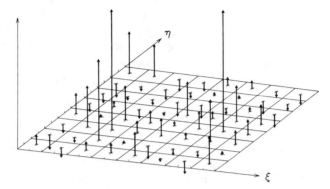

**Figure 5.1** Intensities for two targets at time k − 1.

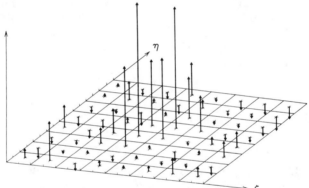

**Figure 5.2** Intensities for two targets at time k.

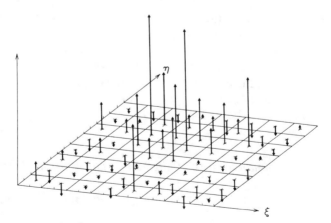

**Figure 5.3** Intensities for two targets at time k + 1.

the correct displacement. Therefore an ambiguity exists in the derived offset measurements that is accounted for by using the data association technique described later. The estimation algorithm assumes two peaks in the correlation matrix. If the signal-to-noise ratio is significantly lower we might have additional peaks, and the algorithm can be modified to account for false peaks [2, 19].

### 5.4.2.4  Summary of the Available Measurements

From the discussion of Subsections 5.4.2.2 and 5.4.2.3 it follows that two kinds of measurement are available during the overlap period for the filter to process: a single merged measurement for the centroid of the mixed image, and two centroid displacement measurements of ambiguous origin.

These will be used to develop the measurement model for the filter described in this chapter. The merged single-centroid measurement has white noise. The centroid displacement measurements have autocorrelated noise. First, a simple tracking filter will be developed, ignoring the autocorrelatedness of the displacement measurement noise, and following this, a full-fledged filter will be developed that accounts for this autocorrelated noise. Later, a comparison will be carried out between the two to show the benefits of the latter.

### 5.4.3  The State Estimation

The state estimation for two crossing targets is done in the following stages:

1. If there are two distinct regions in the distributed image (obtained from segmentation), the states of the two targets under consideration are estimated separately using two filters (one associated with each target, as in Subsection 5.3.1).
2. If the images at the sensor overlap (evaluated by the segmentation algorithm), the measurements available are a single merged measurement for the centroid of the distributed image and two displacement measurements "shared" by both the targets (i.e., have ambiguous origin) during the overlap period. In this situation, the two targets no longer can be tracked reliably with separate filters by using a "nearest neighbor" assignment rule for the ambiguous measurements [2]. The problem can be handled by using the JPDAMCF, which is presented later.

### 5.4.3.1  Estimation with a White Measurement Noise Model

Assuming that the displacement measurement noise is white, the state model is

$$\mathbf{x}(k + 1) = \mathbf{F}\mathbf{x}(k) + \mathbf{G}\mathbf{v}(k) \tag{5.70}$$

where the stacked vector of the states of the two targets under consideration is

$$\mathbf{x}(k) = \begin{bmatrix} x^1(k) \\ x^2(k) \end{bmatrix} \tag{5.71}$$

with the block-diagonal state transition matrix, noise distribution, and stacked process noise vector given by

$$\mathbf{F} = \begin{bmatrix} F^1 & 0 \\ 0 & F^2 \end{bmatrix}; \quad \mathbf{G} = \begin{bmatrix} G^1 & 0 \\ 0 & G^2 \end{bmatrix}; \quad \mathbf{v}(k) = \begin{bmatrix} v^1(k) \\ v^2(k) \end{bmatrix} \tag{5.72}$$

The quantities $x^i(k)$, $F^i$, $G^i$, $v^i(k)$; $i = 1, 2$ are as in Subsection 5.3.1 for the white displacement measurement noise case, where the state vector consists of the present position, current velocity, and previous position.

The measurement model has to be modified due to the *merged* centroid measurement. For each coordinate we have the measurement vector given by

$$\mathbf{z}(k) = \begin{bmatrix} z_c(k) \\ z_{d_1}(k) \\ z_{d_2}(k) \end{bmatrix}$$

$$= \begin{bmatrix} \iota & 0 & 0 & 1-\iota & 0 & 0 \\ 1 & 0 & -1 & 0 & 0 & 0 \\ 0 & 0 & 0 & 1 & 0 & -1 \end{bmatrix} \begin{bmatrix} x_1^1(k) \\ x_2^1(k) \\ x_3^1(k) \\ x_1^2(k) \\ x_2^2(k) \\ x_3^2(k) \end{bmatrix} + \begin{bmatrix} w_c(k) \\ w_{d_1}(k) \\ w_{d_2}(k) \end{bmatrix} \tag{5.73}$$

where the subscripts $c$ and $d_i$, $i = 1, 2$, represent the centroid measurement and the centroid displacement measurements, respectively.

The parameter $\iota$, which depends on the targets' relative intensities [8], has to be found experimentally; and the method to do this is illustrated in Appendix C. The stacked measurement vector in (5.73) has as the first component the merged centroid measurement, and components two and three are from targets 1 and 2, *or* 2 and 1 (in which case they are switched around), respectively, resulting in the ambiguous displacement measurements. We assume there are two peaks in the image correlation; otherwise the algorithm can be modified to account for false peaks [2]. For the SNR considered there were only two peaks.

The parallel procedure, in which the state is updated with the stacked vector of all measurements simultaneously, can be used but is computationally more expensive [3, 24] and difficult with respect to setting up the validation matrix [8, 9] because the ambiguity is associated with only two of the three components of the measurement vector. Instead, the sequential procedure across measurements for estimating the state of the system [5.70] is used as follows.

Two measurements are available at a given sampling time. The measurement $j$ at time $k$ is

$$z(k, j) = H(k, j)x(k) + w(k, j) \qquad j = 1, 2 \tag{5.74}$$

where

$$z(k, 1) = z_c(k); \qquad H(k, 1) = [\iota \quad 0 \quad 0 \quad 1 - \iota \quad 0 \quad 0] \tag{5.75}$$

and

$$z(k, 2) = \begin{bmatrix} z_{d_1}(k) \\ z_{d_2}(k) \end{bmatrix}; \qquad H(k, 2) = \begin{bmatrix} 1 & 0 & -1 & 0 & 0 & 0 \\ 0 & 0 & 0 & 1 & 0 & -1 \end{bmatrix} \tag{5.76}$$

Thus (5.75) and (5.76) represent the merged centroid measurement component and the centroid displacement measurement components in (5.73), respectively. The sequential updating procedure follows.

*Update with the Merged Centroid Measurement*

Denote the predicted state at time $k$ and its covariance as

$$\hat{\mathbf{x}}(k|k, 0) \triangleq \hat{\mathbf{x}}(k|k - 1) \tag{5.77}$$

$$\mathbf{P}(k|k, 0) \triangleq \mathbf{P}(k|k - 1) \tag{5.78}$$

The updated state with the measurement (5.75) at time $k$ is

$$\hat{\mathbf{x}}(k|k, 1) = \hat{\mathbf{x}}(k|k, 0) + W(k, 1)[z(k, 1) - \hat{z}(k, 1)] \tag{5.79}$$

where

$$\hat{z}(k, 1) = H(k, 1)\hat{\mathbf{x}}(k|k, 0) \tag{5.80}$$

$$W(k, 1) = \mathbf{P}(k|k, 0)H(k, 1)'S(k, 1)^{-1} \tag{5.81}$$

$$S(k, 1) = H(k, 1)\mathbf{P}(k|k, 0)H(k, 1)' + R(k, 1) \qquad R(k, 1) = \sigma_c^2 \tag{5.82}$$

$$\mathbf{P}(k|k, 1) = \mathbf{P}(k|k, 0) - W(k, 1)S(k, 1)W(k, 1)' \tag{5.83}$$

*Update with the Centroid Displacement Measurement*

To complete the state update with (5.76) we proceed as follows:

$$\hat{\mathbf{x}}(k|k, 2) = \hat{\mathbf{x}}(k|k, 1) + W(k, 2) \sum_{\theta} P(\theta|Z^k)[z(k, 2, \theta) - \hat{z}(k, 2)] \quad (5.84)$$

where $\theta \in \{\theta_1, \theta_2\}$ (the joint association events $\theta_i$ are detailed later) and

$$z(k, 2, \theta) = \begin{bmatrix} z_{j_1(\theta)}(k, 2) \\ z_{j_2(\theta)}(k, 2) \end{bmatrix} \quad (5.85)$$

is the measurement (5.76) and $j_t(\theta)$ is the index of the measurement associated with target $t$ in event $\theta$ at time $k$ and

$$\hat{z}(k, 2) = H(k, 2)\hat{\mathbf{x}}(k|k, 1) \quad (5.86)$$

Note from (5.85) the possible switching around of the measurements: we have $j_1(\theta_1)$ = 1, $j_2(\theta_1)$ = 2, and $j_1(\theta_2)$ = 2, $j_2(\theta_2)$ = 1.

The conditional probability for a joint association event $\theta$ [2] is

$$P\{\theta|Z^k\} = \frac{1}{c} f_{t_{j_1}, t_{j_2}}[z_{j_1(\theta)}(k, 2), \quad z_{j_2(\theta)}(k, 2)] \quad (5.87)$$

where $f_{t_{j_1}, t_{j_2}}$ is the joint pdf of the measurements of the targets under consideration; $t_j$ is the target to which $z_j(k, 2)$ is associated in event $\theta \in \{\theta_1, \theta_2\}$, and $c$ is the normalizing constant.

The joint probabilities are not mapped into marginal association probabilities as in [8] for use in decoupled JPDA filters. Instead, they are used directly in a *coupled filter* [3, 6]; the combined state (5.71) is updated according to (5.84).

The filter gain in (5.84) is

$$W(k, 2) = \mathbf{P}(k|k, 1)H(k, 2)'S(k, 2)^{-1} \quad (5.88)$$

where the innovation covariance $S(k, 2)$ is given by

$$S(k, 2) = H(k, 2)\mathbf{P}(k|k, 1)H(k, 2)' + R(k, 2) \quad (5.89)$$

where $H(k, 2)$ is as given in (5.76) and

$$R(k, 2) = \begin{bmatrix} \sigma_{d_1}^2 & 0 \\ 0 & \sigma_{d_2}^2 \end{bmatrix} \tag{5.90}$$

is the (diagonal) noise covariance matrix for the two targets under consideration. The covariance update equation is

$$\mathbf{P}(k|k, 2) = \mathbf{P}(k|k, 1) - W(k, 2)S(k, 2)^{-1}W(k, 2)' \triangleq \mathbf{P}(k|k) \tag{5.91}$$

with the final updated state being

$$\hat{\mathbf{x}}(k|k) \triangleq \hat{\mathbf{x}}(k|k, 2) \tag{5.92}$$

This summarizes the JPDAMCF with sequential updating for the centroid and displacement measurements, with the latter assumed to be white. The next subsection presents the corresponding filter for the displacement measurement modeled as autocorrelated.

### 5.4.3.2 Estimation with an Autocorrelated Measurement Noise Model

As shown in Subsection 5.2.3 the autocorrelated displacement measurement noise is the output of the following white noise driven subsystem (of the moving average type):

$$w_d^t(k) = \beta_1 v_2^t(k) + \beta_2 v_2^t(k) \tag{5.93}$$

Augmenting the target state equation with this leads to a state equation with measurement noise and process noise sequences for the two targets that are white but the process noise $v^t(k)$ and the measurement noise $w^t(k)$ are correlated, as pointed out in Subsection 5.3.2. The augmented state equations for each target, for one coordinate and $t = 1, 2$, are given by

$$\begin{bmatrix} x_1^t(k+1) \\ x_2^t(k+1) \\ x_3^t(k+1) \\ x_4^t(k+1) \end{bmatrix} = \begin{bmatrix} 1 & T & 0 & 0 \\ 0 & 1 & 0 & 0 \\ 1 & 0 & 0 & 0 \\ 0 & 0 & 0 & 0 \end{bmatrix} \begin{bmatrix} x_1^t(k) \\ x_2^t(k) \\ x_3^t(k) \\ x_4^t(k) \end{bmatrix}$$
$$+ \begin{bmatrix} T^2/2 & 0 \\ T & 0 \\ 0 & 0 \\ 0 & \beta_2 \end{bmatrix} \begin{bmatrix} v_1^t(k) \\ v_2^t(k) \end{bmatrix} \tag{5.94}$$

and the measurement equation is

$$z^t(k) = \begin{bmatrix} 1 & 0 & 0 & 0 \\ 1 & 0 & -1 & 1 \end{bmatrix} \begin{bmatrix} x_1^t(k) \\ x_2^t(k) \\ x_3^t(k) \\ x_4^t(k) \end{bmatrix} + \begin{bmatrix} w_1^t(k) \\ w_2^t(k) \end{bmatrix} \qquad t = 1, 2 \qquad (5.95)$$

where $v_1^t(k)$ is the motion process noise, $v_2^t(k)$ is the white noise input to the colored noise in the displacement measurement from (5.93) with variance $(\sigma_d^t)^2$, $w_1^t(k)$ is the noise in the centroid measurement, and

$$w_2^t(k) \triangleq \beta_1 v_2^t(k) \qquad (5.96)$$

The second component of the measurement vector in (5.95) corresponds to the displacement measurement.

As long as the targets do not overlap the estimation is done separately for each target with individual filters as indicated earlier. When the targets overlap the filtering is done in a coupled manner as described later. The stacked vector of the states of the two targets under consideration is as in (5.94).

The modified state equation that has the process noise uncorrelated from the measurement noise is

$$x(k + 1) = F^*(k)x(k) + u^*(k) + v^*(k) \qquad (5.97)$$

where the modified block-diagonal state transition matrix is

$$F^*(k) = F(k) - T(k)H(k) \qquad (5.98)$$

The modified stacked input vector in (5.97) is

$$u^*(k) = \begin{bmatrix} u^{1*}(k) \\ u^{2*}(k) \end{bmatrix} \qquad (5.99)$$

and

$$v^*(k) = \begin{bmatrix} v^{1*}(k) \\ v^{2*}(k) \end{bmatrix} = \begin{bmatrix} G^1 v^1(k) - T^1 w^1(k) \\ G^2 v^2(k) - T^2 w^2(k) \end{bmatrix} \qquad (5.100)$$

The elements of the stacked input vector in (5.99) are given by

$$u^{i*}(k) = T^i \sum_\theta P(\theta \mid Z^k) z_{j_i(\theta)}(k) \qquad i = 1, 2, \qquad j = 1, 2 \qquad (5.101)$$

where the notation from (5.87) is used and

$$T^i(k) = G^i(k)U^i(k)R^i(k)^{-1} \qquad i = 1, 2 \tag{5.102}$$

and the stacked block diagonal covariance matrix between the measurement and process noise is

$$U = \begin{bmatrix} U^1 & 0 \\ 0 & U^2 \end{bmatrix} \tag{5.103}$$

Finally, the modified block diagonal process noise covariance matrix is

$$Q^*(k) = Q(k) - G(k)U(k)[R(k)]^{-1}U(k)'G(k)' \tag{5.104}$$

where

$$Q = \begin{bmatrix} Q^1 & 0 \\ 0 & Q^2 \end{bmatrix} \tag{5.105}$$

The measurement equation is

$$
z(k) = \begin{bmatrix} z_c(k) \\ z_{d_1}(k) \\ z_{d_2}(k) \end{bmatrix}
$$

$$
= \begin{bmatrix} \iota & 0 & 0 & 0 & 1-\iota & 0 & 0 & 0 \\ 1 & 0 & -1 & 1 & 0 & 0 & 0 & 0 \\ 0 & 0 & 0 & 0 & 1 & 0 & -1 & 1 \end{bmatrix} \begin{bmatrix} x_1^1(k) \\ x_2^1(k) \\ x_3^1(k) \\ x_4^1(k) \\ x_1^2(k) \\ x_2^2(k) \\ x_3^2(k) \\ x_4^2(k) \end{bmatrix} \tag{5.106}
$$

$$
+ \begin{bmatrix} w_c(k) \\ w_{d_1}(k) \\ w_{d_2}(k) \end{bmatrix}
$$

where the subscripts $c$ and $d_i$, $i = 1, 2$, represent the centroid measurement and the centroid displacement measurements, respectively. The association probabilities for each target are evaluated as in Subsection 5.4.3.1.

The JPDAMCF for the state model (5.97) and measurement model (5.106) is implemented by a corresponding sequential updating procedure, as discussed in Subsection 5.4.3.1, considering first the update with the centroid merged measurement and then the update with the ambiguous centroid displacement measurements.

### 5.4.4 Simulation Results for Crossing Targets

The simulations are carried out for two filters: one assuming the displacement measurement noise white and the other modeling it correctly as autocorrelated. We considered two targets with Gaussian plume images as in Subsection 5.4.2 and with motion described by second-order kinematic models (see [2]) as in Subsection 5.3.1 with white noise acceleration with variance $q = (0.05)^2$ in each of the two coordinates. The image of target 1 was moving with a heading of 135° and a nearly constant speed of 1 pixel per sampling period, and the image of target 2 was moving with a heading of 27° and a nearly constant speed of 2 pixels per sampling period. The sampling period is $T = 1$. The filters were initialized using two-point differencing [2] and the initial state vectors of the targets in the image (pixel) frame were

Target 1: $[-3.5 \quad 1 \quad -4.5 \quad 3.5 \quad -1 \quad 4.5]'$

Target 2: $[-3.5 \quad 1 \quad -4.5 \quad -8.5 \quad 2 \quad -10.5]'$

The target state estimation was done for 10 sampling times. The crossing of the target images takes place at times 3, 4, and 5. The measurement noises have variances $\sigma_c^2 = (0.195)^2$, $\sigma_d^2 = (0.104)^2$.

*Filter with White Measurement Noise Model*

The results of $N = 100$ Monte Carlo runs are shown for target 1 and target 2 in Tables 5.4 and 5.5, respectively. The average normalized errors are seen to be within the bounds of a zero-mean Gaussian random variable with standard deviation $1/\sqrt{N} = 0.1$, and the values of the average normalized state error squared also are close to their theoretical value of 6 (it has a standard deviation of $\sqrt{2 \cdot 8N}/N = 0.35$). The results indicate that the filters are consistent. The results are given only for the $\xi$ coordinate but the average NEES pertains to the entire state.

*Filter with Autocorrelated Measurement Noise Model*

The simulations for the two targets were repeated with the displacement measurement noise modeled by the tracking filter as autocorrelated. The correlation coefficient $\alpha$ is equal to $-0.5$. The results of $N = 100$ Monte Carlo runs are shown for target 1 and target 2 in Tables 5.6 and 5.7, respectively. The average normalized

### Table 5.4
Average Errors in $\xi$ Direction and Average NEES for Entire State for Target 1
(100 Monte Carlo Runs)

| Time k | Avg. Position Error | Position s.d. | Avg. Normalized Position Error | Avg. Velocity Error | Velocity s.d. | Avg. Normalized Velocity Error | Avg. NEES (6 States) |
|---|---|---|---|---|---|---|---|
| 0 | | 0.195 | | | 0.276 | | |
| 1 | −0.004 | 0.14 | −0.025 | 0.0086 | 0.088 | 0.098 | 5.90 |
| 2 | 0.013 | 0.13 | 0.098 | 0.006 | 0.07 | 0.09 | 5.96 |
| 3 | 0.017 | 0.122 | 0.136 | 0.007 | 0.066 | 0.11 | 6.33 |
| 4 | −0.01 | 0.118 | −0.11 | 0.01 | 0.064 | 0.156 | 6.10 |
| 5 | 0.002 | 0.118 | 0.016 | −0.005 | 0.0639 | −0.08 | 5.82 |
| 6 | −0.0004 | 0.1175 | −0.003 | −0.0016 | 0.0637 | −0.025 | 5.86 |
| 7 | 0.007 | 0.1175 | 0.062 | 0.003 | 0.0637 | 0.05 | 6.03 |
| 8 | 0.027 | 0.1175 | 0.23 | 0.011 | 0.0637 | 0.22 | 6.44 |
| 9 | −0.004 | 0.1175 | −0.03 | −0.004 | 0.0637 | −0.06 | 6.11 |

### Table 5.5
Average Errors in $\xi$ Direction and Average NEES for Entire State for Target 2
(100 Monte Carlo Runs)

| Time k | Avg. Position Error | Position s.d. | Avg. Normalized Position Error | Avg. Velocity Error | Velocity s.d. | Avg. Normalized Velocity Error | Avg. NEES (6 States) |
|---|---|---|---|---|---|---|---|
| 0 | | 0.195 | | | 0.276 | | |
| 1 | −0.005 | 0.14 | −0.032 | 0.016 | 0.088 | 0.19 | 6.63 |
| 2 | −0.013 | 0.13 | −0.1 | 0.005 | 0.07 | 0.07 | 6.05 |
| 3 | −0.015 | 0.122 | −0.123 | −0.007 | 0.066 | −0.1 | 5.85 |
| 4 | 0.009 | 0.118 | 0.07 | 0.007 | 0.064 | 0.11 | 5.57 |
| 5 | −0.02 | 0.118 | −0.173 | −0.006 | 0.0639 | −0.2 | 5.66 |
| 6 | 0.004 | 0.1175 | 0.003 | 0.015 | 0.0637 | 0.024 | 6.12 |
| 7 | 0.013 | 0.1175 | 0.113 | 0.013 | 0.02 | 0.094 | 6.20 |
| 8 | −0.008 | 0.1175 | −0.07 | −0.006 | 0.0637 | −0.094 | 5.93 |
| 9 | −0.01 | 0.1175 | −0.09 | −0.001 | 0.0637 | −0.02 | 6.26 |

errors again are seen to be within the bounds of a zero-mean Gaussian random variable with standard deviation $1/\sqrt{N} = 0.1$ and the values of the average NEES also are close to their theoretical value of 8 (standard deviation of $\sqrt{2 \cdot 8N}/N = 0.4$). The results show that the filters are consistent, and best performance is achieved by

**Table 5.6**
Average Errors in $\xi$ Direction and Average NEES for Entire State for Target 1
(100 Monte Carlo Runs)

| Time $k$ | Avg. Position Error | Position s.d. | Avg. Normalized Position Error | Avg. Velocity Error | Velocity s.d. | Avg. Normalized Velocity Error | Avg. NEES (8 States) |
|---|---|---|---|---|---|---|---|
| 0 | | 0.195 | | | | 0.276 | |
| 1 | −0.006 | 0.13 | −0.047 | 0.005 | 0.07 | 0.072 | 9.14 |
| 2 | −0.012 | 0.12 | −0.105 | −0.027 | 0.06 | −0.033 | 8.06 |
| 3 | −0.05 | 0.11 | −0.048 | −0.007 | 0.057 | −0.122 | 7.99 |
| 4 | −0.014 | 0.099 | −0.142 | 0.005 | 0.056 | 0.080 | 8.46 |
| 5 | −0.015 | 0.094 | −0.159 | 0.002 | 0.056 | 0.034 | 8.40 |
| 6 | −0.007 | 0.092 | −0.076 | 0.004 | 0.056 | 0.079 | 8.06 |
| 7 | −0.001 | 0.088 | −0.012 | 0.001 | 0.056 | 0.107 | 7.95 |
| 8 | −0.0001 | 0.088 | −0.001 | −0.0001 | 0.056 | −0.002 | 8.33 |
| 9 | −0.024 | 0.088 | −0.027 | −0.006 | 0.056 | −0.107 | 8.35 |

**Table 5.7**
Average Errors in $\xi$ Direction and Average NEES for Entire State for Target 2
(100 Monte Carlo Runs)

| Time $k$ | Avg. Position Error | Position s.d. | Avg. Normalized Position Error | Avg. Velocity Error | Velocity s.d. | Avg. Normalized Velocity Error | Avg. NEES (8 States) |
|---|---|---|---|---|---|---|---|
| 0 | | 0.195 | | | | 0.276 | |
| 1 | −0.006 | 0.13 | −0.047 | 0.005 | 0.07 | 0.072 | 9.01 |
| 2 | −0.013 | 0.12 | −0.114 | 0.005 | 0.06 | 0.083 | 7.78 |
| 3 | −0.011 | 0.11 | −0.11 | 0.002 | 0.057 | 0.035 | 8.08 |
| 4 | 0.012 | 0.099 | 0.121 | 0.007 | 0.056 | 0.125 | 8.03 |
| 5 | −0.017 | 0.094 | −0.181 | −0.005 | 0.056 | −0.089 | 8.32 |
| 6 | −0.02 | 0.092 | −0.217 | −0.009 | 0.056 | −0.161 | 8.67 |
| 7 | 0.009 | 0.088 | 0.102 | −0.003 | 0.056 | −0.054 | 8.37 |
| 8 | −0.008 | 0.088 | −0.086 | −0.001 | 0.056 | −0.018 | 8.22 |
| 9 | −0.005 | 0.088 | −0.061 | −0.006 | 0.056 | −0.104 | 7.97 |

incorporating the model of the autocorrelated measurement noise (cf. Table 5.6 *versus* Table 5.4) and rms tracking accuracies under one-tenth of pixel are obtained. The results are indicated only for the $\xi$ coordinate but the average NEES pertains to the entire state.

## APPENDIX 5.A: DERIVATIONS FOR THE CENTROID ESTIMATE

The effect of the *image noise* is obtained first. Eq. (5.11) can be rewritten as

$$\hat{\xi}_c = \frac{\Sigma \, \xi_i(s_i + n_i)}{\Sigma \, (s_i + n_i)} = \frac{\Sigma \, \xi_i s_i}{\Sigma \, s_i} \left[ 1 - \frac{\Sigma \, n_i}{\Sigma \, (s_i + n_i)} \right] + \frac{\Sigma \, \xi_i n_i}{\Sigma \, (s_i + n_i)}$$

$$\triangleq \bar{\xi}_c[1 + \epsilon_1] + \epsilon_2 \tag{5.A1}$$

where

$$\bar{\xi}_c \triangleq \frac{\Sigma \, \xi_i s_i}{\Sigma \, s_i} \tag{5.A2}$$

is the centroid estimate in the absence of image noise but with the effect of the image discretization, which will be analyzed later.

The multiplicative noise in (5.A1) is

$$\epsilon_1 \triangleq - \frac{\Sigma \, n_i}{\Sigma \, (s_i + n_i)} \tag{5.A3}$$

Approximating the expected value of the ratio of two random variables by the ratio of their means, which is a reasonably good approximation if the denominator has a small coefficient of variation (standard deviation divided by the mean), as in the present case, the mean of (5.A3) is zero. Its variance, with the same approximation as earlier, in pixel units, is

$$E[\epsilon_1^2] + \frac{E[\Sigma \, n_i \, \Sigma \, n_j]}{E[\Sigma \, (s_i + n_i) \, \Sigma \, (s_j + n_j)]} = \frac{m\sigma^2}{x^2 + m\sigma^2} = \frac{1}{r^2 + 1} \tag{5.A4}$$

*Numerical Example 1*

With $r = 7.5$, the variance of $\epsilon_1$ is

$$\sigma_1^2 \triangleq \text{var}(\epsilon_1) = (0.13)^2 \tag{5.A5}$$

that is, the noise $\epsilon_1$ has variance much less than unity.

The additive noise in (5.A1) is given by

$$\epsilon_2 \triangleq \frac{\Sigma \, \xi_i n_i}{\Sigma \, (s_j + n_j)} \tag{5.A6}$$

and has mean zero and variance

$$\sigma_2^2 \triangleq \text{var}(\epsilon_2) = E \frac{(\Sigma \, \xi_i n_i)(\Sigma \, \xi_j n_j)}{\Sigma \, (s_i + n_i) \, \Sigma \, (s_j + n_j)} \tag{5.A7}$$

$$\approx \frac{\Sigma \, \xi_i^2 E[n_i^2] + \sum_i \xi_i \sum_{j \neq i} \xi_j \, E[n_i n_j]}{E[\Sigma \, (s_i + n_i) \, \Sigma \, (s_j + n_j)]} = \frac{\sigma^2 \, \Sigma \, \xi_i^2}{s^2 + m\sigma^2} = \frac{1}{r^2 + 1} \frac{1}{m} \Sigma \, \xi_i^2$$

where the preceding approximation is justified by (5.A5).

*Numerical Example*

For the $8 \times 8$ array the coordinates of the pixels are $\pm (l - 0.5)$, $l = 1, \ldots, 4$. From this it follows that

$$\Sigma \, \xi_i^2 = 16(0.5^2 + \cdots + 3.5^2) = 336 \tag{5.A8}$$

With this, (5.A7) for $r = 7.5$, in pixel units, becomes

$$\sigma_2^2 \approx 0.09 = (0.3)^2 \tag{5.A9}$$

To evaluate the effect of the *image discretization,* eq. (5.A1) is rewritten as

$$\hat{\xi}_c = (1 + \epsilon_1) \frac{\Sigma \, \xi_i s_i}{\Sigma \, s_i} + \epsilon_2 \tag{5.A10}$$

We assume that the centroid of a pixel $\xi_{i_c}$ is distributed uniformly within the pixel (of size unity) and independently across pixels. Therefore,

$$\xi_{i_c} = \xi_i + \tilde{\xi}_i \tag{5.A11}$$

where

$$E[\tilde{\xi}_i] = 0 \tag{5.A12}$$

$$E[\tilde{\xi}_i \tilde{\xi}_j] = \tfrac{1}{12} \delta_{ij} \tag{5.A13}$$

With this (5.A10) becomes

$$\hat{\xi}_c = (1 + \epsilon_1) \frac{\Sigma \, \xi_{i_c} s_i}{\Sigma \, s_i} - (1 + \epsilon_1) \frac{\Sigma \, \tilde{\xi}_i s_i}{\Sigma \, s_i} + \epsilon_2$$

$$= \xi_c + \xi_c \epsilon_1 + \epsilon_3 + \epsilon_2 \tag{5.A14}$$

where $\xi_c$ is the true centroid and

$$\epsilon_3 \triangleq -(1 + \epsilon_1)\frac{\Sigma \, \tilde{\xi}_i s_i}{\Sigma \, s_i} \tag{5.A15}$$

is the image discretization noise. This noise is zero-mean and uncorrelated with $\epsilon_2$; its correlation with $\epsilon_1$ can be considered negligible because $\sigma_1^2 \ll 1$. Its variance (again using the fact that $\sigma_1^2 \ll 1$) is

$$\sigma_3^2 = (1 + \sigma_1^2)\frac{1}{s^2}\,E[\Sigma\,\tilde{\xi}_i s_i \, \Sigma\,\tilde{\xi}_j s_j] \approx \frac{1}{s^2}\Sigma\,s_i^2 E[\tilde{\xi}_i^2] = \frac{1}{12s^2}\Sigma\,s_i^2 \tag{5.A16}$$

Assuming the signal to be constant over its extent, this becomes

$$\sigma_3^2 \approx \frac{m_s\mu_s^2}{12(m_s\mu_s)^2} = \frac{1}{12m_s} \tag{5.A17}$$

*Numerical Example*

With $m_s = 10$ we have

$$\sigma_3^2 = \frac{1}{12 \cdot 10} \approx (0.09)^2 \tag{5.A18}$$

The measurement equation (5.A14) is of the form

$$z = x + w_c \tag{5.A19}$$

where the *centroid measurement noise:*

$$w_c \triangleq \xi_c\epsilon_1 + \epsilon_2 + \epsilon_3 \tag{5.A20}$$

contains a state-dependent term. All the noises in (5.A20) are zero-mean and uncorrelated.

The variance of the centroid measurement noise is

$$\sigma_c^2 \triangleq E[w_c^2] = \xi_c^2\sigma_1^2 + \sigma_2^2 + \sigma_3^2 \tag{5.A21}$$

where these three variances are given in (5.A4), (5.A7), and (5.A16), respectively.

## APPENDIX 5.B: THE OFFSET MEASUREMENT FROM IMAGE CORRELATION

The errors in the correlation coefficient $\hat{\rho}_{\delta+1}$ are denoted as $\tilde{\rho}_{\delta+1}$, $1 = -1, 0, 1$. As shown later, they are zero-mean, mutually uncorrelated, and with variance $\sigma_p^2$, also derived later. With this, the error in the offset measurement (5.20), using a first-order series expansion, is given by

$$
w_d \triangleq \tilde{d} = -\left(\frac{1}{\alpha_2} - \frac{2\alpha_1}{\alpha_2^2}\right)\tilde{\rho}_{\delta-1} - \frac{4\alpha_1}{\alpha_2^2}\tilde{\rho}_\delta + \left(\frac{1}{\alpha_2} + \frac{2\alpha_1}{\alpha_2^2}\right)\tilde{\rho}_{\delta+1}
$$

$$
\triangleq \sum_{l=-1}^{1} a_l \tilde{\rho}_{\delta-l}
$$

(5.B1)

The variance of (5.B1) is

$$
\sigma_d^2 \triangleq \mathrm{var}(\tilde{d}) = \sigma_p^2 \sum_{l=-1}^{1} a_l^2 \triangleq a\sigma_p^2
$$

(5.B2)

where $a = 2/(\alpha_2^2 + 12\alpha_1^2)$. This is the variance of the "equivalent measurement noise" for the image offset measurement.

To obtain the variance $\sigma_p^2$ of the image correlation (5.18), it is rewritten using (5.19) as

$$
\hat{\rho}_\delta(k) = \frac{\Sigma \left[s_i(k) - \bar{s} + n_i(k)\right]\left[s_{i_\delta}(k-1) - \bar{s} + n_{i_\delta}(k-1)\right]}{\{\Sigma \left[s_i(k) - \bar{s} + n_i(k)\right]^2 \Sigma \left[s_{i_\delta}(k-1) - \bar{s} + n_{i_\delta}(k-1)\right]^2\}^{1/2}}
$$

(5.B3)

where $\bar{s}$ defined in (5.7), is assumed to be time invariant. The average signal $\bar{s}$ can be time varying. This can be rewritten as

$$
\begin{aligned}
\hat{\rho}_\delta(k) = &\{\Sigma \left[s_i(k) - \bar{s}\right]\left[s_{i_\delta}(k-1) - \bar{s}\right] + \Sigma \left[s_i(k) - \bar{s}\right]n_{i_\delta}(k-1) \\
&+ \Sigma \left[s_{i_\delta}(k-1) - \bar{s}\right]n_i(k) + \Sigma n_i(k)n_{i_\delta}(k-1)\} \\
&\cdot \{[\Sigma \left[s_i(k) - \bar{s}\right]^2 + 2\Sigma \left[s_i(k) - \bar{s}\right]n_i(k) + \Sigma n_i(k)^2] \\
&\cdot [\Sigma \left[s_{i_\delta}(k-1) - \bar{s}\right]^2 + 2\Sigma \left[s_{i_\delta}(k-1) \right. \\
&\left. - \bar{s}\right]n_{i_\delta}(k-1) + \Sigma n_{i_\delta}(k-1)^2]\}^{-1/2}
\end{aligned}
$$

(5.B4)

The following simplifying assumption is made: the quantity $\kappa$, which can be termed the *contrast* of the noiseless frame (signal variance over the frame times the number of pixels):

$$\kappa \triangleq \Sigma \left[ s_i(k) - \bar{s} \right]^2 \approx \Sigma \left[ s_{i_\delta}(k - 1) - \bar{s} \right]^2 \gg m\sigma^2 \tag{5.B5}$$

is the dominant term in the denominator of (5.B4), which then becomes $\kappa$. The value of the correlation estimated by (5.B4) is

$$\rho_\delta(k) = \frac{1}{\kappa} \{ \Sigma \left[ s_i(k) - \bar{s} \right] [s_{i_\delta}(k - 1) - \bar{s}] \} \tag{5.B6}$$

The estimate (5.B4) then can be written as

$$\hat{\rho}_\delta(k) = \rho_\delta(k) + \tilde{\rho}_\delta(k) \tag{5.B7}$$

where the estimation error, in view of (5.B4) and (5.B7), is

$$\begin{aligned}
\tilde{\rho}_\delta(k) = \frac{1}{\kappa} \{ &\Sigma \left[ s_i(k) - \bar{s} \right] n_{i_\delta}(k - 1) + \Sigma [s_{i_\delta}(k - 1) - \bar{s}] n_i(k) \\
&+ \Sigma \, n_i(k) n_{i_\delta}(k - 1) \}
\end{aligned} \tag{5.B8}$$

The mean of (5.B8) is zero and the variance is

$$\sigma_p^2(k) = \mathrm{var}[\tilde{\rho}_\delta(k)] = \frac{1}{\kappa^2} [2\kappa\sigma^2 + m\sigma^4] \tag{5.B9}$$

The covariance between the image correlations for two neighboring displacements is assumed to be zero. This then yields (5.B2).

An important question is whether the measurement noise (5.B1) is a white sequence. Because the measurement noise at a given time is a linear combination of the correlation errors (5.B8) at the same time, it is enough to check the whiteness of the latter. To this end, as in (5.B8), consider

$$\begin{aligned}
\tilde{\rho}_\delta(k - 1) = \frac{1}{\kappa} \{ &\Sigma \left[ s_j(k - 1) - \bar{s} \right] n_{j_\delta}(k - 2) \\
&+ \Sigma [s_{j_\delta}(k - 2) - \bar{s}] n_j(k - 1) \\
&+ \Sigma \, n_j(k - 1) n_{j_\delta}(k - 2) \}
\end{aligned} \tag{5.B10}$$

Multiplying (5.B8) and (5.B10) and taking the expected value, all the terms with noises from different times vanish. The only term that contains noise only from time $k - 1$ is

$$
\begin{aligned}
E[\tilde{\rho}_\delta(k)\tilde{\rho}_\delta(k - 1)] = \frac{1}{\kappa^2} E\{ \Sigma\ [s_i(k) - \bar{s}]n_{i_\delta}(k - 1) \Sigma\ [s_{i_\delta'}(k - 2) \\
- \bar{s}]n_j(k - 1)\}
\end{aligned}
\tag{5B.11}
$$

The only nonzero terms in (5.B11) are those with $j = i_\delta$; however, these will be multiplied by a product of displaced deviations of the signal image. A worst case analysis, for a "flat" image yields

$$
E[\tilde{\rho}_\delta(k)\tilde{\rho}_\delta(k - 1)] = \frac{1}{\kappa^2} \kappa\sigma^2 = \frac{\sigma^2}{\kappa}
\tag{5.B12}
$$

This covariance is about half of (5.B9) and, therefore, cannot be neglected; that is, the displacement measurement noise is *autocorrelated*.

## Numerical Example

For the target image considered earlier, the average noiseless image intensity is

$$
\bar{s} = \frac{s}{m} = \frac{60}{64} \approx 1
\tag{5.B13}
$$

The contrast, assuming a 10-pixel image of constant intensity $\mu_s = 6$ with perfectly sharp edges, is

$$
\kappa = 10(6 - \bar{s})^2 + 54(-\bar{s})^2 = 10 \cdot 5^2 + 54 = 304 \approx 300
\tag{5.B14}
$$

The variance of a correlation coefficient between two frames, with $m = 64$ and $\sigma = 1$, from (5.B9), is

$$
\sigma_p^2 = \frac{2 \cdot 300 \cdot 1 + 64 \cdot 1}{300^2} = (0.086)^2
\tag{5.B15}
$$

To obtain the variance of the location of the interpolated offset we assume that

$$
\hat{\rho}_\delta = 0.8 \qquad \hat{\rho}_{\delta-1} = \hat{\rho}_{\delta+1} = 0.6
\tag{5.B16}
$$

Then

$$\alpha_1 = 0 \qquad \alpha_2 = 0.8 \qquad a \approx 3 \tag{5.B17}$$

and, using (5.B12),

$$\sigma_d^2 = \text{var}[\hat{d}] = 3\sigma_\delta^2 \approx (0.15)^2 \tag{5.B18}$$

## APPENDIX 5.C: EVALUATION OF THE "IMAGE-MIXING" PARAMETER

Consider an image plane intensity distribution in which the distributed image has two distinct regions, indicating the existence of two targets with their lines of sight from the sensor not crossing. Because the target images in the array are separated, we assume that the array has been segmented into two nonoverlapping regions $T_1$ and $T_2$ corresponding to each image so

$$T_1 \cap T_2 = \varnothing, \qquad T_1 \cup T_2 = T \tag{5.C1}$$

where $T$ is the set of pixels in the entire array. We assume that the target signal is negligible outside its segmented region $T_j$, $j = 1, 2$.

The estimate of the $\xi$-coordinate of the location of the centroid of the distributed image at time $k$, in pixel units given by (5.11), is

$$\hat{\xi}_c = \frac{\Sigma \, \xi_i I_i}{\Sigma \, I_i} \tag{5.C2}$$

where $\xi_i$ is the $\xi$ coordinate of the center of pixel $i$ and the measured intensity $I_i$ corresponding to this pixel is given by (5.63). The summations are over $T$. Equation (5.C2) can be written approximately as

$$\hat{\xi}_c \approx \frac{\displaystyle\sum_{i \in T1} \xi_i(s_{1i} + n_i)}{\displaystyle\sum_{i \in T} (s_{1i} + s_{2i} + n_i)} + \frac{\displaystyle\sum_{i \in T2} \xi_i(s_{2i} + n_i)}{\displaystyle\sum_{i \in T} (s_{1i} + s_{2i} + n_i)} \tag{5.C3}$$

which after some manipulations yields

$$\hat{\xi}_c \approx \hat{\xi}_{c_1} \iota + \hat{\xi}_{c_2}(1 - \iota) \tag{5.C4}$$

where

$$\iota \triangleq \frac{\displaystyle\sum_{i \in T1} (s_{1i} + n_i)}{\displaystyle\sum_{i \in T} (s_{1i} + s_{2i} + n_i)} \tag{5.C5}$$

is the "image-mixing" parameter. The estimate of this parameter is obtained as

$$\hat{\iota} \triangleq \frac{\displaystyle\sum_{i \in T1} I_i}{\displaystyle\sum_{i \in T} I_i} \tag{5.C6}$$

when the targets do not overlap, to be used later when the targets overlap.

## REFERENCES

[1]   B.D.O. Anderson and J.B. Moore, *Optimal Filtering,* Prentice-Hall, Englewood Cliffs, NJ, 1979.

[2]   Y. Bar-Shalom and T.E. Fortmann, *Tracking and Data Association,* Academic Press, Orlando, FL, 1988.

[3]   Y. Bar-Shalom, "Multitarget-Multisensor Tracking," Short Course Notes, UCLA and University of Maryland, 1988–89.

[4]   Y. Bar-Shalom, H.M. Shertukde, and K.R. Pattipati, "Use of Measurements from an Imaging Sensor for Precision Target Tracking," *IEEE Trans. on Aerospace and Electronic Systems,* Vol. AES-25, November 1989.

[5]   Y. Bar-Shalom, H.M. Shertukde, and K.R. Pattipati, "Precision Target Tracking for Small Extended Objects," *Optical Engineering J.,* Vol. 25, February 1990.

[6]   S. Blake and S.C. Watts, "A Multitarget Track-while Scan Filter," *Proc. IEE Radar-87 Conf.,* London, October 1987.

[7]   T.J. Broida and R. Chellappa, "Estimation of Object Motion Parameters from Noisy Images," *IEEE Trans. on Pattern Analysis and Machine Intelligence,* Vol. PAMI-8, January 1986, pp. 90–99.

[8]   K.C. Chang and Y. Bar-Shalom, "Joint Probabilistic Data Association Filter for Multitarget Tracking with Possibly Unresolved Measurements and Maneuvers," *IEEE Trans. on Automatic Control.* Vol. AC-29, July 1984, pp. 585–594.

[9]   T.E. Fortmann, Y. Bar-Shalom, M. Scheffe, and S. Gelfand, "Detection Threshold for Tracking in Clutter—A Connection Between Estimation and Signal Processing," *IEEE Trans. on Automatic Control,* vol. AC-30, No. 3, March 1985, pp. 221–228.

[10]  J.W. Goodman, *Introduction to Fourier Optics,* McGraw-Hill, New York, 1968.

[11]  J.W. Goodman, *Statistical Optics,* John Wiley and Sons, New York, 1985.

[12]  P.S. Maybeck and D.E. Mercier, "A Target Tracker Using Spatially Distributed Infrared Measurements," *IEEE Trans. on Automatic Control.* Vol. AC-25, April 1980, pp. 222–225.

[13]  P.S. Maybeck, R.L. Jensen, and D.A. Harnly, "An Adaptive Extended Kalman Filter for Target Image Tracking," *IEEE Trans. on Aerospace and Electronic Systems,* Vol. AES-17, March 1981, pp. 173–180.

[14] P.S. Maybeck, and S.K. Rogers, "Adaptive Tracking of Multiple Hot-Spot, Target IR Images," *IEEE Trans. on Automatic Control.* Vol. AC-28, October 1983, pp. 937–943.

[15] P.S. Maybeck and R.I. Suizu, "Adaptive Tracker Field-of-View Variation via Multiple Model Filtering," *IEEE Trans. on Aerospace and Electronic Systems,* Vol. AES-21, No. 4, July 1985, pp. 529–539.

[16] J.H. Mitzel, "Multitarget Tracking Applied to Automatic Target Recognition with an Imaging IR Sensor," Y. Bar-Shalom, (ed.), *Multitarget-Multisensor Tracking: Advanced Applications,* Artech House, Norwood, MA, 1990, Chapter 9.

[17] S.C. Pohlig, "An Algorithm for Detection of Moving Optical Targets," *IEEE Trans. on Aerospace and Electronic Systems,* AES-25, January 1989, pp. 56–63.

[18] S.P. Sage and J.L. Melsa, *Estimation Theory with Applications to Communications and Control,* McGraw-Hill, New York, 1971.

[19] H.M. Shertukde and Y. Bar-Shalom, "Detection and Estimation for Multiple Targets with Two Omnidirectional Sensors in the Presence of False Measurements," *IEEE Trans. on Acoustics Speech and Signal Processing,* Vol. ASSP-38, No. 5, May 1990.

[20] H.M. Shertukde and Y. Bar-Shalom, "Tracking of Crossing Targets with Imaging Sensors," *IEEE Trans. on Aerospace and Electronic Systems,* Vol. AES-27, July 1991.

[21] D.D. Sworder and R.G. Hutchins, "Image Enhanced Tracking," *IEEE Trans. on Aerospace and Electronic Systems,* Vol. AES-25, September 1989, pp. 701–710.

[22] D.M. Tobin and P.S. Maybeck, "Substantial Enhancements to a Multiple Model Adaptive Estimator for Target Image Tracking," Proc. 26th IEEE Conf. Decision and Control, Los Angeles, December 1987.

[23] D.R. VanRheeden and R.A. Jones, "Noise Effects on Centroid Tracker Aim Point Estimation," *IEEE Trans. on Aerospace and Electronic Systems,* Vol. AES-24, March 1988, pp. 177–185.

[24] D. Willner, C.B. Chang, and K.P. Dunn, "Kalman Filter Algorithms for a Multisensor System," Proc. IEEE Conf. Decision and Control, Clearwater Beach, FL, December 1976.

# Chapter 6
# A SYSTEM APPROACH TO MULTIPLE TARGET TRACKING

*Fred Daum*

**Raytheon Company**

## 6.1  INTRODUCTION

This chapter describes an approach to designing systems for tracking in a dense multiple-target environment with clutter, false alarms, missed detections, occasionally
unresolved measurements, and target maneuvers. Nearly all published work on *multiple-target tracking* (MTT) has focused on new algorithms for data association, such
as multiple hypothesis tracking, probabilistic data association, joint probabilistic
data association, and the assignment algorithm. In contrast, this chapter describes
other system components that are important for cost-effective performance. In particular, the sensor design itself is of paramount importance. Moreover, how one uses
a given sensor can be the key to overall system performance.

For example, sensor resolution and waveform design are crucial to system performance. Other sensor characteristics, such as signal-to-noise ratio, measurement
accuracy, and data rate obviously are important and well understood by system
designers; however, resolution and waveform design often are overlooked. Sections
6.3 and 6.4 illustrate the system-level effects of resolution and waveform design for
a number of different sensors, including microwave radars, laser radars, and passive
infrared trackers. For many systems, resolution is a more important issue than data
association. This conclusion is striking, because less than 1% of the literature on
MTT mentions resolution, whereas 99% is devoted to data association algorithms
that ignore resolution.

For a given sensor, the specific way in which the sensor is used has a large effect
on tracking performance. For example, most system engineers routinely assume that
targets will be tracked with a uniform data rate. However, as shown in Section 6.2,

the pattern of measurements in time can be designed to enhance estimation accuracy on single targets or the probability of correct data association in a dense multiple-target environment with clutter. Very little theoretical work has been devoted to this topic, but simple heuristic ideas can be used to produce superior designs. Essentially arbitrary, nonuniform measurement patterns are straightforward to implement using phased array radars, but specific nonuniform measurement patterns also can be achieved by using certain passive IR sensors.

A new theoretical tool will be described in Section 6.5 that allows the optimization of measurement patterns for a given sensor in a given environment. This theory is analogous to the well-known Cramér-Rao bound, in that it provides a bound on system performance independent of a particular algorithm. Therefore, this theory allows the system engineer to understand the fundamental limits of tracking imposed by sensor resolution, sensor measurement accuracy, sensor signal-to-noise ratio, data rate, *et cetera*.

Many discussions on MTT include a popular misconception about tracking performance. On the rare occasion when this erroneous notion is stated explicitly, it goes something like this: the optimal MTT algorithm run on a machine with unlimited throughput and memory can achieve whatever performance was promised. Unfortunately, nothing could be further from the truth. Sensor resolution, sensor measurement accuracy, sensor data rate, clutter, noise, jamming, missed detections, target density, target maneuvers, and sensor waveform repertoire place a fundamental limit on tracking performance that cannot be alleviated by an exact implementation of the optimal algorithm. This misconception is widespread for two reasons. First, up to now, no theory could predict the fundamental limits of MTT performance. At a recent meeting of experts on MTT, the lack of performance bounds was identified as a critical issue. Indeed, one MTT expert noted that "There is no Cramér-Rao bound for MTT." The new theoretical bound in this chapter rectifies this situation.

Second, this misconception about fundamental limits on MTT performance has been propagated by a coalition of five special-interest groups: (1) sellers of new processing technology, (2) sellers of new processing architectures, (3) sellers of new MTT algorithms, (4) naive customers, and (5) sensor designers who promised too much performance.

The new theoretical bound presented in Section 6.5 is analogous to the Cramér-Rao bound for nonlinear estimation problems. In particular, the best possible MTT performance can be determined without implementing the optimal algorithm. This new theory provides a lower bound on the estimation error covariance matrix, as in the Cramér-Rao bound. The computational complexity for the new MTT bound is slightly more than that for Monte Carlo simulations of suboptimal MTT algorithms. This bound allows the system engineer to quantify the fundamental limits of MTT rather than pursue an endless quest for better algorithms, faster processors, or more efficient architectures. On the other hand, the use of this new bound could show that there is substantial room for improved algorithm-architectures or processors.

For some important MTT tracking problems many people believe that yet to be developed algorithm-architectures can substantially improve performance. For the same applications, others believe that the current suboptimal algorithms are close to the best possible performance achievable. The use of this new theoretical bound can help answer such questions.

To put this system-level approach into practice, several factors are required over and above design tools. In particular, MTT performance must be considered very early in the sensor concept formulation. After the sensor has been designed it is too late to add on fundamental performance enhancements for MTT; changing sensor resolution, waveform repertoire, or measurement patterns cannot be done after the fact. Second, the system must be designed by engineers who can balance cost and performance tradeoffs involving sensor design, algorithms, data processing, signal processing, measurement patterns, and system-level performance. Figure 6.1 symbolizes this interdisciplinary approach to system design for successful multiple target tracking; algorithms are only part of this picture. A number of examples of phased array radars will be described in which this system-level design was successfully accomplished. Unfortunately, not all programs have benefited from this system-level approach. Rather, sometimes the sensor specialists design the sensor and the algorithm specialists attempt to "make it work" after the fact. Hypothetical examples of this type also will be described for infrared sensors.

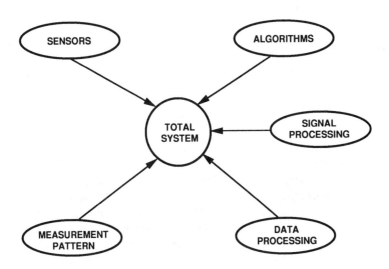

**Figure 6.1** Interdisciplinary approach to system design for multiple-target tracking.

## 6.2 MEASUREMENT PATTERN OPTIMIZATION

Most system engineers assume that a given sensor will make measurements that provide a constant data rate into the data association and tracking algorithms. For many types of sensors, this is a very natural assumption. For example, with a conventional mechanical scanning radar or a dish tracking radar with a fixed-pulse transmission rate, there is very little choice in this matter. However, many sensors, such as phased array radars, can produce essentially any nonuniform measurement pattern desired. Certain types of passive infrared sensors also can realize highly nonuniform measurement patterns.

There is no reason to suppose that a constant data rate is optimal or close to optimal for tracking. In fact, it is well known that velocity estimation accuracy for phased array radars tracking multiple nonmaneuvering targets is optimized with a highly nonuniform measurement pattern. In particular, all sensor measurements are concentrated at the beginning and end of the observation time interval, with no observations in the middle. The accuracy improvement obtained by using this simple idea is dramatic. Under certain assumptions, the one-sigma velocity estimation error is cut almost in half. For example, if we assume a constant one-sigma position measurement error ($\sigma$) for each observation, a fixed number of measurements ($n$), a fixed time interval ($T$), with zero process noise and zero acceleration target dynamics in one spatial dimension, then the one-sigma velocity estimation error for a constant data rate is approximately

$$\sigma_v \approx \frac{\sqrt{12}\sigma}{T\sqrt{n}} \text{ for } n \gg 1 \tag{6.1}$$

whereas the highly nonuniform measurement pattern results in

$$\sigma_v \approx \frac{\sqrt{2}\sigma}{T\sqrt{n/2}} \tag{6.2}$$

The nonuniform measurement pattern puts half the observations at the beginning of the time interval and the other half at the end; no measurements are in the middle. The ratio of $\sigma_v$ for the uniform *versus* nonuniform measurement pattern is about 1.73; for a radar, this would be equivalent to a factor of 3 in increased radar power.

Figure 6.2 shows the two measurement patterns just analyzed. The measurements shown in Figure 6.2 are on a given target or cluster of targets close together in angle, so that all targets can be illuminated with a single radar beam or a single transmitted radar waveform. Other targets or target clusters are illuminated with similar measurement patterns. Almost all radars are designed to transmit energy at a constant rate averaged over a time interval shorter than 1 s. If the radar is not utilized in

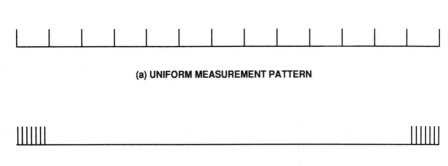

(a) UNIFORM MEASUREMENT PATTERN

(b) NON-UNIFORM MEASUREMENT PATTERN

**Figure 6.2** Measurement patterns.

this way, potential system performance is wasted. Therefore, the overall goal of scheduling radar pulses for a phased array is to transmit waveforms on individual targets or clusters as in Figure 6.2(b), so that the total radar energy is distributed uniformly in time. If hundreds or thousands of targets or clusters are to be tracked, we can imagine that this desirable situation is easy to approximate. If there are fewer targets or clusters, then radar operation is less efficient, but there are plenty of radar resources to provide good performance.

A detailed analysis of optimal measurement patterns for phased array radars is given in [16]. The same basic ideas apply to any other type of sensor that has the flexibility to realize nonuniform measurement patterns on individual targets or clusters. For example, certain types of passive infrared sensors have this flexibility, but others do not. Considering the profound effect on system performance, all other things being equal, we would prefer a sensor with this flexibility. Designing a sensor with this capability requires early planning; such flexibility cannot be added as an afterthought.

The discussion of optimal measurement patterns given earlier (as well as in [16]) ignores several practical aspects of tracking. The most glaring omission is that the so-called optimal measurement pattern in Figure 6.2(b) might produce very poor performance in a dense multiple-target environment. In particular, it might be difficult to associate the final $n/2$ measurements with the initial $n/2$ measurements. For this reason, practical radar systems almost never use the theoretically optimal pattern in Figure 6.2(b). Instead, other measurements are added between the initial and final bursts to help associate these data. No systematic theory is available in the literature to distribute these extra measurements for improved association. Nevertheless, many practical systems have been designed using intuition and ad hoc techniques.

So far, measurement pattern optimization has been discussed under the following assumptions: (1) velocity estimation accuracy is the criterion of performance, (2) one-sigma measurement noise errors are fixed, (3) no target maneuvers or zero process noise, (4) no measurement-to-track association errors, and (5) no consideration of real-time computational complexity. If any of these assumptions is changed, then the so-called optimal measurement pattern will change. For example, if acceleration estimation accuracy is desired rather than velocity accuracy, then the optimal measurement pattern consists of three bursts of measurements rather than two. Second, if the criterion of performance is velocity estimation accuracy, but the target can maneuver, then the optimal measurement pattern looks more like Figure 6.2(a) than Figure 6.2(b). Finally, if data misassociation errors or computational complexity is considered, then both patterns in Figure 6.2 can be highly suboptimal.

The fundamental problem in a dense multiple-target environment with clutter, false alarms, missed detections, occasionally unresolved measurements, and so forth is the uncertain origin of measurements. A given measurement might be from any of several targets, or no target at all, rather it might be due to clutter or noise. There are many hypotheses about the actual origin of measurements, and a real-time algorithm must sort out these many possibilities and come to a decision about measurement-to-track association or measurement-to-measurement association. This decision is made by some kind of algorithm, such as *multiple hypothesis tracking* (MHT), probabilistic data association, joint probabilistic data association, and so on. Almost the entire literature on multiple target tracking is devoted to the discussion of such algorithms. In contrast, essentially no papers have been published about optimal or good measurement patterns for MTT.

As noted, no systematic theory for optimization of measurement patterns for MTT has been published. Nevertheless, a superior design can be obtained by using simple intuitive ideas, as explained later. Furthermore, a systematic optimization method can be formulated using the new theoretical bounds described in [8]; this methodology will be sketched later.

The basic intuitive idea can be grasped by comparing Figures 6.3 and 6.4. These figures plot multiple measurements of target range *versus* time. Both figures use eight discrete measurement times ($t_1, t_2, \ldots, t_8$), and both span the same time interval from $t_1$ to $t_8$. The radar expends exactly the same total transmitted energy for both figures. On the other hand, it is very difficult to associate measurements using the data in Figure 6.3, whereas it is relatively easy to associate data in Figure 6.4. The difference is the measurement pattern: Figure 6.3 has a standard uniform pattern, which is poor for MTT, whereas Figure 6.4 is a specially designed measurement pattern that is vastly superior. Figures 6.5 and 6.6 show exactly the same measurement data as in Figures 6.3 and 6.4, with straight lines to indicate the correct object paths. Dots without lines correspond to clutter or noise detection, and some lines have fewer than eight dots owing to missed detections.

Figures 6.3 to 6.6 illustrate the power of a measurement pattern specifically designed for MTT. These figures were created by using simple target dynamics of zero range acceleration. The same basic idea applies to the more general case of

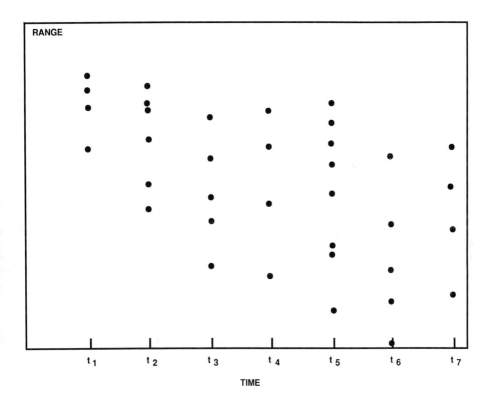

**Figure 6.3** Track initiation problem in dense multiple-target environment with uniform data rate.

curved trajectories, however. In fact, a mix of trajectories with different curvatures creates a more difficult data association problem than straight-line paths, and therefore a measurement pattern specifically designed for MTT is even more valuable. If the trajectory curvature is due to external forces (such as gravity, coriolis, and centrifugal acceleration), which are modeled by known differential equations, then the data association problem essentially is the same as depicted in Figures 6.3 to 6.6 using zero acceleration trajectories.

Data association obviously is easier using Figure 6.4 than Figure 6.3; that is, data association is both quicker and more accurate. The same is true for automatic algorithms. Figure 6.4 is superior to Figure 6.3: better association performance as well as lower computational complexity. In particular, a number of phased-array radars have been designed by using fully automatic track-initiation and track-maintenance algorithms with uniform measurement patterns (like Figure 6.3) as well as nonuniform patterns (Figure 6.4). The automatic algorithms using the nonuniform

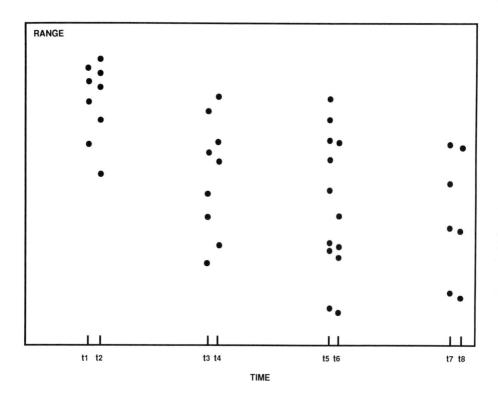

**Figure 6.4** Track initiation problem in dense multiple-target environment with nonuniform data rate.

pattern are simpler to code, run much faster in real-time, and produce better data association than the traditional uniform pattern.

Intuitively, data association is improved by the nonuniform pattern for three reasons. First, association is trivial for measurements that are very close together in time. Second, the associated measurement pairs provide rate information to help associate pairs with each other. Third, we have four pairs rather than eight individual measurements, which reduces the problem size that mitigates the combinatorial explosion in computational complexity.

Figures 6.3 to 6.6 illustrate the power of special measurement patterns in the context of radar range measurements. The same basic ideas apply, however, to radar measurements of doppler, elevation and azimuth angles, and target amplitude. That is, the ideas illustrated by the one-dimensional example in Figures 6.3 to 6.6 apply to multidimensional measurements as well. Needless to say, we have great difficulty absorbing and making decisions based on such multidimensional data; however, automated algorithms do not have the same threshold at two dimensions. In fact, for

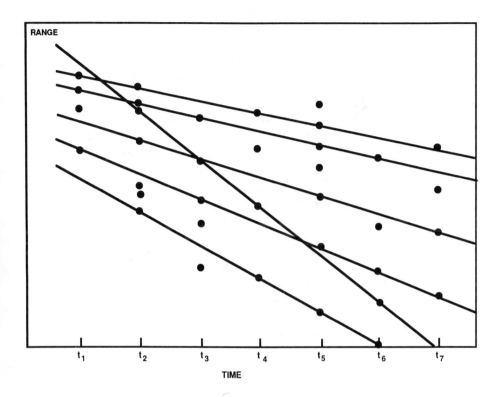

**Figure 6.5** Track initiation solution in dense multiple-target environment with uniform data rate.

automatic algorithms, association performance can be improved significantly by using multidimensional data with a relatively moderate increase in computational complexity as a function of data dimensionality.

Along the same lines, the ideas illustrated in Figures 6.3 to 6.6 for radar range measurements can be applied to passive infrared sensors that measure angle and radiometric data but not range. Some passive infrared sensors cannot realize the nonuniform measurement patterns required for superior MTT performance. On the other hand, certain types of passive infrared sensors can achieve the desired non-uniform sampling strategy shown in Figure 6.4. Designing a sensor to realize supe-rior nonuniform measurement patterns requires thinking ahead; it cannot be done as an afterthought.

So far, the discussion of superior measurement patterns for MTT has been entirely intuitive and ad hoc, using simple pictures, and it has been devoid of equa-tions or design algorithms. There are several approaches to systematize the design of measurement patterns for MTT: (1) characterize the measurement pattern in terms

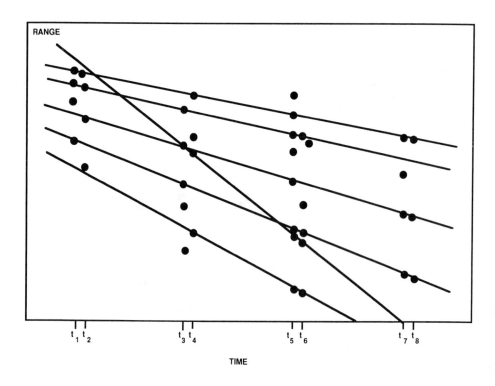

**Figure 6.6** Track initiation solution in dense multiple-target environment with nonuniform data rate.

of a few parameters and vary these continuously until good MTT performance is obtained; (2) allow arbitrary measurement patterns and vary these randomly until good MTT performance is achieved; and (3) use a combinatorial optimization algorithm to design the measurement pattern. Other methods also could be used, as well as hybrid combinations of these three.

In all three methods, we need a criterion to judge MTT performance. This criterion could be either some function of the estimation error covariance matrix (e.g., the trace or determinant or a quadratic form), or the probability of correct data association. Finally, we need some method to compute the value of the performance criterion for a given measurement pattern. There are two basic approaches here as well: evaluate a specific algorithm using a Monte Carlo simulation, or use the theoretical performance bound derived in [8], which is independent of any particular algorithm. The new theory in [8] will be summarized in Section 6.5 of this chapter. Each of the three basic methods of measurement pattern optimization (parametric, random, and combinatorial) will be addressed in the following paragraphs.

The best way to describe the parametric method is by several specific examples. First, a two-parameter characterization of a measurement pattern might be the number of measurements in a burst ($MB$), as well as the number of bursts ($NB$). We assume that the total time interval for all observations is fixed, and the bursts are uniform in time. Referring to Figure 6.2, pattern (a) would have $MB = 1$ and $NB = n$, whereas pattern (b) would have $MB = n/2$ and $NB = 2$. A variation on this theme might be a pattern designed for good acceleration estimation, in which $MB = n/3$ and $NB = 3$. A second example of a simple parametric description of a measurement pattern might be the superposition of other elementary patterns described by two parameters. We can imagine further elementary three-parameter and four-parameter patterns. The basic idea is to characterize the pattern by a few parameters, and vary these to obtain good or optimal MTT performance. In particular, for two-parameter patterns, we could plot the MTT criterion as a function of these two parameters. As the number of free parameters increases, the utility of a simple graphical presentation decreases. An automated algorithm would be required to find good or optimal patterns characterized by many free parameters.

The second method of pattern optimization would generate random times of measurements according to some specified probability distribution. Each random measurement pattern would be evaluated by using the criterion of MTT performance, and the best pattern would be selected. The simplest probability distribution is uniform in time; the measurement times would be independently, randomly distributed according to a uniform distribution. The only parameter needed to specify this random pattern generator is the average density of measurement times per unit time. A two-parameter random pattern generator could use a first-order Markov model to specify correlation between measurement times. This would tend to cluster together measurement times. A three-parameter random pattern could use a second-order Markov process in time, and so on. Simulated annealing could be used to perform this random search in a systematic way; however, the simple method just described would be effective for some applications.

The third method of combinatorial optimization is much more systematic and formal than the two methods discussed so far. In particular, several papers and books deal specifically with the design of measurement patterns using combinatorial optimization algorithms; for example, [33, 26, 43]. None of these, however, treats multiple-target tracking or issues of data association. Nevertheless, much of the theory in [33, 26, 43] can be applied to the MTT problem. The most recent work in this area is reported in [33], which uses an accelerated greedy algorithm to solve the combinatorial optimization problem. The performance criterion used in [33] is the determinant of the Fisher information matrix of the estimation problem. The origin of measurements is known exactly; the underlying set function in this problem formulation is "submodular." Submodular functions are the combinatorial analog of convex performance criteria in continuous optimization problems. The submodularity allows use of the accelerated greedy algorithm, with a consequent speed-up of several orders of magnitude for a typical problem.

Use of the Fisher information matrix in [33] is analogous to use of the lower bound on MTT performance [8] suggested earlier. The Fisher information matrix is the inverse of the estimation error covariance matrix in the Cramér-Rao bound. The new bound reported in [8] for MTT problems is analogous to the Cramér-Rao bound for nonlinear estimation problems.

The three methods described produce good or optimal measurement patterns computed off-line prior to collecting the real-time data. This might be called *open-loop* or *a priori* measurement pattern design. Another possibility is to compute measurement patterns on-line in real time as a function of the measured data. For example, we could use higher data rates in space-time volumes that are difficult in some sense (e.g., a very dense target environment, during ostensible target maneuvers, at lower signal-to-noise ratio, or in high clutter). In relatively benign space-time regions, a lower track rate could be used. Adaptive sampling methods of this type are discussed in [pp. 333–343 in 3]. Track rate is a one-parameter characterization of measurement patterns. The same basic idea could be generalized to adapt multiple-parameter measurement patterns to the immediate tracking environment; for example, use measurement pairs (Figure 6.4) in difficult MTT regions, but not elsewhere. Many variations on this theme have been applied in practical systems, despite the lack of a systematic theory. With sufficient real-time computational resources, we can imagine designing a good or optimal measurement pattern as a function of the measured data using one of the three methods sketched earlier for open-loop design.

In summary, measurement patterns have a significant effect on MTT performance. This has been demonstrated by using several simple examples. The connection between measurement patterns and MTT has not been mentioned in the literature before, and therefore there are no systematic algorithms that have been used to design good or optimal measurement patterns. Nevertheless, simple intuitive ideas can be used to obtain superior designs. Moreover, the new lower bounds on MTT performance reported in [8] can be used to develop systematic methods for the design of good or optimal measurement patterns.

## 6.3  WAVEFORM OPTIMIZATION

Many system engineers address the problem of multiple-target tracking by trying to invent more advanced data association algorithms, without considering the possibility of selecting waveforms that are good or optimal for MTT. For example, two excellent books have been published on MTT [3 and 2], but neither book mentions the issue of waveform design. Moreover, the vast literature on MTT focuses on advanced algorithms, and waveform optimization is almost never considered. In contrast, this section will describe the benefits of waveform optimization for MTT performance in a dense multiple-target environment with clutter, missed detections, noise, and so on.

There are several reasons why waveform design rarely is considered by system engineers for MTT. First, by definition, only active sensors, such as microwave radars and laser radars, can transmit waveforms. Passive sensors, such as many infrared and acoustic sensors, transmit no energy at all, and hence the received waveform cannot be controlled by the system engineer. The most that can be done in passive sensors is to process the received energy in different ways. The second possible reason for the neglect of waveform design for MTT is that many system engineers are accustomed to working with a given sensor rather than designing the sensor itself. Historically, tracking and data association algorithms have fallen into the bailiwick of software engineers. Many sensors are designed by hardware engineers, but the data association algorithms are designed after the fact by software engineers. What is required, obviously, is the joint consideration of sensor and algorithm design for MTT performance. Time and forethought are required, however, to realize this ideal synthesis; sometimes these ingredients are lacking. A third potential reason for the rarity of waveform design for MTT is that system engineers who can perform cost and effectiveness trade-offs involving MTT performance, waveform design, and algorithm design are few and far between.

In a broad sense, the issues and mathematics for waveform design are the same as for measurement pattern optimization as discussed in Section 6.2. One clear distinction, however, is that active sensors can control the transmitted waveform, whereas passive sensors cannot. On the other hand, measurement pattern optimization is relevant for both active and passive sensors, as explained in Section 6.2. For example, the issues and mathematics for waveform design in [1] largely are the same as in [16, 33, 26, and 43], which deal with measurement patterns. Both waveform and measurement pattern design use similar mathematical algorithms to optimize a given performance criterion, subject to the physical constraints of time, energy, bandwidth, *et cetera*. There is an extensive literature on waveform design for radar: [1, 6, and 32, 22, 34, 5, and 24] are the tip of the iceberg in this enormous and growing literature. This radar literature has focused on issues of clutter rejection, robustness to jamming, range and doppler measurement accuracy, range and doppler resolution, range and doppler sidelobes, sensitivity to unknown doppler shift, and so on. Some papers deal implicitly with dense multiple-target environments but only a handful discuss MTT and waveform design explicitly.

As in Section 6.2, the power of waveform design for MTT performance will be illustrated by using simple pictures rather than equations. Recall that Figure 6.3 showed radar range measurements at eight discrete times in a multiple-target environment. The transmitted radar waveform in Figure 6.3 has no capability of measuring range-rate at each discrete time. In contrast, the data shown in Figure 6.7 shows exactly the same multiple-target environment, with the same missed detections, the same false alarms, and the same data rate; but the big difference is that range-rate is measured at each discrete time. The range-rate (doppler) data are represented as arrows attached to each data point. The power of this extra type of information is dramatic. Both people and automated data association algorithms have improved performance as well as reduced computational complexity by using range

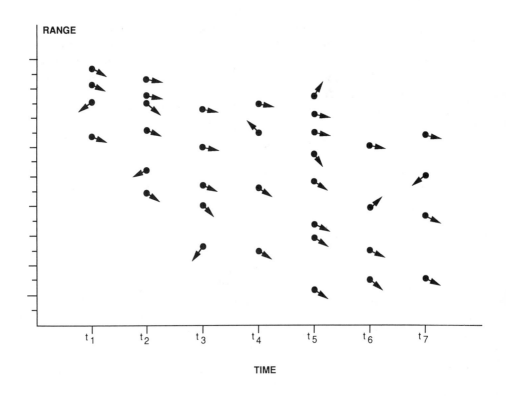

**Figure 6.7** Track initiation in a dense multiple-target environment.

and doppler data instead of range only. This improvement is analogous to the comparison of Figures 6.3 and 6.4, which was due to measurement pattern design. Precisely the same amount of radar energy is transmitted to obtain Figures 6.3 and 6.7, but the resulting information is vastly better for MTT in Figure 6.7.

Various techniques can be used to obtain both range and doppler measurements at each discrete time. These are discussed in detail in [6, 32, 22, 34, 5, 24, and 10]. Suffice it to say that there are very interesting trade-offs and system-level implications of range *versus* range-rate measurement accuracy. This fundamental trade-off is explained in [22]; the Cramér-Rao bound is extremely optimistic about this trade-off for waveforms with a large time-bandwidth product. This cautionary tale is told in [10].

We can combine the waveform and measurement pattern ideas discussed so far to improve MTT performance and reduce computational complexity. For example, the ideas illustrated in Figures 6.4 and 6.7 can be combined to yield excellent track-initiation and track-maintenance performance with extremely small computational complexity compared to algorithms like MHT or JPDA. This synthesis of waveform and measurement pattern design has been used in several microwave and laser radars [20]. The waveform idea is to use a so-called up-chirp and down-chirp linear FM waveform [see p. 250 in 32]. The measurement pattern idea is to arrange these waveforms into pairs as shown in Figure 6.4. This technique is called *up-down chirp pulse-pairs*. Alternatively, we can think of the resulting measurements as represented in Figure 6.7, in which an up-down chirp pulse-pair corresponds to a single measurement at one discrete time. Up-down pulse-pairs are designed to provide both accurate range and range-rate measurements. At the same time, the range-resolution can be very high, and data association is easy.

A linear FM pulse does not measure range, but a linear combination of range and range-rate:

$$R_M(t) = R(t) + (S\tau f/B)\dot{R}(t) \tag{6.3}$$

in which $R(t)$ and $\dot{R}(t)$ denote range and range-rate at time $t$, the parameter $A = s\tau f/B$ is called the *range-doppler coupling* factor, and its components are

$$S = \begin{cases} 1 \text{ for up-chirp} \\ -1 \text{ for down-chirp} \end{cases} \tag{6.4}$$

and $\tau$ = transmitted pulse length, $f$ = operating frequency at center of the linear FM sweep, and $B$ = chirp bandwidth. By definition, a linear FM pulse is transmitted to sweep from $f - B/2$ to $f + B/2$ for up-chirp and from $f + B/2$ to $f - B/2$ for down-chirp.

The combination of two linear FM pulses, down-chirp at time $t_1$ and up-chirp at time $t_2$ results in two independent measurements:

$$R_m(t_1) = R(t_1) - |A|\dot{R}(t_1) \tag{6.5}$$

$$R_m(t_2) = R(t_2) + |A|\dot{R}(t_2) \tag{6.6}$$

This results in two equations in four unknowns for each measurement association pair. If the times $t_1$ and $t_2$ are sufficiently close, then we can approximate the target dynamics as

$$\dot{R}(t_1) \approx \dot{R}(t_2) \text{ and } R(t_2) \approx R(t_1) + (t_2 - t_1)\dot{R}(t_1)$$

With this approximation, each measurement association pair provides two equations in two unknowns, which can be solved for range and range-rate. Assuming that the range measurement errors are statistically independent from $t_1$ to $t_2$, the one-sigma estimation error in range-rate is

$$\sigma_{\dot{R}} = \frac{\sqrt{2}\sigma}{(2|A| + \Delta t)} \tag{6.7}$$

in which $\Delta t = t_2 - t_1$, and $\sigma$ is the one-sigma range measurement error (assumed to be the same for $t_1$ and $t_2$).

This simple formula for $\sigma_{\dot{R}}$ has several important implications for MTT performance. First, for fixed $\sigma$ and $\Delta t$, the range-rate estimation error can be reduced by enlarging $|A|$. In many practical applications $|A| \gg \Delta t$, and therefore the value of $\sigma_{\dot{R}}$ is essentially independent of $\Delta t$. Second, reducing $\Delta t$ allows the angle measurements and *radar cross section* (RCS) measurements to be used to provide excellent measurement-to-measurement association. In particular, in typical microwave radar and laser radar applications, for sufficiently small $\Delta t$, the angle data and perhaps the RCS data will change very little from $t_1$ to $t_2$ for measurements from the same object. This physical fact provides a very powerful association mechanism in a dense multiple target environment.

Without using up-down chirp pulse-pairs, the formula for range-rate accuracy would be the same as given, but with $A =$ zero. In this case, decreasing $\Delta t$ improves data association within a pulse pair, but it degrades $\sigma_{\dot{R}}$ and hence degrades pair-to-pair data association performance. In contrast, using up-down chirp pulse pairs provides another degree of freedom in this trade-off.

In phased array radar systems that have used the up-down chirp pulse-pair idea, track initiation in a dense multiple-target environment has performed much better than it would without this synthesis of waveform and measurement pattern design. Moreover, the computational complexity was radically reduced. Not all radars have parameters $(\tau, f, B)$ that allow this method to be used effectively. For some systems, $|A|$ is too large to allow reliable pulse-to-pulse data association using range information. For other systems, $|A|$ is too small to provide sufficiently accurate range-rate estimates. For many applications $|A|$ should be on the order of 1 s, although this value depends on data rate, target density, average signal-to-noise ratio and the quality of *a priori* information available. If a given sensor does not have a suitable value of $|A|$, then the system engineer can consider changing other sensor parameters $(\tau, f, B)$ from $t_1$ to $t_2$ to achieve the desired change in range-doppler coupling.

Note that the formula for range-doppler coupling quoted earlier assumes linear FM waveforms with large time-bandwidth products, but not too large. In particular, if the target moves more than a fraction of one range resolution cell within the time of one transmitted pulse, then none of these formulas is valid, and performance generally is degraded. Also, it was implicitly assumed that the radar measurements are resolved in range. The lack of sufficient resolution may be a fundamental problem in a dense multiple-target environment (see Section 6.4).

Finally, it was tacitly assumed that the phase velocity was equal to the group velocity; otherwise, the formula for range-doppler coupling is wrong. Group velocity corresponds to the translational motion of the object, whereas phase velocity is due to both translational and rotational motion for rigid bodies, as well as interparticle motion in plasmas and other nonrigid objects. Phase velocity is what is measured as doppler shift during a single radar waveform. If the doppler shift does not correspond to the translational motion of the object, then the simple theory sketched earlier is wrong. In some microwave radar and laser radar applications this condition might fail owing to the doppler shift induced by rocket exhaust plume, jet engine modulation, doppler glint from target rotation, ionospheric or tropospheric doppler shift, and so forth.

In summary, waveform design can be used to improve MTT performance and reduce computational complexity for active sensors such as microwave radars and laser radars. Moreover, the combination of waveform and measurement pattern optimization is a powerful technique that has been used on several systems with excellent results. The new theoretical bounds on MTT performance [8] can be used to obtain good or optimal waveform-measurement pattern designs along the lines sketched in Section 6.2. Needless to say, this type of system approach to MTT must be done at a very early stage in the development of a sensor. New waveforms for MTT are very expensive to add as an afterthought, but they can be extremely cost effective with sufficient forethought.

## 6.4 RESOLUTION

Resolution is crucial for successful tracking in a dense multiple target-environment. Roughly speaking *resolution* is the ability of a sensor and its algorithms to correctly decide that two closely spaced objects are indeed two distinct targets rather than one or none. Most system engineers believe that unresolved measurements are essentially worthless. Despite the importance of resolution, only a handful of papers in the MTT literature consider unresolved measurements; two of the rare papers on this topic are [38] and [4]. This lack of attention is surprising for three reasons. First, a dense multiple-target environment, in which data association is challenging, is precisely the situation in which sensor measurements might be due to two or more unresolved objects. Second, algorithms that consider the possibility of unresolved measurements have substantially better performance than MTT algorithms that ignore this issue (see [38]). Third, for most practical MTT systems, resolution is actually a more serious problem than failure to associate the correct measurements to form a track. This rather striking conclusion will be derived by comparing the probability of resolution to the probability of correct measurement association; the former is always worse than the latter for most systems of practical interest.

Most system engineers think of resolution as a property of the physical sensor rather than the sensor and its processing algorithms. In particular, for microwave radar and infrared sensors, most system engineers believe that the angular resolution is given by the so-called Rayleigh criterion: $\theta = \lambda/D$, in which $\lambda$ is the sensor wavelength and $D$ is the sensor aperture diameter. That is, if two objects are within an angle of $\theta$ of each other, they are unresolved in angle. Similar criteria exist for range and doppler resolution for microwave radars and laser radars. For example, for a linear FM waveform, the usual range resolution criterion is $\Delta R = c/(2B)$, in which $B$ is the chirp bandwidth and $c$ is the speed of light. For a pure sinusoidal waveform, the usual doppler resolution criterion is $\Delta \dot{R} = \lambda/(2T)$, in which $T$ is the total duration of the waveform. Other radar waveforms have completely different resolution criteria. For example, the conventional range resolution criterion for a pure sinusoidal pulse is $\Delta R = \tau c/2$, in which $\tau$ is the transmitted pulselength. These conventional resolution criteria are described in [13] and [17].

In practice, it is not so easy to state a simple resolution criterion for angle, range, or doppler. The simple Rayleigh resolution criterion is correct to within about a factor of two, depending on the precise quantitative definition of the word *resolution*. For example, angular resolution depends on more than $\lambda$ and $D$. In particular, it obviously depends on the following additional factors:

1. Relative signal strength of the two objects,
2. Signal-to-noise ratio for each object,
3. Probability of detecting one target when there actually is one object,
4. Allowed probability of falsely deciding that there are two targets when there is really one or none,
5. Details of the algorithm that attempt to count targets using sensor data,
6. Quantity of sensor measurements (one or more),
7. Type of data available (e.g., quadrature monopulse data for radars, see [35]),
8. Sample interval in space or time.

The Rayleigh resolution criterion depends only on $\lambda/D$, and it does not consider any of these other eight factors. Therefore, the Rayleigh criterion for angular resolution cannot be complete. The subtleties of defining what *resolution* means when these other factors are considered are explored in [30] and [29].

Despite these eight other factors, the Rayleigh angular resolution criterion is correct to within a factor of about two for most practical microwave and infrared sensors. Moreover, the analogous simple range and doppler resolution criteria quoted earlier also are correct to within approximately a factor of two for most practical microwave radars and laser radars.

Many papers have appeared in the radar literature about "superresolution" in angle, range, or doppler. The term *superresolution* refers to resolving two objects that are much closer than the Rayleigh criterion would predict. In theory, this can be accomplished with a phased array radar under certain conditions by using special algorithms that exploit the large number of degrees of freedom available in a phased array. In practice, however, superresolution is difficult to achieve, owing to the following:

1. Phase and gain errors and uncertainty about the physical array,
2. Ill-conditioning of the special algorithms,
3. Uncertainty about the *a priori* target positions to be resolved,

4. Limited signal-to-noise ratio,
5. Degradation of other sensor characteristics (such as signal-to-noise ratio),
6. Lack of robustness with respect to antenna pattern modeling errors,
7. Multipath,
8. Cost and complexity of hardware,
9. Near-field and wideband effects.

Most experienced radar system engineers are skeptical about the practical application of superresolution theory. Suffice it to say that no operational phased-array radar uses superresolution. Nevertheless, this theory might become practical in the future.

Unlike phased-array antennas for radar, practical infrared sensors lack enough degrees of freedom and the flexible control and processing required for superresolution. Therefore, superresolution is out of the question, even in theory, for most infrared sensors.

Despite the impracticality of superresolution for infrared sensors, a handful of theoretical papers claim that useful information can be deduced about two objects that are much closer than the Rayleigh criterion. For example, [19] describes a maximum likelihood algorithm that reportedly "resolves closely spaced objects (CSOs) well below the Rayleigh limit of resolution," with greater than 95% probability "of correctly identifying 1, 2 or 3 objects at a SNR of 6," and with a position estimation accuracy of 0.1 detector subtense. This performance is theoretically possible, but several practical considerations can severely degrade this superresolution. First, it is implicitly assumed in [19] that the object signal strength is exactly constant over the time interval of observations. In practice, signal strength varies with time. An analysis of superresolution in radar shows that even a slight variation in signal strength completely destroys the theoretical angular accuracy (see [7]). Therefore, the theoretical superresolution performance claimed in [19] may be difficult to achieve in practice.

To gain some insight into the importance of resolution in MTT, Figure 6.8 shows the probabilities of resolution and association for an idealized MTT scenario. We assume that targets are independently randomly distributed in one dimension according to a uniform density with an average separation between objects of $S$. The sensor resolution is assumed to be a fixed value, denoted RES. That is, if two objects are within a distance RES of each other, then they are unresolved by the sensor for a given measurement. We define the ratio of resolution to average object separation as $r = \text{RES}/S$. For fixed $S$, if the sensor resolution is poor, RES is large, and hence the probability of resolution is low, as shown in Figure 6.8. The probability of resolution shown in Figure 6.8 was computed by using a Poisson distribution, which follows from the assumptions of independent uniform distributions for individual objects. The probability of resolution for a given object is simply $p = \exp(-2r)$ for one-dimensional measurements (see the appendix for derivation). It is remarkable

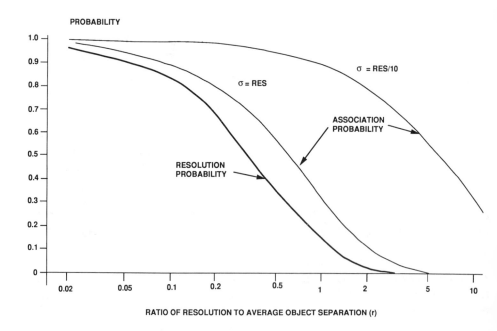

**Figure 6.8** Probability of resolution and association.

that even when the average target separation is ten times the sensor resolution, so that $r = 0.1$, the probability of resolution is as low as 82%. All too often system engineers believe that resolution is not a significant issue for $r = 0.1$; however, Figure 6.8 makes it obvious that this rule of thumb is wrong.

The probability of association in Figure 6.8 was computed by using the theory developed in [27]. In particular, let $N$ denote the average number of objects within a given one-sigma prediction error volume. The probability of correctly associating a given track with its corresponding one-dimensional measurement is approximately $P_c \approx \exp(-N/\sqrt{\pi})$. This amazingly simple formula is in excellent agreement with Monte Carlo simulation results for values of $P_c$ of practical interest. The theory in [27] uses the same basic assumptions about the distribution of random objects that were stated earlier (Poisson, independent, *et cetera*). Useful approximate formula for multidimensional data are given in the appendix. Two curves for $P_c$ are shown in Figure 6.8. The upper curve assumes that the one-sigma prediction error is one-tenth the sensor resolution, whereas the lower curve assumes that the one-sigma prediction error is equal to the sensor resolution. These two extremes should bound most case of practical interest.

The striking conclusion that can be drawn from Figure 6.8 is that, in general, resolution is a more important issue than association! That is, for a given value of $r$ (ratio of sensor resolution to average object separation), the probability of resolving two objects always is worse than the probability of correctly associating a measurement with a track. This conclusion is remarkable because 99% of the MTT literature is devoted to the data association problem, whereas less than 1% of the MTT literature mentions sensor resolution. Moreover, many papers on MTT that ignore sensor resolution evaluate algorithm performance for values of sensor measurement accuracy and target density that imply that there should be a severe resolution problem! For example, if the one-sigma sensor measurement error is $\sigma = $ RES/10 and the average target separation is $S = 5\sigma$, then $r = 2$, in which case the probability of resolution is only 2%. Other examples using different operating points on Figure 6.8 can be constructed, but the general conclusion is the same. Obviously MTT papers that ignore sensor resolution can be extremely misleading.

The measurement-to-track association algorithm assumed in [27] was Munkres's assignment algorithm, which is optimal when the only information used consists of estimated state vectors and error covariance matrices for all tracks, along with all sensor measurements at one discrete measurement time. However, Munkres's algorithm is not optimal for using all sensor measurements at all times; it is suboptimal relative to multiple hypothesis tracking. For some important applications, the assignment algorithm, which is locally optimal, is very poor compared with the globally optimal MHT algorithm. This means that the curves in Figure 6.8 for association probability are pessimistic relative to the globally optimal algorithm (MHT). Therefore, the conclusion drawn in the previous paragraph is still valid, and the conclusion actually is strengthened due to the pessimism of Figure 6.8.

Figure 6.8 shows the probability of correct association for RES/10 $\leq \sigma \leq$ RES, whereas situations in which $\sigma$ exceeds RES are also of interest. There are two main instances in which $\sigma >$ RES: the first is due to target maneuvers or unmodeled acceleration, and the second occurs during the first few measurements of a given track. At a sufficiently low data rate, a target can maneuver to cause the one-sigma prediction error ($\sigma$) to exceed the sensor resolution. On the other hand, if the unmodeled target acceleration is sufficiently small, the only time that $\sigma >$ RES is during the first one or two measurements. After two measurements on an object, the target position can be predicted to within one resolution cell. This means that there can be no association problem unless the measurement data are unresolved. A simple calculation confirms that assertion. Consider a one-dimensional tracking problem, with a uniform data rate and a fixed one-sigma position measurement error of $\sigma_m$. Assume that unmodeled target acceleration is negligible and that there is no useful *a priori* position or velocity information. In this situation, after the first two correctly associated measurements, the one-sigma position prediction error is approximately

$$\sigma = \sqrt{\sigma_x^2 + (3T/2)^2\sigma_v^2 + \sigma_m^2} \tag{6.8}$$

where

$T$ = time between measurements
$\sigma_v$ = one-sigma velocity estimation error at midpoint
$\sigma_v = \sqrt{2}\sigma_m/T$
$\sigma_x$ = one-sigma position estimation error at midpoint
$\sigma_x = \sigma_m/\sqrt{2}$

Combining these results implies that $\sigma \approx \sqrt{6}\sigma_m$ after two measurements. Assuming a typical value of $\sigma_m \approx$ RES/10 results in $\sigma \approx$ RES/4, which is within the upper and lower curves of association probability plotted in Figure 6.8. Unmodeled target acceleration or missed detections can increase $\sigma$ to values exceeding RES/4, and Figure 6.8 includes such cases up to $\sigma$ = RES.

Figure 6.8 showed the probability of resolution for one measurement time, but tracks typically consist of many measurements. Figure 6.9 shows the probability of $n$ measurements from a given target being resolved, assuming statistical independence from one measurement time to the next. In dense multiple-target environ-

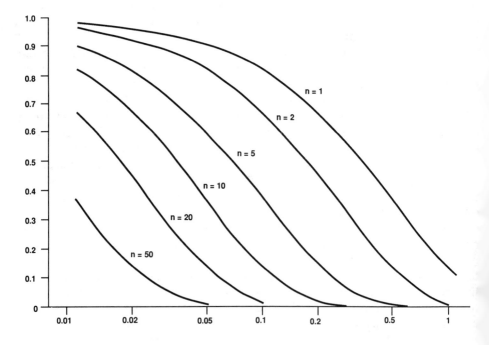

**Figure 6.9** Probability of resolution for multiple measurement times.

ments this often is a good approximation, although we can easily construct examples in which there is a strong correlation from one time to the next. The statistical correlation depends on the data rate, the distribution of object velocities, and the sensor resolution. The basic conclusion from Figure 6.9 is that resolution is a major issue for tracks consisting of more than a few measurements. Even for a ratio of resolution to average object separation of as little as $r = 0.01$, there is still a good chance that 1 or more of the measurements will be unresolved for tracks with more than 10 measurements.

The probability of resolution shown in Figures 6.8 and 6.9 was computed by assuming that unresolved measurements occur randomly for any given track. This mathematical model might approximate the following physical scenario: many objects in one or more large clouds moving relative to each other. Detailed simulations of this physical set-up show that the simple Poisson distribution and the assumption of statistical independence are quite good approximations. The accuracy of this model depends on the number of targets, the sensor resolution, the average target separations, and the dispersive velocities of the objects. In particular, if there are very few objects or if all objects have nearly the same velocity, then this random model will be a poor approximation. In the next paragraph, we consider an extreme case in which there are only two objects with precisely the same velocity. The random model shown in Figures 6.8 and 6.9 are completely inappropriate in this extreme case; nevertheless, sensor resolution is a major issue here as well.

Consider a hypothetical passive infrared sensor as described in [39]. This sensor is postulated for use in an exoatmospheric ballistic missile defense system. The resolution for this IR sensor is varied parametrically from 100 $\mu$rad to 300 $\mu$rad. A similar IR sensor is hypothesized in [42, pp. 82–83], with a resolution of 100 $\mu$rad. According to [42], this hypothetical IR sensor is intended to perform exoatmospheric discrimination to separate *reentry vehicles* (RVs) from decoys or other objects. The physical basis of the discrimination is the IR flux in different IR bands [42, pp. 83–84]. Such discrimination apparently is the underlying reason for attempting to track objects using the algorithms described in [39]. Resolution is crucial for the correct operation of such tracking and discrimination. In particular, suppose that the IR sensor was roughly 1000 km from the objects of interest. This implies that the spatial resolution is about 1000 km $\times$ 100 $\mu$rad = 100 m. With this sensor resolution, a very simple lightweight device can deny discrimination of RVs from balloon decoys. For example, Figure 6.10 shows an emissive balloon tethered to the RV. Both objects are well within the resolution spot size of the hypothetical IR sensor. The IR spectrum of the RV will be completely dominated by the balloon, thereby negating the discrimination capability of the IR sensor. There is no sophisticated tracking algorithm that can overcome this simple tethered emissive balloon. In contrast to the assumptions underlying Figures 6.8 and 6.9, this is an example of only two objects with exactly the same velocity, in which insufficient sensor resolution is a crucial weakness in the overall system.

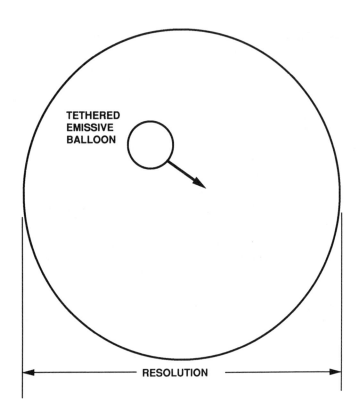

**Figure 6.10** Simple lightweight countermeasure.

It should be emphasized that there are many other versions of such IR sensors for exoatmospheric ballistic missile defense. For example, the sensor postulated in [40, pp. 79–81] has a 5 m aperture with 4 $\mu$m wavelength. This would result in a resolution of roughly $\lambda/D \approx 0.8$ $\mu$rad, assuming that the resolution was limited by diffraction rather than pixel size. This hundredfold improvement in sensor resolution presumably is intended to reduce the effectiveness of the simple idea shown in Figure 6.10.

In summary, resolution is crucial for tracking in a dense multiple-target environment. For many practical systems, resolution is a more serious issue than data association. Therefore, it is surprising that only a handful of papers in the MTT literature mention resolution. This is an example of an MTT issue in which sensor design, waveform design, and signal processing are much more important than data association algorithms.

## 6.5 FUNDAMENTAL LIMITS IN MULTIPLE TARGET TRACKING

A good way to ruin the performance of a tracking filter is to put the wrong data into it. This is the basic problem of tracking in a dense multiple-target environment in many systems using microwave radar, sonar, infrared, and other sensors. The effects of clutter, false alarms, missed detections, unresolved measurements, and target maneuvers make the problem very challenging. The problem is extremely difficult in terms of performance as well as computational complexity. Despite the large number of suboptimal multiple tracking algorithms that have been developed, no nontrivial theoretical bound on performance has been published to date. At a recent meeting of experts on MTT, the lack of theoretical performance bounds was identified as a critical issue. Indeed, one expert noted that: "There is no Cramér-Rao bound for multiple target tracking." The new theory in [8] provides a bound on the error covariance matrix similar to the Cramér-Rao bound. On the other hand, the bound in [8] requires Monte Carlo simulation, whereas a true Cramér-Rao bound, such as reported in [12], does not. The relative merits of the two bounds in [8] and [12] depend on the computational resources available and the specific parameters of a given problem. Both [8] and [12] are lower bounds on the error covariance matrix, and therefore a tighter lower bound could be computed by taking the larger lower bound of the two. In general, it is not obvious *a priori* whether [8] or [12] would result in a larger lower bound.

This section describes a new theoretical bound on estimation accuracy for tracking in a dense multiple-target environment. It is a lower bound on the estimation error covariance matrix, similar to the Cramér-Rao bound for nonlinear estimation problems. Moreover, this bound can be evaluated without implementing the optimal algorithm. The basic problem in MTT is the uncertain origin of measurements. A given measurement might be due to any one of several targets, or no target at all but clutter or noise. Also, a given target might not be detected at a particular time, or its measurement might be unresolved from another target. There are many different hypotheses about the actual origin of measurements. The optimal algorithm must consider all possible hypotheses. The computational complexity of the optimal algorithm is enormous for many practical problems. In contrast, the theoretical bound described here provides an estimate of the best possible tracking performance with a computational complexity that is slightly more than standard Monte Carlo simulations of suboptimal tracking algorithms.

The utility of this new MTT bound is similar to the Cramér-Rao bound. In particular, the best possible tracking performance can be estimated without implementing the optimal algorithm. For example, it is useful to know whether performance is limited by the current suboptimal algorithms or by more fundamental issues. In some important tracking applications, many people believe that future algorithms will substantially improve performance. For the same applications, others believe that the current suboptimal algorithms are close to the best performance achievable. The new theoretical bounds in this chapter can answer such questions.

This new theory can be used to study the fundamental limitations of tracking performance, rather than pursuing an endless quest for better algorithms. On the other hand, for some applications, the use of the new theory could show that there is substantial room for algorithmic improvement.

The fundamental limitations of MTT performance are due to time, energy, sensor aperture size, and bandwidth. Another way to think of fundamental limits is in terms of sensor resolution, sensor measurement accuracy, sensor data rate, signal-to-noise ratio, clutter, target scenario, and the number and geometry of multiple sensors. Optimal tracking and data association algorithms implemented exactly using unlimited throughput and memory cannot overcome these fundamental limitations.

In some applications, the probability of correct data association is the natural performance measure rather than the error covariance matrix. Correct data association means correctly deciding that a sequence of measurement data was generated by one object. This is often referred to as *track purity*. In a dense multiple-target environment, it is easy to confuse one or more measurements from one object with those from another object. Track purity is important for two reasons. First, data association errors degrade the estimation error covariance matrix. Second, data association errors degrade decisions about the tracked objects. Examples of such decisions are friend *versus* foe aircraft, civilian *versus* military aircraft, satellite *versus* missile, reentry vehicle *versus* decoy, and so forth. The theory in [8] and [9] can be used to bound the probability of correct associations.

The new theory in [8] provides a lower bound on the estimation error covariance matrix:

$$E(C) \geq E(C^*)$$

where

$$C = \text{estimation error covariance matrix}$$
$$C^* = \text{covariance matrix computed as shown in Figure 6.11}$$
$$E(\cdot) = \text{expected value of } (\cdot) \text{ with respect to sensor measurements}$$

The matrix $C^*$ is computed with the help of a magic genie as shown in Figure 6.11. The multiple hypothesis tracking algorithm shown in Figure 6.11 is a slight modification of a standard MHT algorithm such as described in [15, 28, 31, and 3, Chapter 10]. The standard MHT algorithm is modified to accept helpful hints from the magic genie; otherwise, the MHT algorithm is unchanged. As noted in Figure 6.11, the MHT algorithm is "suboptimal" in the sense that the total number of hypotheses is limited by standard pruning and combining heuristics. The alternative,

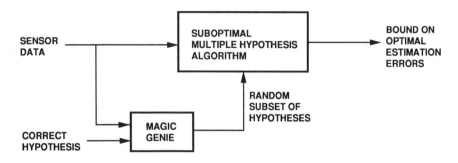

**Figure 6.11** Block diagram of new theoretical lower bound.

an optimal MHT, which has an unlimited number of hypotheses, is completely out of the question owing to its computational complexity.

The suboptimal MHT algorithm is given simulated sensor measurements or real sensor measurements that have been recorded. The MHT algorithm runs off line, and it does not run in real time. Its purpose is to evaluate the best possible system performance, rather than produce such performance.

The magic genie has access to the sensor data, as well as the "correct hypothesis" about measurement-to-measurement association. The genie knows exactly which measurements arise from which targets; the genie also knows which measurements are noise or clutter and which measurements are unresolved. In short, the genie knows everything, but the genie is not allowed to tell the MHT algorithm the whole truth. In particular, the genie supplies the MHT algorithm with a random subset of hypotheses about measurement-to-measurement association, which measurements are due to noise or clutter, and which are unresolved. This random subset of hypotheses must contain the correct hypothesis, but the genie is not allowed to tell the MHT algorithm which hypothesis is correct. If the genie divulged this correct information, then the lower bound on the covariance matrix would degenerate to the trivial bound corresponding to perfectly known origin of measurements. The genie must hide the correct hypothesis within the random subset of other (wrong) hypotheses. This can be done by permuting the order of hypotheses within the subset and by making sure that the number of hypotheses does not give any clue about which one is correct.

Figure 6.12 shows a typical output from the block diagram in Figure 6.11. The lower bound corresponds to $E(C^*)$, which is computed by the MHT algorithm using help from the magic genie. A real-time, on-line MHT algorithm cannot possibly do better than this, because it does not have any help from the magic genie. This is the intuitive "proof" of the inequality $E(C) \geq E(C^*)$. For example, an on-line, real-time MHT algorithm might not consider the correct hypothesis at all. Moreover, even if it did, the correct hypothesis would be competing with an enormous number

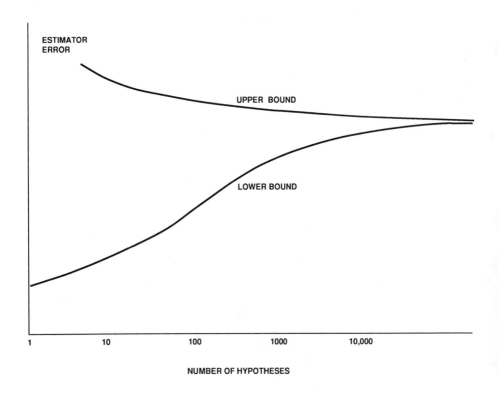

**Figure 6.12** Theoretical bounds.

of other hypotheses, and it would not be obvious which one actually is correct. The genie tells the MHT algorithm which hypotheses might be correct, and thereby limits the total number of hypotheses that must be considered.

The upper bound in Figure 6.12 can be produced by a MHT algorithm that considers a limited number of hypotheses but without any help from the genie. This is exactly what a practical on-line, real-time MHT algorithm would do. The performance of the optimal MHT algorithm, by definition, is no worse than any practical MHT algorithm, hence the upper bound in Figure 6.12. A precise mathematical statement of the new theoretical lower bound is given in [8].

As shown in Figure 6.12, the upper and lower bounds should converge as the number of hypotheses is increased. The upper bound is decreasing because the sub-optimal MHT algorithm is getting better and better as the number of hypotheses is increased. Likewise, the lower bound is increasing, because the magic genie is providing less and less help to the MHT algorithm. If the genie gave all hypotheses to the MHT algorithm, this would be no help at all! The rate at which the upper and lower bounds converge depends on the specific application. We implicitly assume in Figure 6.12 that the hypotheses are selected in a way to speed convergence. One good approach is to use the same pruning and combining heuristics used in standard MHT algorithms: discard the unlikely hypotheses and keep the most likely ones. This strategy speeds convergence for both the upper bound and lower bound.

As noted earlier, in some applications the error covariance matrix is less important than the probability of misassociation. Misassociated data can severely degrade decisions about objects. For example, the underlying reason for tracking often is to support decisions such as civilian *versus* military aircraft, friend *versus* foe aircraft, satellite *versus* missile, or reentry vehicle *versus* decoy. As shown in [9], the new lower bound in Figures 6.11 and 6.12 can be used to bound the probability of data misassociation. The way to do this is to view a decision problem as an estimation problem in disguise. This idea is due to Lainiotis [23], who showed that estimating the indicator function of a set is equivalent to the Bayesian decision rule about membership in the set. Using Lainiotis's idea, the estimation error bound can be used to bound the probability of data misassociation. The other required ingredient is the Bhattacharyya bound [21]. In summary, combining the results in [8, 23 and 21] produces the bound on data misassociation probability described in [9].

On the other hand, we could argue that the theory in [9] is unnecessary and that [8] is sufficient by itself to bound the effect of data misassociation. In particular, we always can include the decision-making variables as part of the state vector, $x$. Errors in $x$ due to misassociation or unresolved measurements are included in the lower bound on covariance matrix, $E(C^*)$. Most engineers think of the state vector as including only *kinematic variables* (KVs), such as position and velocity, but it is easy to include *nonkinematic variables* (NKV) in the state vector. For example, statistics of radar cross section (such as average, variance, maximum values) can be included in the state vector. For infrared sensors, the radiometric variables (emissivity area, apparent temperature, flux density in one or more IR bands, time derivative of apparent temperature, *et cetera*) could be included in the state vector. A third example applies to both radar and IR sensors, and the key decision-making variable is kinematic: drag coefficient to discriminate RVs from decoys or other objects. In summary, there is no need to use the theory in [9] to explicitly bound the probability of misassociation, but rather the theory in [8] is sufficient.

There are five reasons for embedding nonkinematic decision-making variables in the state vector. First, there is an elegant method to embed decision problems into a dynamical estimation context ([18] and [37]). Second, real-time decision rules benefit from quantifying the accuracy of the decision-making variables; propagating an error covariance matrix for the NKVs, which includes the effects of unresolved and misassociated measurements, accomplishes this. Third, in some applications the dynamics of the KVs are coupled to the dynamics of the NKVs; explicitly modeling this dynamical coupling often improves decision-making performance. Fourth, standard techniques to mitigate the effects of data misassociations can be applied to benefit the estimates of NKVs. For example, PDA, JPDA, MHT, or other algorithms can be applied to estimate NKVs as well as KVs. Fifth, inclusion of NKVs in the state vector generally improves the data association performance; this is the case for a simple nearest neighbor chi-square test, as well as MHT, PDA, JPDA, and assignment algorithms. The NKV measurement values help recognize which data should associate with which track. The basic method of embedding decision making into a dynamical estimation context is succinctly explained in [18, p. 250]. For Gauss-Markov models of NKVs, the conditional probability density needed for decision making is propagated by a Kalman filter. The details of this idea were worked out in [37].

Furthermore, we can argue that quantifying the probability of misassociation does not address the fundamental issue of quantifying the decision-making performance. In particular, for a given application, some types of data misassociation are more damaging than others. For example, if a radar uses the average *radar cross section* (RCS) to discriminate RVs from decoys, and if the RCS measurements themselves are used to aid the data association process, then the particular data misassociated are much less damaging to the average RCS statistic than an arbitrary value of measured RCS. This complex interaction between misassociation and NKV estimation accuracy is fully captured in the methodology of Figures 6.11 and 6.12, whereas this complex interaction is lost in factoring the problem into two pieces: compute the probability of misassociation, and attempt to estimate the decision-making performance by using the results of the first step. This issue is not well understood by most system engineers. Moreover, the beneficial effects of using PDA, JPDA, or MHT to mitigate the effects of misassociation are not captured by factoring the total calculation, whereas the good effects of MHT are automatically included in the methodology in [8].

In summary, although it is possible to explicitly compute the probability of misassociation using the theory derived in [9], the simpler and more direct approach of embedding the NKVs into the state vector has five significant advantages, and it captures the complex interactions inherent in this problem. The simple direct approach uses the theory in [8] as illustrated in Figures 6.11 and 6.12, whereas the indirect approach factors the problem into two pieces using the theory in [9]. A significant amount of information may be lost, however, in the factorization.

This section presented a new theoretical bound on MTT performance, which can be used to quantify the fundamental limitations of MTT. No clever algorithm or superfast processing capability can improve this performance. Performance is limited by the sensor characteristics and the target, clutter, and noise. This bound is analogous to the well-known Cramér-Rao bound used by system engineers to quantify performance limits in nonlinear estimation problems. The new MTT bound and the Cramér-Rao bound share a number of interesting properties, as explained in [8]. The main utility of the new MTT bound in [8] is to understand the fundamental limits of MTT performance, rather than pursue an endless quest for better algorithms and faster processors.

## APPENDIX 6.A: PROBABILITIES OF RESOLUTION AND DATA ASSOCIATION

This appendix summarizes some useful formulas to evaluate the probabilities of resolution and data association for $m$-dimensional measurements. This theory was used in this chapter to produce Figures 6.8 and 6.9 for the special case of $m = 1$.

Suppose that two objects $A$ and $B$ are resolved if object $B$ is outside of a volume, $V$, centered on object $A$. This is a rather crude approximation to the physical resolution characteristics of real sensors; however, this simple model yields tractable formulas that provide valuable insight into system design. Further assume that objects are distributed randomly and independently according to a Poisson distribution. The probability that $n$ objects are within a volume $V$ therefore is

$$P_v = \frac{(\lambda V)^n}{n!} \exp(-\lambda V) \tag{6.A1}$$

in which $\lambda$ is the mean object density. Consider any given object ($A$), and ask what is the probability that no other object is within the resolution volume $V$, centered on object $A$. Evaluating $P_V$ for $n =$ zero results in $P_V = \exp(-\lambda V)$. This formula is valid for $m$-dimensional measurements for any integer value of $m = 1, 2, 3, \ldots$ For example, in the one-dimensional case considered in this chapter, $V = 2$ RES, $\lambda = 1/s$, and $r =$ RES$/s$, and therefore $P_V = \exp(-2r)$.

An extremely simple and useful formula for the probability of correct measurement-to-track association is given in [27]. In particular, we assume that an optimal single-scan assignment algorithm (e.g., Munkres's algorithm) is used to associate measurements with tracks. The probability of correct association is approximated by the formula $P_c \approx \exp(-CN)$, where $N =$ average number of objects within the one-sigma ellipsoid corresponding to the innovations covariance matrix

$$C = 2^{m-1} \pi^{-1/2} \Gamma\left(\frac{m + 1}{2}\right) \tag{6.A2}$$

where $\Gamma(\cdot)$ is the gamma function of $(\cdot)$.

For example, this theory was applied to the special case of $m = 1$ in this chapter, in which case $P_c \approx \exp(-N/\sqrt{\pi})$. For $m = 2$, $P_c \approx \exp(-N)$.

The work reported in [27] has several other simple but accurate back-of-the-envelope formulas for tracking performance in a dense multiple-target environment, and it is highly recommended.

# REFERENCES

[1]   M. Athans and F.C. Schweppe, "On Optimal Waveform Design via Control Theoretic Concepts," *Information and Control,* Vol. 10, 1967, pp. 335–337.

[2]   Y. Bar-Shalom and T.E. Fortmann, *Tracking and Data Association,* Academic Press, Orlando, FL, 1988.

[3]   S.S. Blackman, *Multiple-Target Tracking with Radar Applications,* Artech House, Dedham, MA, 1986.

[4]   K.C. Chang and Y. Bar-Shalom, "Joint Probabilistic Data Association for Multitarget Tracking with Possibly Unresolved Measurements and Maneuvers," *IEEE Trans. on Automatic Control,* Vol. AC-29, No. 7, July 1984.

[5]   C.E. Cook and M. Bernfeld, *Radar Signals,* Academic Press, New York, 1967.

[6]   J.P. Costas, "A Study of a Class of Detection Waveforms Having Nearly Ideal Range-Doppler Ambiguity Properties," *IEEE Proceedings,* Vol. 72, No. 8, August 1984.

[7]   F.E. Daum, "Angular Estimation Accuracy for Unresolved Targets," *Proc. American Control Conf.,* 1987.

[8]   F.E. Daum, "Bounds on Performance for Multiple Target Tracking," *IEEE Trans. on Automatic Control,* Vol. AC-35, No. 4, April 1990.

[9]   F.E. Daum, "Bounds on Track Purity for Multiple Target Tracking," *Proc. IEEE Conf. on Decision and Control,* December 1989.

[10]  F.E. Daum, "Doppler Estimation Accuracy of Linear FM Waveforms," *IEEE Int. Radar Conf,* 1985.

[11]  F.E. Daum, "New Exact Nonlinear Filters," J.C. Spall (ed.) *Bayesian Analysis of Time Series and Dynamic Models,* Marcel Dekker, New York, 1988, Chapter 8.

[12]  F.E. Daum, "Cramér-Rao Bound for Multiple Target Tracking," *Proc. SPIE Conf.,* Vol. 1481, April 1991.

[13]  J. Freedman, "Resolution in Radar Systems," *Proc. IRE,* 1951.

[14]  W.F. Gabriel, "Superresolution of Coherent Sources by Adaptive Array Techniques," *IEEE Int. Radar Conf.,* 1980.

[15]  I.R. Goodman, "A General Model for the Multiple Target Correlation and Tracking Problem," *Proc. 18th IEEE Conf. on Decision and Control,* Fort Lauderdale, FL, December 1979, pp. 383–388.

[16]  H. Heffes and S. Horing, "Optimal Allocation of Tracking Pulses for an Array Radar," *IEEE Trans. on Automatic Control,* Vol. AC-15, No. 1, February 1970.

[17]  C.W. Helstrom, "The Resolution of Signals in White Gaussian Noise," *Proc. IRE,* 1955.

[18]  Y.C. Ho and A.K. Agrawala, "On Pattern Classification Algorithms: Introduction and Survey," *Proc. IEEE,* Vol. 56, December 1968.

[19]  J.L. Jenkins and S.F. Rudin, "Single-Frame Velocity Estimation," *SPIE Proc.,* Vol. 1096, 1989.

[20]  A.L. Kachelmyer, "Laser Radar Acquisition and Tracking," *SPIE Conf. Proc.,* Vol. 1103, March 1989.

[21]  T. Kailath, "The Divergence and Bhattacharyya Distance Measures in Signal Selection," *IEEE Trans. on Communications Technology,* February 1967, pp. 52–60.

[22]  J.R. Klauder, "The Design of Radar Signals Having Both High Range Resolution and High Velocity Resolution," *Bell System Tech. J.,* Vol. 39, 1960.

[23]  D.G. Lainiotis, "On a General Relationship Between Estimation, Detection, and the Bhattacharyya Coefficient," *IEEE Trans. on Information Theory,* July 1969, pp. 504–505.

[24]  B.L. Lewis, F.F. Kretschmer, Jr., and W.W. Shelton, *Aspects of Radar Signal Processing,* Artech House, Dedham, MA, 1986.

[25]  R.J. McAulay and J.R. Johnson, "Optimal Mismatched Filter Design for Radar Ranging, Detection, and Resolution," *IEEE Trans. on Information Theory,* Vol. IT-17, No. 6, November 1971.

[26]  R.K. Mehra, "Optimization of Measurement Schedules and Sensor Design for Linear Dynamic Systems," *IEEE Trans. on Automatic Control,* Vol AC-21, No. 1, February 1976.

[27]  S. Mori, K.C. Chang, C.Y. Chong, and K.P. Dunn, "Tracking Performance Evaluation—Track Accuracy in Dense Target Environments," Proc. SPIE 1990 Tech. Symp. on Aerospace Sensing, Orlando, FL, April 1990.

[28]  S. Mori, C.-Y. Chong, E. Tse, and R.P. Wishner, "Tracking and Classifying Multiple Targets Without *A Priori* Identification," *IEEE Trans. on Automatic Controls,* Vol. AC-31, May 1986, pp. 401–409.

[29]  N.J. Nilsson, "On the Optimum Range Resolution of Radar Signals in Noise," *IRE Trans. on Information Theory,* October 1961, pp. 245–253.

[30]  J.W. Parnell, "The Probability of Range Resolution of Closely Spaced Radar Targets," *IEEE Int. Radar Conf.,* 1980.

[31]  D.B. Reid, "An Algorithm for Tracking Multiple Targets," *IEEE Trans. on Automatic Controls,* Vol. AC-24, December 1979, pp. 843–854.

[32]  A.W. Rihaczek, *Principles of High-Resolution Radar,* Mark Resources, Marina del Rey, CA, 1977.

[33]  T.G. Robertazzi and S.C. Schwartz, "An Accelerated Sequential Algorithm for Producing D-Optimal Designs," *SIAM J. on Scientific and Statistical Computing,* Vol. 10, No. 2, March 1989.

[34]  W.D. Rummler, "Clutter Suppression by Complex Weighting of Coherent Pulse Trains," *IEEE Trans. on Aerospace and Electronic Systems,* Vol. AES-2, 1966.

[35]  S.M. Sherman, "Complex Indicated Angles Applied to Unresolved Radar Targets and Multipath," *IEEE Aerospace and Electronic Systems Trans.,* Vol. AES-7, No. 1, 1971.

[36]  J.H. Taylor, "The Cramér-Rao Estimation Error Lower Bound Computation for Deterministic Nonlinear Systems," *IEEE Trans. on Automatic Control,* Vol. AC-24, April 1979, pp. 343–344.

[37]  C.W. Therrien, "A Sequential Approach to Target Discrimination," *IEEE Trans. on Aerospace and Electronic Systems,* Vol. AES-14, May 1978.

[38]  G.V. Trunk and J.D. Wilson, "Track Initiation of Occasionally Unresolved Radar Targets," *IEEE Trans. on Aerospace and Electronic Systems,* Vol. AES-17, No. 1, January 1981.

[39]  M.J. Tsai, L.C. Youens, and K.P. Dunn, "Track Initiation in a Dense Target Environment Using Multiple Sensors," *SPIE Proc.,* Vol. 1096, 1989.

[40]  Y. Velikhov, R. Sagdeev, and A. Kokoshin (eds.), *Weaponry in Space: The Dilemna of Security,* trans. A. Repyev, Mir Publishers, Moscow, 1986.

[41]  A.J. Viterbi, "Error Bounds for Convolutional Codes and an Asymptotically Optimum Decoding Algorithm," *IEEE Trans. on Information Theory,* April 1967, pp. 262–263.

[42]  S. Weiner, "Systems and Technology," A.B. Carter and D.N. Schwartz (eds.), *Ballistic Missile Defense,* The Brookings Institute, Washington, DC, 1984, Chapter 3.

[43]  M.B. Zarrop, *Optimal Experiment Design for Dynamic System Identification,* Springer Verlag, 1979.

## Chapter 7
# PERFORMANCE ANALYSIS OF OPTIMAL DATA ASSOCIATION WITH APPLICATIONS TO MULTIPLE TARGET TRACKING

*Shozo Mori, Kuo-Chu Chang, and Chee-Yee Chong*

**Advanced Decision Systems**
**Mountain View, CA**

## 7.1  INTRODUCTION

The *data association problem* is one of the simplest forms of estimation problems involving *random point sets*. A *random set* is a random element, each sample of which is a set rather than a real number (a random variable), a vector (a random vector), or a function (a random function or field). By a *random point set,* we mean a random set, each sample of which is a finite set of points in a Euclidean space or a hybrid space.[1] Many forms of information can be modeled by random point sets. A typical example may be a set of returns from a radar or a set of observed features in an optical image.

The expected number of points (or objects) or the expected density of the points may determine the nature of an estimation problem expressed in terms of random point sets. When the number of points is enormous or the density is extremely high, there may be no other way to characterize the random sets than through their "group" parameters, such as the centroid or the extent parameters, or

This work is based on research supported by SDIO Contract F19628-85-C-0002. The views expressed are those of the authors and do not reflect the official policy or position of the United States government. The authors are indebted to Dr. Keh-Ping Dunn and Dr. Ming Tsai of M.I.T. Lincoln Laboratory for valuable comments and discussions and are grateful to the editor, Y. Bar-Shalom, for his careful review of our draft.
[1] By a hybrid space, we mean the direct-product of a Euclidean space and a discrete (finite) set.

some other statistical parameters. In such a case, the estimation problem can be expressed in the "traditional" form; that is, problems in terms of random vectors. In another extreme, each point in a random point set may be clearly identified (or "marked") without any ambiguity, and any estimation problem may be reduced into a set of problems of the same nature; that is, in the traditional form. In some intermediate cases estimation concerning individual points is meaningful but there is ambiguity about the identity of each point; hence, the problems are in "nontraditional" forms.

Data association problems appear at least in two applications areas, *multitarget tracking* [9, 5] and *computer vision* [2], both of which have recently attracted rapidly growing interest. A typical problem in multitarget tracking is to assign *tracks,* or a set of estimates of dynamical states of objects, to a set of *measurements* (i.e., a "snapshot") generated by a sensing device such as a radar or an optical sensor. Such a problem sometimes is referred to as the *correlation problem.* In computer vision, a similar problem in which imagery features (such as edges and lines) are associated with respect to their origins is called the *correspondence problem* [1]. When computer vision (or image understanding) is considered as a pattern recognition problem, a similar problem is called the *labeling problem,* in which a set of *objects* in a scene is to be assigned to a set of *labels* [17]. In these applications, a unit of data is a set of points (rather than a vector of variables), which in general are provided by a signal processor connected to a sensing device or an optical image analyzer, as a set of *detections* or *perceived image features.* Such a set, as a unit of information, is often called a *data set, frame,* or *scan.*

The common aspect of the data association problems in these applications will be expressed as a mathematical problem statement in Section 7.2. Although this formulation may not cover all possible variations of the data association problem, it will capture at least the essence or the common thread. Many algorithms have been developed to solve the data association problem. It is not our purpose, however, to discuss or compare such algorithms. Instead, our goal is to estimate a tight upper bound on the performance of such algorithms; that is, to predict the performance of an optimal data association algorithm. This is equivalent to characterizing a given data association problem by its degree of difficulty, as a function of given parameters such as the data density and the observation errors. The importance of this kind of analysis is twofold. First, it may eliminate the necessity for generally expensive (time-consuming) Monte Carlo simulations to measure the performance of algorithms. This may become more important when such performance analysis leads to a method for predicting the performance of a composite data processing algorithm (such as a multiple target tracking algorithm we will discuss in Section 7.6) relying on a series of data association problems. Second, this kind of performance analysis provides a reference point with which the performance of "suboptimal" algorithms can be compared. This is important when run-time constraints do not allow implementation of any optimal algorithm, and hence, the run-time and performance trade-offs become crucial. Our goal is to develop an analytic model that can relate the performance of optimal data association to relevant parameters. In Section 7.3, we show that in fact there is a very simple analytic model, which we may call an *exponential law,* to predict the performance of optimal data association with satisfactory accuracy.

Figure 7.1 is meant to illustrate the nature of the data association problem. In Figure 7.1, two frames of data (i.e., two random point sets) are shown. They can be considered two "distorted" pictures of one "true" pattern of two-dimensional points. In other words, each point in each frame originates from a "true" point that generates one point in one frame and another in another frame, in a one-to-one fashion. The position of each point in each frame deviates from its "true" position because of some "measurement error." The data association problem is to identify a pair of points, one from each of the two sets, that share the same origin. The example shown in Figure 7.1 is an "easy" problem and human eyes will have little difficulty in identifying pairs of points originating from the same "objects," probably through random patterns which appear identical in both sets. One easy way is to make copies of the two images on transparent sheets and overlay them. Figure 7.2 shows a similar pair of random point sets but with larger measurement errors. Now it is not so "easy" to perform data association. Many local patterns are so distorted that matching them becomes difficult. Both examples in Figures 7.1 and 7.2 have the same density in the average sense; that is, the same number of points in the identical total area. The only difference is the average magnitude of the measurement errors. This suggests to us that the "difficulty" of the data association problem may not depend on the object density in the absolute sense; rather, it is determined by the object density relative to the measurement error magnitudes. Actually this is exactly what we will show in Section 7.3; that is, the association performance can be

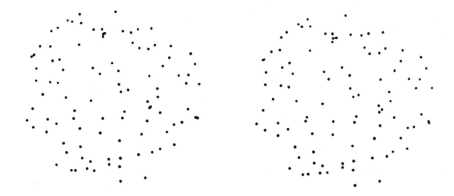

**Figure 7.1** Data association problem—low object density.

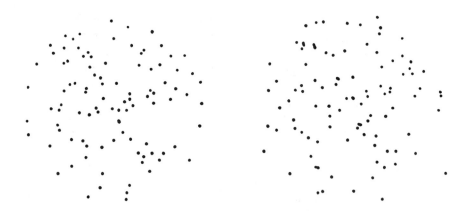

**Figure 7.2** Data association problem—high object density.

expressed as a function of the *object density normalized by the measurement error variance.*

We may imagine that each pair of point sets shown in Figures 7.1 and 7.2 is a pair of observations meant to provide a stereo vision [35]. In such a case, the ultimate goal is to estimate the "depth" (i.e., the three-dimensional position) of each object recognized by each pairing of points. Likewise, in many estimation problems involving random point sets, an ultimate goal often is to estimate the "state" of each object based on a result of optimal data association. Therefore, we would like to express the performance of such estimation, *state estimation*, as a part of the data association performance. When the data association performance is perfect, the (state) estimation problem becomes one in which a random vector is estimated based on a vector measurement; that is, a traditional estimation problem. If the data association performance is not perfect, i.e., if there are some misassociations, however, the performance of the estimation may be degraded. In Section 7.4, we show that we can express the effects of misassociations on the estimation performance by a very simple expression, which we call the *linear-times-exponential law.* Up to Section 7.4, we treat rather simplified data association problems in each of which there is a "true" one-to-one correspondence between the two given point sets. In reality, for one reason or another, there may be extraneous points in one or both point sets in a problem. Such cases are treated in Section 7.5.

The study we present here was motivated by our desire to develop simple yet reliable (hence useful) analytic models that relate the performance of multiple-target tracking in dense target environments to key threat or sensor parameters. The application of the analysis in Sections 7.2 through 7.5 to multiple-target tracking is presented in Section 7.6. In this section, our focus is to predict average *track purity,* defined as the average percentage of the correctly associated observations contained in a track (as in [5, 11, 12]). This kind of analysis is very important when a final goal of object tracking is to identify or classify each object; and such object classification is possible only after successfully tracking each object, by measuring distinguishable features apparent only in time-series data. We describe two models that provide the necessary parameters to predict the performance of the track-to-measurement association problem in each frame (or scan). One is a model to predict the object density as a function of time, and the other predicts the average track accuracy at each epoch as necessary.

## 7.2 PROBLEM STATEMENT

Let us consider a data association problem with the two random point sets in a Euclidean space, $\mathcal{R}^m$, with a given dimension $m > 0$. We assume the two sets have the same cardinality[2] $N$ for the moment.[3] Let an enumeration of the members of the first random point set $Y$ be[4] $(y_i)_{i=1}^N$ and, for each $i$, let

$$y_i = x_i + u_i \tag{7.1}$$

where $x_i$ and $u_i$ are both $m$-dimensional random vectors. Let an enumeration $(z_j)_{j=1}^N$ of the second random point set $Z$ be modeled as

$$z_{q(i)} = x_i + v_i \tag{7.2}$$

where each $v_i$ is an $m$-dimensional random vector and $q$ is a random permutation on the set, $\{1, \ldots, N\}$. Because $Y$ and $Z$ are random point sets, the enumeration of each set is *totally arbitrary*. The relative difference of the enumeration for the two sets is modeled by the random permutation $q$. In eqs. (7.1) and (7.2), $x_i$ can be considered as a "true" position of each object $i$ in $\mathcal{R}^m$, and $u_i$ and $v_i$ are "measurement errors" contained in $Y$ and $Z$.

Throughout Sections 7.2 to 7.5, we will maintain the following assumptions.

*Assumption* [A1]: The error vectors, $u_i$ and $v_i$, are zero-mean Gaussian vectors, *i.e.*, $\mathcal{E}(u_i) = \mathcal{E}(v_i) = 0$, with variance matrices[5]

$$\mathcal{E}(u_i u_i^T) = Q \quad \text{and} \quad \mathcal{E}(v_i v_i^T) = R \tag{7.3}$$

---

[2]That is, the number of members (elements) of a set
[3]We will consider the cases where the cardinalities are not the same in Section 7.5.
[4]$(\xi_i)_{i=1}^n$ is a shorthand expression of a finite sequence, $(\xi_1, \xi_2, \ldots, \xi_n)$, of real numbers or vectors $\xi_i$, with length $n$.
[5]The *mathematical expectation operator* is denoted by $\mathcal{E}(\cdot)$. We will also use the *variance operator* $\mathcal{V}(\cdot)$ defined by $\mathcal{V}(\xi) \triangleq \mathcal{E}((\xi - \mathcal{E}(\xi))(\xi - \mathcal{E}(\xi))^T)$ for a multi-dimensional random vector $\xi = [\xi_1, \xi_2, \ldots]^T$. For a vector or matrix $X$ by $X^T$ we denote the transpose of $X$. The $ij$-element $V_{ij}$ of the *variance matrix* $V$ of a random vector $\xi$ is the variance of $i$th element $\xi_i$ when $i = j$, and is the covariance of the $i$th element $\xi_i$ and the $j$th element $\xi_j$ when $i \neq j$.

for all[6] $i$, such that

$$S = Q + R \qquad (7.4)$$

is strictly positive definite.

*Assumption* [A2]: The permutation is *totally random* in the sense that all of its $N!$ realizations are equally probable[7]; that is,

$$P(q) = \frac{1}{N!} \qquad (7.5)$$

*Assumption* [A3]: Assume that $y_1, \ldots, y_N, u_1, \ldots, u_N, v_1, \ldots, v_N$ and $q$ are all independent from each other, and $(y_i)_{i=1}^N$ is a system of *independent, identically distributed* random vectors with a common distribution that is uniform on an $m$-ball[8] with a large enough radius $r$.

At a casual glance, the following alternative to Assumption [A3] may look more "natural."

*Assumption* [A3′]: Assume that $x_1, \ldots, x_N, u_1, \ldots, u_N, v_1, \ldots, v_N$ and $q$ are all independent of each other, and $(x_i)_{i=1}^N$ is a system of *independent, identically distributed* random vectors with a common distribution that is uniform on an $m$-ball with a large enough radius $r$.

The main reason why we have chosen [A3] rather than [A3′] is that we were motivated by multiple-target tracking. In such a context as well as other contexts in which point-set data are processed in a recursive way, we implicitly assume that, for object $i$, the "true" position $x_i$ in the observation space $\mathcal{R}^m$ is a (in general nonlinear) projection[9] of another higher-dimensional random vector $\xi_i$; that is, the state of the object $i$. With such a state vector, each $y_i$ can be thought of as the conditional expectation of the projection $x_i$ of each state $\xi_i$ onto the measurement state $\mathcal{R}^m$, based on

---

[6]Namely, the uniform magnitude of errors in a given random set, $Y$ or $Z$, is assumed. As apparent in the next section, relaxation of this assumption makes the subsequent analysis very difficult. We may use a *local average* when, as in some applications, this assumption does not hold.

[7]We will use $P(\cdot)$ to denote the probability measure on the underlying probability space, or a probability distribution, its density, probability mass, *et cetera*, as appropriate. The precise meaning should be apparent from the context in which it is used. We also use a similar notation $P(\cdot \mid \cdot)$ for conditional probabilities.

[8]An $m$-ball centered at the origin with radius $r$ is the set of all the $m$-dimensional vectors whose Euclidean norms are less than or equal to $r$. An $m$-ball is an arbitrary translation of it, but we assume it is centered at the origin unless noted otherwise.

[9]By a projection, we mean a composite image of a *linear projection operator* and a (in general) nonlinear coordinate transformation, generally reducing the dimension.

certain information accumulated in the "past." On the other hand, the second set $Z$ can be considered as a "new" conditionally independent observation. In general, a least-square (minimum mean-square error) linear estimate is orthogonal to its estimation error. Assumption [A3] is a stronger version of this orthogonality (see *Remark 1* at the end of this section for a related discussion). With this background, we call the first set $Y$ the *prediction set* and the second set $Z$ the *measurement set*, and their members *predictions* and *measurements*, respectively. Furthermore, borrowing a term from the innovations theory [18], we call the (strictly) positive definite matrix $S$ defined by (7.4) the *innovations variance matrix*.

With our mathematical model defined by (7.1) and (7.2) with assumptions [A1] through [A3], we can state our data association problem as a problem of estimating the random permutation (i.e., association) $q$ given by the two random point sets $Y$ and $Z$. Because of the Gaussian assumption [A1] and the independence assumption [A3], we have[10]

$$P[(y_i)_{i=1}^N, (z_i)_{i=1}^N | q] = P[(z_i)_{i=1}^N | (y_i)_{i=1}^N, q]P[(y_i)_{i=1}^N]$$

$$= P[(y_i)_{i=1}^N][\det(2\pi S)]^{-1/2} \exp\left[-\frac{1}{2}\sum_{i=1}^N \|z_{q(i)} - y_i\|_{S^{-1}}^2\right]$$

$$(7.6)$$

assuming $N$ is given. Because the permutation $q$ is totally random ([A2]) and the distribution of each $y_i$ is uniform, that is, $P[(y_i)_{i=1}^N]$ is constant ([A3]), a most probable (maximum *a posteriori* probability) estimate as well as a maximum likelihood estimate of $q$ *minimizes*, over all the permutations, the *assignment cost*, defined as

$$J(q) = \sum_{i=1}^N \|z_{q(i)} - y_i\|_{S^{-1}}^2 \tag{7.7}$$

which is the well-known sum-of-$\chi^2$ data association metric. The *a posteriori* probability, $P(q | Y, Z)$, can be obtained by normalizing (7.6) over all the possible realizations of $q$.

It is interesting to note that the problem for obtaining an optimal estimate $\hat{q}$ that minimizes the functional (7.7) is a classical integer linear programming problem, known as the *assignment problem* [26] in operation research; for example, a problem of assigning $N$ men to $N$ jobs. Many algorithms have been developed, including a form of primal-dual method [26] (which has been constantly "improved"), heuristic "suboptimal" algorithms (e.g., A*-algorithm [16]), and a neural-net approach ([32]). As mentioned earlier, it is not our goal here to investigate

---

[10]By $\|x\|_A$, we denote a semi-norm of a vector $x$ in a Euclidean space defined by a nonnegative symmetric matrix $A$ as $\|x\|_A = \sqrt{x^T A x}$. When $A = I$; i.e., the identity matrix, $\|\cdot\|_I$ is the usual Euclidean norm and denoted as $\|\cdot\|$. We should remember that the transpose of a vector or a matrix $X$ is denoted by $X^T$.

various algorithms. Instead, we are interested in predicting the performance of optimal data association (i.e., an optimal $\hat{q}$ that minimizes the association cost defined by (7.7), in terms of the average probability for each object $i$ being associated with the correct measurement $q(i)$,

$$P_C = P\{\hat{q}(i) = q(i)\} \tag{7.8}$$

which we call the *correct association probability*. The cardinality $N$ may be random but it will be immediately known once the prediction and measurement sets are given. Nonetheless, we would like to know the "average" performance "beforehand" when only the expected value of $N$ is known. Whenever a distribution on $N$ is needed, we assume that it is a Poisson distribution with a known mean $\nu$.

*Remark 1*

The alternative assumption [A3'] is more appropriate in more "symmetric" situations where the two sets $Y$ and $Z$ actually are two conditionally (given the values of $x_i$) independent observation sets. With [A3'], the distribution $P(y_i)$ no longer is uniform but is the convolution of the uniform distribution (of $x_i$) and a Gaussian distribution (with the variance matrix $Q$). However, when the variance matrix $Q$ is small compared to the radius $r$ of the uniform distribution assumed for the values of $x_i$ (with [A3'] instead of [A3]), the distribution of $P[(y_i)_{i=1}^N]$ in (7.5) still can be considered (approximately) as a constant and the objective function (7.7) is still valid. The association performance with respect to a particular object may depend on its relative position within a group: if an object is located near the edge of a group, the chance of its being associated with the correct measurement is higher, sometimes substantially higher, than if it were in the middle of a group. However, we would like to average out such an effect, by considering a large number of objects spreading out over a large area. In other words, we consider a large object group extent radius $r$ and a large number $N$ of objects, parameterizing the situations by the object density. Thus the difference in the distribution of $P(y_i)$ due to the choice of the two different assumptions [A3] and [A3'] should be insignificant. The results shown in the subsequent sections depend critically on the assumption of the uniform distribution of $P(y_i)$. For the reason mentioned earlier, however, they should not be affected significantly by the choice between the two assumptions, [A3] and [A3'].

## 7.3 PROBABILITY OF CORRECT ASSOCIATION

The expressions for the exact evaluation of the correct association probability, defined by (7.8), may be very complex because the probabilistic properties of an optimal estimate of the "true" data association $q$ cannot be expressed in a simple form.

On the other hand, our goal is to obtain a simple expression as a function of a few key parameters. To reconcile this dilemma, we must employ an effective approximation. To do this, we start with an analysis with only two objects, then with $N$ objects, and finally with a Poisson distribution on the number of objects. The appropriateness of our approximation will be proven through Monte Carlo simulations at the end of this section.

## Two-Object Association Problem

Let us consider two objects, $i$ and $j$ ($i \neq j$). An optimal data association $\hat{q}$ is correct, that is, $\hat{q}(i) = q(i)$ and $\hat{q}(j) = q(j)$, if and only if the cost of the correct association $q$ is less than that of the incorrect association,

$$
\begin{aligned}
\Delta J_{ij} &\triangleq \|z_{q(i)} - y_i\|_{S^{-1}}^2 + \|z_{q(j)} - y_j\|_{S^{-1}}^2 \\
&\quad - [\|z_{q(j)} - y_i\|_{S^{-1}}^2 + \|z_{q(i)} - y_j\|_{S^{-1}}^2] \\
&= -2(z_{q(i)} - z_{q(j)})^T S^{-1}(y_i - y_j) \leq 0
\end{aligned}
\tag{7.9}
$$

or, in other words, if and only if

$$
(\Delta u_{ij} - \Delta v_{ij})^T S^{-1} \Delta y_{ij} \leq \|\Delta y_{ij}\|_{S^{-1}}^2
\tag{7.10}
$$

where

$$
\begin{aligned}
\Delta u_{ij} &\triangleq u_i - u_j \\
\Delta v_{ij} &\triangleq v_i - v_j \\
\Delta y_{ij} &\triangleq y_i - y_j
\end{aligned}
\tag{7.11}
$$

Because $\Delta u_{ij}$, $\Delta v_{ij}$, and $\Delta y_{ij}$ are independent ([A3]), the correct association probability can be calculated as[11]

$$
\begin{aligned}
P_C &= P\{\hat{q}(i) = q(i)\} = P\{\Delta J_{ij} \leq 0\} \\
&= P\{(\Delta u_{ij} - \Delta v_{ij})^T S^{-1} \Delta y_{ij} \leq \|\Delta y_{ij}\|_{S^{-1}}^2\} \\
&= \mathcal{E}(P\{(\Delta u_{ij} - \Delta v_{ij})^T S^{-1} \Delta y_{ij} \leq \|\Delta y_{ij}\|_{S^{-1}}^2 \mid \Delta y_{ij}\}) \\
&= \mathcal{E}(\text{erf}(\alpha_{ij}))
\end{aligned}
\tag{7.12}
$$

---

[11] The term $\text{erf}(\cdot)$ is the error function defined as $\text{erf}(c) \triangleq \dfrac{1}{\sqrt{2\pi}} \displaystyle\int_{-\infty}^{c} e^{-t^2/2} \, dt$. By $\text{erfc}(\cdot)$ we mean its complement, defined by $\text{erfc}(c) \triangleq 1 - \text{erf}(c)$.

where

$$\alpha_{ij} \triangleq \frac{\|\Delta y_{ij}\|_{S^{-1}}}{\sqrt{2}} \tag{7.13}$$

First, let us consider the case where $y_i$ is at the origin. By [A3], $y_j$ is distributed uniformly on the $m$-ball with radius $r$. Hence we have

$$\mathcal{E}[\mathrm{erf}(\alpha_{ij}) \mid y_i = 0] = \frac{\int_{\|\Delta y_{ij}\| \leqslant r} \mathrm{erf}(\alpha_{ij}) \, d\Delta y_{ij}}{\int_{\|\Delta y_{ij}\| \leqslant r} d\Delta y_{ij}} = 1 - \frac{\int_{\|\Delta y_{ij}\| \leqslant r} \mathrm{erfc}(\alpha_{ij}) \, d\Delta y_{ij}}{\int_{\|\Delta y_{ij}\| \leqslant r} d\Delta y_{ij}}$$

$$= 1 - (B_m r^m)^{-1} \int_{\|\Delta y_{ij}\| \leqslant r} \mathrm{erfc}(\alpha_{ij}) \, d\Delta y_{ij}$$

$$= 1 - (B_m r^m)^{-1} 2^{m/2} \, [\det(S)]^{1/2} \int_{\sqrt{2}\|\eta\|_S \leqslant r} \mathrm{erfc}(\|\eta\|) \, d\eta$$

$$= 1 - B_m^{-1} 2^{m/2} \left(\frac{\bar{\sigma}}{r}\right)^m \int_{\sqrt{2}\|\eta\|_S \leqslant r} \mathrm{erfc}(\|\eta\|) \, d\eta \tag{7.14}$$

where $B_m$ is the volume of the unit $m$-ball; that is,[12]

$$B_m \triangleq \frac{\pi^{m/2}}{\Gamma\left(\dfrac{m}{2} + 1\right)} \tag{7.15}$$

and $\bar{\sigma}$ is the *average innovations standard deviation* defined by

$$\bar{\sigma} \triangleq [\det(S)]^{\frac{1}{2m}} \tag{7.16}$$

In the derivation in (7.14), we have used a transformation[13] $\Delta y_{ij} = \sqrt{2} S^{1/2}\eta$ that implies $d\Delta y_{ij} = 2^{m/2}[\det(S)]^{1/2} \, d\eta$.

Assuming that the radius $r$ is large enough, we can approximate the last integral in (7.14) by

$$\int_{\sqrt{2}\|\eta\|_S \leqslant r} \mathrm{erfc}(\|\eta\|) \, d\eta \approx \int_{\mathcal{R}^m} \mathrm{erfc}(\|\eta\|) \, d\eta \tag{7.17}$$

---

[12]$\Gamma(\gamma) \triangleq \int_0^\infty t^{\gamma-1} e^{-t} \, dt$ is the gamma function.

[13]$S^{1/2}$ is a matrix square root of the positive definite symmetric matrix $S$; that is, $S^{1/2}$ is any of $m \times m$ (nonsingular) matrices $A$ that satisfy $S = AA^T$.

By using a kind of spherical integral (7.A1) shown in Appendix 7.A, we have

$$
\int_{\mathcal{R}^m} \mathrm{erfc}(\|\eta\|) \, d\eta = mB_m \int_0^\infty \alpha^{m-1} \, \mathrm{erfc}(\alpha) \, d\alpha
$$

$$
= B_m \frac{1}{\sqrt{2\pi}} \int_0^\infty \acute{\alpha}^m e^{-\alpha^2/2} \, d\alpha \tag{7.18}
$$

$$
= B_m \pi^{-1/2} 2^{\frac{m-1}{2}} \Gamma\left(\frac{m+1}{2}\right)
$$

It follows then from (7.14), (7.17), and (7.18) that

$$
\mathcal{E}(\mathrm{erf}(\alpha_{ij}) \mid y_i = 0) \approx 1 - \check{C}_m \left(\frac{\bar{\sigma}}{r}\right)^m \tag{7.19}
$$

where

$$
\check{C}_m \triangleq 2^{m-1} \pi^{-1/2} \Gamma\left(\frac{m+1}{2}\right)
$$

$$
= \begin{cases}
\dfrac{1}{2} \dfrac{m!}{(m/2)!} & \text{if } m \text{ is even} \\[2ex]
2^{m-1} \pi^{-1/2} \left(\dfrac{m-1}{2}\right)! & \text{if } m \text{ is odd}
\end{cases} \tag{7.20}
$$

From (7.12), we can conclude that the correct association probability $P_C$ can be given by (7.19) when the prediction $y_i$ of the first object $i$ is at the origin. When the radius $r$ is large enough, we can replace this condition ($y_i = 0$) by "when the first object is well inside the $m$-ball." With that condition, we have

$$
P_C = P\{\hat{q}(i) = q(i)\} = P\{\Delta J_{ij} \leq 0\} \approx 1 - \check{C}_m \left(\frac{\bar{\sigma}}{r}\right)^m \tag{7.21}
$$

when there are only two objects.

## N-Object Association Problem

Now let us consider cases where $N > 2$. A rigorous analysis even with $N = 3$ is very difficult mainly because we no longer can write the condition for the correct association to take place in a simple form. To overcome this difficulty, we approximate the event in which an object $i$ is correctly associated by *the event in which there is no transposition*, i.e., *two-way switch that involves the object i*. As we have seen earlier, transposition of two objects, $i$ and $j$, happens if and only if $\Delta J_{ij} > 0$. Hence, this approximation can be written as

$$\{\hat{q}(i) = q(i)\} = \bigcup_{\substack{j=1 \\ j \neq i}}^{N} \{\Delta J_{ij} \leq 0\} \qquad (7.22)$$

Furthermore, when we assume that the event $\{\Delta J_{ij} \leq 0\}$ is independent for each $j$, that is, each "potential" transposition is independent, we have an approximate formula:

$$P_C = P\{\hat{q}(i) = q(i)\} = \prod_{\substack{j=1 \\ j \neq i}}^{N} P\{\Delta J_{ij} \leq 0\} = \left[ 1 - \tilde{C}_m \left( \frac{\bar{\sigma}}{r} \right)^m \right]^{N-1} \qquad (7.23)$$

*Poisson N*

We now assume that the number $N$ of objects is a Poisson random variable (integer) with a mean $\nu$; that is

$$P(N) = e^{-\nu} \frac{\nu^N}{N!} \qquad (7.24)$$

It follows from (7.23) and (7.24) that

$$
\begin{aligned}
P_C &= \sum_{N=0}^{\infty} P\{\hat{q}(i) = q(i) \mid N\} P(N) \\
&\approx e^{-\nu} \left\{ 1 + \sum_{N=1}^{\infty} \left[ 1 - \tilde{C}_m \left( \frac{\bar{\sigma}}{r} \right)^m \right]^{N-1} \frac{\nu^N}{N!} \right\} \\
&= \frac{e^{-\nu \tilde{C}_m (\bar{\sigma}/r)^m} - \tilde{C}_m (\bar{\sigma}/r)^m \, e^{-\nu}}{1 - \tilde{C}_m (\bar{\sigma}/r)^m} \\
&\approx \exp\left[ -\nu \tilde{C}_m \left( \frac{\bar{\sigma}}{r} \right)^m \right] \\
&= \exp(-\tilde{C}_m \tilde{\beta}) \\
&= \exp(-C_m \beta \bar{\sigma}^m)
\end{aligned}
\qquad (7.25)
$$

where[14]

$$\beta = \frac{\nu}{B_m r^m} \tag{7.26}$$

is the object density as the expected number of objects in a unit volume of the measurement space $\mathcal{R}^m$, and

$$\tilde{\beta} = B_m \beta \bar{\sigma}^m = \nu \left(\frac{\bar{\sigma}}{r}\right)^m \tag{7.27}$$

is a normalized object density defined as the expected number of objects in the one-sigma ellipsoidal volume defined by the innovations variance matrix $S$. $C_m$ in the last line of (7.25) is another constant defined by

$$
C_m = B_m \tilde{C}_m = 2^{m-1} \pi^{(m-1)/2} \frac{\Gamma\left(\dfrac{m+1}{2}\right)}{\Gamma\left(m/2 + 1\right)} \tag{7.28}
$$

$$
= \begin{cases}
\dfrac{1}{2} \pi^{m/2} \dfrac{m!}{[(m/2)!]^2} & \text{if } m \text{ is even} \\[3ex]
2^{2m} \pi^{(m/2)-1} \dfrac{[(m-1)/2]![(m+1)/2]!}{(m+1)!} & \text{if } m \text{ is odd}
\end{cases}
$$

Equation (7.25) is one of our main results. We may call it an *exponential law* to predict the average correct association probability in terms of the normalized object density. As we have seen by now, this simple expression was obtained through several approximations, the validity of which is yet to be proven. In the rest of this section, we show the appropriateness of our approximations by means of Monte Carlo simulations.

Figure 7.3 shows the results obtained by Monte Carlo simulations. The dimension of the observation space is two (i.e., $m = 2$) and hence we have $C_m = \pi$. Each

---

[4]The second approximation in (7.25) is justified by our assumption that, in general, a large number $N$ of objects is uniformly distributed in a large area (i.e., with a large $r$). This approximation shows that the difference between $N - 1$ (the number of "other" objects) and $N$ (the number of all the objects) does not affect the conclusion of (7.25).

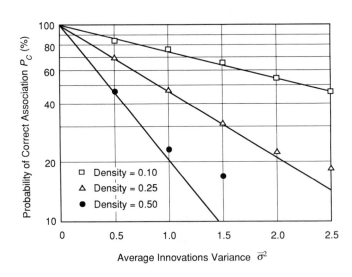

**Figure 7.3** Correct association probability as function of average innovations variance—theoretical performance *versus* simulation results.

point in Figure 7.3 was obtained by repeatedly solving the optimal assignment problem (as formulated in Section 7.1) and by averaging over 50 independent samples. The expected total number $\nu$ of objects was set to be 100. The absolute object densities were varied by changing the object extent radius $r$. Both variance matrices $Q$ and $R$, were set to be diagonal matrices with appropriate identical elements. To solve the assignment problem, a version of the Munkres algorithm was used. Figure 7.3 plots the correct association probability $P_C$ as a function of the *average innovations variance* $\bar{\sigma}^2$ and each point is compared with our theoretical prediction by (7.25). As seen in the figure, the simulation results agree very well with the theoretical prediction, except for in the high object density region where the correct association probability $P_C$ is about 30% or lower. This agreement is rather remarkable considering the approximations we have adopted, including some rather "bold" ones such as the independent transposition assumption. Figure 7.4 shows the same results as in Figure 7.3, but the correct association probability $P_C$ is now expressed as a function of the normalized object density $\tilde{\beta}$. Also in this figure, the persistent downward departure of our theoretical prediction from the simulation results is apparent when the normalized object density $\tilde{\beta}$ is more than 1.2 (corresponding to about 30% of the correct association probability $P_C$). This "pessimistic" tendency of the theoretical prediction for large object densities will not matter very much as it appears only when the correct association probability is extremely low (and hence not of much interest). Nonetheless this will be discussed in Section 7.5.

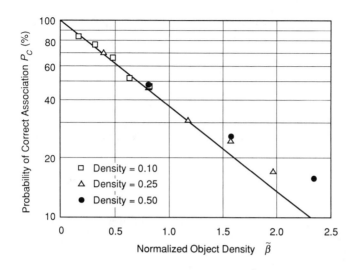

**Figure 7.4** Correct association probability as function of normalized object density—theoretical performance *versus* simulation results.

## 7.4 EFFECTS OF MISASSOCIATION

Having chosen [A3] rather than [A3′] in Section 7.2, we are concerned primarily with situations where the first random point set $Y$ is the set of "predictions" based on the information available in the "past" and the second random point set $Z$ is the "new" observation, which is analogous to the standard filtering setup. The past and new observations are used to estimate the "state" of each object. Before discussing effects of misassociations on the performance of this "state estimation," let us clarify what we mean by *states* first.

For each object $i$, let us consider a state vector $\xi_i$ in another Euclidean space $\mathcal{R}^n$ with $n \geq m$ and let $\overline{Z}$ be some random element that represents the information accumulated in the past. We assume that this information is decomposed in an object-by-object fashion, that is, $\overline{Z} = (\overline{Z}_i)_{i=1}^N$, and that the conditional probability of the joint state $\Xi \triangleq (\xi_i)_{i=1}^N$ is objectwise independent as

$$P(\Xi \mid \overline{Z}) = \prod_{i=1}^{N} P(\xi_i \mid \overline{Z}_i) \tag{7.29}$$

Furthermore, we assume that each $x_i$ in (7.1) and (7.2) is a (in general nonlinear) projection of each state $\xi_i$, that is,

$$x_i = h(\xi_i) \tag{7.30}$$

for each $i$ with an appropriate (sufficiently smooth) function $h: \mathcal{R}^n \to \mathcal{R}^m$, and hence, $P(Z|\Xi) = P(Z|X)$ with $X = (x_i)_{i=1}^N$. We then can interpret the prediction set $Y$ as[15]

$$y_i = \mathcal{E}(x_i|\overline{Z}_i) \quad \text{and} \quad Q = \mathcal{V}(x_i|\overline{Z}_i) \tag{7.31}$$

for all $i$. Furthermore, we implicitly assume that the variance $Q$ is small enough that the Gaussian approximation (7.1) is meaningful.

Because the random permutation $q$ is totally random ([A2]), we have

$$P(\Xi|Z, \overline{Z}) = \frac{P(Z|\Xi)P(\Xi|\overline{Z})}{P(Z|\overline{Z})} = \sum_q P(q|\overline{Z}, Z) \prod_{i=1}^N P(\xi_i|\overline{Z}_i, z_{q(i)}) \tag{7.32}$$

with the summation over the set of all the permutations $q$, where

$$P(\xi_i|\overline{Z}_i, z_{q(i)}) = \frac{P(z_{q(i)}|h(\xi_i))P(\xi_i|\overline{Z}_i)}{P(z_{q(i)}|\overline{Z}_i)} \tag{7.33}$$

for each $i$ and each $q$. First, note that, according to (7.32), *the object states $x_i$ are* not *necessarily independent a posteriori* even if they are independent *a priori* as assumed by (7.29). Dependency among the objects is introduced by the ambiguity in the data association $q$ between the prediction set $Y$ and the measurement set $Z$, which is one of the most important and unique characteristics of the data association problem. Several approaches deal with this dependency. Among them are the following two approaches.

*Best Hypothesis Approach*

Approximate the *a posteriori* probability, $P(q|\overline{Z}, Z)$, of the data association $q$ by letting $P(\hat{q}|\overline{Z}, Z) = 1$, where $\hat{q}$ is the best data association that minimizes the association cost (7.7), and by letting all the other probabilities be zero; that is, by treating the best data association $\hat{q}$ as the "true" one. With this approximation, we have

$$P(\Xi|\overline{Z}, Z) \approx \prod_{i=1}^N P(\xi_i|\overline{Z}_i, z_{\hat{q}(i)}) = \prod_{i=1}^N \frac{P(z_{\hat{q}(i)}|h(\xi_i))P(\xi_i|\overline{Z}_i)}{P(z_{\hat{q}(i)}|\overline{Z}_i)} \tag{7.34}$$

*Probabilistic Data Association Approach*

- For each $i$ and each $q$, approximate the distribution $P(\xi_i|\overline{Z}_i, z_{q(i)})$ by a (in general multivariate) Gaussian distribution, which makes the posterior distribution of (7.32) a *sum-of-Gaussian* (or Gaussian mixture) distribution.

---

[15] $\mathcal{E}(\cdot|\cdot)$ and $\mathcal{V}(\cdot|\cdot)$ are the conditional counterparts of the expectation and variance operators.

- Approximate the sum-of-Gaussian posterior distribution $P(\Xi \mid Z, \overline{Z})$ by a Gaussian distribution by equating the first and the second moments.

Finally, ignore the correlation among the objects by the approximation

$$\mathcal{E}(\xi_i \xi_j^T \mid Z, \overline{Z}) \approx \mathcal{E}(\xi_i \mid Z, \overline{Z})\mathcal{E}(\xi_j^T \mid Z, \overline{Z}) \qquad \text{for } i \neq j. \tag{7.35}$$

In [29], algorithms based on the first approach were referred to as *zero-scan algorithms,* and it was concluded that the approach is probably the simplest and probably the most representative of current practice. The second approach is used by the PDA [5, 3] and the JPDA [5, 4] algorithms for multiple-target tracking.

We can view each of these two approaches as a way of maintaining the object-wise independence[16] (7.29) at each step when $\overline{Z}$ is replaced by $(Z, \overline{Z})$. These two approaches, however, have their own advantages and disadvantages. A disadvantage of the first approach, "best hypothesis approach," may be apparent when there are many data associations, $q$ with similar posterior probabilities; that is, when the "best" data association does not stand out from the others. The approximation by (7.34) is obtained by ignoring data associations other than the best one and, in such a case, may not be a good approximation. On the other hand, the second approach, "probabilistic data association approach," may have a disadvantage when there are only a few (yet multiple) "outstanding" data associations, resulting in distinguishable estimation results. This may happen when the measurement variance $R$ is significantly smaller than the prediction variance $Q$, as illustrated in Figure 7.5, in which a sum-of-Gaussian distribution is compared with its Gaussian approximation. As seen in Figure 7.5, by forcing the distribution to be Gaussian, it becomes more "diffused" than necessary.[17] On the other hand, when the first approach is used in this situation, the effect of misassociations might be excessively large.

Yet another approach may be to use only the previous approximation and maintain several significant values of $q$ or equivalently to maintain the sum-of-Gaussian distribution possibly with some simplification such as *pruning* and *combining* of Gaussian terms. Recently such manipulation was discussed in connection with the PDA algorithm [30]. We have chosen to analyze the performance of the state estimation when the first approach, the "best hypothesis approach," is used for a couple of reasons. First, some analysis already was made for the probabilistic data association (the second approach) and presented in [15] and [19]. Second, when the object density is high, the first approach coupled with additional "recovery" type of algorithms probably may produce better results than the second approach, especially

---

[5]Recently modifications to improve the performance of the JPDA algorithm have been made by eliminating the last step; that is, by maintaining the correlation among the object states created by "combining" all the association hypotheses in the first step [8].

[7]We can see more discussions on Gaussian approximation of sum-of-Gaussian distributions (Gaussian mixtures) in [6].

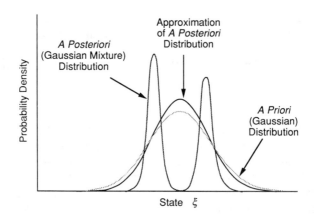

**Figure 7.5** Gaussian approximation—probabilistic data association approach.

if identification of each individual object is of significant importance. Thus we present our analysis in the rest of this section assuming the object state estimation by using the first approach.

When the "best hypothesis" approach (7.33) is used, to analyze the effects of misassociations on the object state estimation represented by $P(\xi_i | \overline{Z}_i, z_{\hat{q}(i)})$, it suffices to evaluate $P(z_{\hat{q}(i)} | x_i) = P[z_{\hat{q}(i)} | h(\xi_i)]$, which can be expanded as

$$P[z_{\hat{q}(i)} | x_i] = P[z_{\hat{q}(i)} | x_i, \hat{q}(i) = q(i)] P\{\hat{q}(i) = q(i)\} \tag{7.36}$$
$$+ P[z_{\hat{q}(i)} | x_i, \hat{q}(i) \neq q(i)] P\{\hat{q}(i) \neq q(i)\}$$

when $\hat{q}(i) = q(i)$ (i.e., when there is no misassociation) we have $z_{\hat{q}(i)} = x_i + v_i$. When $\hat{q}(i) \neq q(i)$ (i.e., the object $i$ is misassociated) there is a $j \neq i$ so that $\hat{q}(i) = q(j)$, and hence $z_{\hat{q}(i)} = x_j + v_j = x_i + (x_j - x_i) + v_j$. In other words, the measurement error for object $i$ is $v_i$ when object $i$ is correctly associated, and $x_j - x_i + v_j$ otherwise. When object $i$ is misassociated, the distribution of the prediction $x_j$ of the misassociated object $j$ may be considered *symmetric* unless the object $i$ is located toward the edge of the object group (which we exclude). Thus, we may conclude that the conditional mean of $P(z_{\hat{q}(i)} | x_i)$ is $x_i$. With a Gaussian approximation, this conditional distribution may be characterized by the second moment, in other words, the variance of the *effective measurement error* defined as $z_{\hat{q}(i)} - x_i$; that is, the difference between the assigned measurement (through an optimal assignment $\hat{q}$) and the "true" position of object $i$ in the measurement space $\mathcal{R}^m$. Figure 7.6 illustrates the concept of effective measurement errors.

Thus, the effects of misassociations on object state estimation (at a given time) have been reduced to the evaluation of the *effective measurement error variance*

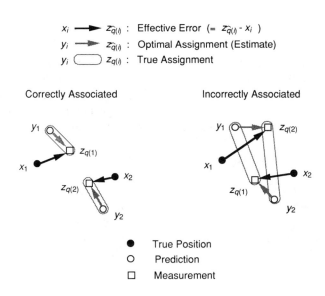

Figure 7.6 Effective measurement errors.

*matrix,* $R_E$; that is, the variance matrix of the effective measurement error, $z_{\hat{q}(i)} - x_i$. The information gained by adding the new measurement set $Z$ to the prediction set $Y$ can be measured by the inverse matrix of $R_E$. From (7.36), it is apparent that the effective measurement error variance matrix $R_E$ approaches the original variance matrix $R$ when the object density approaches zero (and hence $P_C \rightarrow 1$). When the object density is high and, consequently, the possibility of misassociations is high, we *generally*[18] expect the effective error variance $R_E$ to be larger than the original measurement variance $R$. The increment $\Delta R_E \triangleq R_E - R$ measures the effects of misassociation on state estimation performance. In the rest of this section, we describe a method for estimating this increment.

For an arbitrary event $A$, let us define[19] $\mathcal{E}(\cdot \,; A) = E(\cdot \,|A)P(A)$, and similarly, let $\mathcal{V}(\cdot \,; A) \triangleq \mathcal{V}(\cdot \,|A)P(A)$. With the latter notation, we have

$$R_E \triangleq \mathcal{V}(z_{\hat{q}(i)} - x_i) = \mathcal{V}[z_{\hat{q}(i)} - x_i \,; \hat{q}(i) = q(i)]$$
$$+ \mathcal{V}[z_{\hat{q}(i)} - x_i \,; \hat{q}(i) \neq q(i)] \tag{7.37}$$

In the following, we will evaluate the two terms on the right-hand side separately.

---

[18]Interestingly, we will see this increase in $R_E$ is not always "monotone" later in this section.
[19]Namely, $\mathcal{E}(X \,; A) \triangleq \int_A X(\omega)P(d\omega)$.

## When Assignment Is Correct

We would like to evaluate $\mathcal{V}[z_{\hat{q}(i)} - x_i ; \hat{q}(i) = q(i)]$, or equivalently $\mathcal{V}[v_i ; \hat{q}(i) = q(i)]$ because $z_{\hat{q}(i)} = z_{q(i)} = x_i + v_i$ when the assignment is correct; that is, $\hat{q}(i) = q(i)$. This evaluation is rather difficult if done directly, mainly because the condition becomes multiple (rather than a single condition described by a half space). For this reason, we will use the complementary relation:

$$R = \mathcal{V}(v_i) = \mathcal{V}[v_i ; \hat{q}(i) = q(i)] + \mathcal{V}[v_i ; \hat{q}(i) \neq q(i)] \tag{7.38}$$

As in the previous section, let us assume for the moment that there is only one other object $j$ besides the object $i$ in question. Because we have assumed only two objects $i$ and $j$, $\{\hat{q}(i) \neq q(i)\} = \{\hat{q}(i) = q(j)\}$, and as shown in the previous section, this event is equal to $\{\Delta J_{ij} \geq 0\}$. We can rewrite the condition $\Delta J_{ij} \geq 0$ as $a^T W \geq b$ with

$$W = \begin{bmatrix} u_i \\ u_j \\ v_i \\ v_j \end{bmatrix} \tag{7.39}$$

$$a = \begin{bmatrix} I_m \\ -I_m \\ -I_m \\ I_m \end{bmatrix} S^{-1} \Delta y_{ij} \tag{7.40}$$

and[20]

$$b = \|\Delta y_{ij}\|_{S^{-1}}^2 = 2\alpha_{ij}^2 \tag{7.41}$$

where $\alpha_{ij}$ was introduced by (7.13) in the previous section.

Because the values of $y$ are independent of $u$ and $v$, conditioned by $\Delta y_{ij} \triangleq y_i - y_j$, the second moment of the Gaussian random vector $W$ can be calculated using (7.B3) in Appendix 7.B (noting that $\mathcal{E}(W | \Delta y_{ij}) = 0$) as

$$\mathcal{E}(\mathcal{V}(W ; \Delta J_{ij} \geq 0) | \Delta y_{ij}) = \mathcal{E}[\mathcal{V}(W ; a^T W \geq b) | \Delta y_{ij}] \tag{7.42}$$

$$= \text{erfc}(\alpha_{ij}) V + \frac{1}{\sqrt{2\pi}} \alpha_{ij} \exp\left(-\frac{1}{2} \alpha_{ij}^2\right) \frac{V a a^T V}{\|a\|_V^2}$$

---

[20] By $0_m$ and $I_m$ we denote the $m \times m$ zero and identify matrices, respectively.

where $V$ is the variance matrix of $W$; that is, a block-diagonal matrix with $(Q, Q, R, R)$ as its diagonal blocks. Because $v_i = HW$ with $H = [0_m\, 0_m\, I_m\, 0_m]$, (7.42) is followed by

$$\mathcal{E}[\mathcal{V}(v_i\ ;\ \Delta J_{ij} \geqslant 0)|\Delta y_{ij}] = \mathcal{E}[H\mathcal{V}(W\ ;\ \Delta J_{ij} \geqslant 0)H^T|\Delta y_{ij}]$$

$$= \mathrm{erfc}(\alpha_{ij})HVH^T \tag{7.43}$$

$$+ \frac{1}{4}\frac{1}{\sqrt{2\pi}}\,\alpha_{ij}^{-1}\exp\left(-\frac{1}{2}\,\alpha_{ij}^2\right)\frac{HVaa^TVH^T}{\|a\|_V^2}$$

Substituting $\|a\|_V = \sqrt{2}\|\Delta y_{ij}\|_{S^{-1}} = 2\alpha_{ij}$, $HVT^T = R$, and $HVa = -RS^{-1}\Delta y_{ij}$, into (7.43), we have

$$\mathcal{E}[\mathcal{V}(v_i\ ;\ \Delta J_{ij} \geqslant 0)|\Delta y_{ij}] = \mathcal{V}(v_i|\Delta J_{ij} \geqslant 0, \Delta y_{ij})P\{\Delta J_{ij} \geqslant 0|\Delta y_{ij}\}$$

$$= \mathrm{erfc}(\alpha_{ij})R \tag{7.44}$$

$$+ \frac{1}{4}\frac{1}{\sqrt{2\pi}}\,\alpha_{ij}^{-1}\,e^{-\alpha_{ij}^2/2}RS^{-1}(\Delta y_{ij}\Delta y_{ij}^T)S^{-1}R$$

We now are ready to take the average with respect to $\Delta y_{ij}$. To do this, we use the same approach used to derive the *exponential law* (7.25); that is, we ignore the *edge effects* by putting $y_i$ at the origin and assuming a uniform distribution on an $m$-ball with a *large* radius $r$ for $y_j$. To calculate the average of the first term of (7.42), we only have to rewrite (7.19) as

$$\mathcal{E}[\mathrm{erfc}(\alpha_{ij})|y_i = 0] \approx \tilde{C}_m\left(\frac{\bar{\sigma}}{r}\right)^m \tag{7.45}$$

with $\tilde{C}_m$ and $\bar{\sigma}$ defined by (7.20) and (7.16), respectively. To take the average of the second term of (7.44), we can apply the same coordinate transformation as that used in (7.14) in the previous section and a kind of spherical integral (shown in Appendix 7.A as (7.A8))

$$\int_{R^m}\|\eta\|^{-1}\exp\left(-\frac{1}{2}\|\eta\|^2\right)\eta\eta^T\,d\eta = \left[B_m 2^{(m-1)/2}\Gamma\left(\frac{m+1}{2}\right)\right]I_m \tag{7.46}$$

(with $B_m$ being the volume of the unit $m$-ball) to obtain

$$\mathcal{E}\left[\alpha_{ij}^{-1}\exp\left(-\frac{1}{2}\alpha_{ij}^2\right)RS^{-1}\Delta y_{ij}\Delta y_{ij}^TS^{-1}R\,|\,y_i = 0\right]$$

$$\approx \frac{\displaystyle\int_{\|\Delta y_{ij}\|\leqslant r}\alpha_{ij}^{-1}\exp\left(-\frac{1}{2}\alpha_{ij}^2\right)RS^{-1}(\Delta y_{ij}\Delta y_{ij}^T)S^{-1}R\,d\Delta y_{ij}}{\displaystyle\int_{\|\Delta y_{ij}\|\leqslant r}d\Delta y_{ij}}$$

$$\approx (B_m r^m)^{-1}RS^{-1}\left(\int_{\mathcal{R}^m}\alpha_{ij}^{-1}\exp\left(-\frac{1}{2}\alpha_{ij}^2\right)\Delta y_{ij}\Delta y_{ij}^T\,d\Delta y_{ij}\right)S^{-1}R$$

$$= (B_m r^m)^{-1}2^{\frac{m}{2}+1}[\det(S)]^{1/2}RS^{-T/2}\left(\int_{\mathcal{R}^m}\|\eta\|^{-1}\exp\left(-\frac{1}{2}\|\eta\|^2\right)\eta\eta^T\,d\eta\right)S^{-1/2}R$$

$$= 2^{3/2}\pi^{1/2}\tilde{C}_m\left(\frac{\bar{\sigma}}{r}\right)^m RS^{-1}R$$

$$\tag{7.47}$$

It then follows from (7.44) through (7.47) that

$$\mathcal{E}[\mathcal{V}(v_i\;;\;\Delta J_{ij}\geqslant 0)\,|\,y_i = 0] \approx \Upsilon_1(Q, R)\tilde{C}_m\left(\frac{\bar{\sigma}}{r}\right)^m \tag{7.48}$$

where

$$\Upsilon_1(Q, R) = R + \tfrac{1}{2}RS^{-1}R \tag{7.49}$$

By ignoring the "edge effects," we can then drop the condition $y_i = 0$ from (7.48).

So far we have considered only two objects, $i$ and $j$. Now we assume that there are $N$ other[21] objects beside the object $i$ in question. By identifying the event in which the assignment of track $i$ is incorrect with the event in which one and only one trans-

---

[21] More precisely, $N - 1$ other objects. But as discussed in the previous section, the difference between $N$ and $N - 1$ should not make any significant difference in the results.

position involving the object $i$ occurs, we have

$$
\begin{aligned}
\mathcal{V}[v_i \; ; \; \hat{q}(i) \neq q(i)] &\approx \sum_{\substack{j=1 \\ j \neq i}}^{N+1} \mathcal{V}[v_i \; ; \; \hat{q}(i) = q(j)] \\
&\approx \sum_{\substack{j=1 \\ j \neq i}}^{N+1} \mathcal{V}(v_i \; ; \; \Delta J_{ij} \geqslant 0) \prod_{\substack{k=1 \\ k \neq i \\ k \neq j}}^{N+1} \mathcal{P}(\Delta J_{ik} \leqslant 0)
\end{aligned}
\tag{7.50}
$$

Namely, we are equating the event $\{\hat{q}(i) \neq q(i)\}$ with the union of independent events in which (a) there is a transposition between $i$ and $j$ and (b) there is no transposition between $i$ and $k$ for $k \neq i$ or $j$ (for some $j \neq i$). We also ignore the effect of condition (b) on the variance of $v_i$. Substituting (7.21) (Section 7.3) and (7.48) into (7.50), we have

$$
\mathcal{V}[v_i \; ; \; \hat{q}(i) \neq q(i)] = N \Upsilon_1(Q, R) \tilde{C}_m \left(\frac{\overline{\sigma}}{r}\right)^m \left[1 - \tilde{C}_m \left(\frac{\overline{\sigma}}{r}\right)^m\right]^{N-1}
\tag{7.51}
$$

Now let $N$ be a Poisson random variable with mean $\nu$ as in (7.24). It follows from (7.51) that

$$
\begin{aligned}
\mathcal{V}[v_i \; ; \; \hat{q}(i) \neq q(i)] &\approx \Upsilon_1(Q, R) \tilde{C}_m \left(\frac{\overline{\sigma}}{r}\right)^m e^{-\nu} \sum_{N=0}^{\infty} \frac{\nu^N}{N!} N \left[1 - \left(\frac{\overline{\sigma}}{r}\right)^m\right]^{N-1} \\
&= \Upsilon_1(Q, R) \tilde{C}_m \left(\frac{\overline{\sigma}}{r}\right)^m \nu \exp\left[-\tilde{C}_m \left(\frac{\overline{\sigma}}{r}\right)^m \nu\right] \\
&= \Upsilon_1(Q, R) \tilde{C}_m \tilde{\beta} \exp(-\tilde{C}_m \tilde{\beta})
\end{aligned}
\tag{7.52}
$$

where $\tilde{\beta}$ is the normalized object density defined by (7.27). Finally, by using the complementary relation (7.38), we have

$$
\begin{aligned}
\mathcal{V}[z_{\hat{q}(i)} - x_i \; ; \; \hat{q}(i) = q(i)] &= \mathcal{V}[v_i \; ; \; \hat{q}(i) = q(i)] \\
&= R - \Upsilon_1(Q, R) \tilde{C}_m \tilde{\beta} \exp(-\tilde{C}_m \tilde{\beta})
\end{aligned}
\tag{7.53}
$$

### When Assignment Is Incorrect

Now we would like to evaluate $\mathcal{V}(z_{\hat{q}(i)} - x_i; \hat{q}(i) \neq q(i))$. This can be done in a way very similar to that used to derive (7.52). We should note that the expression (7.52) also is conditioned by the "incorrect" assignment. As previously, let us assume that there is only one other object $j$ besides object $i$. Note first that, in such a case, if the assignment is incorrect, $\hat{q}(i) \neq q(i)$ or $\hat{q}(i) = q(j)$, we must have

$$z_{\hat{q}(i)} - x_i = z_{q(j)} - x_i = v_j - \Delta x_{ij} = v_j + \Delta u_{ij} - \Delta y_{ij} \tag{7.54}$$

where $\Delta x_{ij} \triangleq x_i - x_j$ and $\Delta u_{ij} \triangleq u_i - u_j$. Let $w = v_j + \Delta u_{ij} = v_j + u_i - u_j$. Then, if the assignment is incorrect, $\hat{q}(i) \neq q(i)$ or $\hat{q}(i) = q(j)$, we have $z_{\hat{q}(i)} - x_i = w - \Delta y_{ij}$. With this $w$, we have

$$\begin{aligned}
\mathcal{V}[x_{\hat{q}(i)} - x_i \; ; \; \Delta J_{ij} \geq 0] &= \mathcal{V}(w - \Delta y_{ij} \; ; \; \Delta J_{ij} \geq 0) \\
&= \mathcal{V}(w \; ; \; \Delta J_{ij} \geq 0) \\
&\quad - \mathcal{E}(w\Delta y_{ij}^T + \Delta y_{ij}w^T \; ; \; \Delta J_{ij} \geq 0) \\
&\quad + \mathcal{V}(\Delta y_{ij} \; ; \; \Delta J_{ij} \geq 0)
\end{aligned} \tag{7.55}$$

Now let us calculate the three terms in the last expression of (7.55) one by one.

*First Term.* By replacing the definition of $H$ by $H = [I_m \; -I_m \; O_m \; I_m]$, a derivation similar to that by (7.39) through (7.49) leads us to

$$\mathcal{V}(w \; ; \; \Delta J_{ij} \geq 0)$$
$$= \tilde{C}_m \left(\frac{\sigma}{r}\right)^m \left[ (2Q + R) + \frac{1}{2}(2Q + R)S^{-1}(2Q + R) \right] \tag{7.56}$$

with $R$ in $\Upsilon_1(Q, R)$ defined by (7.49) being replaced by $2Q + R$.

*Second Term.* As done earlier, first fix $\Delta y_{ij}$ and then take the average over it. Using the calculation of the first moment of a Gaussian vector conditioned by the linear inequality (described in Appendix 7.B), we have

$$\begin{aligned}
\mathcal{E}[\mathcal{E}(w \; ; \; \Delta J_{ij} \geq 0)|\Delta y_{ij}] &= \mathcal{E}[\mathcal{E}(HX \; ; \; \Delta J_{ij} \geq 0)|\Delta y_{ij}] \\
&= \frac{1}{\sqrt{2\pi}} \exp\left(-\frac{1}{2}\alpha_{ij}^2\right) \frac{HVa}{\|a\|_V} \\
&= \frac{1}{2}(2Q + R)S^{-1}\left[\frac{1}{\sqrt{2\pi}}\alpha_{ij}^{-1}\exp\left(-\frac{1}{2}\alpha_{ij}^2\right)\Delta y_{ij}\right]
\end{aligned} \tag{7.57}$$

with the new definition of $H$. Now we can take the average over $\Delta y_{ij}$ in exactly the same way as we derived (7.44) from (7.43); that is,

$$\mathcal{E}(w\Delta y_{ij}^T \; ; \; \Delta J_{ij} \geq 0) = \frac{1}{2}(2Q + R)S^{-1}\mathcal{E}\left[\frac{1}{\sqrt{2\pi}}\alpha_{ij}^{-1}\exp\left(-\frac{1}{2}\alpha_{ij}^2\right)\Delta y_{ij}\Delta y_{ij}^T\right]$$

$$= \tilde{C}_m\left(\frac{\bar{\sigma}}{r}\right)^m(2Q + R) \tag{7.58}$$

*Third Term.* Because $\mathcal{E}(\Delta y_{ij} | \Delta J_{ij}) = 0$ and $P\{\Delta J_{ij} \geq 0 | \Delta y_{ij}\} = \text{erfc}(\alpha_{ij})$, we have

$$\mathcal{V}(\Delta y_{ij} \; ; \; \Delta J_{ij} \geq 0) = \mathcal{E}(\Delta y_{ij}\Delta y_{ij}^T \; ; \; \Delta J_{ij} \geq 0)$$

$$= \mathcal{E}(\Delta y_{ij}\Delta y_{ij}^T P\{\Delta J_{ij} \geq 0 | \Delta y_{ij}\})$$

$$= \mathcal{E}[\text{erfc}(\alpha_{ij})(\Delta y_{ij}\Delta y_{ij}^T)] \tag{7.59}$$

$$= \frac{\displaystyle\int_{\|\Delta y_{ij}\| \leq r} \text{erfc}(\alpha_{ij})(\Delta y_{ij}\Delta y_{ij}^T) \, d\Delta y_{ij}}{\displaystyle\int_{\|\Delta y_{ij}\| \leq r} d\Delta y_{ij}}$$

$$\approx \frac{2^{\frac{m}{2}+1}[\det(S)]^{1/2}\displaystyle\int_{\mathcal{R}^m} \text{erfc}(\|\eta\|)(S^{1/2}\eta\eta^T S^{T/2}) \, d\eta}{B_m r^m}$$

According to the second formula (7.A8) of Appendix 7.A, we have

$$\int_{\mathcal{R}^m} \text{erfc}(\|\eta\|)\eta\eta^T \, d\eta = B_m\left(\int_0^\infty \rho^{m+1}\,\text{erfc}(\rho)\,d\rho\right)I_m$$

$$= B_m\frac{1}{m + 2}\pi^{-1/2}2^{m/2}\Gamma\left(\frac{m + 3}{2}\right)I_m \tag{7.60}$$

$$= B_m\frac{1}{2}\frac{m + 1}{m + 2}\pi^{-1/2}2^{m/2}\Gamma\left(\frac{m + 1}{2}\right)I_m$$

Substituting (7.60) into (7.59), we have

$$\mathcal{V}(\Delta y_{ij} \; ; \; \Delta J_{ij} \geq 0) \approx 2\tilde{C}_m\left(\frac{\bar{\sigma}}{r}\right)^m\frac{m + 1}{m + 2}S \tag{7.61}$$

Finally, putting all the three terms (7.56), (7.58) and (7.61) together into (7.55), we have

$$\mathcal{V}(y_{\hat{q}(i)} - z_i \; ; \; \Delta J_{ij} \geqslant 0) \approx \Upsilon_2(Q, R)\tilde{C}_m \left(\frac{\bar{\sigma}}{r}\right)^m \tag{7.62}$$

assuming that there are only two objects, with $\Upsilon_2$ being defined by

$$\Upsilon_2(Q, R) = \frac{1}{2}(2Q + R)S^{-1}(2Q + R) - (2Q + R) + 2\frac{m + 1}{m + 2}S \tag{7.63}$$
$$= \frac{1}{2}QS^{-1}Q + \frac{3m + 2}{2m + 4}S$$

As before, let us consider the case where there are $N$ other objects. Then we replace (7.61) by

$$\mathcal{V}[z_{\hat{q}(i)} - x_i \; ; \; \Delta J_{ij} \geqslant 0] \approx N\Upsilon_2(Q, R)\tilde{C}_m \left(\frac{\bar{\sigma}}{r}\right)^m \left[1 - \left(\frac{\bar{\sigma}}{r}\right)^m\right]^{N-1} \tag{7.64}$$

Finally, by using the Poisson assumption and averaging over the number of objects surrounding the object $i$, we have

$$\mathcal{V}[z_{\hat{q}(i)} - x_i \; ; \; \hat{q}(i) \neq q(i)] \approx \Upsilon_2(Q, R)\tilde{C}_m \tilde{\beta} \exp(-\tilde{C}_m \tilde{\beta}) \tag{7.65}$$

*Overall Variance.* By substituting (7.53) and (7.65) into (7.37), we have

$$\mathcal{V}(z_{\hat{q}(i)} - x_i) \approx R_E \triangleq R + \Upsilon(Q, R)\tilde{C}_m \tilde{\beta} \exp(-\tilde{C}_m \tilde{\beta}) \tag{7.66}$$

where[22]

$$\Upsilon(Q, R) \triangleq \Upsilon_2(Q, R) - \Upsilon_1(Q, R)$$
$$= \frac{1}{2}(QS^{-1}Q - RS^{-1}R) + \frac{3m + 2}{2m + 4}S - R \tag{7.67}$$
$$= \frac{2m + 2}{m + 2}Q - \frac{2}{m + 2}R$$
$$= \frac{2}{m + 2}[(m + 1)Q - R]$$

---

[22]Equation (7.67) uses the equality, $QS^{-1}Q - RS^{-1}R = Q - R$, which is implied by (Remember (7.4)) $2(Q - R) = (Q - R)S^{-1}(Q + R) + (Q + R)S^{-1}(Q - R) = 2(QS^{-1}Q - RS^{-1}R)$.

Equation (7.66) is our second main result, and we call it *linear-times-exponential law* (in contrast to the *exponential law* (7.25)) to describe the effects of misassociations on object state estimation.

We have just characterized the effects of misassociations on state estimation performance (i.e., performance of information fusion of two random point sets, $Y$ and $Z$) in terms of the *effective measurement error variance, $R_E$*, by (7.66). We can explicitly express the results of updating the object state estimate based on an optimal data association as

$$\mathcal{E}(\xi_i | \overline{Z}, Z, \hat{q}) \approx \mathcal{E}(\xi_i | \overline{Z}, z_{\hat{q}(i)}) \approx y_i + G_i[z_{\hat{q}(i)} - y_i] \tag{7.68}$$

$$\mathcal{V}(\xi_i | \overline{Z}, Z, \hat{q}) \approx \mathcal{V}(\xi_i | \overline{Z}, z_{\hat{q}(i)}) \approx \left( I - G_i \frac{\partial h}{\partial \xi} \right) \mathcal{V}(\xi_i | \overline{Z}) \tag{7.69}$$

for each $i$, where $G_i$ is the *gain matrix* defined by

$$G_i = \mathcal{V}(\xi_i | \overline{Z}) \left( \frac{\partial h}{\partial \xi} \right)^T (Q + R_E)^{-1} \tag{7.70}$$

and $\partial h / \partial \xi$ is the *matrix of the observation partials.*[23] Equation (7.68) through (7.70) constitute a standard Kalman or extended Kalman (filtering) updating formula, with the measurement error variance matrix $R$ replaced by the effective measurement error variance matrix $R_E$. As naturally expected, (7.66) claims that, as the (normalized) object density $\tilde{\beta}$ approaches zero, $R_E$ approaches $R$. As before, however, the expression (7.66) has been derived through a (rather long) series of approximations, and there is no clear way to describe the effects of these approximations. Hence, its verification through numerical experiments is in order. Monte Carlo simulations were conducted based on the model described in Section 7.2. We found that the results for a fixed number of objects tend to agree fairly well with those with a (Poisson) random number of objects with the same mean. The only significant difference was larger statistical variances when randomizing the number of objects. Based on this observation, we decided that a fixed number of objects, say, 30, would be used for each combination of parameters.

*Two-Dimensional Case*

Figure 7.7 shows that the results of a case of two-dimensional measurement space ($m = 2$). Both $Q$ and $R$ are taken as an identity matrix. In this figure, the vertical axis represents the average of the two diagonal elements of the effective measurement

---

[23] We should note that we have assumed that $Q = (\partial h / \partial \xi) \mathcal{V}(\xi_i | \overline{Z}) (\partial h / \partial \xi)^T$ is the same for all values of $i$.

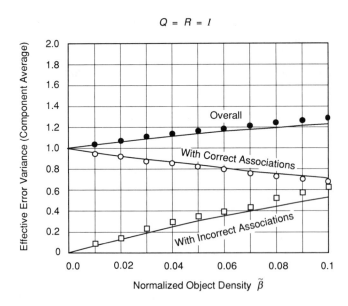

**Figure 7.7** Effective measurement errors—Monte Carlo simulations: a two-dimensional case.

error variance matrix $R_E$; that is, the average of the two eigenvalues of $R_E$. This figure shows three values—the average variance with correct associations, with incorrect associations, and overall error variance—as functions of the normalized object density $\tilde{\beta}$. For each quantity, theoretical curves determined by (7.52), (7.65), and (7.66), respectively, are compared with the simulation results. Although we can observe a consistent trend of the simulation results moving away from the theoretical curves, both theoretical and simulation results in general agree with each other reasonably well when the object density is small. Each simulation point in the figure was obtained by averaging over 300 independent runs.

*One-Dimensional Case*

Figure 7.8 shows the results of the simulations in a one-dimensional measurement space ($m = 1$). As in Figure 7.7, the vertical axis of Figure 7.8 represents the average of effective measurement error variance $R_E$, and theoretical and simulation results are compared. But Figure 7.8 shows only the overall variance. The results of two cases, $Q = R = 1$, and $Q = 2, R = 1$, are shown. Like Figure 7.7, Figure 7.8 shows reasonable agreement between theoretical and simulation results. Figure 7.8 indicates that, as the object density increases, the increment of the effective measurement error due to misassociation increases initially almost linearly with respect to the

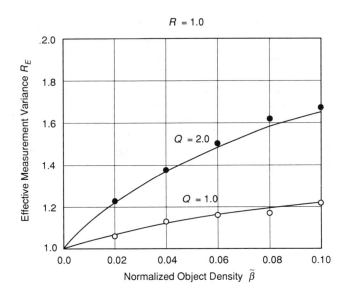

**Figure 7.8** Effective measurement errors—Monte Carlo simulations: a one-dimensional case.

object density, but the slope decreases as the object density increases. This may be explained as follows. The possibility of misassociation increases monotonically as the object density increases, in most cases resulting in increased (effective) measurement errors (hence, diminishing the amount of newly obtained information). However, when the object density is relatively low, misassociation, although very rare, tends to produce "large" errors if it indeed does happen. On the other hand, when the object density is relatively high, the impact of misassociation may not be very high because "misassociated" data may be found to be close to "true" ones because of the high density. The expression (7.66) may be considered a combination of these somehow "offsetting" effects. The results of numerical experiments shown in Figures 7.7 and 7.8 confirm this theoretical prediction, and the agreement of the numerical predictions with simulation results is very good within the region where the correct association probability $P_C$ is reasonably high.[24]

*Extremely High Object Density Case*

Equation (7.66) also claims that the increment $\Delta R_E$ of effective measurement error variance converges to zero as the normalized object density $\tilde{\beta}$ goes to infinity. Figure

---

[24] $P_C \approx 90\%$ for $\tilde{\beta} = .1$ (Figure 7.7 ... $m = 2$), and $P_C \approx 55\%$ for $\tilde{\beta} = 1$ (Figure 7.8 ... $m = 1$).

7.9 shows the second case ($Q = 2$, $R = 1$) in Figure 7.8, with a larger range for the object densities. As in Figure 7.7, the breakdowns (by (7.52) and (7.65), with overall by (7.66)), are shown in Figure 7.9. Simulation results, shown by circles and boxes in the figure, indicate a systematic disagreement in high object density region, although numerical results still exhibit overall structural agreements; that is, initial increase followed by a leveling off and then slow asymptotic decrease. This experiment exhibits a certain limit on the theoretical prediction by (7.66). However, also note that the results in Figure 7.9 show the region where the object densities are extremely high. In reality, however, with such a high density, other factors, such as sensor resolution that determines the ability to recognize each individual object separately, may become dominant. On the other hand, even with perfect resolution, with such a high density (e.g., normalized density $\tilde{\beta} = 2$ with $P_C \approx 30\%$), any effort to associate data themselves may not be meaningful.

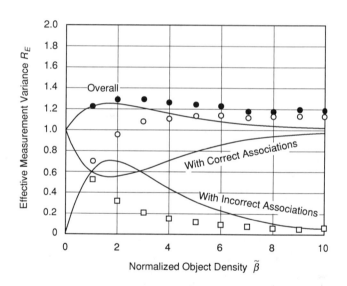

**Figure 7.9** Effective measurement errors—Monte Carlo simulations: cases with extremely high object density

*Case of Extremely Large Measurement Errors*

In (7.66), note that the coefficient $\Upsilon(Q, R)$ defined by (7.67) can be either positive or negative. In one-dimensional cases ($m = 1$), $\Upsilon(Q, R)$ is positive if and only if $Q > 1/2R$. When $Q \ll R$ (i.e., when the prediction errors are much smaller than the measurement errors) the coefficient becomes negative. If the coefficient is negative, the effective measurement error variance $R_E$ *decreases* as the object density increases. Figure 7.10 shows simulation results that confirm this. For Figure 7.10, $R = 1$ and $Q = .1$ are used so that the coefficient $\Upsilon(Q, R)$ becomes negative. Although simulation results tend to disagree with theoretical results as the object density increases, the general trend unmistakably follows the theoretical results. This result seems to suggest the increase in the object density may work in two ways: to confuse the assignments further by deteriorating track accuracy or to provide more *collective* information. Figures 7.7 to 7.9 show examples of the first case whereas Figure 7.10 shows the second.

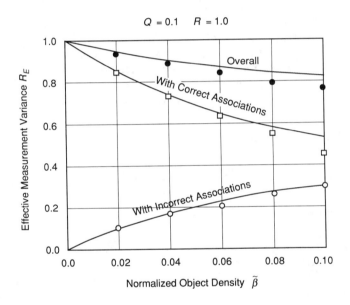

**Figure 7.10** Effective measurement errors—Monte Carlo simulations: cases with extremely large measurement errors.

## 7.5  EFFECTS OF EXTRANEOUS OBJECTS

In previous sections, we assumed that the numbers of objects in the two given random point sets, $Y$ and $Z$, are the same. In reality, the cardinalities of the two sets may not always coincide. We call objects in either set that do not correspond to any other object in the other set *extraneous objects*. In this section, we discuss the effects of such extraneous objects on data association performance in terms of the correct association probability $P_C$ when there are extraneous objects only in the observation set $Z$.

Effects of extraneous objects, one the other side, in $Y$, on data association performance may be analyzed in a similar way. The effect of extraneous objects on state estimation (information fusion) performance, however, is left to future research. Again our goal is to obtain a simple but practical and reliable analytic expression.

Suppose that there are $N$ prediction points in set $Y$ and $N + N_e$ measurement points in set $Z$, where $N_e$ is the number of extraneous objects in $Z$. In this situation, we must modify the optimal assignment problem by adding an extra step in which $N_e$ extraneous objects in $Z$ are identified (and then excluded) before obtaining an optimal assignment $\hat{q}$. There are many algorithms to obtain an optimal assignment $\hat{q}$ in this new situation. Among them is an extension of the Munkres algorithm that allows a rectangular cost matrix [10]. The correct association probability $P_C$ is defined as the average probability for each prediction $y_i$ being assigned correctly; that is, $P_C = P(E_C)$ where $E_C = \{\hat{q}(i) = q(i)\}$. Assuming this object is well inside the object group, we can let $y_i = 0$ without loss of generality. The event $E_C$ can be written as $E_C = E_{C0} \cap E_{Ce}$, where $E_{C0}$ is the event in which there is no transposition of the object $i$ with any other object, and $E_{Ce}$ with any "extraneous" object. The first approximation is to consider the two events as independent:

$$P_C \triangleq P(E_C) \approx P(E_{C0})P(E_{Ce}) \tag{7.71}$$

Then we use the result (7.25) in Section 7.3 for $P(E_{Ce})$:

$$P(E_{C0}) \approx \exp(-\tilde{C}_m \tilde{\beta}) = \exp(-C_m \beta \bar{\sigma}^m) \tag{7.72}$$

where $\beta$ and $\tilde{\beta}$ are the unnormalized and normalized object densities and $C_m$ and $\tilde{C}_m$ are constants, all defined in Section 7.3.

For an object $i$, let $P_{ie}$ be the probability that, given an extraneous measurement $z_e$ and the correct measurement $z_{q(i)}$, the extraneous measurement is not associated with the object $i$, i.e.:

$$P_{ie} = P\{\|z_{q(i)}\|_{S^{-1}} \leqslant \|z_e\|_{S^{-1}}\} \tag{7.73}$$

The distribution of $\|z_{q(i)}\|_{S^{-1}}^2 = \|v_i - u_i\|_{S^{-1}}^2$ is a $\chi^2$ distribution with degree of freedom $m$. Assuming that the extraneous observation $z_e$ is distributed uniformly on the $m$-ball with radius $r$, the distribution of $\|z_e\|_{S^{-1}}$ can be expressed as $P\{\|z_e\|_{S^{-1}} \leqslant \rho\} = [(\bar{\sigma}\rho)/r]^m$. Hence, (7.73) can be calculated as the probability of a random variable $\|z_{q(i)}\|_{S^{-1}}$ being less than another random variable $\|z_e\|_{S^{-1}}$ (see, e.g., [27]), as

$$P_{ie} = 1 - \tilde{D}_m \left(\frac{\bar{\sigma}}{r}\right)^m \tag{7.74}$$

where

$$\tilde{D}_m \triangleq \frac{\int_0^\infty \chi^{2m-1} e^{-\chi^2/2}\, d\chi}{\int_0^\infty \chi^{m-1} e^{-\chi^2/2}\, d\chi} = 2^{m/2}\, \frac{\Gamma(m)}{\Gamma(m/2)}$$

$$= \begin{cases} 2^{m/2}\, \dfrac{(m-1)!}{[(m/2)-1]!} & \text{if } m \text{ is even} \\[2ex] 2^{1-\frac{m}{2}}\pi^{-1/2}\left(\dfrac{m-1}{2}\right)! & \text{if } m \text{ is odd} \end{cases}$$

(7.75)

Then, as a crucial approximation, we will assume that *the probability of object i not being associated with any of the $N_e$ extraneous measurements is $(P_{ie})^{N_e}$.* With this independence assumption (approximation), we have

$$P(E_{Ce}) = e^{-\nu_e} \sum_{N_e=0}^{\infty} \frac{(\nu_e)^{N_e}}{N_e!}\, (P_{ie})^{N_e} = \exp[-\nu_e(1-P_{ie})]$$

$$= \exp(-\tilde{D}_m\tilde{\beta}_e) = \exp(-D_m\beta_e\bar{\sigma}^m)$$

(7.76)

where the number $N_e$ of extraneous observations has a Poisson distribution with mean $\nu_e$,

$$\beta_e \triangleq \nu/(B_m r^m)$$

(7.77)

is the density of the extraneous observations,

$$\tilde{\beta} \triangleq B_m \beta_e \bar{\sigma}^m$$

(7.78)

is the normalized density of extraneous observations, and

$$D_m \triangleq B_m \tilde{D}_m = \begin{cases} \pi^{m/2} 2^{m/2}\, \dfrac{(m-1)!}{(m/2)![(m/2)-1]!} & \text{if } m \text{ is even} \\[2ex] \dfrac{\pi^{m/2}}{2m} & \text{if } m \text{ is odd} \end{cases}$$

(7.79)

is another constant. Finally, substituting (7.72) and (7.76) into (7.71), we have

$$P_C = \exp[-(\tilde{C}_m\tilde{\beta} + \tilde{D}_m\tilde{\beta}_e)] = \exp[-(C_m\beta + D_m\beta_e)\bar{\sigma}^m]$$

(7.80)

The derivation of (7.76) depends heavily on the independence assumption. The probability $P(E_{C_e})$ may have been evaluated without this assumption. To do this, first note that, given $z_{q(i)}$, there is no extraneous measurement $z_e$ in an $m$-ellipsoid defined by

$$\{z \in \mathcal{R}^m \mid \|z\|_{S^{-1}} \leqslant \|z_{q(i)}\|_{S^{-1}}\}$$

in the event $E_{Ce}$, and that the Poisson assumption on the number of extraneous measurements holds true even when restricted within this $m$-ellipsoid. The result then can be integrated with respect to $z_{q(i)}$, which yields to

$$P(E_{Ce}) = \frac{\displaystyle\int_0^\infty e^{-\tilde{\beta}_e x^m} \chi^{m-1} e^{-x^2/2} \, d\chi}{\displaystyle\int_0^\infty \chi^{m-1} e^{-x^2/2} \, d\chi} \tag{7.81}$$

This is shown in a pioneer paper by R.G. Sea in 1971 [31] on data association performance analysis. Our counterpart (7.76) is an exponential function, whereas it can be shown that Sea's result (7.81) is asymptotically proportional to $1/\tilde{\beta}_e$. Because both expressions (7.76) and (7.81) share the same linear approximation at the origin, the probability calculated by (7.76) will always yield values smaller than that predicted by (7.81). We can attribute this difference to the independence assumption. Although the expression (7.81) is more accurate than (7.76), the right-hand side of (7.81) cannot be expressed in a closed form except for special values of $m$. To our best knowledge, there is no known closed form except for $m = 1$,

$$P(E_{Ce}) = 2\exp(\tilde{\beta}_e^2/2)\, \text{erfc}(\tilde{\beta}_e) \tag{7.82}$$

for $m = 2$,

$$P(E_{Ce}) = \frac{1}{1 + 2\tilde{\beta}_e} \tag{7.83}$$

and for $m = 4$,

$$P(E_{Ce}) = \frac{1}{8\tilde{\beta}_e}\left[ 1 - \frac{1}{2}\sqrt{\frac{\pi}{\tilde{\beta}_e}}\, \exp\left(\frac{1}{16\tilde{\beta}_e}\right) \text{erfc}\left(\frac{1}{\sqrt{8\tilde{\beta}_e}}\right) \right] \tag{7.84}$$

Moreover, the most apparent advantage of (7.76) over (7.81) or any of its known close forms, (7.82) through (7.84), is in its exponential form, which yields a very compact form for the overall expression (7.80).

Figure 7.11 shows the result of a numerical experiment similar to that described in Section 7.3 ($m = 2$). In each sample, extraneous observations were added according to given densities. Each point in Figure 7.11 was obtained by a 50-sample Monte Carlo simulation with the average number of objects being 100 and the normalized object density $\tilde{\beta}$ of 0.1. Figure 7.11 shows two theoretical predictions: one from our derivation (7.80) (solid curve) and the other from (7.71) with $P(E_{Ce})$ replaced by the Sea's equation (7.81) (dotted curve). The figure indicates relatively good fit for both formulas when the density of extraneous observations is low. In the high object density area, the Sea's formula (7.81) exhibits a better fit than our counterpart (7.76).

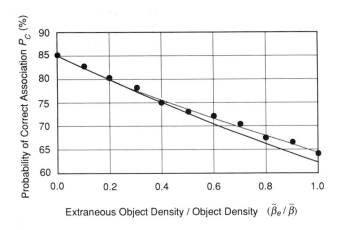

**Figure 7.11** Correct association probability—Monte Carlo simulations: with extraneous objects.

*Remark 2*

R.G. Sea [31] derived (7.81) to evaluate the data association performance by a *nearest neighbor algorithm* that results from removal of the requirement that the association $q$ be one to one. When a nearest neighbor algorithm is used, all the objects in the set to be correlated become "extraneous" (of course except for the "real" one). It is interesting to see the difference between the effects from "other objects" and those from "extraneous" measurements. For example, in two-dimensional cases ($m = 2$), we have $\tilde{C}_2 = 1$ and $\tilde{D}_2 = 2$, implying that the presence of extraneous objects is "twice" as bad as the presence of other objects. A possible explanation is that, when the optimal assignment algorithm is used, occasional (potential) misfits with respect to the association likelihood of one object may be prevented by considering the "global" fit (i.e., the request on the one-to-one assignment $q$), resulting in an improvement of "$\tilde{D}_2/\tilde{C}_2 = 2$" over a nearest neighbor algorithm. This argument may not be as valid when the object density is very high, where the improvement due to the one-to-one requirement becomes less noticeable. In Figure 7.4 (Section 7.3), we noticed a similar deviation of numerical results from the theoretical predictions by (7.25). This disagreement in the high object density region may be explained as follows. First, as the object density becomes extremely high, the data association performance of optimal assignment approaches that of a nearest neighbor algorithm. Second, approximations used to derive our theoretical prediction (7.25) are accurate when the object density is low enough that the use of an optimal assignment algorithm is noticeably advantageous over a nearest neighbor algorithm. These observations are evident in Figure 7.12, which shows the same numerical results as those shown in Figure 7.4 but with a linear scale. In Figure 7.12, the theoretical prediction by (7.25) is shown by a solid curve and that by (7.81) (nearest-neighbor assignment curve, i.e., (7.81) as the correct association probability with the extraneous object density $\tilde{\beta}_e$ replaced by the object density $\tilde{\beta}$) by a dotted curve.

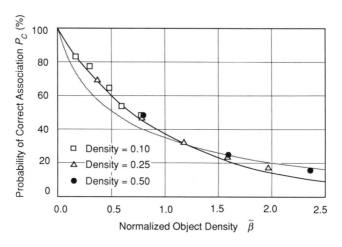

**Figure 7.12** Correct association probability—Monte Carlo simulations: plotted with linear scale (no extraneous object).

## 7.6 APPLICATION TO MULTITARGET TRACKING

As mentioned before, the analysis presented in the previous sections was motivated by the problem of tracking multiple targets in very dense target environments. In a typical multitarget-tracking problem, many data sets (possibly from multiple sensors) are given, modeled by random point sets as described in Section 7.2. In short, the objective of multitarget tracking is to recognize and track *objects,* which are called *targets* in the multitarget-tracking literature, present in multiple data sets. A key aspect of multitarget tracking is to associate data in multiple data sets, which makes the problem a direct extension of the two-set data association problem formulated in Section 7.2. Our goal was to develop simple analytic models that express tracking performance as a function of key tracking parameters. The results, however, may be applied to other data association applications, notably the correspondence problem in computer vision, as mentioned in Section 7.1. In this section, we present a multitarget-tracking application as a typical application of our data association performance analysis.

As discussed earlier, the aim of our analysis is to establish a practical upper bound on data association performance by a simple analytic model. This means that we would like to *evaluate* an optimal algorithm. A general theory of optimal multiple target tracking was established in [21] as a generalization of Reid's multiple hypothesis algorithm [29], based on the concepts of *tracks* and *data association hypotheses* first introduced by [20]. As pointed out clearly in [29], however, the optimal implementation of a multiple hypothesis tracking algorithm generally is *impossible* in dense target environments. This is because the number of possible tracks and hypotheses grows very rapidly as data sets (frames or scans) are accumulated. Some auxiliary algorithms always are needed to control this growth and yet maintain satisfactory performance. On the other hand, we can view the multiple-target tracking problem as a kind of integer linear programming problem (i.e., an extension of the assignment problem formulated in Section 7.2), and effective algorithms from this perspective have been developed.[25] Such algorithms are the *batch-process* type as opposed to *recursive* algorithms such as Reid's algorithm [29]. However, the computational requirements in dense target environments still are dominated by the large number of possible tracks, and hence, some sort of *track pruning* must be incorporated.

Establishing an upper bound on these optimal or suboptimal algorithms is extremely difficult, because, first of all, any process of data association over three or more data sets (random point sets) is too complex to allow simple probabilistic performance analysis. We should remember that, even for the two-set problem, we still needed to use a rather long series of simplifications and approximations. Second, any tracking algorithm involves several complex procedures for data processing, probability assessment, process management, and so forth, that make our analysis more difficult. Recently, an attempt was made to solve this difficult problem of directly evaluating multiple-hypothesis tracking algorithms in [13]. However, the analytical results obtained there must be combined with some Monte Carlo simulations to establish bounds on the performance in a particular situation.

To overcome this difficulty, we need some "bold" approximations, or in other words, we need models, greatly simplified yet capable of capturing the essential fac-

---

[25]Including [20] and very recently in [28].

tors in complex tracking processes, possibly sacrificing some accuracy in performance prediction. In this section, we base our analysis on the following *model* of tracking processes:

1. Given a collection of data sets, consider first a set of "magical" or "ideal" tracks that consist of only "true" measurements for each data set.
2. Then, for each data set, consider the data association problem between these ideal tracks and the actual measurements in this data set.
3. Finally, the tracking performance is measured by accumulating the performance of such data associations over given (in general a subcollection of) data sets.

According to this approach, the *track accuracy* is given as that of ideal tracks as an upper bound. As mentioned later in this section, this upper bound may be modified by using the analysis presented in Section 7.4; that is, the analysis of effects of misassociations on track accuracy.

Our choice for the performance measure for tracking systems is the *track purity* that will be defined as the average percentage of correctly associated measurements in each track. To our best knowledge, the concept of the track purity was first introduced in [11] and [12] as a tracking performance measure. The underlying assumptions for this choice are

1. The track purity is a good indicator of the "quality" of outputs of tracking systems, that is, tracks. This may be particularly true when target classification must be performed on correlated data as time-series data.
2. The detection probability over multiple data sets is high enough that detecting targets to form tracks is no problem. In other words, some targets may not be detected in some of the data sets but each target cannot escape detection in many data sets so that a track will be established eventually for every target.
3. The false alarm rate is modest at most so that target groups are recognized without significant difficulty. Again this justifies the assumption that tracks be well established after a sufficient number of data sets.

Let us consider a sequence of $K$ consecutive data sets $(Z_k)_{k=1}^K$. The sequence may be from a single sensor or multiple sensors. We are interested in the average quality of tracks in this collection of data sets. In our simple model for a tracking process, consider a track, say the $i$th track, and let $d_i$ be the number of misassociated measurements in this track within these $K$ scans. Let $e_i(k)$ be a binary random variable that is 0 when this track is associated with the correct measurement at the $k$th data set and 1 otherwise. Then we have

$$d_i = \sum_{k=1}^{K} e_i(k) \tag{7.85}$$

Assuming the detection probability is unity,[26] we can apply the result (7.25) of Section 7.3 to the tracking process model as

$$P_C(k) \triangleq P\{e_i(k) = 0\}$$

$$= 1 - \mathcal{E}[e_i(k)] \tag{7.86}$$

$$= \exp\{-[C_{m_k}\beta(k) + D_{m_k}\beta_{FA}(k)][\bar{\sigma}(k)]^{m_k}\}$$

$$= \exp[-\tilde{C}_{m_k}\tilde{\beta}(k) - \tilde{D}_{m_k}\tilde{\beta}_{FA}(k)]$$

where $P_C(k)$ is the (average) correct association probability for the $k$th data set, $m_k$ is the dimension of the measurement space of the $k$th scan, $\beta(k)$ is the target density in the $k$th scan measurement space, $\mathcal{R}^{m_k}$, with its normalized version $\tilde{\beta}(k)$, and $\beta_{FA}(k)$ is the false alarm density (in place of the density $\beta_e$ of extraneous measurements used in Section 7.5) with its normalized version $\tilde{\beta}_{FA}(k)$. The constants $C_m$, $D_m$, $\tilde{C}_m$, and $\tilde{D}_m$ all are given in Section 7.3. Then the expected (average) track purity can be calculated as

$$\mu = \frac{1}{K}\sum_{k=1}^{K} P_C(k) = 1 - \frac{1}{K}\mathcal{E}(d_i) \tag{7.87}$$

that is, the average percentage of the correctly associated measurements in a track. If each $P_C(k)$ is large enough, we may approximate $d_i$, the number of misassociations, by a Poisson random variable (integer)[27] with mean $\Sigma_{k=1}^{K}[1 - P_C(k)]$.

To calculate the prediction for the average track purity through (7.86) and (7.87), we must determine the parameters in (7.86) for each data set; that is, the target density $\beta(k)$ in the measurement space and the average innovations standard deviation $\bar{\sigma}(k)$ for the $k$th data set. In the following, we will describe two models to produce these two parameters.

*Track Accuracy Model*

We are to estimate the average innovations standard deviation $\bar{\sigma}(k)$. For this, let us assume a single group of $N$ targets that share identical dynamics defined by a common differential equation:

$$\frac{d}{dt}\xi_i(t) = f[\xi_i(t)] \tag{7.88}$$

---

[26]See Remark 3 at the end of this section for discussions concerning the detection probability.
[27]The approximation is justified by Poisson's law of small numbers.

222

with a smooth enough function $f:\mathcal{R}^n \to \mathcal{R}^n$ and (continuous) time parameter $t$. In other words, we assume deterministic dynamics and $\xi_i(\cdot)$ is the trajectory of the $i$th target in the target state space $\mathcal{R}^n$. For each $k$, let us assume that the "true" position (projection) of each target $i$ in the measurement space $\mathcal{R}^{m_k}$ be

$$x_i = h_k[\xi_i(t_k)] \tag{7.89}$$

where $t_k$ is the time for the $k$th data set with a smooth enough function $h_k:\mathcal{R}^n \to \mathcal{R}^{m_k}$. Then the $k$th data set $Z_k$ is a random point set that can be written as

$$Z_k = \{x_i + v_i | i \in [1, \ldots, N]\} \cup Z_k^{FA} \tag{7.90}$$

where each $v_i$ is an additive zero-mean Gaussian measurement error with a common variance matrix $R_k$, and $Z_k^{FA}$ is the set of *false alarms*, measurements that do not originate from any target.

Let $\bar{\xi}(t)$ be the trajectory of the "centroid" of the group. Assuming that the group extent in the target state space $\mathcal{R}^n$ is small enough, we may consider the centroid trajectory $\bar{\xi}(t)$ to obey the same differential equation (7.88); that is,

$$
\begin{aligned}
\frac{d}{dt}\bar{\xi}(t) &= \frac{1}{N}\sum_{i=1}^{N}\frac{d}{dt}\xi_i(t) \\
&= \frac{1}{N}\sum_{i=1}^{N}f[\xi_i(t)] \\
&\approx \frac{1}{N}\sum_{i=1}^{N}\left\{f[\bar{\xi}(t)] + \frac{\partial f}{\partial\xi}[\bar{\xi}(t)][\xi_i(t) - \bar{\xi}(t)]\right\} \\
&= f[\bar{\xi}(t)]
\end{aligned}
\tag{7.91}
$$

Again assuming that the target group spatial extent is small enough, each track that has been "pure" prior to the $k$th can be considered to share the same Cramér-Rao lower bound on the estimation error variance of the target state at time $t_k$ along the centroid trajectory. Let the $n \times n$ positive definite matrix $P_k$ be such a Cramér-Rao bound, a lower bound on the target state estimation error variance matrix.[28] Then the average prediction error variance matrix $Q_k$ can be calculated as

$$Q_k = \left\{\frac{\partial h_k}{\partial\xi}[\bar{\xi}(t_k)]\right\}P_k\left\{\frac{\partial h_k}{\partial\xi}[\bar{\xi}(t_k)]\right\}^T \tag{7.92}$$

---

[28]With respect to the ordering induced by the positive definiteness of symmetric matrices; that is, $A \geqslant B$ when $A - B$ is nonnegative definite.

from which we can calculate the innovations variance matrix

$$S_k = Q_k + R_k \tag{7.93}$$

where $R_k$ is the (average) measurement error variance matrix for the $k$th data set. Following the definition (7.16) (Section 7.3) of the average innovations error standard deviation, we then have

$$\overline{\sigma}(k) = [\det(S_k)]^{1/(2m_k)} \tag{7.94}$$

We can show [34] that, because of the assumed deterministic nature of the dynamics, the Cramér-Rao bound $P_k$ can be calculated as the target state estimation error for the extended Kalman filter along the known target trajectory, in our case, the centroid trajectory $\overline{\xi}(t)$. Namely, we can express $P_k$ as

$$P_k = \left\{ \Psi(t_k, t_0)^T P_0^{-1} \Psi(t_k, t_0) \right.$$
$$\left. + \sum_{l=1}^{k} \Psi(t_k, t_l)^T \left[ \frac{\partial h_l}{\partial \xi}(\overline{\xi}(t_l)) \right]^T R_l^{-1} \left[ \frac{\partial h_l}{\partial \xi}(\overline{\xi}(t_l)) \right] \Psi(t_k, t_l) \right\}^{-1} \tag{7.95}$$

where $\Psi(\cdot, \cdot)$ is the inverse matrix of the *transition matrix* derived from the (in general time-varying) linear differential equation:

$$\frac{d}{dt} \Delta\xi(t) = \left\{ \frac{\partial f}{\partial \xi}[\overline{\xi}(t)] \right\} \Delta\xi(t) \tag{7.96}$$

that is, a unique solution to the matrix differential equation:

$$\frac{\partial}{\partial t} \Psi(t, s) = - \left\{ \frac{\partial f}{\partial \xi}[\overline{\xi}(t)] \right\} \Psi(t, s) \tag{7.97}$$

with the boundary condition $\Psi(s, s) = I_n$. The $P_0$ in (7.94) is the variance matrix corresponding to the *a priori* information (not given by any sensor but nonetheless given to the tracker) on the target state at time $t_0$. In other words, $P_k$ is calculated in exactly the same way as the state estimation error variance matrix in an extended Kalman filter for continuous-time, sampled-data systems. When the dynamics are not deterministic, as when an additional white noise term appears on the right-hand side of (7.88), we still may use the extended Kalman filtering equations to calculate $P_k$ but no longer claim that it is a Cramér-Rao bound.[29]

---

[29]When the "process" noise (an additive white noise to the dynamics) is small enough, however, we may expect the extended Kalman filtering algorithm to produce a very good approximation of the Cramér-Rao bound.

So far, we have not considered the effects of misassocation on the track accuracy captured by the Cramér-Rao bound, $P_k$, which should be a rather "non-tight" upper bound on data association performance. We may do so by incorporating our analysis on the effects of misassociation on track accuracy (Section 7.4). To do this, we can simply replace $R_k$ in (7.96) by

$$
\begin{aligned}
R_k^E &= R_k + \Upsilon(Q_k, R_k)\tilde{C}_{m_k}\tilde{\beta}(k) \exp[-\tilde{C}_{m_k}\tilde{\beta}(k)] \\
&= R_k + \Upsilon(Q_k, R_k)C_{m_k}\beta(k)[\bar{\sigma}(k)]^{m_k} \exp\{-C_{m_k}\beta(k)[\bar{\sigma}(k)]^{m_k}\}
\end{aligned}
\tag{7.98}
$$

which is the effective measurement error variance matrix, where $\Upsilon(\cdot, \cdot)$ is defined by (7.67). Note, however, that, in deriving (7.98), we ignored the effects of false alarms (extraneous measurements). A simple way to compensate for this may be obtained by adding the false alarm density $\beta_{FA}(k)$ to the target density $\beta(k)$, or by adding $\tilde{D}_{m_k}\tilde{\beta}_{FA}(k)$ to $\tilde{C}_{m_k}\tilde{\beta}(k)$, where $\tilde{\beta}_{FA}(k)$ is the normalization of $\beta_{FA}(k)$.

## Target Density Model

We are to calculate the target density $\beta(k)$ in the measurement space $\mathcal{R}^{m_k}$. To do this, let us consider the second moment

$$
V(t) = \frac{1}{N} \sum_{i=1}^{N} [\xi_i(t) - \bar{\xi}(t)][\xi_i(t) - \bar{\xi}(t)]^T
\tag{7.99}
$$

of the spatial distribution of the targets in the target state space $\mathcal{R}^n$. This can be calculated, similar to the first moment calculation (7.91), as

$$
\begin{aligned}
\frac{d}{dt} V(t) &= \frac{d}{dt} \left\{ \frac{1}{N} \sum_{i=1}^{N} [\xi_i(t)\xi_i(t)^T - \bar{\xi}(t)\bar{\xi}(t)^T] \right\} \\
&\approx \frac{1}{N} \sum_{i=1}^{N} \left\{ \left[ \frac{\partial f}{\partial \xi}(\bar{\xi}(t)) \right] [\xi_i(t) - \bar{\xi}(t)]\xi_i(t)^T \right. \\
&\quad \left. + \xi_i(t)[\xi_i(t) - \bar{\xi}(t)]^T \left[ \frac{\partial f}{\partial \xi}(\bar{\xi}(t)) \right]^T \right\} \\
&= \left\{ \frac{\partial f}{\partial \xi}[\bar{\xi}(t)] \right\} V(t) + V(t) \left\{ \frac{\partial f}{\partial \xi}[\bar{\xi}(t)] \right\}^T
\end{aligned}
\tag{7.100}
$$

which is a quadratic matrix (Riccati) equation identical to the variance matrix extrapolation equation of the continuous-time, sampled-data extended Kalman filter.[30] Equation (7.100) is equivalent to

$$V(t) = \Phi(t, t_0) V_0 \Phi(t, t_0)^T \tag{7.101}$$

where $\Phi(\cdot, \cdot)$ is the fundamental solution matrix to the differential equation (7.96), defined as a unique solution to the matrix differential equation:

$$\frac{\partial}{\partial t} \Phi(t, s) = \left\{ \frac{\partial f}{\partial \xi} [\bar{\xi}(t)] \right\} \Phi(t, s) \tag{7.102}$$

with the boundary condition $\Phi(s, s) = I_n$. The matrix $V_0$ is the initial spatial variance that is the initial condition for the differential equation (7.100); that is, $V(t_0) = V_0$.

The first and the second spatial moments of the target positions in the measurement space can then be calculated as

$$\bar{x}_k \triangleq \frac{1}{N} \sum_{i=1}^{N} h_k[\xi_i(t_k)] \approx h_k[\bar{\xi}(t_k)] \tag{7.103}$$

and

$$\begin{aligned} \mathbf{\Gamma}_k &= \frac{1}{N} \sum_{i=1}^{N} \{h_k[\xi_i(t_k)] - \bar{x}_k\}\{h_k[\xi_i(t_k)] - \bar{x}_k\}^T \\ &\approx \frac{1}{N} \sum_{i=1}^{N} \{h_k[\xi_i(t_k)] - h_k[\bar{\xi}(t_k)]\}\{h_k[\xi_i(t_k)] - h_k[\bar{\xi}(t_k)]\}^T \\ &\approx \left\{ \frac{\partial h_k}{\partial \xi} [\bar{\xi}(t_k)] \right\} P_k \left\{ \frac{\partial h_k}{\partial \xi} [\bar{\xi}(t_k)] \right\}^T \end{aligned} \tag{7.104}$$

Suppose now that the number $N$ of targets in the given group is a Poisson random variable with mean $v$, and the target spatial distribution can be modeled by a Gaussian distribution. Then the average target density can be written as

$$\beta(k) = c_{m_k} \frac{v}{\sqrt{\det(\mathbf{\Gamma}_k)}} \tag{7.105}$$

---

[30]Namely, the extended Kalman filter for continuous-time systems where measurements are available only at discrete times.

with an appropriate constant $c_{m_k}$. Three choices for this constant are listed together with the reason for each choice and some comments:

1. $c_{m_k} = (2\pi)^{-m_k/2}$, which is obtained from the target density at the center, when we assume the target density (defined as the expected number of targets in a unit volume in the measurement space $\mathcal{R}^{m_k}$), $\gamma(\cdot)$, to be Gaussian with the given variance matrix $\Gamma_k$, that is,

$$\gamma(x) = \frac{\nu}{\sqrt{\det(2\pi\Gamma_k)}} \exp\left( -\frac{1}{2} \|x - \bar{x}_k\|^2_{\Gamma_k^{-1}} \right) \tag{7.106}$$

Of course, the center is the place where the target density is highest; hence, this choice may result in a slightly pessimistic prediction on the data association performance.

2. $c_{m_k} = B_m^{-1}\chi^{-m_k}$ with an appropriate $\chi^2$ value, assuming the Gaussian density defined by (7.106). A choice for a "good average value" may be obtained by setting the $\chi^2$ value corresponding to the one-sigma ellipsoidal volume.

3. $B_m^{-1}(m_k + 2)^{-m_k/2}$, which is obtained assuming a uniform target density (rather than (7.106)) on a given ellipsoidal volume with the identical spatial variance matrix $\Gamma_k$. This seems to be an ideal choice for the average target density. We should remember, however, that a projection of a uniformly distributed target group in the target state space $\mathcal{R}^n$ onto the measurement space $\mathcal{R}^m$ is not distributed uniformly unless $n = m$.

Thus the choice of the constant $c_{m_k}$ is not conclusive. Any reasonable choice, however, should give reasonable prediction on the data association performance for the $k$th scan because of the exponential expression of (7.86).

## Remark 3

When the detection probability is significantly less than 1, we must modify our results accordingly. For the track accuracy estimation, this modification may be done easily by discounting the *information matrix* $R_k^{-1}$ in (7.95) by the detection probability $P_D(k)$ for the $k$th data set; that is, by replacing $R_k^{-1}$ with $P_D(k)R_k^{-1}$. This will be justified assuming that, when a target is undetected in the $k$th data set, no new information about its state is obtained. The definition of track purity, however, must be reconsidered in this new situation. The first question is how to count the misdetections in the track purity calculation. We may say the data association is correct when an undetected target is correctly associated with "no measurement." On the other hand, any missing data might be considered an element contributing to the "impurity" of the track when considering the "quality" of tracks. In the latter case, we may simply discount the correct association probability $P_C(k)$ by the detection probability $P_D(k)$.

In this section, we assumed only a single target group. We may apply the results of this section to multiple-group cases. Of course, if the groups are well separated, the extension is obvious. When some groups overlap in some data sets, we may use some kind of "averaging" for each parameter; that is, the target density and the innovations error standard deviation. The same kind of averaging may be used when the track accuracy or measurement error variance is not uniform.

## 7.7 CONCLUSIONS

The data association problem was formulated as the general problem of processing the information contained in multiple random point sets. A simple analytic model for predicting association performance in terms of the correct association probability was derived. The effect of misassociation on the information processing performance (i.e., state estimation performance) also was analyzed, as well as the effect of the presence of extraneous objects on the data association performance. Finally, we showed how this analysis may be applied to performance analysis of multi-target tracking systems. Some preliminary results were presented in [22, 23, 24, and 25]. The effect of uneven target density also was studied in [22]. A rather small example of tracking performance evaluation was presented in [22]. Validity of the analysis presented in Section 7.6 (tracking performance evaluation), however, is yet to be demonstrated through more extensive Monte Carlo simulations. We believe that the results shown in Section 7.6 may be applied to suboptimal multiple hypothesis tracking algorithms even though the results were derived based on an extremely simplified model for tracking processes. This may be so because, in a multiple hypothesis tracker, for each detected target, there should be a track surviving somehow in a hypothesis or several hypotheses, maintaining as much purity as possible and eventually prevailing in the sense that it acquires a high probability. The possible application of the kind of analysis we presented to areas other than multiple target tracking would be of great interest.

As for multiple-target tracking, we concentrated on its data association aspect. Therefore our primary concern was track accuracy and purity. Another important function of multitarget-tracking systems is the *track-level target detection:* a multitarget tracking system can be viewed as a system that performs secondary hypothesis testing on a set of tracks, whereas sensing devices and signal processors providing detections to the tracker may be viewed as systems to perform the primary hypothesis testing function. From this point of view, the important performance measures may be the probability of establishing tracks from "true" targets and the density of "false" tracks. As shown in several works (including [9, Chapter 7, and 7]) along this line, the nature of the analysis is very different from that presented in the chapter, and analysis on general models is extremely difficult. The detection probability and false track density, however, are related intimately to the data association performance in any tracking system. It will be very interesting to see if the results presented here can be incorporated into such an analysis.

Besides R.G. Sea's pioneering work [31] on performance analysis, our work was inspired by an early report by P.W. Soule [33], who analyzed exactly the same data association problem as formulated in Section 7.2. In his study, however, the prediction and measurement error variance matrices ($Q$ and $R$) are assumed in general to be different from object to object. This may be a realistic assumption but it leads to significant difficulty, forcing him to resort to FFT-like numerical analysis for probability of transposition, thereby providing no simple analytic expression. The analysis in Section 7.4, the analysis of the effects of misassocation on track accuracy, was influenced largely by an early work ([15] and its earlier version [14]) on the performance analysis of the probabilistic data association algorithm.

## APPENDIX 7.A:   SOME SPHERICAL INTEGRALS

This appendix describes a couple of useful equations concerning integrating functions over balls in Euclidean space, $\mathcal{R}^n$. They were used in several places in Sections 7.3 and 7.4. Most of the results in this appendix were taken from [14].

1. Let $n$ be a positive integer and $f$ be a real valued measurable function defined on $[0, \infty)$ such that $f(a) \geq 0$ for all $a$ (actually bounded from below is probably enough). Then we have

$$\int_{\|x\|<r} f(\|x\|)\,dx = nB_n \int_0^r \rho^{n-1} f(\rho)\,d\rho \tag{7.A1}$$

for $0 \leq r \leq +\infty$, where $\|x\|$ is the Euclidean norm on $\mathcal{R}^n$, the $n$-dimensional vector space, and $B_n$ is the volume of the unit ball in $\mathcal{R}^n$; that is,

$$B_n = \frac{\pi^{n/2}}{\Gamma\left(\dfrac{n}{2}+1\right)} \tag{7.A2}$$

*Proof:* It is well known that $\mathcal{R}^n \backslash \{0\}$ is homeomorphic to $(0, \infty) \times \mathcal{S}^{n-1}$ where $\mathcal{S}^{n-1}$ is the unit sphere in $\mathcal{R}^n$, and that, for all positive-valued measurable functions $\phi$ defined on $\mathcal{R}^n$, we can integrate the function in "polar" coordinates, as

$$\int_E \phi(x)\,dx = \int_{E\backslash\{0\}} \phi\left(\|x\|\frac{x}{\|x\|}\right)dx$$

$$= \int_G \phi(\rho u)\rho^{n-1} m\,(d\rho \times du) \tag{7.A3}$$

where $E$ is an arbitrary measurable set in $\mathcal{R}^n$ and $G$ is its image on the polar coordinate space; that is,

$$G = \left\{ \left( \|x\|, \frac{x}{\|x\|} \right) \,\middle|\, x \in E\backslash\{0\} \right\} \tag{7.A4}$$

and $m$ is a direct product measure so that $m = \mu \times \sigma_{n-1}$ with $\mu$ being the Lebesgue measure on $\mathcal{R}$ and $\sigma_{n-1}$ being the Lebesgue (surface) measure on $S^{n-1}$. Thus,

$$\sigma_{n-1}(\mathcal{S}^{n-1}) = nB_n \tag{7.A5}$$

is the total area of the unit sphere $\mathcal{S}^{n-1}$.

Noting that

$$\{x \,|\, 0 < \|x\| < r\} = \{\rho u \,|\, \rho \in (0, r) \text{ and } u \in \mathcal{S}^{n-1}\} \tag{7.A6}$$

it is easy to see that (7.A3) actually implies (7.A1).

To calculate the value of $B_n$ (i.e., to prove (7.A2)), we may use the following equalities:

$$\begin{aligned}
(2\pi)^{n/2} &= \prod_{i=1}^{n} \int_{-\infty}^{\infty} e^{\frac{1}{2}x_i^2}\, dx_i \\
&= \int_{\mathcal{R}^n} e^{-\frac{1}{2}\|x\|^2}\, dx \\
&= \sigma_{n-1}(\mathcal{S}^{n-1}) \int_{0}^{\infty} e^{-\frac{1}{2}\rho^2} \rho^{n-1}\, d\rho \\
&= nB_n 2^{n/2-1}\Gamma(n/2) \\
&= B_n 2^{n/2}\Gamma(n/2 + 1)
\end{aligned} \tag{7.A7}$$

2. Let $f$ be the same as before. Then, we have

$$\int_{\|x\|<r} xx^T f(\|x\|)\, dx = \left( B_n \int_0^r \rho^{n+1} f(\rho)\, d\rho \right) I_n \tag{7.A8}$$

for $0 \leqslant r \leqslant +\infty$, where $x^T$ is the transpose of $x$ and $I_n$ is the $n \times n$ identity matrix.

*Proof:* Applying (7.A3) to the integral of each component, we have

$$\int_{\|x\|<r} xx^T f(\|x\|)\, dx = \int_0^r \rho^{n+1} f(\rho)\, d\rho \int_{s^{n-1}} uu^T \sigma_{n-1}\,(du) \tag{7.A9}$$

Therefore, it suffices to show

$$\int_{s^{n-1}} uu^T \sigma_{n-1}\,(du) = B_n I_n \tag{7.A10}$$

which can be proved by

$$\begin{aligned}
\delta_{ij}(2\pi)^{n/2} &= \int_{\mathcal{R}^n} x_i x_j e^{-\|x\|^2/2}\, dx \\
&= \int_0^\infty \rho^{n+1} e^{-\rho^2/2}\, d\rho \int_{s^{n-1}} u_i u_j \sigma_{n-1}\,(du) \\
&= 2^{n/2}\Gamma(n/2 + 1) \int_{s^{n-1}} u_i u_j \sigma_{n-1}\,(du)
\end{aligned} \tag{7.A11}$$

where $\delta_{ij}$ is Kronecker's delta, and $x_i$ and $u_i$ are the *i*th component of the vectors $x$ and $u$, respectively.

## APPENDIX 7.B:  CONDITIONAL GAUSSIAN DISTRIBUTIONS

The appendix describes the calculation of the first two moments of Gaussain random vectors when conditioned by half-plane type constraints. We use the following notations: erfc($\cdot$) is the complementary error function defined by erfc($x$) $\triangleq (2\pi)^{-1/2}\int_x^\infty \exp(-\xi^2/2)\, d\xi$. The probability measure and the expectation operator for the underlying probability space are denoted by $P(\cdot)$ and $\mathcal{E}(\cdot)$. For a vector or a matrix $X$, its transpose is denoted by $X^T$. The term $\|x\|_A$ is a seminorm of a vector $x$ defined by a symmetric nonnegative definite matrix $A$ as $\|x\|_A \triangleq \sqrt{x^T A x}$, and if $A$ is the identity matrix $I$, $\|x\|_I$ is the standard Euclidean norm, denoted by $\|x\|$.

*Proposition:* Let $X$ be a Gaussian random *n*-vector with mean $\bar{x}$ and variance matrix $V$. Let $a$ be an *n*-vector such that $\|a\|_V > 0$, and $b$ be a scalar. Then we have

$$P\{a^T X \geq b\} = \text{erfc}(\alpha) \tag{7.B1}$$

$$\mathcal{E}(X \mid a^T X \geq b) = \bar{x} + \frac{\exp(-\frac{1}{2}\alpha^2) \, Va}{\sqrt{2\pi} \, \text{erfc}(\alpha) \|a\|_V} \qquad (7.B2)$$

$$\mathcal{E}(XX^T \mid a^T X \geq b) = V + \bar{x}\bar{x}^T \qquad (7.B3)$$

$$+ \frac{\exp(-\frac{1}{2}\alpha^2)}{\sqrt{2\pi} \, \text{erfc}(\alpha)} \left( \frac{Va\bar{x}^T + \bar{x}a^T V}{\|a\|_V} + \alpha \frac{Vaa^T V}{\|a\|_V^2} \right)$$

where

$$\alpha = \frac{b - a^T \bar{x}}{\|a\|_V} \qquad (7.B4)$$

*Proof:* Equation (7.B1) can be calculated directly from the mean and the variance of the Gaussian random variable $a^T X$. Let us assume that the variance matrix $V$ is positive definite. The proposition may be proven without this assumption, but we will keep it for the sake of simplicity. To calculate (7.B2), consider the linear transformation

$$\xi = V^{-1/2}(x - \bar{x}) \qquad (7.B5)$$

where $V^{1/2}$ is a matrix square root of $V$ such that

$$V = V^{1/2} V^{T/2} \qquad (7.B6)$$

Such a square root $V^{1/2}$ may not be uniquely determined. We may choose one, however, so that

$$V^{T/2} a = \|a\|_V e_1 \qquad (7.B7)$$

is true, where (as well as in the following) we use the notations, $V^{T/2} \triangleq V^{1/2})^T, V^{-T/2} \triangleq [(V^{1/2})^T]^{-1} = [(V^{1/2})^{-1}]^T$, and so forth, and $e_1$ is the $n$-vector defined by

$$e_1 = \begin{bmatrix} 1 \\ 0 \\ \cdot \\ \cdot \\ \cdot \\ 0 \end{bmatrix} \qquad (7.B8)$$

Using the transformation (7.B5), we have

$$\mathcal{E}(X \mid a^T X \geqslant b) \, P\{a^T X \geqslant b\}$$

$$= \det(2\pi V)^{-1/2} \int_{a^T x \geqslant b} x \exp\left(-\frac{1}{2} \|x - \bar{x}\|^2_{V^{-1}}\right) dx$$

$$= \bar{x} \, \mathrm{erfc}(\alpha) + (2\pi)^{-n/2} V^{1/2} \int_{e_1^T \xi \geqslant \alpha} \xi \exp\left(-\frac{1}{2} \|\xi\|^2\right) d\xi \qquad (7.B9)$$

$$= \bar{x} \, \mathrm{erfc}(\alpha) + (2\pi)^{-\frac{1}{2}} \exp\left(-\frac{1}{2} \alpha^2\right) V^{1/2} e_1$$

$$= \bar{x} \, \mathrm{erfc}(\alpha) + (2\pi)^{-1/2} \exp\left(-\frac{1}{2} \alpha^2\right) \frac{Va}{\|a\|_V}$$

from which (7.B2) follows.

Using the same transformation (7.B5), we have

$$\mathcal{E}(XX^T \mid a^T X \geqslant b) P\{a^T X \geqslant b\}$$

$$= \det(2\pi V)^{-1/2} \int_{a^T x \geqslant b} xx^T \exp\left(-\frac{1}{2} \|x - \bar{x}\|^2_{V^{-1}}\right) dx \qquad (7.B10)$$

$$= (2\pi)^{-n/2} \int_{e_1^T \xi \geqslant \alpha} (\bar{x} + V^{1/2}\xi)(\bar{x} + V^{1/2}\xi)^T \exp\left(-\frac{1}{2} \|\xi\|^2\right) d\xi$$

In one of the steps in (7.B9), we already calculated

$$(2\pi)^{-n/2} V^{1/2} \int_{e_1^T \xi \geqslant \alpha} \xi \exp\left(-\frac{1}{2} \|\xi\|^2\right) d\xi$$

To calculate (7.B10), it suffices to evaluate

$$W \triangleq (2\pi)^{-n/2} \int_{e_1^T \xi \geqslant \alpha} \xi\xi^T \exp\left(-\frac{1}{2} \|\xi\|^2\right) d\xi \qquad (7.B11$$

The (1, 1)-element of matrix $W$ is calculated as

$$W_{11} = \left[\int_{\alpha}^{\infty} \xi_1^2 \frac{\exp\left(-\frac{1}{2} \xi_1^2\right)}{\sqrt{2\pi}} d\xi_1\right] \left[\prod_{i=2}^{n} \int_{-\infty}^{\infty} \frac{\exp\left(-\frac{1}{2} \xi_i^2\right)}{\sqrt{2\pi}} d\xi_i\right]$$

$$= \mathrm{erfc}(\alpha) + (2\pi)^{-1/2} \alpha \exp(-\tfrac{1}{2}\alpha^2)$$

Similarly, we have $W_{ii} = \text{erfc}(\alpha)$ for all $i > 1$ and $W_{ij} = 0$ for $i \neq j$. We thus have

$$W = \text{erfc}(\alpha)I + (2\pi)^{-1/2}\alpha\, \mathbf{e}^{-\alpha^2/2} e_1 e_1^T \tag{7.B12}$$

where $I$ is the identity matrix, and hence

$$V^{1/2}WV^{T/2} = \text{erfc}(\alpha)V + (2\pi)^{-1/2}\alpha\, \mathbf{e}^{-\alpha^2/2}\frac{Vaa^TV}{\|a\|_V^2} \tag{7.B13}$$

Equation (7.B3) then follows from (7.B9), (7.B10), and (7.B13).    Q.E.D.

By replacing $a$ and $b$ in (7.B1) through (7.B3) with $-a$ and $-b$, we can obtain the following "dual" results. Namely, under all the assumptions made for the Proposition, we have

$$P\{a^TX \leq b\} = \text{erf}(\alpha) \tag{7.B14}$$

$$\mathcal{E}(X\,|\,a^TX \leq b) = \bar{x} - \frac{\exp(-\frac{1}{2}\alpha^2)}{\sqrt{2\pi}\,\text{erf}(\alpha)}\frac{Va}{\|a\|_V} \tag{7.B15}$$

$$\mathcal{E}(XX^T\,|\,a^TX \leq b) = V + \bar{x}\bar{x}^T \tag{7.B16}$$

$$- \frac{\exp(-\frac{1}{2}\alpha^2)}{\sqrt{2\pi}\,\text{erf}(\alpha)}\left(\frac{Va\bar{x}^T + \bar{x}a^TV}{\|a\|_V} + \alpha\frac{Vaa^TV}{\|a\|_V^2}\right)$$

where $\alpha$ is defined by (7.3) and $\text{erf}(\cdot)$ is the error function defined by

$$\text{erf}(\alpha) = 1 - \text{erfc}(\alpha) \tag{7.B17}$$

## REFERENCES

[1] J.K. Aggarwal, L.S. Davis, and W.N. Martin, "Correspondence Processes in Dynamic Scene Analysis," *Proc. IEEE*, Vol. 69, No. 6, May 1981, pp. 562–572.

[2] D.H. Ballard and C.M. Brown, *Computer Vision*, Prentice-Hall, Englewood Cliffs, NJ, 1982.

[3] Y. Bar-Shalom and E. Tse, "Tracking in a Cluttered Environment with Probabilistic Data Association," *Automatica*, Vol. 11, September 1975, pp. 451–460.

[4] Y. Bar-Shalom, T.E. Fortmann, and M. Scheffé, "Joint Probabilistic Data Association for Multiple Targets in Clutter," *Proc. 1980 Conf. Information Science Systems*, Princeton University, Princeton, NJ, March 1980.

[5] Y. Bar-Shalom, and T.E. Fortmann, *Tracking and Data Association*, Academic Press, 1988.

[6] Y. Bar-Shalom, "Multitarget-Multisensor Tracking: Principles and Techniques," UCLA Extension Short Source Notes, 1989.

[7] Y. Bar-Shalom, L.J. Campo, and P.B. Luh, "From Receiver Operating Characteristic to System Operating Characteristic: Evaluation of a Track Formation System," *IEEE Trans. on Automatic Control*, Vol. AC-35, No. 2, February 1990, pp. 172–179.

[8]    Y. Bar-Shalom, K.C. Chang, and H.A.P. Blom, "Tracking of Splitting Targets in Clutter Using an Interactive Multiple Model Joint Probabilistic Data Association Filter," Chapter 4 of this book.

[9]    S.S. Blackman, *Multiple Target Tracking with Radar Application,* Artech House, Dedham, MA, 1986.

[10]   F. Bourgeois and J.-C. Lassalle, "An Extension of the Munkres Algorithm for the Assignment Problem to Rectangular Matrices," *Communications of the ACM,* Vol. 14, No. 12, December 1971, pp. 802–804.

[11]   C.B. Chang, K.P. Dunn, and L.C. Youens, "An Algorithm for Multiple Target Tracking and Data Correlation," Tech. Rep. 643, Lincoln Laboratory, M.I.T., AD-A1131313, June 1983.

[12]   C.B. Chang, K.P. Dunn, and L.C. Youens, "A Tracking Algorithm for Dense Target Environments," *Proc. of American Control Conf.,* San Diego, CA, June 1984.

[13]   F.E. Daum, "Bounds on Performance for Multiple Target Tracking," *IEEE Trans. on Automatic Control,* Vol. AC-35, No. 4, April 1990, pp. 443–446. See also Chapter 6 of this book.

[14]   T.E. Fortmann, Y. Bar-Shalom, M. Scheffé, and S. Gelfand, "Detection Thresholds for Multi-Target Tracking in Clutter," BBN Rep. No. 5495, BBN Laboratory, Inc., Cambridge, MA, December 1983.

[15]   T.E. Fortmann, Y. Bar-Shalom, M. Scheffé, and S. Gelfand, "Detection Thresholds for Tracking in Clutter—A Connection Between Estimation and Signal Processing," *IEEE Trans. on Automatic Control,* Vol. AC-30, No. 3, March 1985, pp. 221–229.

[16]   P.E. Hart, N.J. Nilsson, and B. Raphael, "A Formal Basis for the Heuristic Determination of Minimum Cost Paths," *IEEE Trans. on Systems Science and Cybernetics,* Vol. SSC-4, No. 2, 1968, pp. 217–234.

[17]   R.A. Hummel, "On the Foundations of Relaxation Labeling Processes," *IEEE Trans. on Pattern Analysis and Machine Intelligence,* Vol. PAMI-5, No. 3, May 1983, pp. 267–287.

[18]   T. Kailath, "An Innovations Approach to Least-Squares Estimation, Part I: Linear Filtering in Additive White Noise," *IEEE Trans. on Automatic Control,* Vol. AC-13, No. 6, 1968, pp. 646–654.

[19]   X.R. Li and Y. Bar-Shalom, "Stability Evaluation and Track Life of the PDFA for Tracking in Clutter," *Proc. 29th IEEE Conf. on Decision and Control,* Honolulu, December 1990, pp. 2264–2269.

[20]   C.L. Morefield, "Application of 0–1 Integer Programming to Multi-Target Tracking Problems," *IEEE Trans. on Automatic Control,* Vol. AC-23, June 1977, pp. 302–312.

[21]   S. Mori, C.-Y. Chong, E. Tse, and R.P. Wishner, "Tracking and Classifying Multiple Targets without *A Priori* Identification," *IEEE Trans. on Automatic Control,* Vol. AC-31, No. 5, May 1986, pp. 401–409.

[22]   S. Mori, K.C. Chang, C.Y. Chong, and S. Spain, "Tracking Performance Evaluation," Tech. Rep. ADS-TR-1196-01, Advanced Decision Systems, Mountain View, CA, December 1988.

[23]   S. Mori, K.C. Chang, C.Y. Chong, and S. Spain, "Tracking Performance Evaluation: Phase II Final Technical Report," Tech. Rep. ADS-TR-2228-01, Advanced Decision Systems, Mountain View, CA, November 1989.

[24]   S. Mori, K.C. Chang, C.Y. Chong, and K.P. Dunn, "Tracking Performance Evaluation—Prediction of Track Purity," *Proc. SPIE 1989 Tech. Symp. on Aerospace Sensing,* Orlando, FL, March 1989.

[25]   S. Mori, K.C. Chang, C.Y. Chong, and K.P. Dunn, "Tracking Performance Evaluation—Track Accuracy in Dense Target Environments," *Proc. SPIE 1990 Tech. Symp. on Aerospace Sensing,* Orlando, FL, April 1990.

[26]   J. Munkres, "Algorithm for the Assignment and Transportation Problems," *J. Soc. Industrial Applied Mathematics,* Vol. 5, No. 1, March 1957, pp. 32–38.

[27]   A. Papoulis, *Probability, Random Variables, and Stochastic Processes,* 2d Ed., McGraw-Hill, New York, 1984, Chapter 6, pp. 139–140.

[28]   K.R. Pattipati, S. Deb, Y. Bar-Shalom, and R.B. Washburn, "Passive Multisensor Data Association Using a New Relaxation Algorithm," Y. Bar-Shalom (ed.), *Multitarget-Multisensor Tracking: Advanced Applications,* Artech House, Norwood, MA, 1990, Chapter 7, pp. 219–246.

[29]   R.D. Reid, "An Algorithm for Tracking Multiple Targets," *IEEE Trans. on Automatic Control,* Vol. AC-24, December 1979, pp. 843–854.

[30]   D.J. Salmond, "Mixture Reduction Algorithms for Target Tracking in Clutter," *Proc. of SPIE 1990 Tech. Symp. on Aerospace Sensing,* Orlando, FL, April 1990.

[31]   R.G. Sea, "An Efficient Suboptimal Decision Procedure for Associating Sensor Data with Stored Tracks in Real-Time Surveillance Systems," *Proc. IEEE Conf. Decision and Control,* Miami Beach, December 1971, pp. 33–37.

[32]   W. Smith, L. Ekchian, and D. Johnson, "Neural Net Implementation of Plot/Track Association," *Proc. SPIE 1990 Tech. Symp. on Aerospace Sensing,* Orlando, FL, April 1990.

[33]   P.W. Soule, "Performance of Two-Way Association of Complete Data Sets," Rep. No. TOR-0074(4085)-15, The Aerospace Corporation, El Segundo, CA, January 1974.

[34]   J.H. Taylor, "The Cramér-Rao Estimation Error Lower Bound Computation for Deterministic Nonlinear Systems," *IEEE Trans. on Automatic Control,* Vol. AC-24, No. 2, April 1979, pp. 343–344.

[35]   P.R. Wolf, *Elements of Photogrammetry,* McGraw-Hill, New York, 1974.

# Chapter 8
# MULTITARGET TRACKING WITH AN AGILE
# BEAM RADAR

## S. S. Blackman*

### Hughes Aircraft Company
### Los Angeles, California

## 8.1  INTRODUCTION

Future radar multiple-target tracking systems will utilize the agile beam (*electronically scanned array* [ESA] or phased array) radar. The agile beam radar can perform adaptive sampling by directing the radar beam without inertia in any direction. Thus, the transition from the search for new targets to the update illumination of an existing target track can be achieved almost instantaneously (within a few microseconds). This property gives the agile beam radar the potential to achieve MTT performance significantly improved over that obtainable with a *mechanically scanned antenna* (MSA) radar, which is severely limited by mechanical inertia.

The agile beam radar allows for the separation of the search and track update functions for an MTT system. It can illuminate existing target tracks one at a time and interleave search for new targets among update illuminations of existing tracks. This allows it to track targets outside the standard search volume. Therefore, for the agile beam radar it is appropriate (and can significantly improve performance) to adaptively choose a track update-sampling rate and search-illumination volume based on such considerations as target importance, track quality, proximity between

*Most of the concepts presented in this chapter were originally formulated jointly by the author and Dr. T. J. Broida and with the encouragement of J.N. Hoffner. Other major contributors were Dr. D. Goudey, Dr. J. Hashimi, S. Ickovic, Dr. K. Krikorian, Dr. R. Popoli, and R. Rosen.

tracks, and prior knowledge of expected target input flux into the potential search region.

This chapter is concerned primarily with the airborne tracking problem for which the postulated future environment includes the potential for many closely spaced targets, highly maneuverable targets, and low cross-section (low observable) targets. Therefore, the increased capabilities of the agile beam radar must be utilized efficiently. This leads to a number of options and trade-offs between performance and complexity.

References [13, 15, 17, 39] contain overview discussions of many of the issues involved in agile beam radar tracking system design. This chapter will extend those discussions and present conclusions obtained from recent studies. It will present a design strategy that covers all significant aspects involved in the definition of an agile beam radar MTT system.

Section 8.2 outlines methods for system evaluation. These methods are used later to illustrate the design process. Section 8.3 gives an overview of the detection process. For an agile beam radar the processes of detection and tracking are closely interrelated. Thus, the basic detection issues and methods must be understood to design the tracking system.

Section 8.4 discusses resource allocation issues. The effective utilization of radar resources probably is the most important (and interesting) challenge in agile beam radar tracking system design. Resource allocation is important and rarely discussed in the radar tracking literature; therefore, this chapter is heavily devoted to allocation. Issues to be discussed in detail include the choice of time on target for track update illumination and the definition of an overall strategy for the allocation between search for new targets and the update illumination of existing target tracks.

Sections 8.5 and 8.6 discuss methods that can be used for filtering and prediction and data association. A wide variety of techniques are available for these functions, and the choice of technique will depend highly on the particular application. Therefore, a broad survey of the available techniques is presented. The chapter concludes with a discussion of the tracking of low observable targets and the interaction of the radar with the other sensors in a multiple sensor suite.

## 8.2 PERFORMANCE PREDICTION

To design tracking system algorithms and predict performance, we must first use approximate analytic methods and then perform more detailed and more accurate evaluations using Monte Carlo simulation. In the case of agile beam radar tracking, the design options are so numerous that full use of analytic methods is particularly important. Then, by using the results of approximate analysis, the Monte Carlo simulation study can be more effective.

### 8.2.1   Analytic Methods for Predicting Track Accuracy

Reference [15] has summarized the use of covariance analysis for estimating track prediction performance. However, other techniques are available for determining steady state track accuracy in an even quicker and more direct manner. These include use of the curves presented in [5, 24, 26, 40] giving track accuracy as a function of the environment for position measurement. The curves presented in [27] extend the results of [26] by giving track accuracy where a velocity measurement also is available. Thus, the results of [27] are particularly convenient for predicting the performance of a radar-range tracker in which range rate is measured in addition to range.

Due to the difficulty in extrapolating among the published curves of [5, 24, 26, 40] it is convenient to use closed-form analytical expressions. Reference [8] presents a closed-form solution that can be used to determine steady-state track accuracy for the case of a position measurement. When considering the position prediction error for a position measurement, an even simpler approach is to use the expression, first presented in [46] and modified in [15], to include the effects of nonunity probability of detection ($P_D$). This expression is

$$T = 0.4 P_D \left[ \frac{\sigma_0 \sqrt{\tau_m}}{\sigma_m} \right]^{0.4} \frac{v_0^{2.4}}{1 + 0.5 v_0^2} \tag{8.1}$$

where

$$T = \text{sampling interval,}$$
$$\sigma_0 = \text{position observation standard deviation,}$$
$$\sigma_m, \tau_m = \text{target maneuver standard deviation, time constant from Singer model [40],}$$
$$v_0 = \sigma_p / \sigma_0$$
$$\sigma_p = \text{position prediction error standard deviation.}$$

The stated limits of applicability of (8.1) for Cartesian position are [46]

$$\sigma_0 = 30 \text{ to } 1500 \text{ ft}, \qquad \sigma_m = 8.0 \text{ to } 96 \text{ ft/s}^2 \tag{8.2}$$
$$\tau_m > 20 \text{ s}, \qquad T = 0.1 \text{ to } 5.0 \text{ s}$$

However, as indicated in [15], experience indicates that the region of applicability typically can be extended to shorter values of the target maneuver time constant ($\tau_m \geqslant 10$ s). Given system parameters, (8.1) can be solved conveniently for the track prediction accuracy, and this method will be used for the allocation study presented later.

## 8.2.2 Analytic Methods for Predicting Correlation (Association) Performance

Reference [15] presents convenient expressions for evaluating track correlation performance for an isolated target in a false-alarm environment. However, for typical radar system design the correlation performance for closely spaced targets is of more concern. For this application approximate expressions [19, 34] have proven to be very useful for preliminary design (see also Chapter 7 in this book).

First, consider two targets separated by distance vector **d** in an $M$-dimensional measurement space. Then, under the conditions that both targets are in track and that a detection is received from each target, the probability of false correlation, $P_{FC2}$, can be approximated by [19, 34]

$$P_{FC2} = 1 - \text{erf}\left(\sqrt{W/2}\right) \tag{8.3}$$

where

$$
\begin{aligned}
W &\triangleq \mathbf{d}^T S^{-1} \mathbf{d} \\
S &= \text{residual covariance matrix} = HPH^T + R, \\
H &= \text{measurement matrix}, \\
P, R &= \text{Kalman prediction, measurement error covariance matrices}, \\
\text{erf}(x) &\triangleq (2\pi)^{-1/2} \int_{-\infty}^{x} \exp(-u^2/2)\, du
\end{aligned}
$$

The derivation leading to (8.3) has assumed that the same Kalman filter covariance matrix, $P$, is valid for both tracks and that the same measurement noise covariance matrix, $R$, can be used for both observations.

For a single detection (one detection is missed due to nonunity $P_D$), the approximate probability of false correlation is given by

$$P_{FC1} = 1 - \text{erf}\left(\sqrt{W/2}\right) \tag{8.4}$$

Then, the overall probability of correlation error as a function of $P_D$, tracking system performance (through $P$) and radar system measurement accuracy (through $R$) is given by

$$P_{FC} = \frac{P_D^2 P_{FC2} + 2P_D(1 - P_D)P_{FC1}}{P_D^2 + 2P_D(1 - P_D)} \tag{8.5}$$

Thus, when considering a given radar system design, preliminary tracking performance estimates can be obtained by using covariance analysis or the other methods discussed earlier, and correlation performance for typical target spacings, **d**, can be estimated using (8.3) through (8.5).

Use of $P_{FC}$, as defined earlier, is a very approximate way to determine expected system performance as measured, for example, by track stability and accuracy. Given a simple correlation method, such as the sequential, nearest-neighbor method described in Chapter 4 of [15], typical results, such as presented in [31], indicate accurate, stable tracking as long as $P_{FC}$ can be maintained at a few percent. As $P_{FC}$ increases to 0.1 or beyond, tracks typically become erratic due to miscorrelation as long as only the single, most likely, hypothesis is maintained. On the other hand, multiple hypotheses tracking will greatly improve performance but $P_{FC}$ is a rough measure of the number of hypotheses that must be maintained.

### 8.2.3    Monte Carlo Simulation

Reference [30] discusses in more detail the design of a simulation used to evaluate tracking performance for an agile beam radar system. Many of the conclusions presented later in this chapter are based on the examination of results from this simulation. The major principles in the design of this, or any other, simulation of an agile beam radar tracking system are summarized next.

First, the simulation must be modularized so that individual functions are contained in completely independent (stand-alone) modules. Examples are the elements of the allocation logic and the tracking filters, which are designed and tested independently. Modules also should be generalized as much as possible for ease in future expansion.

Several levels of radar process modeling should be available. For ease in obtaining adequate Monte Carlo statistics, one version should use just basic detection and measurement models in the form of formulas or simple curve fits. However, the option to obtain results with a more detailed radar model must be available as well. This more detailed radar model, for example, might simulate scintillation and eclipsing in detail rather than use detection curves averaged over these phenomena. There is a trade-off, however, between detailed modeling and the number of Monte Carlo runs that can be used to obtain performance statistics.

A comprehensive set of graphic output statistics for an agile beam radar simulation must include at least four basic categories: track number statistics, data association performance, kinematic estimation accuracy, and radar resource allocation statistics. A provision must be made to examine the most interesting (or anomalous) Monte Carlo runs in more detail. This is conveniently done by producing a short summary table for individual Monte Carlo runs and specifying the random number that initiated each run. Then, individual runs can be repeated and more detailed printouts conveniently obtained for program debugging and system design.

## 8.3   DETECTION: OBSERVATION GENERATION AND PROCESSING

### 8.3.1   Enhancing Detection and Measurement Performance

As discussed in [15, 21] there are three main techniques for enhancing detection performance with the agile beam radar. The first method varies the *time-on-target* (TOT) spent during target illumination at a particular beam position. This feature allows the use of longer TOT for longer range or lower cross-section targets. As will be shown in Section 8.4, theoretically we can determine an optimal TOT given the system performance goals and assuming knowledge of the target characteristics.

One unfortunate characteristic of an agile beam radar is that the radar antenna beam typically broadens when the antenna is pointing off the mechanical boresight. This beam broadening is accompanied by a corresponding loss in the signal-to-noise ratio associated with a target offset by angle $\theta$ from the boresight. The attenuation factor in SNR is approximately $\cos^2\theta$. Thus, because SNR also typically is taken to be proportional to TOT, the variable TOT feature also can be used to compensate for the loss that otherwise would occur for targets offset from the mechanical boresight.

A second method for improving detection performance is the adaptive choice of radar waveform. As discussed in [17], there are a variety of potential waveforms, as defined by the radar pulsewidth, the *pulse repetition frequency* (PRF), and the radar *carrier frequency* (RF). Again, because the functions of track update and search for new targets can be separated, we can tailor the choice of waveform to the function and, within the function of track update, choose the waveform based on the estimated target characteristics.

During track illumination the waveform can be chosen based on the estimated target position. For example, for a high PRF radar, the PRF can be chosen to minimize the effects of the eclipsing phenomenon [15, 17] that can be predicted as a function of the estimated target range. Similarly, during search, the waveform can be adaptively chosen to best accommodate the alert-confirm detection process discussed next.

The third, and probably the most significant, detection feature associated with the agile beam radar is the use of a two stage detection sequence typically denoted *alert-confirm* (or *alert-verify*) processing [17, 21]. Using this approach, the initial (alert) detection, usually obtained from a lowered detection threshold, triggers the transmission of a second (confirm) waveform. The time interval between the alert and confirm stages typically is small as the delay needs to be only long enough to accommodate the required alert phase signal processing. Thus, because the target characteristics can be assumed to be relatively unchanged, the same basic waveform (RF, PRF) should be used for confirm as for alert. However, the confirm stage typically is characterized by a longer time on target to reduce false alarms, and a more complex waveform is used to provide the information required to initiate an accurate track.

A typical alert-confirm detection sequence might utilize a *velocity search* (VS) alert waveform in which the target angular position and range rate would be measured but for which no range would be obtained. The RF could be changed so that a given target typically would be illuminated during search by more than one radar frequency. Use of multiple frequencies utilizes the effects of radar target cross-section scintillation to enhance detection [15].

The alert stage threshold crossing received using the VS waveform would be followed by a more complex waveform to accommodate the FM ranging technique discussed in [17] for high PRF. Alternatively, a medium or low PRF confirm dwell might also be considered. Finally, a more accurate angle measurement may be obtained during the confirm dwell through use of the monopulse measurement technique.

The delay between the alert dwell and the application of the corresponding confirm dwell typically is the time required to apply several search alert beams. This delay results from the time required for alert dwell signal processing and the necessity to recognize multiple detections that may occur on successive alert beams from the same target. Also, interruption of the alert search process to confirm a prior alert should occur only after completion of the current alert. However, the correlation time of the radar signal typically is much longer than the delay time between alert and confirm dwells.

The choice of antenna beam spacing in search also presents some interesting trade-offs. Decreasing the spacing between beams leads to less loss for targets between adjacent beam centers. However, decreased spacing typically means that a longer time (more beams) may be required to search a given volume. Alternatively, as beam spacing is decreased, less power (time at that beam position) will be required. References [10, 13] discuss the choice of beam spacing and other search considerations in more detail. As discussed there, the typical criterion for choice of search parameters is the cumulative probability of detection for a closing target. For example, the analysis of [11] indicates that the spacing between beam positions should be about 0.8 beamwidths.

Alert-confirm processing also may be used for track illumination. The options here include the use of multiple RF or PRF waveforms for alert to determine the best waveform for use in confirm.

## 8.3.2 Reducing the Effects of Jet Engine Modulation

As discussed in [15, 36], the effects of *jet engine* (or turbine) *modulation* (JEM) on the radar return can lead to multiple apparent range-rate detections from a single target. Although highly dependent on the particular conditions, the deviations of the spurious JEM returns from the true (skin) return may be about the same as typical deviations between true and expected returns resulting from a target maneuver. Thus, JEM returns may be interpreted falsely as target maneuvers and cause difficulty in determining the presence of multiple closely spaced targets.

The characteristics of JEM can be used to reduce its effects on tracking. First, the true target (skin) return and the JEM returns typically are characterized by harmonic relationships, with the skin return expected to have the largest amplitude. The JEM induced range-rate measurements typically appear as distinct components separated from the true range rate by integer multiples of engine-dependent fundamental components [36]. Also, the range of separations between skin and JEM returns can be predicted. Thus, combined amplitude, harmonic and spacing information can be used to form likelihoods for the skin return and the potential presence of multiple targets (as opposed to the skin and JEM returns from a single target).

The fast update rate capability of the agile beam radar can lead to a very accurate estimate of range rate. Thus, it may be possible to maintain distinct tracks on the return estimated to be the skin and the returns estimated to be JEM lines. Then, by examining the range measurement residual, we can determine if the skin return has been correctly identified, and if not, the skin estimate can be shifted according to the range measurement residual. This process could best be performed within a structure such as MHT.

To summarize, some processing typically is performed during the detection and observation stage of the processing to identify potential JEM returns. This may reduce some of the observations formed, and it will produce likelihoods for those observations formed and sent to the data association function of the ESA tracking system. However, the presence of JEM returns probably will necessitate more sophisticated data association, such as the JPDA and MHT methods discussed later, for future systems.

## 8.4   RADAR RESOURCE ALLOCATION

Given the postulated difficult tracking environment for future agile beam radar systems, the efficient allocation of radar resources is crucial to the success of these systems. The overall allocation problem includes several issues. The main issue is the proportion of resources to be allocated to the various target tracks for track illumination and target identification and to the search for new (previously undetected) targets. However, given that an overall proportion of radar resources is to be allocated to a given target track, another important issue is the trade-off between time on target and revisit rate. Thus, the issue of choosing TOT will be addressed first, and then the more global allocation issues will be discussed.

### 8.4.1 Choice of Optimal TOT

Assume that a given proportion ($C$) of radar resources typically is to be allocated to a given target track. This proportion is given by the ratio of TOT to the average revisit time ($T$). As an example, consider a system that typically must maintain tracks on 30 targets and should spend at least 40% of its time searching for new targets. Then, the average proportion of resources that can be allocated for each track is

$$C = \frac{0.6}{30} = 0.02 = \frac{\text{TOT}}{T}$$

To determine the optimal choice of TOT for a given value of $C$, we use the analytic expressions given by (8.1) through (8.5) and consider as figures of merit the azimuth angular prediction error standard deviation ($\sigma_p$), the angular residual error standard deviation ($\sigma_r = \sqrt{\sigma_p^2 + \sigma_0^2}$), and the probability of false correlation ($P_{FC}$). The azimuth angle prediction error is chosen because angle prediction accuracy is a key factor in weapon delivery and angle separation typically is the most useful discriminant for data association with closely spaced radar targets. Reference [29] presents a study with similar methods and conclusions.

For a given radar system, the assumed TOT and the target characteristics can be used to compute the SNR. To evaluate tracking performance for a given value of SNR, standard relationships can be used to compute the probability of detection ($P_D$) and the measurement standard deviation ($\sigma_0$). For the purposes of illustration, two such simple relationships that are applicable under fairly general conditions [7, 13, 17] will be used:

$$P_D = (P_{FA})^{1/(1+\text{SNR})}, \qquad \sigma_0 = \frac{\theta_{HP}}{k\sqrt{2(\text{SNR}+1)}} \tag{8.6}$$

where

$P_{FA}$ = probability of false alarm per detection element,
$\theta_{HP}$ = half-power radar beamwidth,
$k$ = slope factor associated with the monopulse measurement process.

Representative values taken for an example to follow are

$$P_{FA} = 10^{-5}, \qquad \theta_{HP} = 2.5°, \qquad k = 1.37$$

SNR can be assumed to be directly proportional to TOT. Thus, given the nominal values, $SNR_n$ and $TOT_n$, the SNR for other (than nominal) TOT can be computed directly by using

$$\text{SNR} = \frac{\text{TOT}}{\text{TOT}_n} \text{SNR}_n \qquad (8.7)$$

Then, using $C$ to determine $T$ and using (8.6) and (8.7) to determine $P_D$ and $\sigma_0$, (8.1) can be used to evaluate prediction accuracy. Finally, given system parameters and prediction accuracy, (8.3) through (8.5) can be used to estimate correlation performance.

To illustrate the approach, assume typical targets at 30 nmi and with maneuver time constant ($\tau_m$) and standard deviation ($\sigma_m$) of 10 s and 1.0 g (32 ft/s²). Converting target acceleration to angular units and noting that 1 nmi is about 6000 ft:

$$\sigma_m = 32/(30 \times 6 \times 10^3) = 0.18 \text{ mrad/s}^2$$

Also, for illustration, assume values for $TOT_n$ and $SNR_n$ of 0.04 s and 25, respectively. Finally, to evaluate correlation performance, assume closely spaced targets separated only in azimuth angle and with a separation of 1.0°.

Figures 8.1–8.3 show illustrative results that would be used to determine the choice of TOT for our hypothetical radar system. Figure 8.1 shows the prediction

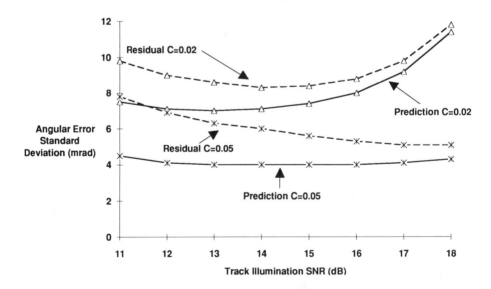

**Figure 8.1** Comparison of tracking error for varying illumination SNR: target at 30 nmi.

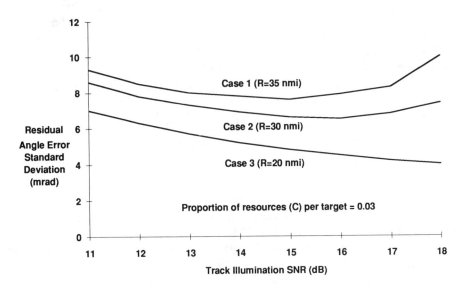

**Figure 8.2** Comparison of residual error for three ranges as function of illumination SNR.

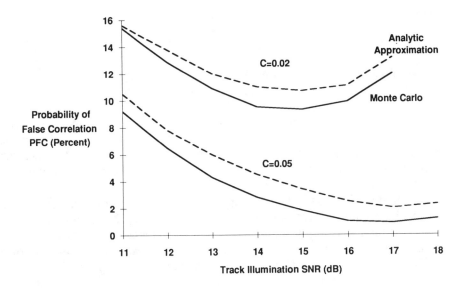

**Figure 8.3** Correlation performance as function of illumination SNR: two targets separated by 1°.

and residual error standard deviations for the target conditions defined above and for the cases of 2 and 5% of resources allowed per target ($C = 0.02, C = 0.05$). Figure 8.2 shows the residual standard deviation for three assumed encounter ranges. A standard operational assumption of increased target maneuverability at a shorter range is used. Also, using standard SNR relationships, the required nominal TOT to achieve SNR of 25 is taken to be proportional to $R^4$. The cases are defined

Case 1: $R = 35$ nmi, $\sigma_m = 0.5$ g, $TOT_n = 0.074$

Case 2: $R = 30$ nmi, $\sigma_m = 1.0$ g, $TOT_n = 0.04$

Case 3: $R = 20$ nmi, $\sigma_m = 2.0$ g, $TOT_n = 0.008$

For all cases shown in Figure 8.2 the proportion of resources allocated to each target was 0.03.

Figure 8.3 relates radar system parameters and prediction accuracy to correlation performance by showing estimated $P_{FC}$ for the two cases ($R = 30$ nmi, $\sigma_m = 1.0$ g, $C = 0.02, 0.05$) considered in Figure 8.1. One set of results presented in Figure 8.3 was derived using (8.3) through (8.5). Also, a simple Monte Carlo simulation was run to give comparative results and determine the result of the approximations involved in the use of (8.3) through (8.5).

In Figure 8.3, the analytic approximation is somewhat pessimistic. This is particularly true for the smaller values of $P_{FC}$. However, the same general conclusions regarding the allocation of illumination SNR are apparent from the analytic and the Monte Carlo results.

Using standard radar conventions, results in Figures 8.1–8.3 are presented as a function of SNR expressed in dB, as defined

$$SNR \ (dB) = 10 \log_{10} SNR$$

This was done to illustrate the main conclusion, which is that an operating point in SNR can be defined and the appropriate TOT chosen from that operating point. For our example, it would appear that an SNR of about 15 dB provides an operating point for a wide variety of conditions. A somewhat more refined allocation logic would increase the amount of power allocated per track illumination when more overall resources are available for track illumination. However, to a first order approximation, an efficient allocation procedure would require always choosing TOT so that 15 dB SNR is obtained.

Finally, note that this conclusion of a 15 dB operating point is dependent on the assumed detection and measurement models of (8.6) and the assumed allowable $P_{FA}$ ($10^{-5}$ in this case). In particular, for advanced systems, a more sophisticated radar signal processing technique will lead to better detection performance for a given SNR. Thus, results using other models have indicated a 13–14 dB operating point to be more appropriate. However, the analysis techniques presented here have been found to be equally valid for other radar models.

## 8.4.2 Global Allocation Strategy

When considering the allocation of radar resources, it is generally required that the radar sensor manager be designed to have autonomous capability. However, for future systems the radar sensor manager and the radar tracking system will operate within an *integrated multiple sensor* (MSI) system framework [9]. Thus, the radar sensor manager must be designed to integrate the MSI sensor manager and other external inputs with an internal radar-generated task list. Figure 8.4 presents an overview of a proposed approach to the radar resource allocation problem. This representation and the discussion to follow are similar to that presented in [17], and a more complete discussion of an MSI system is given in [9].

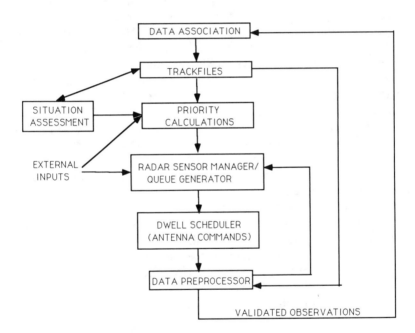

**Figure 8.4** Overview of radar sensor allocation.

The radar sensor manager will determine a set of task priorities based on the radar track file and other internal radar information. The three major task categories are update or target identification for existing tracks and the search for new targets. The assignment of priorities to these tasks can be accomplished using utility theory or expert system methods that will be discussed later. The computation of utilities will be aided by a situation assessment function whose purpose is to determine track and search region priorities. In addition, there may be external input such as track importance weighting and the establishment of a radiation policy from the MSI sensor manager. Finally, based on this information and the existing track quality, as determined by the Kalman filter covariance matrices, figures of merit, or utilities, can be determined for the potential radar tasks.

The queue generator will form a queue of tasks that will be entered into the dwell scheduling function, where the actual radar antenna commands are generated. In addition to the tasks generated internally, other tasks may be added from external sources such as the aircraft pilot, the fire control system, and the MSI sensor manager. Also, it may be necessary to integrate tasks that are to be performed on a fixed time schedule with the other required tasks. An example of a fixed time task is the transmission of an update message to a missile in flight.

The dwell scheduling function will produce radar beam position commands and determine the choice of parameters such as radar waveform and TOT for the tasks as they are performed. The choice of TOT is based on a trade-off between accurate measurement and timely updates. Guidelines for this choice will be defined *a priori*, based on analysis such as given in the previous section.

Once radar sensor allocation is performed, the observation data is entered into the data association function. However, a preprocessor also will assess the quality of the data and provide a fast feedback to the queue generator. For example, the preprocessor will determine when a track update was unsuccessful so that the track update may be repeated as soon as possible. Also, as discussed later, the preprocessor may inhibit the allocation of a confirm waveform on an alert received during search and found to correlate with an existing target track or determined to be from an unwanted target, such as a bird [12].

Radars designed to operate against low observable targets may detect many unwanted small targets, such as birds, in the alert stage. These unwanted targets probably can be rejected (so that a confirm illumination is not wasted) only based on their combined small measured component of radial velocity and small signal amplitude. This rejection process may lead to some loss of target sensitivity. However, the low amplitude targets that are not closing on the tracking platform, which may be rejected falsely, probably will be of lesser priority.

### 8.4.3   Determining Task Figures of Merit

A modern efficient allocation algorithm must direct the agile beam radar (and other sensors) among the options to search for new targets, to perform kinematic update or identification for existing target tracks, or (for active sensors) to remain covert. As discussed in more detail by Waltz and Llinas [47], the decision must be based on such factors as expected target threat, offensive opportunity, availability of other sensors, and overall mission objectives. Thus, the basic issue in the design of an allocation algorithm is the manner in which these alternative tasks are assigned *figures of merit* (FOM).

The two basic methods that have been proposed for determining task FOM are through utility theory [9, 15] and expert system [1, 20, 37] approaches. However, these two methods actually are very similar in application. They both use the same type of criteria, such as target lethality, tracking error, and time since revisit of a given search region, and assign measures of usefulness, or FOM, in the interval (0, 1) to the allocation alternatives. The difference between the methods is that utility theory computes the FOM through mathematical expressions, called *utility functions,* whereas the expert system uses a set of "IF-THEN" rules to determine FOM. We next discuss in more detail the actual implementation of these methods.

### 8.4.4   Utility Theory Allocation

A multiattribute utility function $U(x_1, x_2, \ldots, x_n)$ is defined as a measure of usefulness (or utility) of the attributes $x_1, x_2, \ldots, x_n$ relative to other values or consequences. For our application the attributes are quantities such as range and angle tracking error variances, the number of newly detected targets, the uncertainty in target type estimation, *et cetera.* The goal of the allocation algorithm will be to maximize expected utility.

To define a system that can be implemented readily, we found it desirable to make several simplifications that result from assumed independence conditions. For example, considering two attributes $(x_1, x_2)$, making the assumption of additive independence leads to a multiattribute utility function which is the weighted sum of single attribute utility functions

$$U(x_1, x_2) = aU_1(x_1) + bU_2(x_2) \tag{8.8}$$

The assumption of additive independence can be interpreted loosely to state that the desirability of $x_1$ does not depend on the value of $x_2$.

Using the assumption of additive independence, the overall utility of all tracks can be defined as a weighted sum of the individual track utilities. Also, for a given track it is very convenient to assume that the utilities for the kinematic attributes (such as range and angle tracking error) are independent. This leads to an overall track kinematic utility that is a weighted sum of the utilities for each of the kinematic components.

The choice of utility functions, in effect, is an art similar to the design of an expert system. The expert knowledge of the designer is contained in the form and the parameters chosen for the utility function. Before presenting the forms for the utility functions that have proven useful for this application, it is necessary to define the attribute set. The values of the members of this set will be used to measure the usefulness of performing a given allocation action. The attribute sets are

$S$ = The set of all Kalman filter error variances of all currently held tracks.

$P$ = The set of probability distributions over the possible target types.

$N_s$ = The expected number of targets within a potential search volume.

The overall utility function is defined to be an additive function of the utilities for update, search, and target ID ($U_U$, $U_S$, $U_{ID}$, respectively):

$$U(S, N_s, P) = K_U U_U(S) + K_S f(N, S) U_S(N_s) + K_I U_{ID}(P) \tag{8.9}$$

The parameters $K_U$, $K_S$, and $K_I$ are appropriately chosen scaling factors and $f(N, S)$ is chosen as a function of the number ($N$) and quality of existing tracks. Finally, the update and ID utilities can be expressed more explicitly in terms of the contributions from the $N$ individual tracks (again assuming additive independence):

$$U_U(S) = \sum_{n=1}^{N} I_n U_U(S_n) \tag{8.10}$$

$$U_{ID}(P) = \sum_{n=1}^{N} I_{Gn} U_{ID}(P_n) \tag{8.11}$$

where, for track $n$,

$I_n, I_{Gn}$ = target type and geometrical importance weighting terms,
$U_U(S_n), U_{ID}(P_n)$ = kinematic and ID utilities for track $n$.

There are $2N + 1$ allocation events to consider, and as discussed in more detail later, the expected change in utility (the marginal utility) associated with each of these $2N + 1$ possible actions can be computed. For example, when considering track update we can measure track quality for a state $X$ by

$$Q = \frac{\sigma_{\hat{x}}}{\sigma_D} = \frac{\text{error standard deviation}}{\text{desired error standard deviation}} \tag{8.12}$$

Given the expression of (8.12), each track will have two potential qualities. These are the quality ($Q_{NU}$) if the track is not updated and the quality ($Q_U$) if the track is updated. The quality $Q_U$ can be computed by using the expected error standard deviation that will result from track update. This computation requires solution, or estimation, of the anticipated Kalman filter covariance matrix. Then, as illustrated by Figure 8.5, a marginal utility for quantity $X$ can be computed. Thus, if

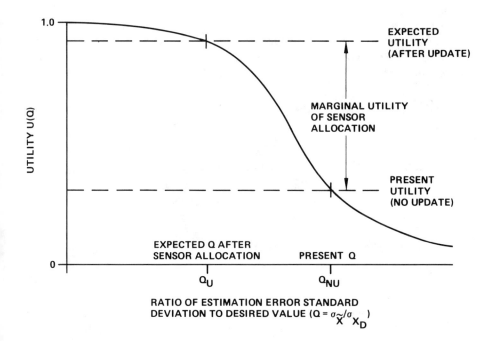

**Figure 8.5** Illustration of utility computation for sensor allocation.

allocation decisions are made to maximize marginal utility, the result will be that the overall system utility will be maximized.

The marginal utility, $M_U(n)$, for the update of track $n$ can be computed as a sum over the marginal utilities, $M_U(n, i)$, for each measured state $i$:

$$M_U(n) = P_D(n) \sum_{i=1}^{M} r_i I_n M_U(n, i) \tag{8.13}$$

where

$$\begin{aligned} M &= \text{measurement dimensionality,} \\ P_D(n) &= \text{probability of detecting track } n, \\ r_i &= \text{weight associated with state } i, \text{ such that } \sum_{i=1}^{M} r_i = 1. \end{aligned}$$

The marginal utility associated with use of the radar for target ID for a given track can be computed by using the present ID vector, $P_n$, the utilities, $U_{lm}$, of declaring target type $l$ given true target type $m$ and the expected ID performance of the radar. This involves a direct application of Bayes's rule as illustrated in [15].

A convenient expression for defining the utility of searching to acquire an expected number, $N_s$, of new tracks is given by

$$U_S(N_s) = [1 - \exp(-N_s V_{nt}/N_{max})]N_{max} \qquad (8.14)$$

where

$V_{nt}$ = expected value of a new target track. Given that track utilities range from 0 to 1, a typical value for $V_{nt}$ is 0.25 .

$N_{max}$ = maximum number of tracks that the system is required (or able) to maintain.

The expected number of targets detected in search can be computed from

$$N_s = P_{DS}\hat{\theta} \qquad (8.15)$$

where $P_{DS}$ is the probability of detection in search and $\hat{\theta}$ is the expected number of new (previously undetected) targets in the search volume. A simple recursive formula for computation of $\hat{\theta}$ is

$$\hat{\theta}(k + 1) = [1 - \gamma P_{DS}] \hat{\theta}(k) + \lambda T \qquad (8.16)$$

where

$$\gamma = \begin{cases} 1.0; & \text{search performed on frame } k \\ 0; & \text{search not performed} \end{cases}$$
$\lambda$ = new target flux rate,
$T$ = time interval between frames.

As outlined earlier, the computation of FOM through utility functions can be quite complex. However, as discussed in [9, 47], this problem can be reduced by categorizing targets and storing precomputed utilities as a function of the target track category. Thus, the track utility computations are reduced to a table look-up.

### 8.4.5 Expert System Allocation

Following Popoli and Blackman [37], and as discussed in more detail in Chapter 10 of this book, an allocation expert system can be defined to be situation driven, using a simplified situation assessment. The expert system consists of a knowledge base and a reasoning scheme (or inference engine). The knowledge base is a codification of the expert's knowledge as typically defined by a knowledge base of "IF-THEN" rules. The reasoning scheme draws conclusions from the knowledge base.

The system described here employs an inexact reasoning scheme based on fuzzy set theory. As illustrated, this approach starts with root concepts and builds higher-order concepts by using fuzzy set operations as logical connectives. The method starts by assigning fuzzy memberships of tracks and search regions to root concepts such as close and lethal for tracks and large flux of undetected targets for search regions.

The membership of quantity $x_i$ in set $A$ is defined by the membership function, $\mu_A(x_i)$, which quantifies the degree to which $x_i$ belongs to $A$. For example, if $x_i$ is track $n$ the degree to which the track $(T_n)$ belongs to the set of close tracks may be defined

$$\mu_{\text{CLOSE}}(T_n) = \frac{1}{1 + aT_{\text{GO}}(n)} \tag{8.17}$$

where $T_{\text{GO}}(n)$ is the time to go (range divided by magnitude of range rate) and $a$ is an appropriately chosen weighting coefficient.

Membership functions, such as given by (8.17), are defined over the interval (0, 1). The ultimate goal of the system is to define the membership of each track in that set of tracks that require update and to define the membership of each search region in that set of search regions that should be illuminated for the detection of new targets. These membership functions thus are the analogy of the utilities computed for track update and search by the utility theory method. Thus, as noted earlier, the methods are very similar with the major difference being that the mathematical utility functions are replaced by the rules and reasoning scheme of the expert system.

The expert system approach to allocation is illustrated through the decision tree given in Figure 8.6. This decision tree computes the membership function of a track in the set of tracks to be updated. Each box represents a node, and there are two types of nodes. The nodes that have lines branching out below them to other nodes are called *branch nodes*. Otherwise, the node is called a *root*.

Each branch node's value is computed from the values of the nodes below it. A branch connected with an arc is a conjunction such as defined by the rule "If the target is hostile and imminent, then the target is attacking." The value for a branching node that is a conjunction is taken to be the minimum of the values of its children. Thus, for this example,

$$\mu_{\text{ATTACKING}} = \text{MIN}[\mu_{\text{HOSTILE ID}}, \mu_{\text{IMMINENT}}]$$

If the nodes below a branching node are not connected by an arc, the branching node is a disjunction. In this case, the value of the branching node is taken to be the

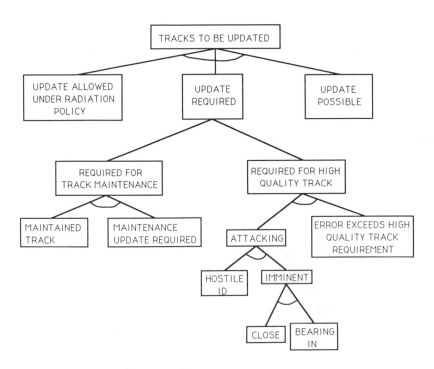

**Figure 8.6** Sensor allocation decision tree.

maximum of the values of its children. For our example, the degree to which a track update is required is the maximum of the values for which update is required for track maintenance or high quality. Note that the requirement for a high-quality track also is based on the degree to which the target is attacking. The top three nodes together represent the implication, "If an update for a given track is required, is allowed under the radiation policy, and is possible, then that update should be performed." Note that, for example, an update might not be possible due to the off-boresight angle of the target.

The decision tree given in Figure 8.6 does not include all the nodes that typically would represent the factors involved in determining the value of track update. However, this example does illustrate that there will be at least two classes of tracks. One class of tracks requires only sufficient accuracy so that the track is not lost, whereas the second class of higher-quality tracks, such as for attacking targets, requires greater accuracy.

The example in Figure 8.6 is designed to illustrate the flexibility of the expert system approach to sensor management. The value of a branch node is determined by the values of its children. The values of the root nodes are determined by defining membership functions such as that given by (8.17). More examples of membership functions for root nodes are given in Popoli and Blackman [37].

The use of an expert system sensor management system appears to have several distinct advantages over the utility theory method. In general, it is easier to define, modify, and add rules than to choose utility functions and their parameters. Also, it is easier to trace back decisions through the rules than to evaluate utility functions. Thus, using an expert system, it is easier to explain the operation of the sensor management system to a user and changes based on user input can be made more directly.

### 8.4.6 Other Allocation Issues

#### 8.4.6.1 Efficient Use of Alert-Confirm Search

Using the alert-confirm method, a lower threshold alert detection during search triggers the application of a longer TOT confirm dwell for which a second threshold exceedance is required to declare target presence. This approach is an application of sequential detection theory that, for typical conditions, can be equivalent to an increase in target signal power of about 4 dB [12]. This equivalent gain is dependent on the system parameters that determine the loss that occurs due to the necessity to allocate confirm dwells to false alarms [7]. Another potential loss in system efficiency may occur if confirm dwells are allocated unnecessarily to targets already in track.

It may be inefficient (and unnecessarily slow down the search process) to allocate confirm dwells to targets that are already in track and that do not require an immediate update. Also, search observations typically are less accurate than those received during track illumination. Thus, the information gain may be low and the potential for miscorrelation high for search observations used for track update. On the other hand, for a very dense target environment it may be necessary to use all possible information to maintain tracks on all targets.

An approach that utilizes search observations, when appropriate, first identifies "good" tracks for which an immediate search observation update would not be of significant value. Then, alert observations falling within the gates of these tracks would be ignored, and no confirm would be applied. On the other hand, alert detections within the gates of higher-priority tracks that require update will cause the transmission of a confirm. Finally, alert detections within the gates of low-priority tracks may not lead to a confirm but may be used for track update so that the track can be maintained.

The alert stage typically uses a velocity search waveform that measures only angle and range rate (no range is measured). Therefore, ignoring alert returns within the gates of existing tracks may lead to a delay in track initiation for the stream raid target case in which two or more targets are at the same angle and closing rate but different ranges. This problem can be addressed by periodically performing a search for new targets while illuminating existing tracks.

### 8.4.6.2 Supersearch Track Update Illumination

Ideally, the track update schedule should be such that targets remain within the beamwidth of the predicted track positions. However, under conditions of severe target maneuver or unusual demand on radar resources the ideal may not be possible. Therefore, in difficult tracking environments track uncertainty can grow so that there will be a significantly degraded probability of detection if an update illumination is performed using a single radar beam position. For high-priority targets, this can lead to the requirement for a supersearch about the predicted position of the track being illuminated. The supersearch could consist of anywhere from three to nine beam positions centered about the predicted track angular position. An alternative is to use the capability to electronically broaden the radar beamwidth (at the cost of lower SNR).

### 8.4.6.3 Group Illumination

Potential data association problems can arise if the members of a closely spaced group are illuminated individually [15]. This problem results, due to incomplete information, when observation-to-track assignment occurs without observations from all target tracks. The problem can be alleviated through use of branching or the multiple hypothesis tracking methods discussed later in this chapter. However, it may be advantageous to perform a supersearch that illuminates all members of a target group simultaneously.

### 8.4.7 Typical Allocation Example

Figure 8.7 generically illustrates the typical allocation that occurs when a large number (approximately 50) of targets must be tracked, and a search for new targets is performed as well. It is based on results obtained from the Monte Carlo simulation described earlier and in [30]. We assume that search begins as several waves of targets enter the surveillance regions. Initially, before tracks are established, all resources are devoted to search. However, as tracks are initiated, more resources are allocated to track update. Thus, as tracks are being acquired and before firm tracks are established, the proportion of resources allocated to track update typically exceeds 50%.

As firm tracks are established and the targets close in range, the proportion of resources required for track illumination may decrease. Note that, as range decreases, the TOT required to achieve the optimal SNR decreases. However, it typ-

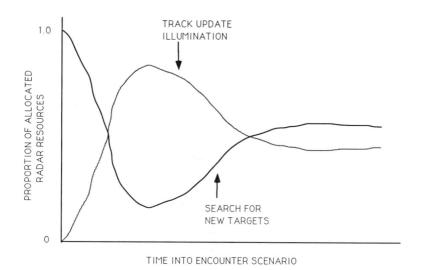

**Figure 8.7** Typical allocation time history for dense-target scenario.

ically is assumed that potential target maneuverability increases as target range decreases. Also, even for invariant target maneuverability, target angle dynamics increase with decreasing range. Thus, a complex set of trade-offs is presented to the allocation logic to resolve.

The allocation pattern shown in Figure 8.7 results from either utility or expert system allocation schemes. Simulation results also indicate that both methods adapt well to the number of targets. More total resources, of course, are allocated to track illumination for scenarios with large numbers of targets. However, to maintain search capability and service all the tracks in large-target scenarios, less resources per track are allocated for scenarios with large numbers of targets.

It might be argued that the allocation pattern shown in Figure 8.7 gives an inordinate proportion of radar resources to track update. However, as also noted in the translation of the Russian book by Shishov and Voroshilov [39], it is reasonable that the emphasis should be to apply radar resources to existing tracks because resources already have been invested in the establishment of these tracks. If inadequate resources are applied to existing tracks, these tracks may be lost with the result that further resources will be expended to reacquire the tracks. It is much more efficient to allocate resources to adequately maintain a track than to later have to repeat the track initiation and confirmation processes.

Another important factor is that search performance may not be significantly degraded by an increase in the proportion of radar resources allocated to track update. For example, Billam [10, 12] gives an example where the allocation of half the radar resources to tracking leads to a reduction of only 10% in the 90% cumulative probability of detection range. A similar result is shown in Chapter 12 of [15].

## 8.5  FILTERING AND PREDICTION

The development of tracking filters for an agile beam radar system depends highly on the application. This section gives an overview of the major issues involved. More details on applicable techniques are given in the references.

### 8.5.1  Choice of Tracking Coordinates and States

The first major issue is the choice between the use of Cartesian *versus* polar coordinates. Performing all tracking in a Cartesian system clearly is most convenient for internetted system operation. Also, target-track extrapolation is performed most accurately in Cartesian coordinates. However, the conversion of the radar measurements (range, range rate, and angle) to Cartesian coordinates for the purpose of track update leads to a nonlinear measurement that typically requires the use of a fully coupled, extended Kalman filter [24]. However, Daum and Fitzgerald [22] and Baheti [4] discuss practical methods for radar tracking using Cartesian coordinates.

The use of polar coordinates (range and angles) has the advantage of using measured quantities directly as states. Thus, no nonlinear measurement is required and filter decoupling is facilitated. However, problems can arise in the extrapolation for a conventional polar tracking coordinate system where angle rates and possibly angle accelerations are used as states.

As discussed further in [15], extrapolation, and tracking in general, with a polar system can be improved greatly by applying a filter that uses angle along with Cartesian velocity and acceleration as states. This choice of tracking coordinates has proven to be very accurate in both simulation and actual flight test studies for a single airborne-tracking platform. However, the use of any type of polar system for individual platforms will require the conversion to Cartesian coordinates for internetted operation.

The issue of decoupling is of extreme practical importance [22]. This refers, for example, to the use of three separate tracking filters for range, azimuth, and elevation angles (or $x$, $y$, $z$ in Cartesian coordinates). The fully coupled alternative refers to the use of one tracking filter for all tracking coordinates. For example, the possible alternatives might be the use of three three-state filters (uncoupled) *versus* the use of a single nine-state filter (coupled). As discussed in [22], by using the $n^3$ (where $n$ is the number of states) rough rule of thumb, decoupling leads to a reduction in the number of required computations by a factor of about nine for this case.

Another factor, recently discussed by Rogers [38], is the potential error introduced into a polar tracking system by using uncoupled filters due to target *line-of-sight* (LOS) rotation. The polar tracking coordinates rotate with the LOS and this rotation introduces a coupling so that the decoupled tracking filters no longer are independent. The effects of this phenomenon are a strong function of the relative accuracies of the decoupled filters and the LOS rate.

Simulation results indicate that the filter instability discussed in [38] does not occur for typical airborne agile beam radar applications. However, the unmodeled coupling may lead to somewhat inaccurate Kalman filter covariances with resulting problems in gating for maneuvering, high-LOS rate targets. Thus, some adjustment to the Kalman covariance may be required.

### 8.5.2  Target Maneuver Modeling and Detection

The Singer model [40] has a long history of application but, as discussed in [3, 33, 45], it may be desirable to augment the tracking filter design with models for the physical constraints applicable to maneuvering aircraft. In particular, typical aircraft accelerations are primarily perpendicular to the aircraft velocity. This constraint can be introduced through a more general target dynamic model [3, 33] or as a pseudo-measurement [45].

Many techniques have been proposed for maneuver detection and filter adaptation to target maneuvers. Surveys are presented in [5, 17]. Use of an agile beam radar introduces the additional flexibility to adapt the track update rate to the target maneuver level [14, 15, 35].

Recent experience has indicated that the use of maneuver detection along with radar resource allocation methods, such as described earlier, can lead to very efficient allocation. The first step is to appropriately increase the track Kalman filter covariance matrix after the detection of target maneuver. The increased error, as reflected in the Kalman covariance, then is included in the trade-off between updating the track in question *versus* performing other allocation options. This approach automatically leads to the increased allocation of resources to maneuvering targets [31].

Recently developed *interacting multiple model* (IMM) methods [16] should be considered for future agile beam radar systems. Again, the output track covariance, that now also includes model uncertainty, is directly applicable for use in the radar resource allocation logic.

### 8.5.3  Modified Spherical Coordinates

Radar tracking in the presence of *electronic countermeasures* (ECM) typically is made difficult by the lack of range and range-rate measurements. Thus, the tracking system must be designed to operate in the presence of angle-only measurements. This constraint favors the use of a polar type of coordinate system.

Use of the *modified spherical coordinates* (MSC) filter, as discussed by Stallard [41], has been proposed primarily for use with passive sensors. In this six-state filter, the set of coordinates used are two angles, two angle rates, inverse time-to-go ($\dot{R}/R$) and inverse range ($1/R$). The advantages of this system are that all but the sixth state ($1/R$) are observable with angle-only data and that the estimation of these states (and the associated Kalman covariance matrix) is not degraded by the lack of a range measurement.

Preliminary results indicate that use of an MSC filter is appropriate for a radar tracking system in which ECM may be employed. When available, range and range rate can be given the filter as nonlinear measurements. Otherwise, in the presence of ECM, the filter operates in a stable manner using angle-only information.

The MSC filter estimates the quantity $\dot{R}/R$ with angle-only measurements. Thus, given a range-rate measurement, in addition to angle, a range estimate can be developed as well. This means that it may be possible to maintain sufficiently accurate tracks (including range estimates) on low-priority targets by using only the alert velocity search waveform. This property of the MSC filter can have important implications for radar resource allocation.

## 8.6  DATA ASSOCIATION

Data association, which involves the partitioning of observations into tracks, is the major issue in the design of any tracking system. This general problem is discussed in great detail in five books [5, 6, 15, 24, 47] and in numerous articles. This section will outline the applicability of various data association approaches to the agile beam radar MTT problem.

### 8.6.1  Conventional Data Association

The conventional approach to data association for radar tracking systems, as summarized in Chapter 4 of [15], might be described as sequential, nearest-neighbor single-hypothesis tracking. Using this approach, on the receipt of a set of observation data, a unique pairing of observations to existing tracks is determined by using likelihood theory. Observations not assigned to existing tracks typically are used to initiate new tracks. The best data association hypothesis, in terms of maximizing likelihood, is chosen, and this decision is irrevocable. This approach was appropriate when considering the limited requirements and computational capabilities of early radar track-while-scan systems but must be extended for future systems.

Chapter 12 of Blackman [15] and [14, 31] outline an approach by which conventional data association methods can be extended for application to a future agile beam radar system. This approach utilizes several levels of gating, and a limited amount of branching (or deferred decision) is used for cases of ambiguous data association.

An example of the use of multiple gates and branching occurs when a search observation falls within the large (or maneuver) gate (but not the standard gate) of a given track. The track is assigned a high priority for update illumination, and the observation is saved for potential use later. Then, if the track is illuminated and no resulting illumination observation is assigned to the track, the search observation is assigned to the track. If, as a result of track illumination, a standard gate observation is assigned to the track, the large gate search observation may be used to initiate a new tentative track.

Simulation results indicate that relatively simple extensions to conventional data association methods can lead to excellent tracking performance [31]. These results were obtained by using an allocation logic that gave high priority to tracks involved in data association conflicts. Thus, branches were established and quickly resolved by allocation of update illuminations. However, a limited number ($\leq 10$) of targets was simulated, and this approach may not be successful for larger scenarios of closely spaced targets.

### 8.6.2 Multiple Hypothesis Tracking

By using the MHT method, the full capability of the agile beam radar can be achieved theoretically. New hypotheses are formed as observations are received, and later data are used to resolve uncertainty. By using MHT rather than conventional methods, successful tracking performance will depend much less on the simultaneous illumination of all target tracks and the immediate allocation of radar resources to resolve uncertainty.

Simulation studies have indicated that the MHT methods described in Chapters 10 and 14 of [15] can be applied directly to agile beam radar MTT with excellent performance resulting. Furthermore, preliminary sizing and timing studies have indicated the feasibility of implementing both the MHT algorithm of [15] and the structured branching [23] approach to MHT on future airborne computers. Other studies, such as reported in the chapters by Kurien and Chong in [6], also clearly indicate that MHT will be the preferred data association method for future systems.

One important issue is that sensor allocation is less direct using the MHT approach. Because several alternative tracks may be formed for a given target, it becomes more difficult to position the antenna for track update. One approach to this problem is to use the coordinated presentation described in [18]. By using the coordinated presentation, the centroid, extent, and expected number of targets within a cluster are computed, and this information can be used for sensor allocation.

### 8.6.3 Joint Probabilistic Data Association

The JPDA method also forms multiple data association hypotheses after the receipt of each data set. However, these hypotheses are combined before the next data set is processed. The result is that the updated estimate for a given track may contain contributions from more than one observation, and a given observation can be used to update more than one track.

The JPDA method has been shown to have better performance than conventional methods for a variety of applications [5], and the JPDA computational requirements will be much less than those for MHT. However, the agile beam radar MTT problem typically is characterized by closely spaced targets flying in parallel. Also, we must initiate new tracks in the vicinity of existing tracks as targets become newly detected or resolved. Both of these problems require the development of special logic for JPDA application. However, the chapter by Fitzgerald in [6] and [42] address these issues for the practical application of the JPDA method to radar MTT.

The *jet engine modulation* problem discussed earlier is characterized by multiple observations from the same target. These are produced by the target skin and the modulation resulting from the motion of internal components of the jet engine. Given a set of JEM returns, the JPDA method will form a weighted sum of the returns to update the track and appropriately increase the track Kalman filter covariance matrix to reflect the uncertainty. Thus, the JPDA methods appear to be directly applicable to JEM data processing.

### 8.6.4 Group Tracking

As discussed in Chapter 11 of [15] and in [44], group tracking has many advantages for closely spaced radar targets in formation. Group tracking provides a stable centroid and an estimate of group extent. This information can be used for sensor allocation with the advantage that multiple targets can be illuminated during a single allocation. Also, computer resources can be conserved by tracking several targets as a group with a single Kalman filter and state vector being utilized for the entire group.

As discussed further in [44], group tracking has the advantage (over conventional tracking methods) of stability in the presence of missing detections that occur due to target fades and difficulties in resolving closely spaced targets. However, a considerable logic is required to handle the conditions of splitting, merging, and crossing groups. Also, because some precision may be lost, it may be necessary to restrict group tracking to targets not considered to be an immediate threat to the tracking platform.

### 8.6.5   Other Implementation Issues

Several other important implementation issues are involved in agile beam radar MTT data association and must be addressed regardless of the method chosen. First, due to the flexibility inherent in the allocation of the agile beam radar, the observation data will be received in an asynchronous manner. Thus, for practical purposes, the track position can be predicted for the expected time of the next target illumination. This position and the associated prediction covariance are used for initial gating and possibly for observation-to-track association. However, for final track update the track prediction should be corrected to coincide with the actual observation time.

Degraded tracks must be deleted and one component of the deletion logic typically is a penalty for missed update attempts and a reward for track update. Therefore, update attempts are defined to occur either when a specific track update is allocated or when a search volume containing the track is illuminated.

### 8.7   OTHER FUTURE SYSTEM ISSUES

### 8.7.1   Track Confirmation for Low-Observable Targets

It is well known that low-observable (or dim) targets pose a prime threat for future radar tracking systems [12, 43]. First, note that the alert-confirm processing method discussed earlier is a very efficient allocation of radar resources. It effectively uses the principle of sequential detection theory to acquire tracks on low-observable targets. However, several other methods, outlined here, also are being developed for this problem.

Both MHT [23, 28, 32] and JPDA [Chapter 2 of 6] methods have been proposed for dim targets, and the results are presented in those references. Furthermore, [23] has defined an approach whereby the problem of track confirmation on dim targets is recognized as an application of the classical *sequential probability ratio test* (SPRT). Using this analogy, the expected decision times associated with the SPRT can be used to predict MHT performance in terms of the expected true target track confirmation time and the expected number of false tracks that must be maintained.

Either MHT or JPDA track confirmation logic could be designed to operate on returns that satisfy a relatively low threshold. For example, a dual thresholding approach could be used for search. Using this approach, a return that exceeds the standard (alert) threshold would lead to the immediate application of a confirm waveform. However, an observation that exceeds the second (lowered) threshold but not the higher (alert) threshold will lead to the initiation of a tentative track and the subsequent application of special track confirmation logic. Again, should the tentative track reach an intermediate confidence level, as computed by the MHT scoring procedure [15], the application of a confirm waveform could be made.

Both MHT and JPDA methods for acquiring tracks on dim targets require that thresholding be applied to each set of observation data as it is received. Other techniques, that have been given the term *track-before-detect* (TBD), attempt to map the measured signal into an appropriate target state space so that integration occurs over several scans of data, and thresholding is deferred until after track processing. The *dynamic programming algorithm* (DPA) discussed by Arnold [2] and the processing methods discussed by Farina and Russo [25] are examples of the application of the TBD approach to the detection and tracking of dim radar targets. A detailed discussion of the DPA method is given in the chapter by Barniv in [6].

An interesting tracking problem will be introduced by the extreme sensitivity of future radars designed to detect very low cross-section targets. As discussed by Billam [12], these radars may detect a large number of small, unwanted targets, such as birds or even worker bees. Thus, a logic, based on range rate or other discriminating features, will be required to assure that radar resources (such as a confirm dwell) are not wasted on these "targets."

### 8.7.2 Radar as Part of Multiple Sensor System

For modern systems, the radar tracking system will operate as part of a multiple sensor system. As discussed earlier, the radar sensor manager must be defined to accept input from an MSI sensor manager. Also, radar data must be integrated into the multiple sensor track file [48].

As discussed in Chapter 6 of [6] and in [48], multiple sensor data can be integrated in several ways. However, probably the preferred architecture for future airborne systems will have each sensor maintain sensor-level tracks formed from its own data. Then, the multiple sensor track file is formed by track fusion. The major reasons for maintaining sensor-level tracks are to reduce data transmission requirements, to ensure greater survivability by maintaining distributed tracking capabilities, and to reduce the effects of ECM. Also, the features of the particular set of sensors—radar, *infrared search and track* (IRST), and electronic *support measure* (ESM)—are such that the potential loss in tracking performance associated with track fusion is minimized.

When considering the radar, IRST, and ESM sensors, note that track fusion essentially will take the radar range and range rate, the IRST angle, and the ESM emitter-target ID information. Thus, in effect, the process that occurs is merging rather than averaging, and as noted in [48], the potential problems associated with track fusion probably are not of significant consequence for this sensor suite.

## 8.8  CONCLUSION

The full utilization of the agile beam radar for MTT is a relatively new subject. Also, due to classification restrictions, the amount of published literature, and in particular performance predictions, presently is limited. In addition, until recently, computational limitations have curtailed full development of agile beam radar tracking systems. This chapter attempted to summarize the key issues and present a broad overview of the methods being proposed. Next, recommendations are made for future system development.

The key issue in agile radar system design is the development of resource allocation logic. Clearly, an optimal SNR can be defined for track update illumination and an optimal beam spacing can be defined for search. Then, an expert system approach is probably the most flexible and most easily developed method for defining the overall allocation between the functions of track update, target identification, and search for new targets, as well as other radar duties such as missile update. The radar allocation expert system must be integrated with the overall situation assessment and the MSI sensor manager.

More sophisticated filtering and data association methods will be applicable for future systems. These include the use of improved target dynamics models and probably multiple maneuver models. The use of maneuver detection or multiple maneuver models will be integrated into the resource allocation logic so that maneuvering targets are automatically allocated more resources.

The MHT method will lead to very accurate data association for all future tracking systems. Recent advances in computational capabilities mean that MHT will be feasible to implement even for airborne agile beam radar tracking systems.

The increasing emphasis on low-observable targets will lead to applications of sophisticated techniques, such as the DPA, for the detection and tracking of low cross-section targets. The low-observable target threat also will lead to greater use of combined multiple sensor data for track initiation. Further, the sensitivity to low cross-section targets that will be a feature of future radars will require special logic to reject unwanted small targets, such as birds, that now become detectable.

## REFERENCES

[1]    E.R. Addison, "Design Issues for a Knowledge Based Controller for a Track-While-Scan Radar System," *Proc. Applications of Artificial Intelligence III, 1986,* SPIE, Vol. 635, pp. 276–279.

[2]    J. Arnold, "A Dynamic Programming Approach to Target Detection with MTI Radar," *Proc. 1986 Tri-Service Radar Symp,* October 1986.

[3]    S.J. Asseo and R.J. Ardila, "Sensor-Independent Target State Estimator," *Proc. NAECON 1982,* May 1982, pp. 916–924.

[4]    R.S. Baheti, "Efficient Approximation of Kalman Filter for Target Tracking," *IEEE Trans. on Aerospace and Electronic Systems,* Vol. AES-22, January 1986, pp. 8–14.

[5] Y. Bar-Shalom and T.E. Fortmann, *Tracking and Data Association,* Academic Press, New York, 1988.

[6] Y. Bar-Shalom, *Multitarget-Multisensor Tracking: Advanced Applications,* Artech House, Norwood, MA, 1989.

[7] D.K. Barton, *Modern Radar System Analysis,* Artech House, Norwood, MA, 1988.

[8] M. Beuzit, "Analytical Steady-State Solution for a Three-State Kalman Filter," *IEEE Trans. on Aerospace Electron System,* Vol. AES-25, November 1989, pp. 828–835.

[9] S.G. Bier, P.L. Rothman, and R.A. Manske, "Intelligent Sensor Management for Beyond Visual Range Air-to-Air Combat," *Proc. NAECON 1988,* May 1988, pp. 264–269.

[10] E.R. Billam, "Design and Performance Considerations in Modern Phased Array Radar," *Proc. 1982 IEEE Int. Radar Conf.,* 1982, pp. 15–19.

[11] E.R. Billam, "The Optimization of Beam Position Separation in Phased Array Radar," *Proc. First Int. Conf. on Radar,* Nanjing, 1986, pp. 878–882.

[12] E.R. Billam, "Phased Array Radar and the Detection of Low Observables," *Proc. of 1990 IEEE Int. Radar Conf.,* 1990, pp. 491–495.

[13] D.R. Billetter, *Multifunction Array Radar Design,* Artech House, Norwood, MA, 1989.

[14] S.S. Blackman, T.J. Broida, and M.F. Cartier, "Applications of a Phased Array Antenna in a Multiple Maneuvering Target Environment," *Proc. of 1981 IEEE Conf. on Dec. and Control,* December 1981, pp. 1413–1418.

[15] S.S. Blackman, *Multiple Target Tracking with Radar Applications,* Artech House, Norwood, MA, 1986.

[16] H.A.P. Blom and Y. Bar-Shalom, "The Interacting Multiple Model Algorithm for Systems with Markovian Switching Coefficients," *IEEE Trans. on Automatic Control,* Vol. AC-33, August 1988, pp. 780–783.

[17] P.L. Bogler, *Radar Principles with Applications to Tracking Systems,* John Wiley and Sons, New York, 1990.

[18] I.P. Bottlik and S.S. Blackman, "Coordinated Presentation of Multiple Hypotheses in Multitarget Tracking," *Proc. Signal and Data Processing of Small Targets 1989,* SPIE, Vol. 1096, March 1989, pp. 152–157.

[19] T.J. Broida, "Performance Prediction for Multi-Sensor Tracking Systems: Kinematic Accuracy and Data Association Performance," *Proc. of Sensor Fusion II: Human and Machine Strategies,* SPIE, Vol. 1198, November 1989, pp. 256–271.

[20] R. Cowan, "Improved Tracking and Data Fusion Through Sensor Management and Control," *Proc. of 1987 Tri-Service Data Fusion Symp.,* Vol. 1, June 1987, pp. 669–675.

[21] R.A. Dana and D. Moraitis, "Reliable Single Scan Target Acquisition Using Multiple Correlated Observations," *Proc. of 1982 IEE Int. Radar Conf.,* October 1982, pp. 61–65.

[22] F.E. Daum and R.J. Fitzgerald, "Decoupled Kalman Filters for Phased Array Radar Tracking," *IEEE Trans. on Automatic Control,* Vol. AC-28, March 1983, pp. 269–283.

[23] G. Demos et al., "Applications of MHT to Dim Moving Targets," *Proc. of Signal and Data Processing of Small Targets 1990,* SPIE, Vol. 1305, April 1990.

[24] A. Farina and F.A. Studer, *Radar Data Processing,* Vols. 1 and 2, John Wiley and Sons, New York, 1985.

[25] A. Farina and A. Russo, "Radar Detection of Correlated Targets in Clutter," *IEEE Trans. on Aerospace and Electronic Systems,* Vol. AES-22, September 1986, pp. 513–532.

[26] R.J. Fitzgerald, "Simple Tracking Filters: Steady-State Filtering and Smoothing Performance," *IEEE Trans. on Aerospace Electronic Systems,* Vol. AES-16, November 1980, pp. 860–864.

[27] R.J. Fitzgerald, "Simple Tracking Filters: Position and Velocity Measurements," *IEEE Trans. on Aerospace and Electronic Systems,* Vol. AES-18, September 1982, pp. 531–537.

[28] W. Fleskes and G. VanKeuk, "On Single Target Tracking in Dense Clutter—Quantitative Results," *Proc. of 1987 Int. Radar Conf.,* October 1987, pp. 130–134.

[29]   W.H. Gilson, "Minimum Power Requirements for Tracking," *Proc. of 1990 Int. Radar Conf.,* 1990, pp. 417–421.

[30]   J.R. Hashimi, S.S. Blackman, and S.P. Ickovic, "Simulation of an Air-to-Air Tracking System for an Electronically Steered Antenna," *Proc. of 1987 Summer Computer Simulation Conference,* Montreal, July 1987, pp. 279–284.

[31]   J. Hashimi, "Multitarget Tracking with an ESA," presented at UCLA Short Course, Multitarget/ Multisensor Tracking II: Advanced Applications, January 11–15, 1988.

[32]   H. Iwama, *et al.,* "Track Initiation Using MHT in Dense Environments," *Proc. of the 1989 Int. Symp. on Noise and Clutter Rejection in Radars and Imaging Sensors,* pp. 608–613.

[33]   P.S. Maybeck, W.H. Worslay, and P.M. Flynn, "Investigation of Constant Turn-Rate Dynamic Models in Filters for Airborne Vehicle Tracking," *Proc. NAECON 1982,* May 1982, pp. 896–903.

[34]   S. Mori, K.C. Chang, and C.Y. Chong, "Tracking Performance Evaluation: Prediction of Track Purity," *Proc. Signal and Data Processing of Small Targets 1989,* SPIE, Vol. 1096, March 1989, pp. 215–223.

[35]   A.M. Navarro, "Procedure for Tracking Maneuvering Targets with a Multi-Purpose Phased-Array Radar System," *Proc. of 1977 Int. Radar Conf.,* October 1977, pp. 150–154.

[36]   N. Nelson, "Aircraft Tracking Problems from Range Rate Turbine Modulation," *Proc. NAECON 1977,* May 1977, pp. 679–682.

[37]   R. Popoli and S. Blackman, "Expert System Allocation for the Electronically Scanned Antenna Radar," *Proc. of 1987 American Control Conf.,* June 1987, pp. 1821–1826.

[38]   S.R. Rogers, "Instability of a Decoupled Kalman Tracking Filter," *IEEE Trans. on Automatic Control,* Vol. AC-34, March 1989.

[39]   Y.A. Shishov and V.A. Voroshilov, *Multichannel Radar with Time-Division Multiplexing,* Moscow, 1987, Controlling Office of English Translation, National Security Agency, W312, Fort George C. Meade, Maryland, 20755-6000.

[40]   R.A. Singer, "Estimating Optimal Tracking Filter Performance for Manned Maneuvering Targets," *IEEE Trans. on Aerospace Electronic Systems,* Vol. AES-5, July 1970, pp. 473–483.

[41]   D.V. Stallard, "An Angle-Only Tracking Filter in Modified Spherical Coordinates," *Proc. 1987 AIAA Guidance, Navigation and Control Conf.,* pp. 542–550.

[42]   G.M. Stuart, R.I. Odom, and F.D. Gorecki, "Implementation of a JPDAF Tracker for an Electronically Scanned Radar," *Proc. of 1989 AIAA Guidance, Navigation and Control Conf.*

[43]   W.S. Sweetman, *Stealth Aircraft,* Motorbooks International, Osceola, WI, 1986.

[44]   E. Taenzer, "Tracking Multiple Targets Simultaneously with a Phased Array Radar," *IEEE Trans. on Aerospace and Electronic Systems,* Vol. AES-16, September 1980, pp. 604–614.

[45]   M. Tahk and J.L. Speyer, "Target Tracking Problems Subject to Kinematic Constraints," *IEEE Trans. on Automatic Control,* Vol. AC-35, March 1990, pp. 324–326.

[46]   G. VanKeuk, "Software Structure and Sampling Strategy for Automatic Target Tracking with a Phased Array Radar," *AGARD Conf. Proc. No. 252, Strategies for Automatic Track Initiation,* Monterey, CA, October 1978, pp. 11-1 to 11-13.

[47]   E. Waltz and J. Llinas, *Multisensor Data Fusion,* Artech House, Norwood, MA, 1990.

[48]   R.M. Yannone, "UD Factorization Applied to Airborne Kalman-Filter-Based Fusion," *Proc. of MAECON 1988,* May 1988, pp. 326–333.

# Chapter 9
# AUTONOMOUS NAVIGATION WITH UNCERTAIN REFERENCE POINTS USING THE PDAF

*Jean Dezert**

**ONERA, France**

## 9.1 INTRODUCTION

This chapter presents a new application of the PDAF to autonomous navigation of a vehicle flying at low altitude. As in most autonomous navigation problems, we attempt to update the vehicle position automatically with respect to a navigation map to guide the vehicle toward the target. This updating uses a finite number of sensors and a navigation map stored aboard the vehicle. The originality of this new method lies in its use of multiple sensors to determine the position of the vehicle relative to a detected landmark and also to recognize its identity. Each landmark has one of several preestablished identities. This method offers an interesting alternative to traditional methods using image correlation techniques. The ambiguities of association appearing between the landmarks referenced on the navigation map and those detected during the mission are taken into account by the probabilistic data association method. The navigation map is a register of the landmarks that might be flown over. These landmarks are referenced both by their geographical coordinates and their identities (for example, crossroads, bridges, *et cetera*). The methods developed in this chapter also allow us to take into account uncertainty in the identity and

---

*The author, formerly of ONERA, is currently visiting the University of Connecticut under the sponsorship of European Space Age.

The author would like to express his thanks to Pascal Bondon and Christian Riché for their many helpful comments and suggestions as well as to Alain Appriou who gave him the support to carry out this research.

---

location of the landmarks referenced in the navigation map. These new autonomous navigation methods have a very simple real-time structure and a low computational load. They offer many advantages over traditional methods, which are very expensive to implement, in particular for mission planning and changes.

Section 9.2 presents the discrete-time state and observation models for the vehicle, the landmark validation test, and the formulation of the autonomous navigation filter using only landmark position information. Section 9.3.1 discusses the incorporation of the identity of the detected landmarks (assumed to be Bayesian) to improve the rustic navigation filter presented in Section 9.2. Section 9.3.2 discusses the incorporation of uncertain identity information concerning the detected landmarks by using the Dempster-Shafer approach. This leads to the development of a new autonomous navigation filter called a *Shaferian navigation filter*. Section 9.3.3 discusses the incorporation of a decision maker based on Bayesian or uncertain identity information into the rustic autonomous navigation filter developed in Section 9.2. Simulations results, comments, and the prospects of these new autonomous navigation methods are discussed in Sections 9.4 and 9.5.

## 9.2 AUTONOMOUS NAVIGATION WITHOUT LANDMARK RECOGNITION

### 9.2.1 Discrete-Time State and Observation Models

We assume that the discrete-time linear dynamic (plant) equation of the state is

$$\mathbf{x}(k + 1) = \mathbf{F}(k + 1, k)\mathbf{x}(k) + \mathbf{u}(k) + \mathbf{v}(k) \qquad k = 0, 1, \ldots \qquad (9.1)$$

where $\mathbf{x}(k)$ is the state vector of dimension $n_x$ (i.e., kinematic components), $\mathbf{F}(k + 1, k)$ is the transition matrix, $\mathbf{u}(k)$ is the (known) input, $\mathbf{v}(k)$ is a sequence of zero-mean white Gaussian process noises with covariance $\mathbf{Q}(k)$:

$$E[\mathbf{v}(k)\mathbf{v}(j)'] = \mathbf{Q}(k)\delta(k, j) \qquad (9.2)$$

We also assume, as in Figure 9.1, it is possible to extract from sensors the relative location information:

$$\mathbf{z}(k) \triangleq [R(k), \theta(k)]' \qquad (9.3)$$

where $R(k)$ is the distance between the vehicle and the detected landmark and $\theta(k)$ is the angle between the line of sight and a particular direction $Dp$.

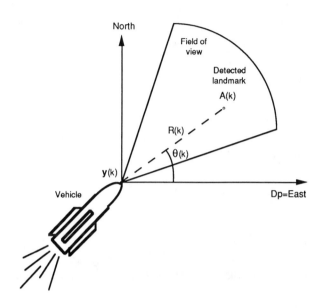

**Figure 9.1** Position of the vehicle relative to the detected landmark.

From the geographical position $(x_A, y_A)$ of the detected landmark $A(k)$ (if it is known) and from $\mathbf{z}(k)$, we can infer the potential position $\mathbf{y}(k)$ of the vehicle in the navigation map coordinates as

$$\mathbf{y}(k) = \mathbf{A}(k) - \mathbf{f}[\mathbf{z}(k)] \qquad (9.4)$$

where $\mathbf{A}(k) \triangleq [x_A, y_A]'$ are the coordinates of the landmark $A$ at time $k$ in the frame of the map, $\mathbf{y}(k) \triangleq [x(k), y(k)]'$ are the coordinates of the vehicle, and $\mathbf{f}[\mathbf{z}(k)]$ is a nonlinear function given by

$$\mathbf{f}[\mathbf{z}(k)] \triangleq \begin{bmatrix} R(k)\,\cos\theta(k) \\ R(k)\,\sin\theta(k) \end{bmatrix} \qquad (9.5)$$

However, in practical situations, the relative position measurement $\mathbf{z}(k)$ corresponding to the real relative position $\mathbf{z}_{\text{real}}(k)$ is corrupted by an additive zero-mean Gaussian white noise $\mathbf{b}_z(k)$ having a covariance

$$\mathbf{R}_z(k) = \begin{bmatrix} \sigma_R^2 & 0 \\ 0 & \sigma_\theta^2 \end{bmatrix} \qquad (9.6)$$

where $\sigma_R$ is the standard deviation for the distance noise and $\sigma_\theta$ for the angular noise. The measurement $\mathbf{z}(k)$ can then be written

$$\mathbf{z}(k) = \mathbf{z}_{\text{real}}(k) + \mathbf{b}_z(k) \tag{9.7}$$

with

$$\mathbf{z}_{\text{real}}(k) \triangleq \begin{bmatrix} R_{\text{real}}(k) \\ \theta_{\text{real}}(k) \end{bmatrix} \text{ and } \mathbf{b}_z(k) \triangleq \begin{bmatrix} b_R(k) \\ b_\theta(k) \end{bmatrix} \tag{9.8}$$

and the potential vehicle position $\mathbf{y}(k)$ is given by

$$\mathbf{y}(k) = \begin{bmatrix} x(k) \\ y(k) \end{bmatrix} = \mathbf{A}(k) - \mathbf{f}[\mathbf{z}_{\text{real}}(k) + \mathbf{b}_z(k)] \tag{9.9}$$

Assuming a small angular noise $b_\theta(k)$ and $b_R(k) \ll R_{\text{real}}(k)$, the relationship (9.9) can be rewritten as

$$\mathbf{y}(k) \approx \mathbf{y}_{\text{real}}(k) + \mathbf{w}(k) \tag{9.10}$$

where

$$\mathbf{y}_{\text{real}}(k) = \mathbf{A}(k) - \mathbf{f}[\mathbf{z}_{\text{real}}(k)] \tag{9.11}$$

$$\mathbf{w}(k) = \begin{bmatrix} -b_R(k) \cos\theta_{\text{real}}(k) + b_\theta(k)R_{\text{real}}(k) \sin\theta_{\text{real}}(k) \\ -b_R(k) \sin\theta_{\text{real}}(k) - b_\theta(k)R_{\text{real}}(k) \cos\theta_{\text{real}}(k) \end{bmatrix} \tag{9.12}$$

where $\mathbf{w}(k)$ is (approximately) a sequence of zero-mean white Gaussian measurement noises with covariance $\mathbf{R}(k)$:

$$E[\mathbf{w}(k)\mathbf{w}(j)'] = \mathbf{R}(k)\delta(k, j) \tag{9.13}$$

with

$\mathbf{R}(k) =$

$$\begin{bmatrix} R_{\text{real}}^2(k) \sin^2\theta_{\text{real}}(k)\sigma_\theta^2 + \cos^2\theta_{\text{real}}(k)\sigma_R^2 & [\sigma_R^2 - R_{\text{real}}^2(k)\sigma_\theta^2] \sin\theta_{\text{real}}(k) \cos\theta_{\text{real}}(k) \\ (\sigma_R^2 - R_{\text{real}}^2(k)\sigma_\theta^2) \sin\theta_{\text{real}}(k) \cos\theta_{\text{real}}(k) & R_{\text{real}}^2(k) \cos^2\theta_{\text{real}}(k)\sigma_\theta^2 + \sin^2\theta_{\text{real}}(k)\sigma_R^2 \end{bmatrix} \tag{9.14}$$

This expression for $\mathbf{R}(k)$ holds whenever the noises are small compared with the components of $\mathbf{z}_{\text{real}}(k)$ (i.e., $\sigma_\theta \ll 1$ and $\sigma_R \ll R_{\text{real}}$).

Thus, the potential position measurement can be described by a classical observation equation with a known observed landmark position and relative position $z(k)$. The relationship (9.10) then can be written in a standard form:

$$\mathbf{y}(k) = \mathbf{H}(k)\mathbf{x}(k) + \mathbf{w}(k) \tag{9.15}$$

with

$$\mathbf{H}(k) \triangleq \begin{bmatrix} 1 & 0 & 0 & 0 \\ 0 & 1 & 0 & 0 \end{bmatrix} \quad \text{if, for example, } \mathbf{x}(k) = [x(k), y(k), \dot{x}(k), \dot{y}(k)]'$$

Unfortunately, the relative position $z_{\text{real}}(k)$ in practice is unknown and the approximate theoretical covariance matrix $\mathbf{R}(k)$ associated with $\mathbf{w}(k)$ is not available. We then must look for another approximation of $\mathbf{R}(k)$. When the measurement uncertainty is assumed to be small, we can approximate the covariance matrix $\mathbf{R}(k)$ by using the relative available measurement $z(k)$ and the covariance matrix is given approximately by

$$\mathbf{R}(k) \approx \mathbf{f}_1[\mathbf{z}(k), \mathbf{R}_z(k)]$$
$$= \begin{bmatrix} R^2(k)\sin^2\theta(k)\sigma_\theta^2 + \cos^2\theta(k)\sigma_R^2 & [\sigma_R^2 - R^2(k)\sigma_\theta^2]\sin\theta(k)\cos\theta(k) \\ (\sigma_R^2 - R^2(k)\sigma_\theta^2)\sin\theta(k)\cos\theta(k) & R^2(k)\cos^2\theta(k)\sigma_\theta^2 + \sin^2\theta(k)\sigma_R^2 \end{bmatrix} \tag{9.16}$$

Other approximations for $\mathbf{R}(k)$ also can be developed [1] when the navigation map and the field of view of the sensors are known. However, the approximation presented here is justified if we assume that distance and angular noises are relatively small.

If the geographical position of the landmarks referenced on the navigation map is uncertain, but can be characterized by a covariance matrix $\mathbf{R}_A$ such as

$$\mathbf{R}_A = \begin{bmatrix} \sigma_{x_A}^2 & 0 \\ 0 & \sigma_{y_A}^2 \end{bmatrix} \tag{9.17}$$

then we must add the matrix $\mathbf{R}_A$ to the matrix $\mathbf{R}(k)$ defined earlier to obtain the total covariance matrix of the noise measurement. Hence, we have

$$\mathbf{R}(k) = \mathbf{f}_1[\mathbf{z}(k), \mathbf{R}_z(k)] + \mathbf{R}_A \tag{9.18}$$

Of course, in practice, the identity and, thus, the position of the detected landmark $A(k)$ is unknown, and all we can deduce from the navigation map and the relative position $\mathbf{z}(k)$ is a set of potential vehicle positions (i.e., $\{y_j(k), j = 1, \ldots,$

$N$)). This is illustrated in Figure 9.2, where there are five landmarks. Depending on whether the landmark is $A_j$, the deduced positions are $y_j$, but $j$ is not known with certainty.

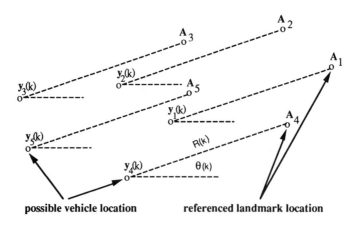

**Figure 9.2** Example of navigation map and possible vehicle locations.

To limit the number of potential measurements, we use the validation test [3] to choose those which are statistically close to the predicted one given by the autonomous navigation filter. As in the PDAF, the problem consists of evaluating the probabilities of the exclusive and exhaustive association events:

$\theta_0(k) \triangleq$ "None of the validated referenced landmarks corresponds to the detected landmark"

$\theta_j(k) \triangleq$ "The validated referenced landmark $\mathbf{A}_j(k)$ corresponds to the detected landmark"

### 9.2.2 Notation

Let $A(k)$ denote the set of $n_k$ landmarks referenced on the navigation map that might correspond to the detected landmark and let $A^k$ denote the cumulative set of landmarks:

$$A(k) \triangleq \{\mathbf{A}_j(k)\}_{j=1}^{n_k} \quad \text{and} \quad A^k \triangleq \{A(i)\}_{i=1}^{k} = \{A^{k-1}, A(k)\} \tag{9.19}$$

Also let $\mathbf{z}^k$ be the cumulative set of relative position measurements $\mathbf{z}$ such as

$$\mathbf{z}^k \triangleq \{\mathbf{z}(i)\}_{i=1}^{k} = \{\mathbf{z}^{k-1}, \mathbf{z}(k)\} \tag{9.20}$$

From the deterministic relationship (9.4) we can define the sets of position measurements for the vehicle

$$Y(k) \triangleq \{\mathbf{y}_j(k)\}_{j=1}^{n_k} \quad \text{and} \quad Y^k \triangleq \{Y(i)\}_{i=1}^{k} = \{Y^{k-1}, Y(k)\} \tag{9.21}$$

The statistical information contained in $Y(k)$ is similar to what is in $[A(k), \mathbf{z}(k)]$, and we have

$$Y(k) = [A(k), \mathbf{z}(k)] = \{\mathbf{y}_j(k)\}_{j=1}^{n_k} = [\{\mathbf{A}_j(k)\}_{j=1}^{n_k}, \mathbf{z}(k)] \tag{9.22}$$

$$Y^k = (A^k, \mathbf{z}^k) = \{Y^{k-1}, Y(k)\} = [A^{k-1}, A(k), \mathbf{z}^{k-1}, \mathbf{z}(k)] \tag{9.23}$$

Let $\hat{\mathbf{y}}(k|k-1)$ be the vehicle position predicted given by the filter and $\hat{\mathbf{A}}(k|k-1)$ the predicted position of the detected landmark given from $\hat{\mathbf{y}}(k|k-1)$ and the measurement $\mathbf{z}(k)$. According to (9.4), we have

$$\hat{\mathbf{y}}(k|k-1) = \hat{\mathbf{A}}(k|k-1) - \mathbf{f}[\mathbf{z}(k)] \tag{9.24}$$

Using (9.24) and (9.4), we see that

$$\tilde{\mathbf{y}}(k) \triangleq \mathbf{y}(k) - \hat{\mathbf{y}}(k|k-1) = A(k) - \mathbf{f}[\mathbf{z}(k)] - \hat{\mathbf{A}}(k|k-1)$$
$$+ \mathbf{f}[\mathbf{z}(k)] = A(k) - \hat{\mathbf{A}}(k|k-1) \triangleq \tilde{\mathbf{A}}(k) \tag{9.25}$$

Consequently we have

$$\mathbf{S}(k) = E[\tilde{\mathbf{y}}(k)\tilde{\mathbf{y}}'(k)| Y^{k-1}] = E[\tilde{\mathbf{A}}(k)\tilde{\mathbf{A}}'(k)|A^{k-1}, \mathbf{z}^{k-1}] \tag{9.26}$$

### 9.2.3 Measurement Validation Test

The measurement validation test is a procedure for selecting potential measurements $\{\mathbf{y}_j(k), j = 1, \ldots, n_k\}$ (deduced from the landmark position on the navigation map and from $\mathbf{z}(k)$) lying in an elliptical region of the map that corresponds to the possible vehicle location. The validation region (i.e., gate volume) thus makes it possible to limit the number of potential vehicle positions to be dealt with by eliminating those statistically too far from the predicted vehicle position calculated by the navigation filter. The validation test at time $k$ is defined by [3]

$$[\mathbf{y}(k) - \hat{\mathbf{y}}(k|k-1)]'[\mathbf{S}(k)]^{-1}[\mathbf{y}(k) - \hat{\mathbf{y}}(k|k-1)] < g^2 \tag{9.27}$$

where $\mathbf{S}(k)$ is the covariance matrix of the innovation corresponding to the true measurement defined in (9.26) and $g^2$ is the gate threshold, which can be determined according to the method given in [3]. From a practical point of view, the measurement validation test can be applied directly to the landmark positions because a bijective relationship exists between the referenced landmark positions and the potential vehicle positions. Therefore, (9.27) is equivalent to

$$[A(k) - \hat{A}(k|k - 1)]'[S(k)]^{-1}[A(k) - \hat{A}(k|k - 1)] < g^2 \tag{9.28}$$

where $\hat{A}(k|k - 1)$ is the predicted position of the detected landmark, calculated by (9.24), and where the covariance matrix $S(k)$ is given by the standard Kalman filter equation

$$S(k) = H(k)P(k|k - 1)H'(k) + R(k) \tag{9.29}$$

As an example of measurement validation test, Figure 9.3 shows the statistical validation gate for three referenced landmarks.

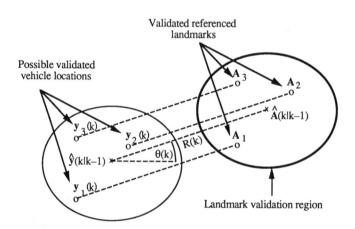

**Figure 9.3** Example for landmark validation test.

### 9.2.4 Formulation of the Autonomous Navigation Filter

The Bayesian equation giving the best estimate of the state (in the sense of minimizing the mean square error) is the conditional mean calculated from all available information given by

$$\hat{x}(k|k) = E[x(k)| Y^k] = E[x(k)|A^k, z^k] \tag{9.30}$$

Assuming each detected landmark to be resolved (i.e., one detected landmark corresponds to only one real landmark) and introducing the $n_k + 1$ mutually exclusive and exhaustive association events $\theta_j(k)$, it follows that

$$\hat{\mathbf{x}}(k\,|\,k) = \sum_{j=0}^{nk} E[\mathbf{x}(k)\,|\,\theta_j(k),\, Y^k]P\{\theta_j(k)\,|\,Y^k\} \qquad (9.31)$$

where $n_k$ is the number of validated landmarks at time $k$, $\theta_j(k)$ the event corresponding to the realization of the association hypothesis "$\mathbf{A}_j$ is the detected landmark," and $\theta_0(k)$ is the event corresponding to the hypothesis "None of validated referenced landmarks is correct." The *a posteriori* probabilities of each association event are

$$P\{\theta_j(k)\,|\,Y^k\} = P\{\theta_j(k)\,|\,A^k,\, \mathbf{z}^k\} \triangleq \beta_j(k) \qquad (9.32)$$

Assuming the landmarks to be uniformly distributed on the navigation map and using the nonparametric PDAF [3], the *a posteriori* probabilities (9.32) are

$$\beta_j(k) = e_j(k)\left[b(k) + \sum_{j=1}^{nk} e_j(k)\right]^{-1} \qquad j = 1,\ldots, n_k \qquad (9.33)$$

$$\beta_0(k) = b(k)\left[b(k) + \sum_{j=1}^{nk} e_j(k)\right]^{-1} \qquad (9.34)$$

where

$$e_j(k) \triangleq (P_G)^{-1}N[\tilde{\mathbf{A}}_j(k);0,\, \mathbf{S}(k)] \qquad (9.35)$$

$$b(k) \triangleq n_k(1 - P_G P_D)[P_G P_D V(k)]^{-1} \qquad (9.36)$$

$P_D$ is the probability of a landmark being detected; $N[a;0,\, \mathbf{S}(k)]$ is the normal probability density function with argument $a$, mean zero, and variance $\mathbf{S}(k)$; $P_G$ is the probability that the correct position of the detected landmark lies within a two-dimensional validation region ("$g$-sigma gate"), the volume of which is

$$\mathbf{V}(k) = g^2\pi\,|\mathbf{S}(k)|^{1/2} \qquad (9.37)$$

and

$$\tilde{\mathbf{A}}_j(k) \triangleq \mathbf{A}_j - \hat{\mathbf{A}}(k\,|\,k-1) = \mathbf{y}_j(k) - \hat{\mathbf{y}}(k\,|\,k-1) \qquad (9.38)$$

is the innovation for landmark $\mathbf{A}_j$. The state estimate conditioned that landmark $\mathbf{A}_j$ is correct (event $\theta_j(k)$) is

$$\hat{\mathbf{x}}_j(k\,|\,k) = \hat{\mathbf{x}}(k\,|\,k-1) + \mathbf{W}(k)\tilde{\mathbf{A}}_j(k) \tag{9.39}$$

with the gain given by

$$\mathbf{W}(k) \triangleq \mathbf{P}(k\,|\,k-1)\mathbf{H}'(k)\mathbf{S}^{-1}(k) \tag{9.40}$$

Here, $\mathbf{P}(k\,|\,k-1)$ is the covariance matrix of the predicted state $\hat{\mathbf{x}}(k\,|\,k-1)$ and $\mathbf{H}(k)$ is the observation matrix. The general formulation of the state estimate can be rewritten [3] as

$$\hat{\mathbf{x}}(k\,|\,k) = \sum_{j=0}^{nk} \beta_j(k)\hat{\mathbf{x}}_j(k\,|\,k) = \hat{\mathbf{x}}(k\,|\,k-1) + \mathbf{W}(k)\tilde{\mathbf{A}}(k) \tag{9.41}$$

where the combined innovation is

$$\tilde{\mathbf{A}}(k) \triangleq \sum_{j=1}^{nk} \beta_j(k)\tilde{\mathbf{A}}_j(k) \tag{9.42}$$

The covariance associated with (9.39), that is, conditioned on knowing the correct landmark, is given by the standard Kalman equation as

$$\mathbf{P}_c(k\,|\,k) = [\mathbf{I} - \mathbf{W}(k)\mathbf{H}(k)]\mathbf{P}(k\,|\,k-1) \tag{9.43}$$

The covariance associated with (9.41) is given by [3]

$$\mathbf{P}(k\,|\,k) = \beta_0(k)\mathbf{P}(k\,|\,k-1) + [1 - \beta_0(k)]\mathbf{P}_c(k\,|\,k) + \tilde{\mathbf{P}}(k) \tag{9.44}$$

where

$$\tilde{\mathbf{P}}(k) = \mathbf{W}(k)\left[\left\{\sum_{j=1}^{nk} \beta_j(k)\tilde{\mathbf{A}}_j(k)\tilde{\mathbf{A}}'_j(k)\right\} - \tilde{\mathbf{A}}(k)\tilde{\mathbf{A}}'(k)\right]\mathbf{W}'(k) \tag{9.45}$$

The state prediction is made according to the standard Kalman filter equation.

We have seen in the preceding that the autonomous navigation problem for a vehicle flying at low altitude can be solved directly by the PDA method using a very simple navigation map stored on board and a relative position measurement (distance and angle) between the detected landmark and the vehicle. Just one modification was made in deriving the measurement noise covariance matrix.

The navigation algorithm developed here has the same properties as the PDAF (modest storage, real-time applicability, recursivity). In this particular application, the track initialization assumption (necessary for the theoretical development of the PDAF) can be removed because we legitimately can assume that the initial vehicle position is known at the beginning of the mission.

Figure 9.4 gives the general flowchart for this "rustic" autonomous navigation filter that uses landmarks without identity. Note that this filter does not utilize any identity information about the landmarks, only location information. Incorporation of identity recognition information is discussed in the next section.

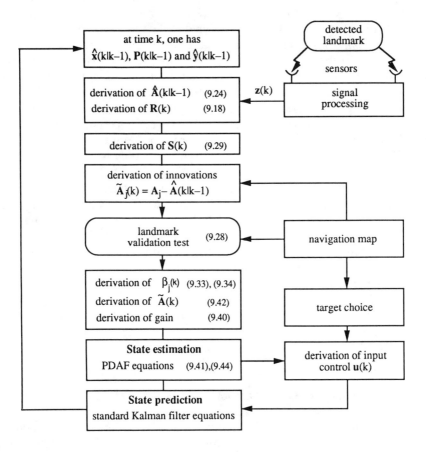

**Figure 9.4** One cycle of the rustic autonomous navigation filter.

## 9.3 AUTONOMOUS NAVIGATION WITH LANDMARK RECOGNITION

To improve the probabilistic data association method, we propose to use a complementary type of information concerning the identification of the landmarks detected during navigation. This recognition information is assumed to be given from the different sensors aboard the vehicle (like MM sensors, IR sensors, and laser). In this case the navigation map must be complemented by the description of the referenced landmarks' identities to take advantage of recognition information obtained from the sensors.

As in most multisensor applications, we assume at first that our recognition information is Bayesian (i.e., statistical information). This assumption is particularly well supported whenever the statistical measurement distributions (given all the possible identities for a detected landmark) are known and sufficiently reliable. Thus the total recognition information to be considered in the navigation filter is a set of conditional probabilities of each possible measurement that might be delivered from every sensor under the different possible identity assumptions. However, in practice, it is difficult, if not impossible, to describe the measurements with reliable statistical distribution modeling. We must assume, though, that we are dealing (from rustic image processing techniques) with a set of uncertain quantities generated by low-grade image processing and lying within an interval of uncertainty [0, 1] that characterizes the relative confidence of each sensor in the identity of the detected landmark. This uncertain recognition information commonly is labeled *Shaferian,* as opposed to the Bayesian, recognition information. The problem is to integrate this Shaferian recognition information in the autonomous navigation filter.

Note that, to take the recognition information (Bayesian or Shaferian) fully into account, a very large quantity of data has to be transferred to the navigation filter. To alleviate this problem, we can try to use the information generated by the sensors to establish a rule (optimal or not) for deciding which is the best identity for the detected landmark. Unfortunately, in practice, observation conditions and sensor quality being what they are, the reliability of this decision rule cannot be taken for granted. So the quality of the decision-making device is characterized by the nonzero probability of an error in the decision. At the level of the navigation filter, then we must be able to take into account both the decision that has been made and the quality of the decision maker itself.

### 9.3.1 Inclusion of Bayesian Recognition Information

Consider a landmark recognition system with $S$ independent sensors $s_l$ having the same field of view in common. We assume that each sensor $s_l$ yields a measurement $m_l$ contributing to the real identity of the detected landmark (i.e., the one nearest the vehicle). We also assume we are given $N + 1$ mutually exclusive and exhaustive identification classes $\{I_0, I_1, \ldots, I_N\}$ for a detected landmark.

Each class $I_i$ $(i = 0, \ldots, N)$ represents one particular identity that might be flown over by the vehicle during its mission. Let $I$ be the identity of the detected landmark and $E_R$ the set of possible realizations for $I$; that is,

$$E_R = \{I_0, I_1, \ldots, I_N\} \tag{9.46}$$

$E_R$ is called the *frame of discernment* of landmark identification.

With the Bayesian model, the measurement $m_j$ delivered from each sensor is assumed to be random and have a known distribution, conditional on the chosen identification hypothesis $I_i$. The known distributions (*probability mass functions* (pmf)) $p(m_l/I_i)$ (for $l = 1, \ldots, S$ and $i = 0, \ldots, N$) are the only Bayesian recognition information that has to be transferred to the filter (see Figure 9.5). But even though there is no problem handling the distributions $p(m_j \mid I_i)$ in theory, we should say modeling of the conditional distributions $p(m_l \mid I_i)$ statistically will be very difficult to obtain in practice. In Figure 9.5, we need to transfer the $S(N + 1)$ quantities $p(m_l \mid I_i)$ to the filter.

Let $M(k)$ be a set of recognition measurements generated by the $S$ sensors at time $k$, and let us denote by $M^k$ the cumulative set of measurements delivered by the sensors:

$$M(k) \triangleq \{m_l(k), \quad l = 1, \ldots, S\} \tag{9.47}$$

$$M^k \triangleq \{M(i)\}_{i=1}^k = \{M^{k-1}, M(k)\} \tag{9.48}$$

The best estimate of the state at time $k$ is the conditional mean, calculated by using all the available information:

$$\hat{\mathbf{x}}(k \mid k) = E[\mathbf{x}(k) \mid Y^k, M^k] \tag{9.49}$$

Using the total probability theorem with respect to the $n_k + 1$ mutually exclusive and exhaustive association events $\theta_j$, the conditional mean of the state at time $k$ can be written as

$$\hat{\mathbf{x}}(k \mid k) = \sum_{j=0}^{n_k} \beta_j(k) E[\mathbf{x}(k) \mid \theta_j(k), Y^k, M^k] \tag{9.50}$$

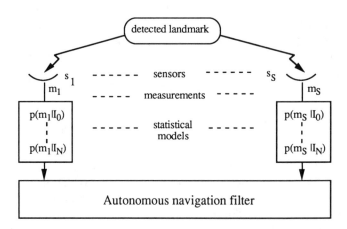

**Figure 9.5** Inclusion of Bayesian recognition information.

where $E[\mathbf{x}(k)|\theta_j(k), Y^k, M^k]$ corresponds to the updated state estimate conditioned on the event that the $j$th validated referenced landmark is the correct one. This is done by updating a standard Kalman filter equation. The conditional probability $\beta_j(k)$ of the event $\theta_j(k)$ can be written out explicitly as follows:

$$\beta_j(k) \triangleq P\{\theta_j(k)|\,Y^k, M^k\} = P\{\theta_j(k)|\,Y^{k-1}, Y(k), n_k, M^k\} \qquad j = 0, \ldots, n_k$$

$$(9.51)$$

Assuming the landmarks to be uniformly distributed over the navigation map (without distinguishing identities) and the sensors to be independent, it is shown in [5] that the association probabilities can be rewritten as

$$\beta_j(k) = e_j(k)Q(\mathbf{A}_j)\left[b(k) + \sum_{j=1}^{n_k} e_j(k)Q(\mathbf{A}_j)\right]^{-1} \qquad j = 1, \ldots, n_k \qquad (9.52)$$

$$\beta_0(k) = b(k)\left[b(k) + \sum_{j=1}^{n_k} e_j(k)Q(\mathbf{A}_j)\right]^{-1} \qquad\qquad\qquad (9.53)$$

with

$$e_j(k) \triangleq (P_G)^{-1}N[\tilde{\mathbf{A}}_j(k);0, \mathbf{S}(k)] \qquad\qquad\qquad\qquad (9.54)$$

$$b(k) \triangleq n_k(1 - P_G P_D)[P_G P_D V(k)]^{-1} \qquad (9.55)$$

$$Q(\mathbf{A}_j) \triangleq \frac{\displaystyle\sum_{i=0}^{N} P\{T(\mathbf{A}_j) = I_i\} P_R\{I_i\} \prod_{l=1}^{S} p[m_l(k)\,|\,T_R = I_i]}{\displaystyle\sum_{i=0}^{N} P_R\{I_i\} \prod_{l=1}^{S} p[m_l(k)\,|\,T_R = I_i]} \qquad (9.56)$$

Here, $N + 1$ is the number of mutually exclusive and exhaustive identification hypotheses, $S$ is the number of sensors aboard, $p[m_l(k)\,|\,T_R = I_i]$ is the measurement pdf from sensor 1 for identification hypothesis $I_i$ and $P_R\{I_i\}$ the *a priori* probability of observing one landmark having an identity $I_i$. This probability must be evaluated from the known navigation map information (e.g., using the percentage of landmarks present on the navigation map with the identity $I_i$). $P\{T(\mathbf{A}_j) = I_i\}$ is the *a priori* probability (assumed to be known in the mapping) that the identity of $\mathbf{A}_j$ should be $I_i$. The coefficient $Q(\mathbf{A}_j)$ is an agreement factor (given from sensors and navigation map) between the identity of the detected landmark and the identity of the landmark $\mathbf{A}_j$.

If we know the identity of the detected landmark with certainty, and if all landmarks referenced on the navigation map have this same identity, then the recognition information will not be informative and of no use in improving the estimation of the vehicle position. The noninformativeness of the recognition information can be written mathematically as

$$\text{for } j = 1, \ldots, n_k \qquad Q(\mathbf{A}_j) \equiv 1 \qquad (9.57)$$

Under these conditions, we again find the classical expression for the posterior association probabilities as in the PDAF development; that is, (9.33) and (9.34). Hence, when the recognition is not informative, the navigation filter will be equivalent to the autonomous navigation filter developed in Section 9.2. Note that, if all the coefficients $Q(\mathbf{A}_j)$ were alike but less than unity (i.e., there is a disagreement between the identity of the detected landmark and the identities of the referenced landmarks), the navigation filter would tend to favor the particular association event $\theta_0(k)$, to take the safer option. The state and covariance updating equations are the same as earlier, and the state prediction is made according to the standard Kalman equation.

As a concluding remark, we may say that the autonomous navigation filter using complete Bayesian recognition information has the same structure as the classical PDAF. Just one modification has to be made in the posterior association probabilities. The analytical expressions of the association probabilities are similar to those developed in the PDAF and pose no difficulty for practical implementation, if we know the conditional measurement distribution models for the different identification hypotheses chosen. The navigation filter structure using Bayesian recognition information will follow the PDAF structure strictly whenever recognition information is not informative. Figure 9.6 illustrates the augmented autonomous navigation filter's flowchart.

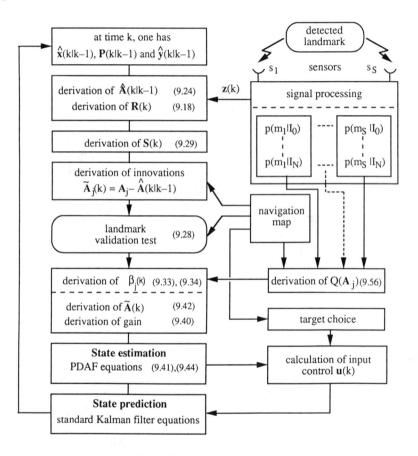

**Figure 9.6** Autonomous navigation filter cycle augmented with Bayesian recognition information.

### 9.3.2 Use of Uncertain Recognition Information

*Information Preprocessing*

In practice Bayesian recognition information is not usable, because the conditional measurement distribution models for the different identification hypotheses chosen are either unknown or can be identified only with great difficulty. Therefore, we must modify the filter structure to take into account the nature of the information delivered by the different sensors aboard the vehicle.

Generally speaking, we assume that the information from each local processor associated with each sensor can be modeled as quantities of some uncertain type (i.e., a set of intervals lying within [0, 1], which corresponds to the relative confidence each sensor accords to every identification hypothesis $I_i$ of the frame of discernment $E_R$). The available information from sensor $l$ then consists of $N + 1$ intervals such that

$$[\epsilon_{il}^{\min}, \epsilon_{il}^{\max}] \subset [0, 1] \qquad i = 0, \ldots, N \tag{9.58}$$

The interval $[\epsilon_{il}^{\min}, \epsilon_{il}^{\max}]$ is called $i$th uncertain quantity relative to sensor $l$. The terms $\epsilon_{il}^{\min}$ and $\epsilon_{il}^{\max}$ represent, respectively, the minimum and maximum confidence accorded by sensor $l$ to the identification hypothesis $I_i$.

It must be possible to take this uncertain recognition information into account in the autonomous navigation filter once each preselected identification hypothesis is evaluated. According to [5], this evaluation, based upon the Dempster-Shafer's inference rule [8], requires a preliminary step in which the uncertain quantities need to be transformed within the evidence theory formalism [6]. This transformation consists of changing uncertain quantities into some basic assignment probabilities (also called *basic assignment masses*) to match every uncertain quantity with a credibility and plausibility measurement [5]. For this, we associate each available uncertain quantity with the basic assignment probabilities defined by (for $i = 0, \ldots, N$ and $l = 1, \ldots, S$):

$$m_i^l(I_i) = \epsilon_{il}^{\min} \tag{9.59}$$

$$m_i^l(\bar{I}_i) = 1 - \epsilon_{il}^{\max} \tag{9.60}$$

$$m_i^l(E_R) = \epsilon_{il}^{\max} - \epsilon_{il}^{\min} \tag{9.61}$$

One can easily verify from this basic probability assignment that the credibility and plausibility of identity $I_i$ delivered by sensor $l$ coincide exactly with the uncertain quantity $[\epsilon_{il}^{\min}, \epsilon_{il}^{\max}]$. Thus, we have

$$\text{Bel}_i^l(I_i) = \epsilon_{il}^{\min} \tag{9.62}$$

$$\text{Pl}_i^l(I_i) = \epsilon_{il}^{\max} \tag{9.63}$$

in which $\text{Bel}_i^l(I_i)$ and $\text{Pl}_i^l(I_i)$ represent, respectively, the credibility and the plausibility accorded by sensor $l$ to the identification hypothesis $I_i$. This transformation step is illustrated in Figure 9.7.

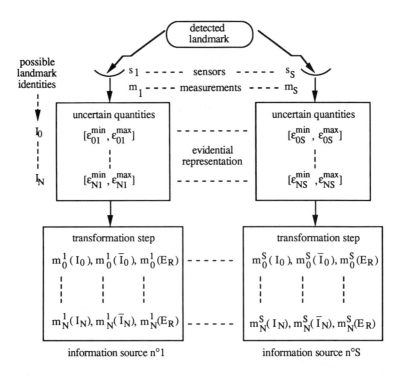

**Figure 9.7** Preliminary transformation step.

From the $S(N + 1)$ basic assignment masses available for the same identification frame of discernment and using the Dempster-Shafer inference, a single set of basic assignment masses $m_R$ can be constructed that is committed to every subset of $E_R$. Index $R$ means that this basic probability assignment is found only from the recognition information delivered from sensors. Denoting by $\oplus$ the Dempster-Shafer's inference rule [8] (i.e., the orthogonal sum operator defined in [5]), the resulting basic probability assignment $m_R$ is obtained mathematically by

$$m_R = m_0^1 \oplus \cdots \oplus m_0^S \oplus m_1^1 \oplus \cdots \oplus m_1^S \oplus \cdots \oplus m_N^1 \oplus \cdots \oplus m_N^S$$

$$(9.64)$$

To reduce the number of operations involved in calculating $m_R$, we can use the associativity property of the Dempster-Shafer rule. Thus, the relationship (9.64) can be rewritten

$$m_R = m_0 \oplus \cdots \oplus m_N \qquad (9.65)$$

with

$$m_i = \bigoplus_{l=1,S} m_i^l \triangleq m_i^1 \oplus \cdots \oplus m_i^S \qquad (i = 0, \ldots, N) \qquad (9.66)$$

After some transformations [5] the final analytical expression of the basic probability functions $m_i$ is given by (for $i = 0, \ldots, N$):

$$m_i(I_i) = \frac{1}{K_i} \left\{ \prod_{l=1}^{S} \epsilon_{il}^{\max} - \prod_{l=1}^{S} [\epsilon_{il}^{\max} - \epsilon_{il}^{\min}] \right\} \qquad (9.67)$$

$$m_i(\bar{I}_i) = \frac{1}{K_i} \left\{ \prod_{l=1}^{S} [1 - \epsilon_{il}^{\min}] - \prod_{l=1}^{S} [\epsilon_{il}^{\max} - \epsilon_{il}^{\min}] \right\} \qquad (9.68)$$

$$m_i(E_R) = \frac{1}{K_i} \prod_{l=1}^{S} [\epsilon_{il}^{\max} - \epsilon_{il}^{\min}] \qquad (9.69)$$

with

$$K_i = \prod_{l=1}^{S} \epsilon_{il}^{\max} + \prod_{l=1}^{S} [1 - \epsilon_{il}^{\min}] - \prod_{l=1}^{S} [\epsilon_{il}^{\max} - \epsilon_{il}^{\min}] \qquad (9.70)$$

We can easily verify that $m_i$ corresponds to a basic probability assignment because

$$m_i(I_i) + m_i(\bar{I}_i) + m_i(E_R) = 1 \qquad \text{for } i = 0, \ldots, N \qquad (9.71)$$

The credibility and plausibility of each identification hypothesis are given by

$$\begin{aligned} \text{Bel}_i(I_i) &= m_i(I_i) = 1 - [m_i(\bar{I}_i) + m_i(E_R)] \\ &= 1 - \frac{1}{K_i} \prod_{l=1}^{S} [1 - \epsilon_{il}^{\min}] \triangleq \epsilon_i^{\min} \end{aligned} \qquad (9.72)$$

$$\text{Pl}_i(I_i) = m_i(I_i) + m_i(E_R) = \frac{1}{K_i} \prod_{l=1}^{S} \epsilon_{il}^{\max} \triangleq \epsilon_i^{\max} \qquad (9.73)$$

The calculation of intermediate masses $m_i$ thus implicitly is the same as grouping the $M$ intervals $[\epsilon_{il}^{\min}, \epsilon_{il}^{\max}]$ into a single interval $[\epsilon_i^{\min}, \epsilon_i^{\max}]$ representing the minimum and maximum confidence given by all sensors with respect to the identification hypothesis $I_i$. In spite of the simplicity of the analytical expression for the $(N + 1)$ basic probability assignments $m_i$ (see (9.67)–(9.69)), note that calculating $m_R$ analytically by using relationship (9.65) is complicated and very difficult to process whenever the cardinality of the frame of discernment is large (because, in the worst case, the basic probability assignment $m_R$ has to quantify $2^{N+1} - 1$ proposed identifications). One way around this problem is to process (9.65) sequentially, as follows:

$$m_R = [[[m_0 \oplus m_1] \oplus m_2] \cdots \oplus m_N] \tag{9.74}$$

Since the Dempster-Shafer's inference rule is commutative and associative, the sequential processing order will have no consequence upon the final result. Figure 9.8 shows how the uncertain information that has to be transferred to the autonomous navigation filter is processed. In such a structure, we see that the filter needs $2^{N+1} - 1$ basic probability assignments relative to the $2^{N+1} - 1$ proposed identifications.

## The Automatic Context Translator

The use of uncertain recognition information in the autonomous navigation filter deserves a particular theoretical discussion of its own, as the two frames of discernment, which are each of a very different nature, have to be used simultaneously in the probabilistic data association method. The two frames of discernment to consider are

- The association frame of discernment, denoted $\Theta(k)$, which consists of the $n_k + 1$ realizations of the mutually exclusive and exhaustive association events $\theta_j(k)$ ($n_k$ being the number of landmarks validated by the statistical validation gate):

$$\Theta(k) = \{\theta_0(k), \theta_1(k), \ldots, \theta_{n_k}(k)\} \tag{9.75}$$

- The recognition frame of discernment, denoted $E_R$, which consists of $N + 1$ possible preselected identification hypotheses $I_i$:

$$E_R = \{I_0, I_1, \ldots, I_N\} \tag{9.76}$$

The problem is to calculate the $n_k + 1$ probabilities $\beta_j(k)$ required for the state estimation updating. We recall that $\beta_j(k)$ represents the posterior probability that the detected landmark is associated with the validated referenced landmark $\mathbf{A}_j$. We also recall that, in the standard probabilistic data association method [3], the probabilities $\beta_j(k)$ are evaluated by using only position information. In other words, the classical calculation of association probabilities (9.33)–(9.34) is similar to constructing a basic Bayesian probability assignment $m_L$ (here called *basic location assignment*) defined by

$$m_L[\theta_j(k)] = P\{\theta_j(k)| Y^k\} \qquad j = 0, \ldots, n_k \tag{9.77}$$

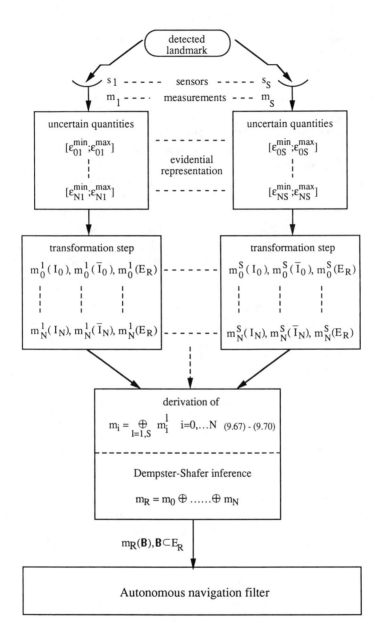

**Figure 9.8** Uncertain recognition information transferred to the filter.

Furthermore, the complementary recognition information that we have at the filter input is a single basic recognition probability assignment $m_R$ that quantifies all proposed identifications:

$$m_R(\mathbf{B}), \qquad \mathbf{B} \subset E_R \tag{9.78}$$

Because the frames of discernment $\Theta(k)$ and $E_R$, on which the basic probability assignments $m_R$ and $m_L$ have been constructed, have different natures, the Dempster-Shafer's inference rule cannot be applied directly to take account of these two types of information (i.e., location and recognition information). The inference of these two basic probability assignments requires the use of the information included on the navigation map and the development of a specific processing module called an *automatic context translator* (ACT). This module, based on a deductive logic mechanism, translates the identification propositions $\mathbf{B} \subset E_R$ into association propositions $\mathbf{A} \subset \Theta(k)$ (compatible with the mapping) and assigns the basic probabilities to propositions $\mathbf{A}$.

Consider for example the recognition frame of discernment $E_R = \{I_0, I_1, I_2\}$, and assume that at time $k$ the validation test gives the three referenced landmarks $\mathbf{A}_1$, $\mathbf{A}_2$, and $\mathbf{A}_3$, which are of types $I_1$, $I_2$, and $I_1$. Respectively, the association frame of discernment is then $\Theta(k) = \{\theta_0(k), \theta_1(k), \theta_2(k), \theta_3(k)\}$. Let us consider all the possible identification propositions $\mathbf{B} \subset E_R$ concerning the detected landmark and examine (independent of the referenced landmark locations) the association propositions to which they may correspond.

If the detected landmark identity is $I_0$, then the only association hypothesis compatible with type $I_0$ is $\theta_0(k)$, because we cannot associate the detected landmark (of type $I_0$) with the landmarks $\mathbf{A}_1$, $\mathbf{A}_2$, or $\mathbf{A}_3$, which we are certain have identities $I_1$ or $I_2$. On the other hand, the detected landmark may correspond to an unknown landmark, which may have an identity $I_0$. Thus, by pure logic the identification proposition $I_0$ is translated into the association proposition $\theta_0(k)$. The same reasoning allows us to translate each identification proposition into one particular association proposition. The translation is the result of one logical deductive mechanism conditioned on prior knowledge of referenced landmark identities. In this simple example, we obtain the following translations (omitting the indices $k$ to simplify the notation)

$$I_0 \rightarrow \theta_0$$
$$I_1 \rightarrow \theta_0 \cup \theta_1 \cup \theta_3$$
$$I_2 \rightarrow \theta_0 \cup \theta_2$$
$$I_0 \cup I_1 \rightarrow \theta_0 \cup \theta_1 \cup \theta_3$$
$$I_0 \cup I_2 \rightarrow \theta_0 \cup \theta_2$$

$$I_1 \cup I_2 \to \theta_0 \cup \theta_1 \cup \theta_2 \cup \theta_3 = \Theta$$

$$I_0 \cup I_1 \cup I_2 = E_R \to \theta_0 \cup \theta_1 \cup \theta_2 \cup \theta_3 = \Theta$$

This logical deductive mechanism must be complemented by the calculation of the basic probability assignment for each resulting association proposition, which is similar to defining a new basic probability assignment denoted $m_{RC}$. This has to simultaneously take into account the basic available recognition probability assignment $m_R$ and the mapping. To evaluate the basic mass of every association proposition compatible with the mapping, we must add the masses of each identification proposition that is committed from the ACT to the association proposition to be considered. The masses of the other association propositions (which are incompatible with the mapping) are taken to be zero. In this particular example, the mass of the four association propositions compatible with the mapping and the recognition are given by

$$m_{RC}(\theta_0) = m_R(I_0)$$

$$m_{RC}(\theta_0 \cup \theta_2) = m_R(I_2) + m_R(I_0 \cup I_2)$$

$$m_{RC}(\theta_0 \cup \theta_1 \cup \theta_3) = m_R(I_1) + m_R(I_0 \cup I_1)$$

$$m_{RC}(\theta_0 \cup \theta_1 \cup \theta_2 \cup \theta_3) = m_R(I_1 \cup I_2) + m_R(I_0 \cup I_1 \cup I_2)$$

The masses of incompatible association propositions that may be taken to zero are

$$m_{RC}(\theta_1), \; m_{RC}(\theta_2), \; m_{RC}(\theta_3),$$

$$m_{RC}(\theta_0 \cup \theta_1), \; m_{RC}(\theta_0 \cup \theta_3), \; m_{RC}(\theta_1 \cup \theta_2), \; m_{RC}(\theta_1 \cup \theta_3), \; m_{RC}(\theta_2 \cup \theta_3),$$

$$m_{RC}(\theta_0 \cup \theta_1 \cup \theta_2), \; m_{RC}(\theta_0 \cup \theta_2 \cup \theta_3), \; m_{RC}(\theta_1 \cup \theta_2 \cup \theta_3)$$

Generally, the navigation map stored aboard the vehicle will have to contain the position information and referenced identification landmarks. In practice, the navigation map may be viewed in any one of three ways, depending on the referenced landmark identification quality. The navigation map is then called *certain* if there is no identification ambiguity for the referenced landmarks; otherwise, it will be called *uncertain*. In the latter case, the identity of each landmark $A_j$ is characterized by a basic recognition probability assignment $m_C^j$. Hence, if we have to construct, for example, a navigation map from three chosen prior identities $I_0$, $I_1$, and $I_2$, we will assign to every referenced landmark $A_j$ the following basic probability (called *cartographical assignment*) $m_C^j$:

$$m_C^j(I_0), \; m_C^j(I_1), \; m_C^j(I_2),$$

$$m_C^j(I_0 \cup I_1), \; m_C^j(I_0 \cup I_2), \; m_C^j(I_1 \cup I_2)$$

and $m_C^j(I_0 \cup I_1 \cup I_2)$

An uncertain navigation map is called *Bayesian* (or *probabilistic*) if the cartographical assignment associated with each referenced landmark is Bayesian (i.e., $m_C^j$ quantifies only singletons $\{I_j\}$). This is implicitly similar to knowing the prior identification probabilities $P\{T(\mathbf{A}_j) = I_i\}$ of the referenced landmarks. To construct a certain navigation map, we have to set one of cartographical masses $m_C^j$ to unity to quantify a particular singleton $\{I_j\}$, and set the other masses to zero.

Even though the translation and evaluation mechanism used to obtain the association propositions just presented (where we assumed the navigation map to be certain) may seem quasi-immediate, the automatic implementation of such a mechanism must be extended to cover the possibility of an uncertain navigation map. To develop the automatic context translator, we must introduce the idea of a fictitious landmark denoted $\mathbf{A}_0$ associated with the particular event $\theta_0$. Under $\theta_0$, none of the validated referenced landmarks stored on the navigation map corresponds to the detected landmark; an equivalent interpretation is to say that the detected landmark may be associated with a fictitious landmark $\mathbf{A}_0$ having an unknown prior identity. Therefore, we have to associate with this unknown landmark $\mathbf{A}_0$ a particular basic cartographical probability assignment $m_C^0$ that does not give preference to any preselected identity. Thus, for a given cartographical frame of discernment $E_C$, we define

$$m_C^0(\mathbf{B}) \equiv 1 \text{ if } \mathbf{B} = E_C \text{ and } m_C^0(\mathbf{B}) = 0 \text{ if } \mathbf{B} \neq E_C \tag{9.79}$$

To simplify the presentation we shall assume from here on that the basic recognition probability assignment $m_R$ and the basic cartographical masses $m_C^j$ ($j = 0, \ldots, n_k$) have been constructed over the same identification frame of discernment $E$, where

$$E \triangleq E_R \equiv E_C \equiv \{I_0, I_1, \ldots, I_N\} \tag{9.80}$$

In general, to construct the masses $m_{RC}$ relative to each possible association proposition $\mathbf{A} \subset \Theta$, we must consider, for every identification proposition $\mathbf{B} \subset E$, all identification propositions $\mathbf{C}$ in accordance with $\mathbf{B}$ (i.e., such that $\mathbf{B} \cap \mathbf{C} \neq \varnothing$) and compatible with $\mathbf{A}$, and simultaneously all identification propositions $\mathbf{C}$ in discordance with $\mathbf{B}$ and incompatible with $\mathbf{A}$. This may be written mathematically in the form of the following fundamental formula [5]:

$$\forall \mathbf{A} \subset \Theta, \qquad m_{RC}(\mathbf{A}) = \sum_{\mathbf{B} \subset E} m_R(\mathbf{B}) \prod_{j \in \mathbf{A}} \alpha_j(\mathbf{B}) \prod_{j \notin \mathbf{A}} [1 - \alpha_j(\mathbf{B})] \tag{9.81}$$

where $\mathbf{A}$ is an association proposition like $\cup_j \theta_j$, $j \in \mathbf{A}$ represents the set of indices $j$ lying in the association proposition $\mathbf{A}$, and $\alpha_j(\mathbf{B})$ is a real number pertaining to $[0, 1]$ and defined by

$$\alpha_j(\mathbf{B}) \triangleq \sum_{\substack{\mathbf{C} \subset E \\ \mathbf{B} \cap \mathbf{C} \neq \varnothing}} m_C^j(\mathbf{C}) \tag{9.82}$$

The validation of the ACT formula (9.81) with two simple examples of application (for a certain and an uncertain navigation map) may be found in [5].

If the identification frames of discernment $E_C$ (relative to cartography) and $E_R$ (relative to the recognition process) are different, then preprocessing is needed to implement the ACT to homogenize the identification propositions entering into (9.81). Preprocessing consists of choosing the smallest frame of discernment between $E_C$ and $E_R$. This frame of discernment, denoted $E$, corresponds to the one that has the minimal cardinality. Thus, we have to choose

$$E = E_R \quad \text{if } |E_R| < |E_C| \tag{9.83}$$

$$E = E_C \quad \text{if } |E_C| < |E_R| \tag{9.84}$$

where $|\cdot|$ denotes cardinality.

The automatic context translator presented here is the theoretical and fundamental expression of this new autonomous navigation method using uncertain recognition information. By using recognition information (i.e., from the basic masses $m_R$) and information stored on the navigation map (i.e., from the cartographical masses $m_C^j$), this original processing unit finds a single basic probability function $m_{RC}$ quantifying the entire set of possible association propositions; Figure 9.9 shows the functional block diagram of the automatic context translator.

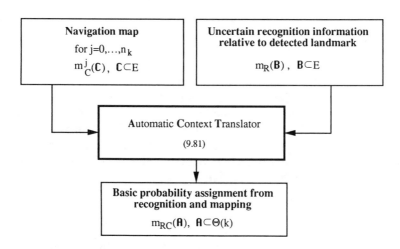

**Figure 9.9** Automatic context translator functional block diagram.

*Calculation of Posterior Association Probabilities*

We recall from the probabilistic data association method that the posterior association probabilities $\beta_j(k)$ to be calculated represent the posterior probabilities for the realization of events $\theta_j(k)$, $j = 0, \ldots, n_k$. The frame of discernment that we have to account for is then the association frame of discernment $\Theta(k)$ defined in (9.75). We also recall that, in the standard PDAF, the calculation of the probabilities $\beta_j(k)$ is based mainly on echo location information and not on echo identification. By leaving out recognition information, we have a single basic Bayesian location probability assignment $m_L$ (defined by (9.77) and where $P\{\theta_j(k) \mid Y^*\}$ is given by the classical relationships (9.33)–(9.34)) that quantifies only singletons $\{\theta_j\}$. Furthermore, by making use of uncertain recognition information, the ACT has been able to construct one basic probability assignment $m_{RC}$ that evaluates the association propositions compatible with the cartography. Note that, in general, singletons $\{\theta_j(k)\}$ are not the only association propositions delivered by the ACT. Therefore, the basic probability assignment $m_{RC}$ is not necessarily a basic Bayesian probability assignment:

$$m_{RC}(\mathbf{A}), \qquad \mathbf{A} \subset \Theta(k) \tag{9.85}$$

From the basic probability assignments $m_L$ and $m_{RC}$ relative to the same frame of discernment $\Theta(k)$, we can now use the Dempster-Shafer inference rule to construct a new basic probability assignment $m_{LRC}$, which combines the location and identification information relative to the referenced landmarks with the identification information relative to the detected landmark. This basic probability assignment $m_{LRC}$ is given mathematically by

$$m_{LRC} \triangleq m_L \oplus m_{RC} = m_{RC} \oplus m_L \tag{9.86}$$

Because $m_L$ is a basic Bayesian probability assignment and, according to a fundamental property of the Dempster-Shafer's inference rule (see theorem 3.7 in [8]), we deduce that $m_{LRC}$ likewise is a basic Bayesian probability assignment for which every focal element is a singleton $\{\theta_j(k)\}$. Thus, this basic Bayesian probability assignment $m_{LRC}$ is homogeneous with a single probability measure $P$. In view of this, the posterior association probabilities $\beta_j(k)$ involved in the probabilistic data association method are given directly by $m_{LRC}[\theta_j(k)]$. Consequently, we have

$$\beta_j(k) \triangleq m_{LRC}[\theta_j(k)] \qquad j = 0, \ldots, n_k \tag{9.87}$$

Thus the association probabilities $\beta_j(k)$ include all available information (i.e. location, recognition, and mapping information). Using the Dempster-Shafer inference, we obtain the following final analytical expression for $\beta_j(k)$

$$\beta_j(k) = \frac{1}{K} m_L[\theta_j(k)] Q(\mathbf{A}_j) \qquad j = 0, \ldots, n_k \tag{9.88}$$

with

$$Q(\mathbf{A}_j) \triangleq \sum_{\substack{\mathbf{A} \subset \Theta(k) \\ \mathbf{A} \cap \theta_j = \theta_j}} m_{RC}(\mathbf{A}) \qquad j = 0, \ldots, n_k \tag{9.89}$$

where

$$K \triangleq \sum_{j=0}^{n_k} m_L[\theta_j(k)]Q(\mathbf{A}_j) \tag{9.90}$$

Recall that the basic location assignments $m_L[\theta_j(k)]$ are given by the classical relationships (9.33)–(9.34):

$$m_L[\theta_j(k)] = e_j(k)\left[b(k) + \sum_{j=1}^{n_k} e_j(k)\right]^{-1} \qquad j = 1, \ldots, n_k \tag{9.91}$$

$$m_L[\theta_0(k)] = b(k)\left[b(k) + \sum_{j=1}^{n_k} e_j(k)\right]^{-1} \tag{9.92}$$

Note that when $m_{RC}$ yields no relevant information (i.e., complete uncertainty), the basic probability mass relative to the association frame of discernment will be maximum and equal to unity:

$$m_{RC}[\Theta(k)] = 1 \tag{9.93}$$

Under these particular conditions, identification information (based on recognition and mapping) will be entirely useless, and we will have for every referenced landmark $\mathbf{A}_j$

$$Q(\mathbf{A}_j) \triangleq \sum_{\substack{\mathbf{A} \subset \Theta(k) \\ \mathbf{A} \cap \theta_j = \theta_j}} m_{RC}(\mathbf{A}) = m_{RC}[\Theta(k)] = 1 \tag{9.94}$$

Therefore, we have

$$\beta_j(k) \equiv m_L[\theta_j(k)] \qquad \forall j = 0, \ldots, n_k \tag{9.95}$$

In other words, when $m_{RC}$ is inconsistent, the posterior association probabilities obtained from the Dempster-Shafer inference are exactly the same as those obtained from the standard probabilistic data association method.

To evaluate the autonomous navigation filter by using uncertain recognition information, in light of (9.88) and (9.89), the automatic context translator has to be programmed to generate the basic probability assignment $m_{RC}$ used in calculating the association probabilities $\beta_j(k)$. Even though there are no difficulties in programming, this specific processing unit may demand a great deal of calculation time and memory space (to store $m_{RC}$), which increases exponentially with the cardinality of the association frame of discernment $\Theta(k)$ (which in turn depends on the number of validated referenced landmarks $n_k$). These two major drawbacks at first would seem to stand in the way of real-time use of the navigation filter and, indeed, of any practical application of this theoretical version of the navigation algorithm. To obtain a real-time (i.e., recursive) filter structure with a limited memory load, we have to look for an equivalent expression for the coefficients $Q(\mathbf{A}_j)$ that does not involve the ACT-generated basic probability assignment $m_{RC}$. After some algebraic transformation (given in [5]), the expression for $Q(\mathbf{A}_j)$ can be written finally as follows:

$$Q(\mathbf{A}_0) \equiv 1 \tag{9.96}$$

$$Q(\mathbf{A}_j) = \sum_{\mathbf{B} \subset E} m_R(\mathbf{B})\alpha_j(\mathbf{B}) \qquad j = 1, \ldots, n_k \tag{9.97}$$

where $\alpha_j(\mathbf{B})$ given in (9.82) is the plausibility of the identification proposition $\mathbf{B}$ relative to the validated referenced landmark $\mathbf{A}_j$. The quantities $\alpha_j(\mathbf{B})$ may be calculated once and for all at the start of the mission but all the $\alpha_j(\mathbf{B})$ for all the referenced landmarks have to be stored. This method becomes very expensive as soon as the number of landmarks on the navigation map and the cardinality of frame of discernment $E$ become large. Another solution is to calculate the quantities $\alpha_j(\mathbf{B})$ at each validation time only for the validated referenced landmarks. However, this solution may call for some redundant calculation of $\alpha_j(\mathbf{B})$ whenever the same referenced landmark appears several times within several validation gates. Considering this, and substituting the basic location masses of (9.91)–(9.92) in (9.88), we finally get (with $b(k)$, $e_j(k)$, and $Q(\mathbf{A}_j)$ as given in (9.55), (9.54), and (9.97))

$$\beta_j(k) = e_j(k)Q(\mathbf{A}_j) \left[ b(k) + \sum_{j=1}^{nk} e_j(k)Q(\mathbf{A}_j) \right]^{-1} \qquad j = 1, \ldots, n_k \tag{9.98}$$

$$\beta_0(k) = b(k) \left[ b(k) + \sum_{j=1}^{nk} e_j(k)Q(\mathbf{A}_j) \right]^{-1} \tag{9.99}$$

In conclusion, we see that the ACT need not be programmed to calculate posterior association probabilities so that a real-time autonomous navigation filter is possible. However, note that the final calculation (9.98)–(9.99) cannot be obtained directly without introducing a specific theoretical automatic context translator. Also note that the inclusion of uncertain quantities in the calculation of posterior association probabilities yields an analytical expression equivalent to the one obtained with Bayesian recognition information. The only difference between relationships (9.33)–(9.34) and (9.98)–(9.99) is in the calculation of the coefficients $Q(\mathbf{A}_j)$. The updating filter equations are made according to standard PDAF equations, and the state prediction is made according to the standard Kalman filter equation.

Before presenting the autonomous navigation filter flowchart, we can verify that this autonomous navigation filter using uncertain recognition information (called a *Shaferian navigation filter* hereafter) is compatible with the navigation filter using only the probabilistic recognition information discussed in Section 9.3.1 (which will be referred to as a *Bayesian navigation filter*). Indeed, whenever the basic cartographical probability masses $m^j_C$ and the recognition masses $m_R$ are strictly Bayesian, for $j = 1, \ldots, n_k$, we have

$$\forall \mathbf{C} = I_i, \quad (i = 0, \ldots, N) \qquad m^j_C(\mathbf{C}) \equiv P\{T(\mathbf{A}_j) = \mathbf{C}\} \qquad (9.100)$$

$$\forall \mathbf{C} \subset E \text{ and } \mathbf{C} \neq I_i, \qquad m^j_C(\mathbf{C}) \equiv 0 \qquad (9.101)$$

$$\forall \mathbf{B} = I_i, \quad (i = 0, \ldots, N) \qquad m_R(\mathbf{B}) \equiv P\{T_R = \mathbf{B} \mid M(k)\} \qquad (9.102)$$

$$\forall \mathbf{B} \subset E \text{ and } \mathbf{B} \neq I_i, \qquad m_R(\mathbf{B}) \equiv 0 \qquad (9.103)$$

Hence, the coefficients $\alpha_j(\mathbf{B})$ are homogeneous with prior probabilities $P\{T(\mathbf{A}_j) = I_i\}$. Under these conditions, (9.97) (for $j = 1, \ldots, n_k$) can be rewritten as follows:

$$Q(\mathbf{A}_j) = \sum_{i=0}^{N} P\{T_R = I_i \mid M(k)\} P\{T(\mathbf{A}_j) = I_i\} \qquad (9.104)$$

Relationship (9.104) corresponds exactly to the analytical expression (9.56) for the coefficients $Q(\mathbf{A}_j)$. Therefore, the Shaferian navigation filter legitimately can be considered a generalization of the Bayesian navigation filter (the Dempster-Shafer inference is commonly considered [4] as the generalization of the Bayesian inference). Figure 9.10 presents the process flowchart of the Shaferian autonomous navigation filter.

## Inconsistency Conditions for Information Provided by the ACT

Now consider briefly the different conditions allowing us to have an inconsistent basic probability assignment $m_{RC}$ at the output of the automatic context translator. From (9.81) and because we always have $\forall \mathbf{B} \subset E, \alpha_0(\mathbf{B}) \equiv 1$, the relationship (9.93) can be rewritten as

$$m_{RC}[\Theta(k)] = \sum_{\mathbf{B} \subset E} m_R(\mathbf{B}) \prod_{j=1}^{nk} \alpha_j(\mathbf{B}) = 1 \qquad (9.105)$$

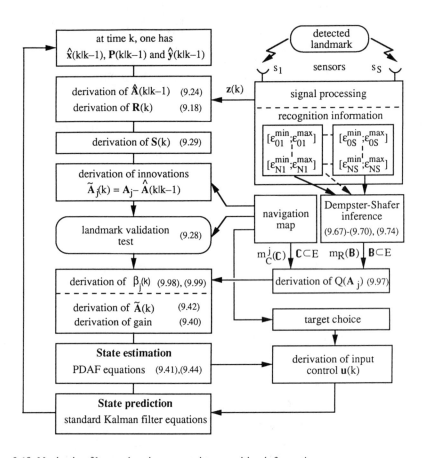

**Figure 9.10** Navigation filter cycle using uncertain recognition information.

It is shown in [5] that (9.105) holds at least in the three following configurations, which are intuitively legitimate.

*First Inconsistent Configuration* This arises when the basic recognition masses are entirely inconsistent; that is

$$m_R(E) \equiv 1 \text{ and } \forall \mathbf{B} \subset E, \quad \mathbf{B} \neq E, \quad m_R(\mathbf{B}) = 0 \tag{9.106}$$

Under this condition, (9.105) holds because despite the type of navigation map (i.e., certain, uncertain, or probabilistic), we always have

$$\prod_{j=1}^{nk} \alpha_j(E) = 1 \tag{9.107}$$

*Second Inconsistent Configuration* This arises when the navigation map is completely inconsistent for every referenced landmark $\mathbf{A}_j$. This assumption can be written mathematically as

$$m_C^j(E) \equiv 1 \text{ and } \forall \mathbf{C} \subset E, \quad \mathbf{C} \neq E, \quad m_C^j(\mathbf{C}) = 0 \tag{9.108}$$

Hence, we have

$$\forall \mathbf{B} \subset E, \quad \alpha_j(\mathbf{B}) \triangleq \sum_{\substack{\mathbf{C} \subset E \\ \mathbf{B} \cap \mathbf{C} \neq \emptyset}} m_C^j(\mathbf{C}) \equiv 1 \tag{9.109}$$

and then

$$\forall \mathbf{B} \subset E, \quad \prod_{j=1}^{nk} \alpha_j(\mathbf{B}) \equiv 1 \tag{9.110}$$

Therefore (9.105) is verified for every type of recognition information (certain, uncertain, or probabilistic) delivered by the sensors, because from the definition of the basic probability assignment [8], we have

$$\sum_{\mathbf{B} \subset E} m_R(\mathbf{B}) \prod_{j=1}^{nk} \alpha_j(\mathbf{B}) = \sum_{\mathbf{B} \subset E} m_R(\mathbf{B}) \equiv 1 \tag{9.111}$$

*Third Inconsistent Configuration* We also may assume we have a Bayesian navigation map and, at the same time, Bayesian recognition information concerning the detected landmark; that is, $m_R$ and $m_C^j$ are basic Bayesian probability assignments defined by relationships (9.100)–(9.103). To obey the inconsistent condition (9.105), we need

$$\forall \mathbf{B} = I_i, i = 0, \ldots, N \quad \prod_{j=1}^{nk} \alpha_j(\mathbf{B}) = \prod_{j=1}^{nk} P\{T(\mathbf{A}_j) = I_i\} = 1 \tag{9.112}$$

with

$$\forall j = 1, \ldots, n_k \quad \sum_{i=0}^{N} \alpha_j(I_i) = \sum_{i=0}^{N} P\{T(\mathbf{A}_j) = I_i\} = 1 \tag{9.113}$$

In view of (9.113), condition (9.112) can hold only in the special case where the mapping and the basic probability recognition assignment $m_R$ are certain and the validated referenced landmarks have the same identity as the detected one (this in fact is the situation discussed at the end of Section 9.3.1).

Indeed, when the recognition and the mapping are certain and compatible (i.e., when $P\{T_R = I_i | M(k)\} = 1$ and $P\{T(\mathbf{A}_j) = I_i\} = 1$ for $j = 1, \ldots, n_k$), we have

$$m_{RC}[\Theta(k)] = \sum_{\mathbf{B} \subset E} m_R(\mathbf{B}) \prod_{j=1}^{nk} \alpha_j(\mathbf{B})$$

$$= P\{T_R = I_i | M(k)\} \prod_{j=1}^{nk} P\{T(\mathbf{A}_j) = I_i\} = 1$$

(9.114)

Searching for these inconsistent conditions in the basic probability assignment generated by the automatic context translator, we find the three special and intuitively legitimate configurations described here, in which the cartography and the recognition information offer no pertinent information with respect to relative location information. Yet note that other configurations also may exist for certain numerical values of basic cartographical and recognition probability assignments, where the inconsistency condition is also verified.

*Conclusion*

We have been able to include both uncertain recognition information and an uncertain navigation map in the autonomous navigation filter strictly by using the theory of evidence and the Dempster-Shafer inference rule. The final structure of the Shaferian filter remains entirely compatible with the structure using Bayesian recognition information and a probabilistic navigation map. The autonomous navigation filter developed is a recursive one. The posterior association probabilities can be calculated in real time with a computation burden equivalent to that required of the PDAF. This navigation filter also is entirely compatible with the PDAF structure as the complementary information given by recognition and navigation map becomes inconsistent. The theoretical development originality of the Shaferian navigation filter lies in the achievement of a new special processing unit called the automatic context translator.

### 9.3.3 Inclusion of a Detected Landmark Identity Classification

We recall that autonomous navigation filters using complementary recognition information require a large data transfer (because we have to transfer $S(N + 1)$ pdf $p(m_l | I_i)$ for the Bayesian navigation filter and $2^{N+1} - 1$ basic masses $m_R$ for the Shaferian navigation filter). To reduce this data transfer between sensors and navigation filters (Bayesian or Shaferian) while reducing computation time, we might introduce a decision maker (called a *classifier*) that will give us the identity of the detected landmark. The classifier's decision then will be transferred to the navigation filter for processing. In practice, the classifier must be developed from measurements delivered by sensors and from the available statistical modelings (if we have Bayesian recognition information) or from uncertain quantities (if we have uncertain recognition information). In this subsection we present the two principal classifier structures for an on-board multisensor system. However, it should be known that some other classifier structures also have been developed in the literature. A survey and discussion of this topic can be found in [9] and [10].

*Centralized Bayesian Classifier*

In such a structure (see Figure 9.11), the optimum decision is constructed by using all the measurements obtained by the sensors and from the conditional probabilities of each possible identification hypothesis, which are chosen beforehand. This implicitly requires a statistical knowledge of the measurement model distribution for each identification hypothesis of the frame of discernment E. The decision given by the classifier at time $k$, denoted $d(k)$, takes its value in the set of all possible decisions $D(k)$ defined by

$$D(k) \triangleq \{d_0, d_1, \ldots, d_N\} \tag{9.115}$$

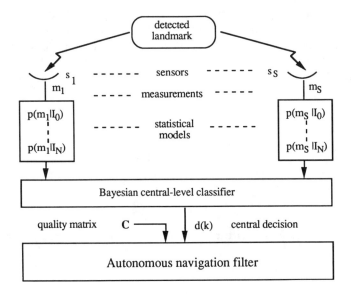

**Figure 9.11** Centralized Bayesian classifier scheme.

The possible decisions $d_i$ at time $k$, are in bijective correspondence with the $N + 1$ identification hypotheses $I_i$, as every decision $d_i$ represents the decision to accept identification hypothesis $I_i$:

$$d(k) = d_i$$

$\Leftrightarrow$ we accept the hypothesis: "Identity I of the detected landmark is $I_i$"

(9.116)

Decision $d_i$ is obtained by choosing a pure decision function $\varphi$ from the measurement space to the decision space $D(k)$:

$$d_i = \varphi[M(k)] \qquad (9.117)$$

where $M(k)$ is the set of measurements generated by the $S$ sensors at time $k$ (defined by (9.47)). The pure decision function $\varphi$ partitions the measurement space by $\{D_0, D_1, \ldots, D_N\}$ and we call the decision region $D_i$ the subset of the measurement space for which $\varphi$ yields the decision $d_i$.

The classification problem [2] consists in finding the optimum decision rule $\varphi$ (i.e., which minimizes the decision error mean) in the set $\Phi_p$ of all possible decision functions. To solve this problem, we assume the parameter $I$ (the landmark identity) to be random. We assume, too, that the conditional probability density functions $p(m_l \mid I_i)$ are known, as are the prior probabilities $P\{I_i\}$, and that there exists a loss function $R$ that yields a positive or null loss $R_{qi} = R(d_q, I_i)$ to each possible situation $[d(k) = d_q, I = I_i]$ for $i = 0, \ldots, N$ and $q = 0, \ldots, N$. This loss function is defined by the known $(N + 1)^2$ coefficients $R_{qi}$. We also assume that the loss due to a correct decision always is strictly less than the loss corresponding to a false decision under the same identification hypothesis:

$$\forall i = 0, \ldots, N, \qquad \forall q = 0, \ldots, N, \qquad R_{qq} \leq R_{qi} \qquad (9.118)$$

Under this condition, the average Bayesian error decision risk is given by

$$R = E[R(d, I)] = \sum_{q=0}^{N} \sum_{i=0}^{N} R_{qi} P\{d_q, I_i\} \qquad (9.119)$$

Introducing all possible sets of measurements and using the total probability theorem, we have

$$R = \int_{M(k)} \sum_{q=0}^{N} \sum_{i=0}^{N} R_{qi} P[d_q, I_i, M(k)] \, dM(k) \qquad (9.120)$$

Using Bayes's formula, we get

$$R = \int_{M(k)} \sum_{q=0}^{N} \sum_{i=0}^{N} R_{qi}P\{I_i\}p[M(k)|I_i]P\{d_q|M(k), I_i\} \, dM(k) \qquad (9.121)$$

The Bayesian solution consists in finding the decision function that will minimize $R$. Assuming the sensors to be independent, we have

$$p[M(k)|I_i] = \prod_{l=1}^{S} p[m_l(k)|I_i] \qquad (9.122)$$

where $S$ is the number of sensors. As shown in [5], (9.121) can be written

$$R = \frac{1}{N+1}\left\{\sum_{q=0}^{N}\sum_{i=0}^{N} R_{qi}P\{I_i\}\right.$$

$$\left. + \int_{M(k)} \sum_{q=0}^{N} \sum_{p=0,p\neq q}^{N} P\{d_p|M(k)\} \sum_{i=0}^{N}(R_{pi} - R_{qi})P\{I_i\}p(M(k)|I_i) \, dM(k)\right\} \qquad (9.123)$$

Because the first Bayesian risk term is independent of the decision that has to be made, minimizing $R$ is equivalent to searching for optimum decision rule that, for every possible set $M(k)$, will minimize the coefficient $S[M(k)]$ appearing in the previous integral and defined by

$$S[M(k)] \triangleq \sum_{q=0}^{N} \sum_{p=0,p\neq q}^{N} P\{d_p|M(k)\} \sum_{i=0}^{N}(R_{pi} - R_{qi})P\{I_i\}p[M(k)|I_i] \qquad (9.124)$$

The minimization of $S[M(k)]$ leads [5] to the following optimum decision:

$$d(k) = \varphi[M(k)] = d_q \Leftrightarrow \forall p \neq q, \qquad \sum_{i=0}^{N} R_{qi}P\{I_i\}p[M(k)|I_i]$$

$$< \sum_{i=0}^{N} R_{pi}P\{I_i\}p[M(k)|I_i] \qquad (9.125)$$

This optimum decision rule, however, must be completed to get a decision for the sets $M(k)$ of measurements if the equality occurs in (9.125). These measurements lie on the border of the decision region $D_p$ such that

$$\exists p, \exists q, \qquad \sum_{i=0}^{N} R_{qi}P\{I_i\}p[M(k)|I_i] = \sum_{i=0}^{N} R_{pi}P\{I_i\}p[M(k)|I_i] \qquad (9.126)$$

In practice we can decide arbitrarily to assign border measurements to one of the regions on either side of the border and so obtain a pure decision rule. But we also can decide to assign a given probability to each decision generated by each measurement of a border region. We then have a randomized decision rule for which, whatever probability is chosen, $R$ is minimized. Note that pure decision rules are special cases of randomized decision rules. If the set of measurements constituting the decision region borders has a nonzero probability for each density function of $M(k)$, conditioned on identification hypothesis $I_i$, the conditional correct and erroneous decision probabilities are dependent on this random decision rule. If they are, the decision function defining the random decision rule may for example be chosen to establish some of these conditional decision probabilities.

After the decision is made, there are $(N + 1)^2$ possible situations: the set of measurements $M(k)$ belongs to class $D_i$ (i.e., the identity of the detected landmark is $I_i$) and the decision is made to assign this realization to the $q$th class. This situation is then characterized by the pair $[d(k) = d_q, I = I_i]$ with $q \neq i$. To each situation there corresponds a conditional probability: either a correct decision $P\{d_q | I_q\}$ for one of the $(N + 1)$ situations where $[d(k) = d_q, I = I_q]$, or a false decision $P\{d_q | I_i\}$ for one of the $N(N + 1)$ situations where $[d(k) = d_q, I = I_i]$ with $q \neq i$.

If we assume that probabilities are given for identification hypotheses (with a prior known probability $P\{I_i\}$ for $i = 0, \ldots, N$), we can associate with each pair $(d_q, I_i)$ the joint probability

$$P\{d_q, I_i\} = P\{I_i\}P\{d_q | I_i\} \tag{9.127}$$

Even if the identification hypothesis is not described in terms of a probability, we always can characterize the quality of a decision rule with the $(N + 1)^2$ conditional probabilities $P\{d_q | I_i\}$ or with some deterministic expression of these conditional probabilities, such as a linear combination with positive real coefficients. In practice, these conditional probabilities will be stored in a $(N + 1)$-order square matrix, called the *classifier quality matrix*, denoted

$$\mathbf{C} \triangleq \begin{bmatrix} P\{d_0 | I_0\} & \cdots & P\{d_0 | I_N\} \\ \cdots & \cdots & \cdots \\ \cdots & \cdots & \cdots \\ \cdots & \cdots & \cdots \\ P\{d_N | I_0\} & \cdots & P\{d_N | I_N\} \end{bmatrix} \tag{9.128}$$

The total probability theorem also requires the sum of matrix elements over each column to be equal to unity. The quality matrix $\mathbf{C}$ characterizes the classifier performances directly, which of course will improve the closer the matrix $\mathbf{C}$ is to the identity matrix. However, in practice, the matrix $\mathbf{C}$ usually will not be diagonal, due to the observation conditions, sensor quality, and the approximate statistical models used in the decision rule. A classifier would be ineffective if all the elements of $\mathbf{C}$ were similar. The quality matrix $\mathbf{C}$ may be calculated from the known conditional statistical distribution models for each possible identification hypothesis. Indeed, introducing the set of $S$-tuples $M(k)$, the elements of $\mathbf{C}$ are given by

$$c_{qi} = P\{d_q | I_i\} = \int_{M(k)} P\{d_q | M(k), I_i\} p[M(k) | I_i] \, dM(k) \tag{9.129}$$

As the measurements from the sensors are assumed to be independent and the centralized decision is constructed solely from the available measurements, it follows that

$$c_{qi} = \int_{M(k)} P\{d_q | M(k)\} \prod_{l=1}^{S} p[m_l(k) | I_i] \, dM(k) \tag{9.130}$$

Using (9.125), we deduce that

$$P\{d_q | M(k)\} = 1 \Leftrightarrow \forall p \neq q, \quad \sum_{i=0}^{N} [R_{qi} P\{I_i\} \prod_{l=1}^{S} p(m_l(k) | I_i)]$$
$$< \sum_{i=0}^{N} [R_{pi} P\{I_i\} \sum_{l=1}^{S} p(m_l(k) | I_i)] \tag{9.131}$$

otherwise

$$P\{d_q | M(k)\} = 0 \tag{9.132}$$

The components of the quality matrix are then given by

$$c_{qi} = \int_{M(k) \in D_q} \prod_{l=1}^{S} p[m_l(k) | I_i] \, dM(k) \tag{9.133}$$

where $M(k) \in D_q$ represents the set of $S$-tuples $M(k)$ yielding decision $d_q$.

Therefore, the quality matrix of the centralized Bayesian classifier may be obtained from the statistical models (assumed to be exact) for the measurement distributions and from the chosen loss function, which defines the Bayesian risk $R$. Note that in practice the theoretical expression (9.133) rarely can be used, because in most cases, the components $c_{qi}$ cannot be calculated analytically. The quality matrix can be evaluated by simulation or by experiment, however.

The simulation approach consists in using conditional probability density functions to simulate the classifier for every possible identity of referenced landmarks. After a very large number of simulations, the rates of correct and false decisions are then calculated to approximate the components of the quality matrix.

The experimental approach consists in carrying out the decision rule for every type of referenced landmark under environmental conditions, in a large number of trials using all sensors simultaneously. By counting the declarations obtained for each identification hypothesis, we can approximate the column elements of the quality matrix corresponding to the identity of the presented landmark.

To characterize the classifier quality, we also define the *mean recognition rate* (MRR) and the *mean confusion rate* (MCR) as follows:

$$\text{MRR} \triangleq \sum_{i=0}^{N} P\{d_i, I_i\} = \sum_{i=0}^{N} P\{d_i | I_i\} P\{I_i\} \tag{9.134}$$

$$\text{MCR} \triangleq \sum_{q=0}^{N} \sum_{i=0, i \neq q}^{N} P\{d_q, I_i\} = \sum_{q=0}^{N} \sum_{i=0, i \neq q}^{N} P\{d_q | I_i\} P\{I_i\} \tag{9.135}$$

One simple case of interest in practice is to choose the loss function so that all losses associated with correct decisions are null and all losses associated with false decisions are equal to unity. That is,

$$\text{if } q = i \quad R_{qi} = 0 \tag{9.136}$$
$$\text{otherwise} \quad R_{qi} = 1 \tag{9.137}$$

This particular loss function is commonly called the *0–1 loss function*. The optimum decision rule (9.125) for this 0–1 loss function can be written as

$$d(k) = \varphi[M(k)] = d_q \Leftrightarrow \forall p \neq q, \quad P\{I_p\} p[M(k) | I_p]$$
$$< P\{I_q\} p[M(k) | I_q] \tag{9.138}$$

Thus, the decision maker makes its decision by choosing the identification hypothesis that will have the maximum posterior probability for the available measurement. The case in which the prior probabilities $P\{I_i\}$ are equal corresponds to the usual maximum likelihood criteria:

$$d(k) = \varphi[M(k)] = d_q \Leftrightarrow \forall p \neq q, \quad p[M(k) | I_p] < p[M(k) | I_q] \tag{9.139}$$

Clearly, minimizing $R$ for the 0–1 loss function is exactly the same as minimizing MCR and simultaneously maximizing MRR because, considering (9.119) and (9.136)–(9.137), we have

$$R = \sum_{q=0}^{N} \sum_{i=0}^{N} R_{qi} P\{d_q, I_i\} = \sum_{q=0}^{N} \sum_{i=0, i \neq q}^{N} P\{d_q, I_i\} \triangleq \text{MCR} \tag{9.140}$$

Moreover using the total probability theorem we have

$$R = 1 - \sum_{q=0}^{N} P\{d_q, I_q\} = 1 - \text{MRR} = \text{MCR} \tag{9.141}$$

When the identification hypotheses are equiprobable, MRR and MCR are given by

$$\text{MCR} = \frac{1}{N+1} \sum_{q=0}^{N} \sum_{i=0, i \neq q}^{N} P\{d_q | I_i\} \tag{9.142}$$

$$\text{MRR} = \frac{1}{N+1} \sum_{q=0}^{N} P\{d_q | I_i\} \tag{9.143}$$

The MRR represents the arithmetical mean of the diagonal terms of the quality matrix and the MCR is the arithmetical mean of the conditional confusion terms.

The most important advantages we can get out of this centralized Bayesian decisional structure are, first, the inclusion of all available information (i.e., measurements from sensors and our prior knowledge of the conditional pdf), second, less data to be transferred, and finally, a certain amount of versatility stemming from the inclusion of statistical modeling, which may be more or less reliable.

We also must note that the classifier decision is not necessarily unique and we sometimes may have a set of equivalent decisions (cf. (9.126)) for some sets of measurements $M(k)$, which all minimize this Bayesian risk $R$. Depending on the specifics of the problem, we may choose a pure decision rule (which arbitrarily settles on one of the possible equivalent decisions) or a random decision rule (which assigns to each equivalent possible decision a prior realization probability). This pure decision or these equivalent decisions with their probabilities (chosen to be equiprobable) then must be taken into account in the navigation filter.

## Centralized Shaferian Classifier

We are interested here in constructing a Shaferian decision rule that will provide the best choice concerning the identity of the detected landmark using all uncertain quantities delivered by each sensor. The Dempster-Shafer theory of evidence [8], which is quite appropriate for considering uncertain quantities in combination, does not provide any solution to optimum decision problems. Because there is no overriding decision rule among all the possible ones given in the literature concerning this topic, we have chosen the one suggested by D. Dubois in [7, pp. 58–59]. As we will see in the following, this decision rule is very simple and has the advantage of becoming coherent with the classical Bayesian decision rule as the uncertainties tend toward zero. Figure 9.12 illustrates the centralized Shaferian classifier scheme.

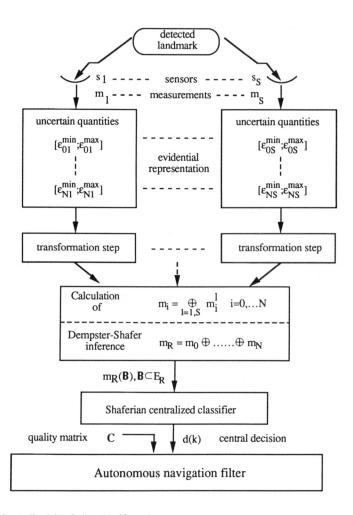

**Figure 9.12** Centralized Shaferian classifier scheme.

The problem is to choose the best of all the possible identification hypotheses concerning the detected landmark (i.e., we have to choose the best singleton $I_i$ pertaining to the identification frame of discernment $E_R$). This choice must be made on the basis of all available information; that is, the basic recognition probability assignments $m_R$ (given in (9.74) by the Dempster-Shafer's inference rule using all uncertain quantities simultaneously). The solution proposed by Dubois consists in approximating the credibility and plausibility measure with a probability measure by distributing weights of evidence $m_R(\mathbf{B})$ equally over all the focal elements. This legitimate approximation gives the following probability measure:

$$\forall I_i \in E_R, \quad \text{we define } P\{I_i\} = \sum_{\substack{\mathbf{B} \subset E_R \\ I_i \in \mathbf{B}}} \frac{1}{|\mathbf{B}|} m_R(\mathbf{B}) \tag{9.144}$$

This approximation is equivalent to the one made in Bayesian inference when, in the absence of information, we use a uniform mass as prior probability. The legitimate decision rule given under this approximation consists in choosing the most probable identification hypothesis. Thus the centralized Shaferian decision rule is given by

$$d(k) = \varphi(m_R) = d_q \Leftrightarrow \forall p \neq q, \quad P\{I_p\} < P\{I_q\} \tag{9.145}$$

This decision rule, as in Bayesian case, must be complemented to assign one decision to all the basic recognition probability assignments $m_R$ for which equality holds. We also can choose a pure or a random decision rule, which takes into account all possible equivalent decisions with their prior probabilities.

As for Bayesian decision rule, we can always characterize the quality of the centralized Shaferian classifier by the $(N + 1)^2$ conditional probabilities $P\{d_q | I_i\}$. But contrary to the Bayesian case, these probabilities cannot be calculated analytically. So we have to evaluate the quality matrix $\mathbf{C}$ of the Shaferian classifier either from decision process simulations or from trials using all sensors. The operational advantages of the centralized Shaferian classifier are similar to those of the centralized Bayesian classifier. Some other decision structures can be found in [9, 10] and a presentation on a (Bayesian and Shaferian) decentralized decision classifier is given in [5].

*Formulation of a Navigation Filter Using a Classifier*

In a general manner, the output of any classifier (optimal or nonoptimal, Bayesian or Shaferian, centralized or decentralized, or with any other decisional structure) consists of either a single decision $\mathbf{d}(k) = I_i$ quantifying a particular identification singleton $I_i$ ($I_i$ corresponds in this case to the best presumed identity) or a set of equivalent possible decisions, denoted $\mathbf{d}(k)$, having some prior probability. The quality of a classifier always can be characterized by an $N + 1$ square quality matrix $\mathbf{C}$, which can be obtained from theoretical calculation, simulations, or experimental trials. The elements of $\mathbf{C}$ represent the probabilities of correct and false decisions.

We denote as $\mathbf{d}^k$ the cumulative set of decisions made by the classifier from the initial time to time $k$:

$$\mathbf{d}^k \triangleq \{\mathbf{d}(i)\}_{i=1}^k = \{\mathbf{d}^{k-1}, \mathbf{d}(k)\} \tag{9.146}$$

The best estimate of the state (in the sense of minimizing the mean square error) is given by the conditional mean calculated from all the available information; that is,

$$\hat{\mathbf{x}}(k|k) = E[\mathbf{x}(k)|Y^k, \mathbf{d}^k] \tag{9.147}$$

Introducing the $n_k + 1$ mutually exclusive and exhaustive association events $\theta_j(k)$ and applying the total probability theorem yields

$$\hat{\mathbf{x}}(k|k) = \sum_{j=0}^{nk} \beta_j(k)E[\mathbf{x}(k)|\theta_j(k), Y^k, \mathbf{d}^k] \tag{9.148}$$

$E[\mathbf{x}(k)|\theta_j(k), Y^k, \mathbf{d}^k]$, which corresponds to the updated state estimate conditioned on the event that the $j$th validated referenced landmark is correct, is obtained by the standard updating Kalman filter equation. The conditional probability $\beta_j(k)$ can be written explicitly as follows (for $j = 0, \ldots, n_k$):

$$\begin{aligned} \beta_j(k) &\triangleq P\{\theta_j(k)|Y^k, \mathbf{d}^k\} = P\{\theta_j(k)|A^k, \mathbf{z}^k, \mathbf{d}^k\} \\ &= P\{\theta_j(k)|Y^{k-1}, Y(k), n_k, \mathbf{d}^k\} \end{aligned} \tag{9.149}$$

Assuming the landmarks to be uniformly distributed on the navigation map (without distinguishing identities) and the sensors to be independent, we show in Appendix 9A that the association probabilities can be written

$$\beta_j(k) = e_j(k)Q(\mathbf{A}_j)[b(k) + \sum_{j=1}^{nk} e_j(k)Q(\mathbf{A}_j)]^{-1} \quad j = 1, \ldots, n_k \tag{9.150}$$

$$\beta_0(k) = b(k)[b(k) + \sum_{j=1}^{nk} e_j(k)Q(\mathbf{A}_j)]^{-1} \tag{9.151}$$

where

$$e_j(k) \triangleq (P_G)^{-1}N[\tilde{\mathbf{A}}_j(k); 0, \mathbf{S}(k)] \tag{9.152}$$

$$b(k) \triangleq n_k(1 - P_GP_D)[P_GP_DV(k)]^{-1} \tag{9.153}$$

$$Q(\mathbf{A}_j) \triangleq \frac{\sum\limits_{i=0}^{N} P\{T(\mathbf{A}_j) = I_i\}P_R\{I_i\}P\{\mathbf{d}(k)|I_i\}}{\sum\limits_{i=0}^{N} P_R\{I_i\}P\{\mathbf{d}(k)|I_i\}} \qquad (9.154)$$

$(N + 1)$ is the number of mutually exclusive and exhaustive identification hypotheses; $P_R\{I_i\}$ is the *a priori* probability of observing a landmark with identity $I_i$. This probability must be evaluated from the knowledge of the navigation map; $P\{T(\mathbf{A}_j) = I_i\}$ is the *a priori* probability that the identity of $\mathbf{A}_j$ is $I_i$ (this *a priori* probability is assumed to be known in the mapping). $P\{\mathbf{d}(k)\}I_i$ is given by the classifier quality matrix $\mathbf{C}$ (see Appendix 9.A). Figure 9.13 gives the general flowchart for the autonomous navigation filter that uses the classification of the landmarks.

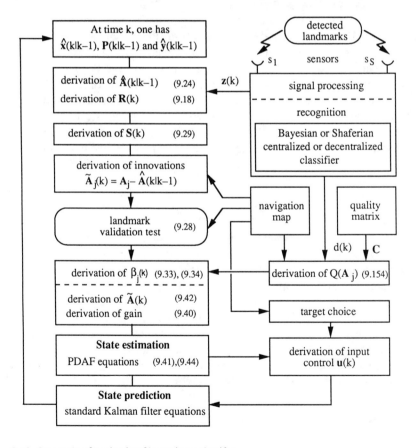

**Figure 9.13** One cycle of navigation filter using a classifier.

As for the Bayesian or Shaferian navigation filter, the coefficient $Q(A_j)$ can be interpreted as an agreement factor (given by the classifier and navigation map) between the identity of the detected landmark and the identity of landmark $A_j$. If the classifier is 100% reliable and if all validated landmarks have the same identity as the presumed identity given by the classifier, then the available recognition information becomes noninformative and cannot be used to improve the state estimate. The noninformative recognition information condition can be written mathematically as

$$\text{for } j = 1, \ldots, n_k \qquad Q(A_j) \equiv 1 \qquad (9.155)$$

Under these particular conditions, we find the classical expression of the *a posteriori* association probabilities as in the standard PDAF. The updating state and covariance equations are the same as those of the PDAF and the state prediction is made according to the standard Kalman equation.

In conclusion, the autonomous navigation filter using a classifier has the same structure as a Bayesian or Shaferian navigation filter discussed earlier. Only one modification appears in the calculation of coefficients $Q(A_j)$ to evaluate the *a posteriori* association probabilities. The analytical expression of the association probabilities is similar to that developed in PDAF and presents no difficulty for real-time implementation if we know the classifier quality matrix. This navigation filter structure becomes exactly equivalent to the PDAF structure whenever the recognition information is noninformative. Also note that this structure does not allow an uncertain navigation map to be taken into account, contrary to the Shaferian navigation filter.

## 9.4 SIMULATION RESULTS

From different randomly generated navigation maps and an arbitrary navigation scenario, a set of simulations was conducted in [5] to display the behavior of these new autonomous navigation filters with respect to parameters such as the MRR, the cartographical density (i.e., number of landmarks per km²), and the minimal probability of landmark detection. Such parameters usually are considered sensitive for these new algorithms. Unfortunately, due to the current lack of knowledge on conditional statistical measurement distributions, we were able to test the behavior only of the Shaferian navigation filter and a navigation filter using a classifier. The navigation results given in [5] confirm the behavior legitimately expected from the theoretical development of the algorithms, that is, an improvement in navigation quality with

- The use of additional recognition information,
- An increase in the MRR of the recognition system aboard,
- An increase in the alignment frequency.

In practice, the increase in the MRR could be obtained either by improving the sensor quality (in the case of a single-sensor system) or using a multisensor system (with sensors judiciously chosen for their good complementarity) in which the recognition system could discriminate among a large diversity of landmarks. As for the alignment frequency, it depends mainly on the cartographical density of the navigation map and the minimal detection probability of the chosen detection and recognition system.

Furthermore, the robustness and the consistency of these two navigation filters for different types of navigation map (i.e., certain map, uncertain map, or probabilistic map), for various landmark densities and different recognition information qualities, has been verified from a set of simulations based upon 50 Monte Carlo runs. However, some inconsistency problems in the navigation algorithms have appeared when we used low minimal-detection probability. This behavior is due mainly to the nonlinear filter structure and from nonlinearities of the dynamical state models involved in navigation simulations.

For example, Figures 9.14 and 9.15 illustrate (for one run) the behavior of the Shaferian navigation filter and the navigation filter using a classifier. In these simulations, the real initial vehicle position is (20 km, 20 km), the real initial velocity is

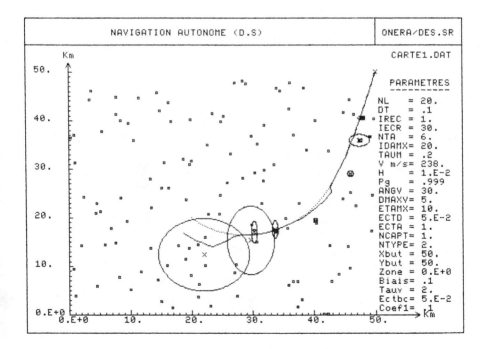

**Figure 9.14** Behavior of the Shaferian autonomous navigation filter (one run).

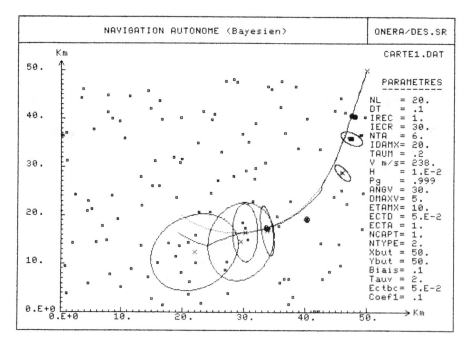

**Figure 9.15** Behavior of the navigation filter using a classifier (one run).

238 m/s and the initial heading (i.e., angle between velocity vector and *x*-axis) is
−45°. The initial state error $x(0) - \hat{x}(0|0)$ is 2 km for position in each coordinate,
2 m/s for velocity, and 2° for heading. The guidance law to be used in simulations is
the classical proportional navigation law. The sampling time was $T = 0.1$ s and the
target position was chosen at (50 km, 50 km). In this scenario, we used a navigation
map that had a cartographic density equal to 0.05 landmarks per km² with six different landmark identities.

The simulated recognition system consists of one sensor able to discriminate
only three types of landmarks among the six possible identities present on the navigation map. The maximal vision distance (see Figure 9.1) is 5 km with an angle of
60°. The landmark detection probability is assumed to be high ($0.95 \leq P_D \leq 1$) and
probability $P_G$ entering in landmark validation test is 0.999. The MRR corresponding to the quality matrix of the classifier (for the navigation filter using a classifier)
lies within the interval [0.5, 0.6]. Uncertain recognition information used in the
Shaferian navigation filter is generated to be compatible with the chosen MRR (if the
centralized Shaferian decision rule were applied).

The axes appearing in Figures 9.14 and 9.15 correspond to the *x*-axis and *y*-axis of the simulated navigation map and the black points correspond to the different referenced landmark positions (to be randomly generated). The dashed-line curve represents the real motion of the vehicle during navigation and the solid curve represents the estimated trajectory given by autonomous navigation filters. The ellipses represent the "$2\sigma$" confidence regions for the detected landmark position as calculated by the filters when a landmark is detected in the sensor's field of view. For convenience, not all validation gates (calculated at each landmark detection) have been represented on the figures; only the gates with a minimal period of 3 s are shown.

These two autonomous navigation runs demonstrate the alignment ability of the algorithms to guide the vehicle toward the target. The validation gate dimensions also show an improved accuracy of the vehicle state estimate during navigation. The deviation between the estimated trajectory and real trajectory (appearing in the middle of navigation) results from the difference between the simulated real state evolution model (where some bias and some colored noises were introduced to account for some wind effects and some uncertainty concerning vehicle lift) and the simplified evolution model used in the navigation filters (i.e., without bias and colored noises). This navigation period also corresponds to a blind navigation period during which alignment was impossible because no landmarks had been detected in the sensor's field of view.

## 9.5   SUMMARY AND CONCLUSIONS

A new application of the probabilistic data association method is presented for solving the problem of autonomous navigation for a vehicle flying at low altitude. The new algorithms are an interesting alternative to traditional methods based on image correlation techniques that involve many difficulties in their operational implementation. From a finite number of sensors and a navigation map stored aboard the vehicle, navigation algorithms allow the vehicle position to be aligned automatically with respect to the navigation map to guide the vehicle autonomously toward the target. The target (assumed to be fixed) generally is chosen at the beginning of the mission but also could be chosen (or changed) during the mission through a sophisticated communication system (hence, we also may guide a vehicle toward a moving target).

The originality of the new autonomous navigation methods lies in the use of the information provided by different types of sensors (such as MM sensors, IR sensors, or radar sensors) with simple specific data processing to recognize in real time the identity of landmarks being flown over. When the conditional distribution probability function of each measurement given by each sensor relative to each possible identification hypothesis is available, the Bayesian inference is the optimal solution for recognition information fusion. In addition, the Bayesian inference rule is entirely compatible with the Bayesian structure of the PDAF. The introduction of Bayesian recognition information in the PDAF leads to modifying the calculation of the *a posteriori* association probabilities. The Bayesian navigation filter also allows us to consider the *a priori* identification probabilities of referenced landmarks possibly with their position uncertainties.

Unfortunately, in an operational context, the recognition processing does not generally yield a statistical representation of the required information used in the navigation algorithm. However, this recognition information may be modeled in terms of uncertain quantities that can be taken judiciously into account in the probabilistic data association method. The theory of evidence with the Dempster-Shafer inference rule appears to be the best tool for solving the problem of fusion of uncertain information because this inference rule commonly is considered a generalization of the Bayesian inference. The introduction of the Dempster-Shafer inference rule in the probabilistic data association method yields a new recursive navigation filter structure; the Shaferian navigation filter, which is usable in real time and entirely compatible with the standard PDAF. From a theoretical viewpoint, the Shaferian navigation filter can be considered a generalization of the Bayesian navigation filter.

Finally, to reduce the transfer of recognition information to the filter, we can use a particular classifier structure adjusted to the nature of the available recognition information. The introduction of a classifier yields a new recursive navigation filter structure that, once again, is compatible with the standard PDAF.

The advantages of these new methods over traditional methods (based on complete navigation map and image correlation techniques) lies mainly in the low computation burden, the simplicity of their operational implementation both for mission planning and real-time running, and their ease of use. In addition, by taking recognition information into account, the navigation algorithms also allow position uncertainties and referenced landmark identification to be considered. For instance, this flexibility could allow real-time transmission to the vehicle of the target chosen and the navigation map, obtained from a satellite observation, of the area to be flown over (battlefield or enemy territory, for example). Thus, the navigation map could be more or less reliable according to satellite image resolution and the image processing used to identify landmarks to be referenced. Table 9.1 summarizes the principal characteristics of navigation filters.

In this chapter, data processing is considered independent of the nature of the sensors in order to cover a very wide range of applications. We already can envisage the use of these new alignment techniques for other applications involving autonomous vehicle motion (autonomous robot guidance in a partially known or hostile environment, for example). The research now to be done should focus on the choice of sensors and the processing required to provide recognition information for use by these new navigation methods.

**Table 9.1**
Characteristics of Navigation Filters

| Properties \ Filter category | rustic (§ 2) | Bayesian (§ 3.1) | Shaferian (§ 3.2) | with classifier (§ 3.3) |
|---|---|---|---|---|
| real-time | yes | yes | yes | yes |
| $P_D \leq 1$ | yes | yes | yes | yes |
| Landmark recognition | no | yes | yes | yes |
| Certain map | no | yes | yes | yes |
| Bayesian map | no | yes | yes | yes |
| Uncertain map | no | no | yes | no |
| Bayesian recognition | no | yes | yes | yes |
| Uncertain recognition | no | no | yes | yes |

## APPENDIX 9.A: CALCULATION OF THE ASSOCIATION PROBABILITIES FOR A FILTER USING A CLASSIFIER

We seek to calculate the following association probabilities:

$$\beta_j(k) \triangleq P\{\theta_j(k)|Y^k, \mathbf{d}^k\} = P\{\theta_j(k)|Y^{k-1}, Y(k), n_k, \mathbf{d}^k\} \tag{9.A1}$$

Applying Bayes's rule yields

$$\beta_j(k) = p_1^j(k)P_2^j(k)\left[\sum_{j=0}^{nk} p_1^j(k)P_2^j(k)\right]^{-1} \tag{9.A2}$$

with

$$p_1^j(k) \triangleq p[Y(k)|\theta_j(k), Y^{k-1}, n_k, \mathbf{d}^k] = p[A(k)|\theta_j(k), A^{k-1}, \mathbf{z}^{k-1}, n_k, \mathbf{d}^k] \tag{9.A3}$$

$$P_2^j(k) \triangleq P\{\theta_j(k)|Y^{k-1}, n_k, \mathbf{d}^k\} = P\{\theta_j(k)|A^{k-1}, \mathbf{z}^{k-1}, n_k, \mathbf{d}^k\} \tag{9.A4}$$

The term $p_1^j(k)$ represents the joint location probability density function of validated landmarks conditioned on event $\theta_j(k)$. At this stage, note that location information and recognition information (which is relative only to the identity of the detected landmark) are different by nature and therefore can be considered independent. Hence, the conditioning term $\mathbf{d}^k$ becomes irrelevant and can be eliminated from (9.A3). Thus, we have

$$
\begin{aligned}
p_1^j(k) &= p[A(k)|\theta_j(k), A^{k-1}, \mathbf{z}^{k-1}, n_k, \mathbf{d}^k] \\
&= p[A(k)|\theta_j(k), A^{k-1}, \mathbf{z}^{k-1}, n_k]
\end{aligned}
\tag{9.A5}
$$

The calculation of $p_1^j(k)$ then is identical to that developed in [3] the expression of which is recalled:

$$
p_1^j(k) = (P_G)^{-1} N[\tilde{\mathbf{A}}_j(k); 0, \mathbf{S}(k)] V(k)^{-n_k+1} \qquad j = 1, \ldots, n_k
\tag{9.A6}
$$

$$
p_1^0(k) = V(k)^{-n_k}
\tag{9.A7}
$$

The term $P_2^j(k)$ represents the *a priori* probability of associating the detected landmark with $A_j(k)$ given the number of validated referenced landmarks and the decision to be made by the classifier concerning the identity of the detected landmark. This probability also can be written as

$$
P_2^j(k) \triangleq P\{\theta_j(k)| Y^{k-1}, n_k, \mathbf{d}^k\} = \frac{1}{c_2} P\{\theta_j(k), Y^{k-1}, n_k, \mathbf{d}^{k-1}, \mathbf{d}(k)\}
\tag{9.A8}
$$

with

$$
c_2 \triangleq \sum_{j=0}^{n_k} P\{\theta_j(k), Y^{k-1}, n_k, \mathbf{d}^{k-1}, \mathbf{d}(k)\}
\tag{9.A9}
$$

*Under Hypothesis $\theta_0(k)$*

Applying Bayes's rule, we have

$$
\begin{aligned}
P_2^0(k) &= \frac{1}{c_2} P\{\mathbf{d}(k)|\theta_0(k), Y^{k-1}, n_k, \mathbf{d}^{k-1}\} \\
&\quad \times P\{\theta_0(k)| Y^{k-1}, n_k, \mathbf{d}^{k-1}\} P[Y^{k-1}, n_k, \mathbf{d}^{k-1}]
\end{aligned}
\tag{9.A10}
$$

Note that under hypothesis $\theta_0(k)$, the detected landmark corresponds to any validated referenced landmark and its type *a priori* is completely unknown. Therefore, the occurrence of event $\theta_0(k)$ gives no pertinent information on the identity of the detected landmark and the decision to be made is independent of $\theta_0(k)$. Thus, we have

$$P\{\mathbf{d}(k)|\theta_0(k), Y^{k-1}, n_k, \mathbf{d}^{k-1}\} = P\{\mathbf{d}(k)\} \tag{9.A11}$$

In addition, the *a priori* occurrence of $\theta_0(k)$ is independent of $Y^{k-1}$ and $\mathbf{d}^{k-1}$, and as in PDAF we have

$$P\{\theta_0(k)| Y^{k-1}, n_k, \mathbf{d}^{k-1}\} = P\{\theta_0(k)|n_k\} = 1 - P_G P_D \tag{9.A12}$$

where $P_D$ is the probability of detecting the landmarks and $P_G$ is the *a priori* probability that the detected landmark lies within the validation gate.

*Under Hypotheses $\theta_j(k)$, j $\neq$ 0*

Introducing the set of all possible identities and applying the total probability theorem and Bayes's rule yields

$$P_2^j(k) = \frac{1}{c_2} \sum_{i=0}^{N} [P\{\theta_j(k)| T_R = I_i, Y^{k-1}, n_k, \mathbf{d}^{k-1}, \mathbf{d}(k)\} \tag{9.A13}$$
$$\times P\{T_R = I_i| Y^{k-1}, n_k, \mathbf{d}^{k-1}, \mathbf{d}(k)\} P\{Y^{k-1}, n_k, \mathbf{d}^{k-1}, \mathbf{d}(k)\}]$$

where $T_R$ is the real identity of the detected landmark at time $k$ and $P\{\theta_j(k)| T_R = I_i, Y^{k-1}, n_k, \mathbf{d}^{k-1}, \mathbf{d}(k)\}$ is the *a priori* probability of associating the validated landmark $\mathbf{A}_j$ with the detected landmark conditioned on the knowledge of the detected landmark identity and the number of validated landmarks.

Because the knowledge of decision $\mathbf{d}(k)$ made by the classifier is irrelevant with respect to the knowledge of the real identity of the detected landmark (which *a priori* is independent of its location), we can write

$$P\{\theta_j(k)| T_R = I_i, Y^{k-1}, n_k, \mathbf{d}^{k-1}, \mathbf{d}(k)\} = \frac{1}{n_k} P_G P_D P\{T(\mathbf{A}_j) = I_i\} \tag{9.A14}$$

$$P\{T_R = I_i| Y^{k-1}, n_k, \mathbf{d}^{k-1}, \mathbf{d}(k)\} = P\{T_R = I_i|\mathbf{d}(k)\} \tag{9.A15}$$

$$P[Y^{k-1}, n_k, \mathbf{d}^{k-1}, \mathbf{d}(k)] = P[Y^{k-1}, n_k, \mathbf{d}^{k-1}]P\{\mathbf{d}(k)\} \tag{9.A16}$$

where $P\{T(\mathbf{A}_j) = I_i\}$ is the *a priori* probability that identity of $\mathbf{A}_j$ is $I_i$. In practice, $P\{T(\mathbf{A}_j) = I_i\}$ is given by the mapping. This probability may take into account landmark identification errors during the mapping.

Finally, the expression of $P_2^j(k)$ is

$$P_2^j(k) = \frac{1}{c_2} \frac{1}{n_k} P_G P_D P\{\mathbf{d}(k)\} P[Y^{k-1}, n_k, \mathbf{d}^{k-1}] Q(\mathbf{A}_j) \qquad (9.A17)$$

with

$$Q(\mathbf{A}_j) \triangleq \sum_{i=0}^{N} P\{T(\mathbf{A}_j) = I_i\} P\{T_R = I_i | \mathbf{d}(k)\} \qquad (9.A18)$$

Applying Bayes' rule yields

$$Q(\mathbf{A}_j) = \frac{\displaystyle\sum_{i=0}^{N} P\{T(\mathbf{A}_j) = I_i\} P\{T_R = I_i\} P\{\mathbf{d}(k) | T_R = I_i\}}{\displaystyle\sum_{i=0}^{N} P\{T_R = I_i\} P\{\mathbf{d}(k) | T_R = I_i\}} \qquad (9.A19)$$

$P\{T_R = I_i\}$ is the *a priori* probability of observing one landmark with identity $I_i$. This probability must be evaluated from the knowledge of the navigation map (e.g., by the use of percentage of landmarks with type $I_i$ lying on the navigation map). The term $P\{\mathbf{d}(k) | T_R = I_i\}$ is given by the classifier quality matrix.

Symbolically, we denote

$$P_R\{I_i\} \triangleq P\{T_R = I_i\} \qquad (9.A20)$$

If $\mathbf{d}(k)$ concerns only one identification singleton $\mathbf{B} = \{I_j\}$, $(j \in \{0, 1, \ldots, N\})$, then we have

$$P\{\mathbf{d}(k) | T_R = I_i\} = P\{\mathbf{d}(k) = I_j | T_R = I_i\} \triangleq c_{ji} \qquad (9.A21)$$

If $\mathbf{d}(k)$ concerns any identification proposition $\mathbf{B} \subset E$ and because the detected landmark necessarily has only one particular identity, we can write

$$P\{\mathbf{d}(k) | T_R = I_i\} = P\{\mathbf{d}(k) = \mathbf{B} | T_R = I_i\}$$
$$= \sum_{j \in \mathbf{B}} P\{\mathbf{d}(k) = I_j | T_R = I_i\} = \sum_{j \in \mathbf{B}} c_{ji} \qquad (9.A22)$$

where $j \in \mathbf{B}$ represents the indices of singletons included in the identification propositions delivered by the classifier. The term $c_{ji}$ is the element lying on the $j$th row in the $i$th column of the classifier quality matrix $\mathbf{C}$.

The normalizing constant $c_2$ is given by

$$c_2 = P\{\mathbf{d}(k)\}P[Y^{k-1},n_k,\mathbf{d}^{k-1}]\left[(1 - P_G P_D) + \frac{1}{n_k}P_G P_D \sum_{j=1}^{nk} Q(\mathbf{A}_j)\right] \qquad (9.A23)$$

Replacing $c_2$ by its expression and after some cancellations, we obtain

$$P_2^j(k) = \begin{cases} \dfrac{\dfrac{P_G P_D}{n_k} Q(\mathbf{A}_j)}{(1 - P_G P_D) + \dfrac{1}{n_k}P_G P_D \sum_{j=1}^{nk} Q(\mathbf{A}_j)} & \text{for } j = 1, \ldots, n_k \\[4ex] \dfrac{(1 - P_G P_D)}{(1 - P_G P_D) + \dfrac{1}{n_k}P_G P_D \sum_{j=1}^{nk} Q(\mathbf{A}_j)} & \text{for } j = 0 \end{cases} \qquad (9.A24)$$

Finally replacing $p_1^j(k)$ and $P_2^j(k)$ by their expressions in (9.A2) yields the expression of the *a posteriori* association probabilities:

$$\beta_j(k) = e_j(k)Q(\mathbf{A}_j)\left[b(k) + \sum_{j=1}^{nk} e_j(k)Q(\mathbf{A}_j)\right]^{-1} \qquad j = 1, \ldots, n_k \qquad (9.A25)$$

$$\beta_0(k) = b(k)\left[b(k) + \sum_{j=1}^{nk} e_j(k)Q(\mathbf{A}_j)\right]^{-1} \qquad (9.A26)$$

with

$$e_j(k) \triangleq (P_G)^{-1}N[\tilde{\mathbf{A}}_j(k);0, \mathbf{S}(k)] \qquad (9.A27)$$

$$b(k) \triangleq n_k(1 - P_G P_D)[P_G P_D V(k)]^{-1} \qquad (9.A28)$$

where $Q(\tilde{\mathbf{A}}_j)$ is as given in (9.A18) or (9.A19).

## REFERENCES

[1]  B.D.O. Anderson and J.B. Moore, *Optimal Filtering,* Prentice-Hall, Englewood Cliffs, NJ, 1979.
[2]  P.Y. Arquès, *Décisions en Traitement du Signal,* Collection Technique et Scientifique des Télécommunications, Edition Masson, Paris, 1982.
[3]  Y. Bar-Shalom and T.E. Fortmann, *Tracking and Data Association,* Academic Press, Orlando, FL, 1988.

[4]   Y. Bar-Shalom, *Multitarget-Multisensor Tracking: Advanced Applications,* Vol. 1, Artech House, Norwood, MA, 1990.

[5]   J. Dezert, "Vers un nouveau concept de navigation autonome d'engin. Un lien entre la théorie de l'évidence et le filtrage à association probabiliste de données," Thèse de Doctorat de l'Université de Paris-Sud, Centre d'Orsay, 1990, No. 1393, France (also published as ONERA Tech. Note 1990-11, Châtillon, France).

[6]   R.A. Dillard, "Computing Probability Masses in Rule-Based Systems," Tech. Doc. 545, 55 p, NOSC, San Diego, September 8, 1982.

[7]   D. Dubois, "Modèles Mathématiques de l'imprécis et de l'incertain en vue d'applications aux techniques d'aide à la décision," Thèse de Doctorat d'Etat, Université de Grenoble, France, 1983.

[8]   G. Shafer, *A Mathematical Theory of Evidence,* Princeton University Press, Princeton, NJ, 1976.

[9]   S.C.A. Thomopoulos, R. Viswanathan, and D.P. Bougoulias, "Optimal Decision Fusion in Multiple Sensor Systems," *IEEE Trans. on Aerospace and Electronic Systems,* Vol. AES-23, September 1987, pp. 644–653.

[10]  R. Viswanathan, S.C.A. Thomopoulos, and R. Tumuluri, "Optimal Serial Distributed Decision Fusion," *IEEE Trans. on Aerospace and Electronic Systems,* Vol. AES-24, July 1988, pp. 366–376.

# Chapter 10

# THE SENSOR MANAGEMENT IMPERATIVE

## Robert Popoli

### Hughes Aircraft Co.
### El Segundo, CA

## 10.1   INTRODUCTION

Our purpose in this chapter is to accomplish three tasks:

1. Establish what sensor management is and why it is necessary to include it in the design of modern sensor systems.
2. Explain how sensor management can be accomplished.
3. Show concrete examples of both how sensor management is performed and the benefits we can hope to gain from it.

Increased tactical demand for environment sensing and the advances in sensor technology make sophisticated airborne sensor management schemes a timely topic. Modern fighter aircraft must perform in an environment of steadily increasing complexity. Foreseeable trends in fighter deployment require that a single aircraft simultaneously engage multiple targets or threats. The complexity of the sensing environment and the corresponding complexity of modern sensors could easily outstrip even a dedicated sensor and weapons officer not to mention the pilot of a single-seat fighter. These complex factors alone necessitate the development of automated sensor tasking to reduce the pilot's workload.

As we will discuss, a host of requirements and benefits make up the role of sensor management in a modern avionics sensor suite. We refer to the composite of these sensor management roles and requirements as the *sensor management imperative.*

Sensor management is really just the study of ways to improve or optimize the measurement process in a tracking system. The role of the measurement process is one of the least developed elements in tracking systems. To be sure, many books and papers have been written on the detection process for various sensors, particularly radar; for example, [2, 9, 17, 20, 27]. Also, many good texts concentrate on the issues of target tracking, like [1, 4, 13]. These books, however, tend to deal with the optimization of detection or tracking in isolation of each other. They do not take an overall systematic approach to the composite measurement-tracking-situation assessment problem. Sensor management attempts to achieve this overall system optimization by checking tracking performance relative to certain criteria and generating a feedback control to the sensors. This interpretation of sensor management as a feedback implementation is depicted in Figure 10.1.

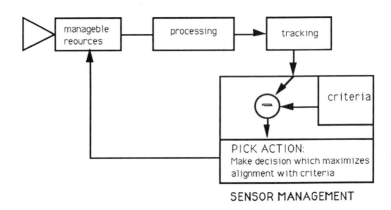

**Figure 10.1** Sensor management as a feedback system.

Therefore, we argue for a more unified approach to the optimization of the measurement process. We argue that, although the traditional criteria for detection optimization are still in force, these criteria must be accompanied by additional criteria that address the overall tracking and tactical performance of the system. These criteria form the basis for the dynamic scheduling of the sensor resource to adapt to changes in the sensing environment. Many authors have recognized the need for dynamic scheduling of sensor resources, particularly for the active array radar [3, 11, 16, 19, 24, 25, 30, 31]. Each of these works focuses on the description of a specific dynamic scheduling approach for achieving specific objectives. Although not overtly mentioned in any of these previous works, a common thread emerges. They all deal to some degree with the following central issues of sensor management:

1. What system performance can be gained by employing sensor management?
2. How can various alternative sensor actions be ranked?
3. How can a dynamically changing time line of sensor tasks be constructed?

These are the central issues we address in this chapter.

Although some of the material in this chapter can be found in other sources, our presentation varies in significant ways from previous works. First, we draw specific attention to what we feel are the issues central to sensor management design. We establish the breadth of these issues by developing a catalog of sensor management imperatives. We attempted to describe these imperatives in a sensor-independent way. Therefore, we take a harder look than previous works at the generality of sensor management for various single and multisensor applications. Second, we provide alternative ways of ranking and scheduling sensor tasks. By discussing some of the alternatives side by side, we hope to provide background to aid designers of such systems rather than simply provide a point design. Finally, we address multisensor architectural issues that are not typically discussed in prior works.

The discussion in this chapter is intended to be applicable to a generalized suite of one or more sensors. Throughout the chapter, we stress the systematic allocation of an *electronically scanned antenna* (*ESA*) radar in a multitarget, multitasking, multisensor environment. Although the sensor management concepts presented can be extended to other sensors, we focus our attention on the *ESA* radar. This emphasis seems justified as a radar (as opposed to an IRST, for example) is always included in fighter sensor suites (as the primary fire control sensor). We focus our attention on ESA radars in particular as they are the most modern type of radar and very amenable to dynamic scheduling. Furthermore, they are the most complicated and therefore the most in need of management.

The chapter begins by defining the sensor management imperative in Section 10.2. This imperative is the central motivating force in the chapter, and facets of the imperative will tie together further discussions of sensor management architectures, approaches, and results.

Section 10.3 discusses how sensor management can be accomplished. It includes discussions of sensor system architectures that utilize sensor management as well as providing technical approaches to sensor management decision making.

Section 10.4 presents results that help to make more concrete all that has proceeded. It will demonstrate some of the benefits sensor management can achieve as well as providing examples of the implementation of sensor management algorithms.

## 10.2 ESTABLISHING THE SENSOR MANAGEMENT IMPERATIVE

In this section, we establish the sensor management imperative. Establishing this imperative is a good vehicle for explaining the *what* (i.e., what is sensor management in terms of its functional role) and the *why* (i.e., why is sensor management important in terms of the benefits it provides). The imperative is expressed in terms of a catalog of the roles sensor management can play in a modern sensor system. We motivate each role through a discussion of its tactical significance in a fighter's tracking system.

Note that many of the imperatives are marked with * to indicate that specific simulation results will be offered in Section 10.4 to demonstrate these imperatives. Thus, in addition to a general motivation for sensor management, this section also serves as a backdrop for the rest of this chapter.

### 10.2.1 General Discussion

Throughout, we stress a tactical fighter vantage point in deriving the sensor management imperatives. The imperatives thus derived easily extend to other types of sensor systems. This emphasis on fighter sensor systems is justified because fighter sensor suites are likely to be the focus of multisensor management for some time to come. A discussion of the factors that have caused the designers of fighter avionics to consider sensor management is a good place to start our discussion.

Multiple target tracking (see [1, 4] for a thorough discussion of MTT) is one of the most basic avionic functions involved in providing the pilot with tactical information about the evolving complex environment and allowing him to deliver firepower. Airborne MTT systems are being designed to use a suite of modern sensors. As we will discuss, the capabilities of many modern sensors cannot be fully realized by using older sensor control strategies. In particular, the distinctive beam agility of an electronically scanned antenna (the ESA is the primary fire control sensor) is virtually lost without the development of intelligent allocation algorithms. Therefore, need for sensor management, in part, is driven by the advances in sensor technology.

Driven by trends in modern air combat, sensor agility and complexity have increased to help collect timely information about the ever increasing complexity of the modern tactical environment. This increase in the data collecting capability of modern sensors could place an enormous additional burden on the sensor operator. Thus, the need for sensor management also is driven by nature of modern warfare.

We argue that these two factors, the advance in sensor technology and the complexity of the tactical environment, have made sensor management algorithms an essential element of modern MTT systems. In other words, these factors lead to the sensor management imperative.

### *The Role of Sensor Management*

The significance of the sensor management imperative becomes clear if we compare the roles of the operator in sensor systems with and without sensor management. Figure 10.2 depicts sensor systems with and without sensor management.

Note that in a system without sensor management the operator forms an integral link in providing feedback between tracking performance and future sensor behavior. On the other hand, in a system with sensor management, primary feedback is provided by the sensor manager, under the possible guiding input from the oper-

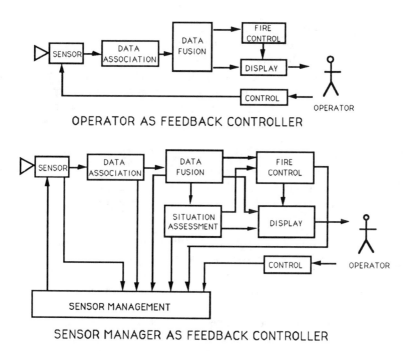

Figure 10.2 Sensor management automates tracking feedback that normally would require operator intervention.

ator. Thus, sensor management's role is to take responsibility for future sensor behavior while still allowing the operator to exercise particular choices.

Sensor management thus can be seen to yield the following benefits:

- Reduced Pilot Workload. Sensor management alleviates the need for the operator to specify each operation the sensors are to perform. The sensor manager uses information previously collected to direct most of the future behavior of the sensors. With sensor management the operator need only establish general sensor tasking criteria (such as override a track's priority or establish the degree of allowable active radiation) or make an occasional request for a special data collection.

- Sensor Tasking Based on Finer Detail. Note that, as shown in Figure 10.2, the primary source of information for the operator about the functioning of the sensors is the sensor displays. Clearly, in a system in which the operator is the primary controller of the sensors, he must be made aware of any aspects of sensor operation that should be dynamically controlled. Therefore, any information relevant to the operator's decision making about sensor tasking must be made available on the display. In a system with sensor management, many more details about the system's incremental behavior than could possibly be displayed can be folded into the decision making about the tasks that need to be performed. Furthermore, even if all the fine details about the operation of every tracking subsystem could be made available to the operator, there are obvious limits to the amount of detail a human operator is capable of dealing with. A human operator is much more comfortable thinking about the tactical objectives the sensors are to achieve rather than the fine details of their operation.

- Faster Adaptation. Finally, the automated feedback of systems with sensor management yields much faster adaptation to the changing environment. The faster adaptation is possible because the finer performance details considered by the sensor manager allow for earlier detection of tracking performance degradation.

The various feedback loops shown in Figure 10.2 can be thought of as representing the various roles that sensor management must play. Each role is related to a tracking criterion we wish to impose on the tracking system. As shown in Figure 10.2, each role is the result of monitoring the performance of some subsystem of the overall sensor system. Each subsystem's performance can be summarized by parameters of its operation. The sensor manager monitors these performance parameters, compares them to some criteria, and then directs the sensors to operate in such a way as to attempt to drive the performance parameters into closer agreement with the criteria.

In the remainder of this section, we discuss in greater detail each role represented by the feedback paths in Figure 10.2. In doing so we establish a catalog of roles that sensor management is to play and performance benefits we hope to achieve. This catalog then will be our sensor management imperative.

### 10.2.2   Effective Use of Limited System Resources

The effective use of limited sensor resource is perhaps the most obvious sensor management imperative. It is directly apparent that one goal of sensor management must be to make the best use of our available sensors' capabilities. We identify three types of limited sensor system resources that necessitate allocation: agile sensor aperture resource; agile multimode resources; and operator resources.

### 10.2.2.1   *Control of Agile Sensor Aperture Resources*

Some modern sensors have an agile "aperture" resource that must be managed. Often this "aperture" resource is limited in nature and therefore must be effectively allocated or scheduled to assure timely interception of pertinent data. We have used the word *aperture* here to refer to any port by which a sensor can admit data. More specifically, we consider the sensors that typically compose a modern tactical fighter sensor suite.

- *Electronically Scanned Antenna Radar System. The ESA radar has an antenna aperture that can be redirected very quickly. Once positioned for a measurement task (e.g., fixed azimuth and elevation for a track update, directed scan for a search region update) the beam must remain dedicated to the task for the length of time required to perform that task. The tasks, of course, must be scheduled into a limited time line. Therefore, the beam positioning constitutes a limited agile resource that must be managed to assure that data about the environment is being collected in a timely fashion. A sensor management scheme should be employed to direct the beam among the various tasks, such as searching for new targets, revisiting tracks for maintenance, or track identification looks.
- Electronic Support Measures System. Another example of a sensor with an agile "aperture" is the modern *electronic support measures* (ESM) receiver (in its simple form also known as a *radar warning receiver,* or RWR). A typical ESM system can simultaneously process signals from a wide field of regard. However, due to hardware limitations of a practical ESM system, only a limited set of frequency bands can be analyzed simultaneously. Thus for an ESM system the "aperture" is that part of the frequency spectrum which the sensor is currently analyzing. This aperture resource then must be allocated to search for as yet undetected threats, revisit previously detected threats, perform special measurements on threats with ambiguous identification, and so forth.
- Infrared Search and Track System. An IRST typically is a mechanically pointed device and therefore has somewhat limited resource agility. The sensor however can be directed to either single-target track or enter into any one of a number of search patterns optimized for various ranges and tactical objectives.

Note that for each of these examples two factors support the need for sensor management: the resource is agile in the sense that it can be readily shifted among various sensing tasks; and the resource is limited in the sense that each of the sensing tasks that could be performed compete for the available resource.

Without these contributing factors the need for sensor management diminishes. For example, if we were dealing with a mechanically scanned antenna radar, the lack of agility limits the value of sensor management severely. To break the antenna out of its nominal search scanning requires a significant amount of mechanical settling time. Thus, it is fairly impractical to do anything with the antenna except follow a simple search scan pattern, updating known tracks as it passes over them. In summary, whether sensor management is required for a sensor depends largely on the degree of agility that the sensor possesses.

### 10.2.2.2 *Control of Agile Multimode Resource*

Many sensors have multiple modes of operation. A radar for example can be reconfigured to operate with a number of different transmit waveforms, each with particular advantages. Differing tactical situations may require a sequence of these modes to effectively collect some desired information or support a particular weapon. Because the timely selection of sensor mode conserves both sensor and weapon resources, it is essential that an automated system be provided to conserve those resources.

### 10.2.2.3 *Reducing Operator Workload*

The human operator often is an essential element of a sensing system. Because he often will be required to make timely top level decisions about the deployment and goals of the sensor suite, it is important that the operator is not burdened by lower level nontactical decision making that may distract him from his mission objectives.

### 10.2.3 Track Maintenance

The primary goal of many sensor systems is the development and maintenance of kinematic tracks on moving objects in the environment. Several factors cause the kinematic tracking quality to change dynamically (e.g., maneuverability of the target, missassociation of data collected from closely spaced targets). Because the amount and type of sensor resource required by tracks the system currently holds varies dynamically, an automated system must be provided to partition the available resource among the tracks in accordance with the needs of the individual tracks. Three general imperatives for track maintenance can be identified.

### 10.2.3.1 *Basic Track Quality Maintenance*

The system should be able to recognize track quality degradation since its last update and schedule track updates only as often as necessary to maintain the track quality within given thresholds. More sophisticated systems may assign different tracking goals for various tracks depending on the tactical importance of the track (or more specifically the type of weapon with which the corresponding target would be engaged).

### 10.2.3.2 *Track Quality in Dense Environments*

In dense tracking environments, special attention has to be paid to clusters of closely spaced targets. When targets get close together the association of target observations to currently held tracks becomes nontrivial. The probability of associating the returns from one target with the track of another target becomes significant. This misassociation results in unstable tracks and eventual track loss. A sophisticated sensor management system could attempt to deal with such situations by spending additional sensor resources on these closely spaced tracks to help improve track stability.

### 10.2.3.3   Adaptive Tracking

The rate of degradation of a track depends on the behavior of the target that generates the track. Furthermore, the degradation is not always directly apparent from the track's covariance. For example, if a track maneuvers in such a way as to violate the modeling assumptions of the Kalman filter, then the tracking error will not be properly reflected by the covariance matrix. However, tracking systems often provide tests on the statistical nature (whiteness) of a track's innovations process. These tests can serve as indicators for target maneuver. Traditionally such maneuver indications have been utilized to temporarily adjust the model of the process noise used by the tracker. More sophisticated sensor management systems similarly could attempt to adaptively modify the tracking filter or shorten the target revisit time to minimize model mismatch.

## 10.2.4   Sensor Fusion and Synergism

Multisensor fusion quickly is becoming a very important technology area for modern tactical sensor systems. For example, future tactical fighters will certainly employ multiple sensors for situation assessment and fire control. Sensor management is a key element of multisensor fusion. It is essential that these sensors operate synergistically. Sensor management in multisensor systems must operate so that full advantage is taken of the strengths of each sensor. Several ways in which sensor management can accomplish this are discussed.

### 10.2.4.1   *Cooperative Reinforcement

Different sensors may have the capability to measure different features of the same target. For example, a radar has range, range-rate, and angle measurement capabilities, whereas an IRST has superior angle and some angle-rate measurement capabilities. Differences in sensor's ID measuring capabilities also are prevalent. The goal of sensor fusion, of course, is to combine the varied sensor data to achieve a better overall picture of the environment. In this process, sensor management plays the essential role of coordinating the data collection processes of the various sensors to support the overall goal. Thus, for example, sensor management may respond to a tactical need for better range accuracy by queuing the radar to support a track that was maintained primarily by the IRST.

## 10.2.4.2  *Emission Control

Sensors fall into two basic categories: passive and active. Passive sensors collect information on elements in the environment by measuring energy the targets emit or that reflects off them from sources in the environment other than the sensor itself. Thus passive sensors can covertly collect information about an element in the environment. Active sensors, on the other hand, actively emit a signal in an attempt to reflect it off an element in the environment. Active sensors may betray their own existence to collect information about other elements in the environment. Thus, in a military environment there is significant advantage to minimizing the use of active sensing equipment. Unfortunately, generally, active sensors provide more information than passive sensors. For example, a radar is an active sensor. It generally can measure range, range-rate, and angle. An IRST is a passive sensor. It generally measures only angle (and perhaps angle-rate). Because the operation of the radar belies the presence of ownship, sensor management should attempt to synergistically employ the radar and the IRST to minimize active radar radiation while maintaining sufficient tracking accuracy.

## 10.2.4.3  *Intersensor Cueing

Sensors vary greatly in their ability to detect the presence of targets or the onset of a particular target behavior. Therefore, sensor management may improve the response time of a sensor by cueing it with information derived from another sensor.

## 10.2.5  Situation Assessment

The raison d'être of many sensor systems is to provide an operator with an assessment of the environment. In current systems, the operator simply is supplied with only the simplest synthesis of sensor data in the form of kinematic tracking and identification displays. The operator's role then is to make all inferences concerning the intent of the targets from these simple displays. Future systems propose that part of this situation assessment function be carried out in an automated fashion. Sensor management would play a role as a feedback link connecting the automated situation assessment function and the sensors. The feedback is provided to improve the data collection process relative to the following two goals.

## 10.2.5.1  *Tactically Efficient Use of Resource

The idea is to use the sensor time line efficiently in terms of providing attention to those elements of the environment assessed to be the most tactically important.

## 10.2.5.2   Collection of Missing Information

A feedback loop from an automated situation assessment function also can be used to cue a sensor to collect any information that would improve situation assessment or confirm what might be tactically inferred by previously collected information. For example, knowledge about enemy force employment tactics might indicate the presence of as yet undetected escort aircraft when a cargo aircraft is detected. Sensor management could use this background information to cue a radar to search for these surmised aircraft.

### 10.2.6   Support of Specific Goals

No sensor management system could ever hope to encompass all sensor tasking decision making. Therefore a necessary role of any sensor management system is servicing sensor tasking requests that come from other sources. Although there are many conceivable sources of sensor tasking requests, consider the following important sources.

## 10.2.6.1   Operator Requests

In some sense, sensor management is an automated system that replaces a human operator in making tasking decisions for the sensors. Generally it would be considered unacceptable to forbid operator control over sensors. Rather, the goal of sensor management should be to ease the burden of sensor system operation without limiting the flexibility of human control. Therefore an operator interface is still to be provided. The nature of this interface, however, may change. Instead of providing an interface that requires the operator to specify low-level details of sensor operation, a "macro" level interface may be deemed more appropriate. For example, if the sensor manager already is setting target priorities to decide on the relative amount of sensor resource they should attain, the operator could be allowed to directly set target priority.

## 10.2.6.2   Fire Control System

If the ultimate purpose of the sensor system is to support the delivery of firepower, then an interface should be provided between the sensor manager and the fire control computer. This interface would allow the fire control computer to request that special data collections be taken if it aids in the fire control solution.

### 10.2.7  Adaptive Behavior in Varying Sensing Environments

The ability of a sensor to collect information can be strongly influenced by the current environmental sensing conditions. The relevant conditions vary from sensor to sensor but can include weather, electronic countermeasures, look angle, background clutter, and clouds. Often sensors can vary operational parameters or even complete methods to optimize their measurement performance for various environmental conditions. The optimization of one data collection task may adversely affect other collection tasks due to increased resource expenditure or intertask interference. Therefore sensor management should potentially trade off the importance of optimizing one task over its negative impact on other tasks.

### 10.2.8  Summary

This chapter has discussed the two major driving forces motivating the need for sensor management: flexibility of modern sensors that make sensor tasking nontrivial, and dense target environments that make a sensor a precious resource. The next two sections will discuss how sensor managers can be designed to satisfy the imperatives and provide demonstrations of the imperatives in action.

### 10.3  SENSOR MANAGEMENT APPROACHES

This section addresses the *how* (i.e., how sensor management can be accomplished) and the *where* (i.e., where sensor management should reside in a complex sensor system). There are at least three facets to the question, How and where do we accomplish sensor management?

- Architectures. This facet deals with where sensor management fits into the overall sensor and tracking system. An integrated fighter fire-control sensor system consists of many subsystems distributed among several processors. Exactly how sensor management functionality is distributed among these subsystems is an important issue. The choices for sensor management location are several: within the sensor itself, within the tracking system (for multisensor fusion systems), within the fire-control system, within the mission computer, or distributed among some subset of these.
- Scheduling Techniques. Sensor management's ultimate role is to task sensors to perform actions. This facet deals with whether the manager should simply issue commands or build a schedule of activity for each sensor. When building a schedule, how exactly should the time line be filled with the important tasks?
- Decision-Making Techniques. This facet deals with the process by which the system is to decide which sensor tasks need to be performed. Decision-making approaches based on distinctively different theoretical bases are available.

### 10.3.1. Architectures for Sensor Management

We investigate, here, architectural issues of sensor systems that employ sensor management. We are concerned with the architecture of the overall sensor system and how sensor management functionality is distributed among the subsystems.

As already discussed in the sensor management imperative, sensor management automates feedback between performance of several subsystems and the sensor's behavior. These subsystems are hosted on several computers, which may be produced by different manufacturers. Where to host the sensor manager is a significant issue, because the location will have an impact on system integration, subsystem interfaces, intersubsystem communication load, and ultimate management functionality.

In fact, we argue that, depending on the application, the scope of sensor management may be so broad that no one location is suitable. This opens the issue of how to break up sensor management into subsystems that can be appropriately located. Finally, once the location or locations have been selected, decisions must be made about the exact nature of the required interfaces and communication links.

Unfortunately, there is no one correct solution to these architectural issues. Each specific application must be considered in turn. We hope, here, at least to draw attention to the architectural decision making that must transpire. In addition, we will make some recommendations for sensor management in single sensor (radar) and multiple sensor fighter systems.

### 10.3.2 The Macro-Micro Architecture

There are three primary considerations in establishing an architecture for a sensor system that employs sensor management:

1. What level of sensor management functionality do we wish to incorporate? This issue is driven primarily by the particular sensor management imperatives most important to the application at hand.
2. How should the sensor management functionality be distributed among the various subsystems of the overall sensor system? This issue is driven primarily by the types of functionality required and the available computing resources.
3. What communication links must be provided between subsystems of the sensor manager (if distributed) and between the sensor manager and the rest of the sensor system? This issue is driven by the first two issues and by the selected schedule techniques.

Note that these considerations all interact. For example, suppose we decide that we want sensor management to synergistically coordinate several sensors. This level of functionality would drive the decision to place this sensor management function at some central location. A good choice might be the same computing resources that handle the multisensor fusion as its data fusion results would be the prime source of information for a sensor manager trying to achieve synergism. On the other hand, if we were most concerned about managing the detailed waveform selection of a radar to combat a dynamic ECM environment, a better choice might be to locate the sensor management decision making in the radar itself. If both functions are desired, then perhaps, an architecture that distributes sensor management functionality among the various subsystems would be best. Furthermore, the choice for the location of sensor management decision making obviously will have an impact on the required communication links. In fact, the most logical place for a piece of sensor management functionality may be predicated on trying to minimize the amount of information that must be passed between subsystems.

The issue of exactly which architecture to pick clearly has no *one* answer. We can offer some guidelines for consideration, however. We propose the following hierarchical classification of two types of sensor management tasking:

$M$ Macro-Level Functionality. This level is to include all high-level tasking best summarized by the expression, Which task should the sensor perform?

$\mu$ Micro-Level Functionality. This level is to include all low-level tasking best summarized by the expression, How can a particular $M$-task best be accomplished?

We advocate partitioning sensor management into one centrally located macro sensor manager and several sensor located micro sensor managers. A sensor management architecture for a multisensor system is shown in Figure 10.3. The macro sensor manager is responsible for making tactical decisions on how to best utilize sensor resources to achieve the mission goals. The micro sensor manager is responsible for establishing the detailed sensor behavior required to carry out the requests of the macro sensor manager.

### 10.3.2.1  *Distribution of the Sensor Management Functionality*

We repeat, here, our list of sensor management imperatives marked with either $M$ and or $\mu$ depending on which manager should be most concerned with them. Comments justifying the partitioning are offered.

1. Effective Use of Limited System Resources

   (a) *Agile Sensor Aperture Resources* ($M$). Because sensor coordination is required to meet this imperative properly, it is important that it be done at the $M$ level. The decisions for each sensor should be driven by all that is known, not by just what is known at each sensor's own level.

   (b) *Agile Multimode Resources* ($\mu$). System integration is improved if sensors are not designed with very low-level interfaces. Generally decisions about

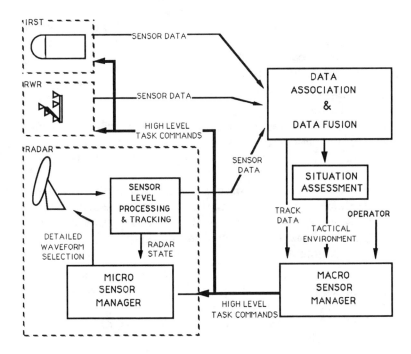

**Figure 10.3** Partitioning sensor management into macro and micro elements for multisensor systems.

exact mode implementation require detailed sensor operating parameters and hence are best done at the sensor level.

    (c) *Reducing Operator Workload (M).* Although it could be argued that any sensor management reduces the operator workload, operators usually do not deal with very low-level sensor commanding anyway, so this imperative really is the domain of the *M* manager.

2. Track Maintenance

    (a) *Basic Track-Quality Maintenance (M).* Because the only basic track quality that matters to the operator is that at the central level, this type of decision making should be done at the central level.

    (b) *Track Quality in Dense Environments* ($\mu$). For single-sensor systems, the details of how the sensor associates measurements with currently held tracks is best handled at the sensor level. For multiple sensor systems, the classification of this imperative may depend on the multisensor fusion method used; however, for distributed fusion techniques this imperative can be primarily handled at the sensor level.

    (c) *Adaptive Tracking (M, $\mu$).* Some aspects of dealing with dynamic target behavior must be handled at each level. Even if adaptive tracking (e.g., maneuver compensation, adaptive dwell times) is performed only at the sensor level, information at the central level may be required to recognize and cue the need for adaptation.

3. Sensor Fusion and Synergism

   (a) *Cooperative Reinforcement* (*M*). This decision making must occur at a central location.

   (b) *Emission Control* (*M*, $\mu$). Both managers play a role here: the *M* manager decides how to coordinate sensors to minimize active emission requests; and the $\mu$ manager attempts to satisfy macro requests without violating a prescribed degree of overtness.

   (c) *Intersensor Cueing* (*M*). Decision making about how sensors cue each other should be arbitrated at the central level. Note that it may be valuable to allow sensors to communicate data collection problems they encounter to the *M* manager to aid in intersensor tasking.

4. Situation Assessment

   (a) *Tactically Efficient Use of Resource* (*M*). Because situation assessment is formed at the central level, decisions about how this assessment affects sensor tasking also should be done at this level.

   (b) *Collection of Missing Information* (*M*). Same comment as the preceding.

5. Support of Specific Goals

   (a) *Operator Requests* (*M*). It is best to provide operator-fire control interface to sensors through the *M* manager so that other decision making required from the *M* manager can be influenced by these requests.

   (b) *Fire Control System* (*M*). Same comment as the preceding.

6. General Sensing Environment Adaptive Behavior

   (a) *Environmental Adaptation* ($\mu$). This type of decision making requires detailed knowledge of sensor operational capabilities. Note that these capabilities could change rapidly depending on the sensing environment, so that they may be available only at the sensor level. It may be valuable to allow the sensors to communicate the level of effort required to collect data to the *M* manager. The *M* manager then may alter task priorities if certain requests would require too much sensor resources.

It should be stressed that these *M* and $\mu$ categories are not hard and fast. We mean only to indicate that these sensor management roles are predominantly the responsibility of the macro or micro sensor managers.

*10.3.2.2  Sensor Management Interfaces*

The *M* manager receives, as input to its decision-making process, the following information.

*Central Tracking Data*

This data is to include all the kinematic and attribute (ID) information available. Also included is information about the quality of the tracks (e.g., filtered and predicted Kalman covariance matrices). Because so much tracking data must be made available to the $M$ manager, it is best to set up this communication link as a database access. Namely, the $M$ manager should have access to the central track files (or sensor track files in a single-sensor system). The $M$ manager then needs only access the data currently relevant to its decision making. The information is used to determine which tracks need attention and where they are located.

*Inferred Tactical Environment*

This data is to include all inferences made from the track data. Specifically, the data is to include inferred track priorities and any inferences concerning shortages of critical data.

*External Tasking from Operator or Fire Control*

Finally, $M$ manager decision making must accommodate operator or fire control desires. These may be expressed indirectly by modifying the priority of tracks or search volume or include a direct sensor request such as a missile update.

The output of the $M$ manager generally is a queue of tasks for the sensors to perform. The choices for the exact nature of this time line tasking is discussed at length in the subsection on scheduling techniques.

Finally, as intimated in some of our discussion on $M$-level–$\mu$-level classification of sensor management imperatives, a valuable feedback path could be provided from $\mu$ manager to $M$ manager. This path would allow a sensor's $\mu$ manager to inform the $M$ manager of the cost or difficulty of performing a task. Thus this path could influence $M$-level task generation and intersensor cueing.

*10.3.2.3   Some Alterations to the Architecture*

Two alternatives to the preceding architecture should be noted. If situation assessment is only to set limited track update priorities, then it could be included as part of the $M$ manager itself. If, on the other hand, situation assessment is to provide information to many subsystems (e.g., display, $M$ manager, fire control) then it may be best to think of it as a separate function. Furthermore, situation assessment could be thought of as higher-order data fusion, in which case it may be logical to include it in the central data association and tracking function.

## 10.3.2.4 Some Advantages of the Architecture

This $M$-level–$\mu$-level architecture has several advantages:

- Distributes Processing. The most basic advantage of this architecture is that it provides a natural distribution of the processing load among multiple processors.
- Partitions Code Cycle Times. The partition separates the decision making that has an inherently rapid cycle time from that which can be run at slower rates. For example, decisions about waveform use or dwell times must occur at a much higher rate than decisions about target priority.
- Minimizes Communication Load. Communication between subsystems is kept simple and logical by associating the various sensor management functionalities with the subsystem for which the particular functionality is most pertinent.
- Improves System Integration. System integration is improved in several ways. First, subsystem specification (recall that various manufacturers may be responsible for the different subsystems) is simpler because each system is responsible for its own internal decision making. System test is simpler because each sensor must be able to accept high level operator-like commands.

With minor modifications the same macro-micro philosophy can be applied to single-sensor systems. Figure 10.4 shows a radar system with a partitioned sensor manager. If the situation assessment function is not a centrally located asset, then the entire system can reside in the sensor. We would still advocate a $M$-$\mu$ partition to maintain some of the advantages noted earlier.

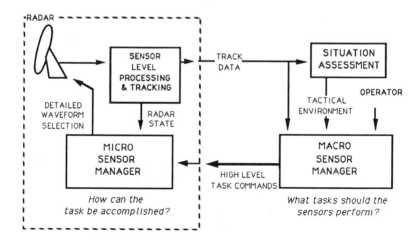

**Figure 10.4** Partitioning sensor management into macro and micro elements for single-sensor systems.

### 10.3.3  Scheduling Techniques

#### *10.3.3.1  The Scheduling Problem*

The scheduling problem can be stated as given the ability to decide which tasks are important (this ability is the topic of the next section), how do we set up a time line of tasks for the sensor to perform. This may seem a trivial problem until we consider the various characteristics of the tasks to be performed. A list of typical *M*-level task characteristics is

- Some tasks are time critical "hard deadline tasks" (i.e., tasks that are of value only if performed within a small window of opportunity).
- Some tasks may not be time critical ("fluid deadline tasks") but still may have weak constraints (e.g., start times before which they cannot be set up).
- Tasks may have significant differences in priority.
- Some tasks may not be interruptible.
- Tasks may differ significantly in length.
- Some tasks may become suddenly necessary.
- Some tasks may become suddenly unnecessary.
- Some tasks may be of uncertain duration.

The goal for tasking is to devise a scheme that respects these constraints as much as possible.

#### *10.3.3.2  Two Approaches to Scheduling*

For simplicity, we will restrict our attention to a discussion of scheduling techniques for the *M* manager. For the *M* manager, two general approaches for scheduling sensor tasks suggest themselves: the "myopic" or "best first" approach; and the "local optimum" or "brick packing" approach. We describe each of these techniques and discuss why we advocate the myopic or best first approach.

#### *Brick Packing*

The basic idea behind the brick packing approach is to break the scheduling time line, *T*, into smaller tasking intervals, say $\Delta T$. Then we pack this time interval according to some measure of optimality. Variants of this approach are described by the method of choosing $\Delta T$, the measure of optimality, and the method of optimization. Most of the sensor management scheduling techniques discussed in the literature are some variant of the brick packing approach (e.g., [24, 25, 30]). To make this discussion more concrete, consider the operation of a system that can build time lines similar to that shown in Figure 10.5.

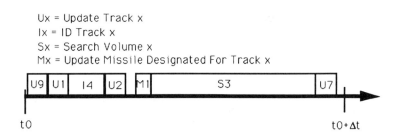

**Figure 10.5** Sample sensor tasking time line.

The scheduler is to build a schedule that will begin execution at time $t_0$ and last until time $t_0 + \Delta t$. The goal of the algorithm is to pack as many of the important tasks as possible into the interval $[t_0, t_0 + \Delta t)$. In building this schedule, the algorithm will need the following task information available before time $t_0$.

1. The priority of all tasks that might be scheduled.
2. The nominal duration of all tasks to be scheduled.
3. The time constraints within which fluid deadline tasks must be accomplished.
4. The time constraints within which hard deadline tasks must be accomplished.

Algorithms of the brick packing type must rely on the following assumptions:

1. The duration of tasks will be close to some standard nominal duration.
2. No unexpected task will need to be scheduled before the next scheduling opportunity at time $t_0 + \Delta t$.
3. No task will become unnecessary or detrimental due to information not available at time $t_0$.

In the example shown in Figure 10.5, assume that the missile update is the only hard deadline task; all other tasks are fluid. The brick pack scheduling functions as follows. First, place the hard deadline tasks into the schedule (arbitrating on priority if two time critical tasks compete for the same time slot). Then place the fluid tasks around these fixed blocks. Two forces are at work in determining the exact order in which fluid tasks actually are packed into the schedule: epoch goals (making sure the most tasks possible get accomplished within the time constraint) and priority goals (making sure the higher priority tasks get accomplished). The general approach is to exercise the epoch goal first and arbitrate any competitions based on priority.

As a final step, the algorithm can check if any of the remaining unscheduled fluid tasks have greater priority and can be scheduled in lieu of the scheduled hard time tasks (one final caveat, replacing a hard deadline task with one or more fluid tasks may make room for a hard deadline task that previously competed with the hard deadline task just removed).

Note that the epoch goal of the problem can be achieved by an exhaustive tree search to find the schedule that contains the most tasks. A less expensive, suboptimal approach is to use some heuristically guided depth-first tree search to select tasks. There are a host of obvious epoch oriented heuristics, including [12] select task with earliest start deadline, select task with earliest completion deadline, and select task with the tightest scheduling window. Although the heuristic tree search is less expensive than the exhaustive search, both could require significant processing. This processing load motivates us to make the following observation.

Note that, for the epoch-oriented part of the decision making to be significant, start and stop times are required for every fluid task. If the nature of the fluid deadline tasks is that they have no significant timing constraints within the interval $[t_0, t_0 + \Delta t)$, then the epoch-oriented nature of the scheduling problem becomes irrelevant. The approach degenerates into a purely priority-oriented approach, as all decisions will have to be arbitrated based on priority. This observation is important because most sensor scheduling tasks are truly fluid (the rate is more critical than any absolute times). We will show how a myopic or best first approach eliminates the need for epoch tree search altogether.

We also note difficulties with the brick-packing approach when any of its underlying assumptions is violated. For example, as stated earlier, the brick-packing approach relies on the assumption that no unexpected tasks will need to be performed before the next scheduling period at $t_0 + \Delta t$. Figure 10.6 shows an example where the update U1 on track 1 failed. It may be important to achieve this update quickly as, for example, the effectiveness of the missile update may depend on it. The brick-packing technique cannot directly accommodate this problem (i.e., we would need to apply a software "bandaid").

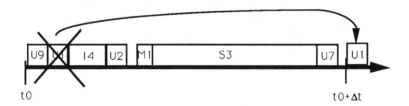

**Figure 10.6** Brick-packed time line with a failed task.

*Best First*

The desire for an alternative to the brick-packing approach is motivated in two ways. First, most tasks, particularly for $M$-level tasking, are very fluid and the epoch nature of the scheduling problem is minimal. Second, it is important to be able to handle pop-up events. Under these observations, it is natural to suggest shortening the scheduling window $[t_0, t_0 + \Delta t)$ of the brick-packing method as much as possible. This would expedite the service of pop-up tasks as well as take advantage of the fact that the epoch nature of the scheduling problem has little impact. This is exactly the motivation for the best first approach.

We will explain the best first approach in terms of the example shown in Figure 10.7. The gist of the best first approach is to produce a queue of priority-ordered fluid tasks every $\Delta t$ and a separate list of time-ordered hard deadline tasks. The fluid queue represents the best $N$ tasks to perform during the next $[t_0, t + \Delta t)$ interval. The algorithm steps through time (current time is $t$) picking tasks according to the following algorithm:

1. Retrieve top hard deadline task; call it $H$; get the earliest start time of $H$ and call it $T_b$.
2. If $t \geq T_b$, schedule $H$ and remove it from the list; return to step 1.
3. Otherwise, calculate latest valid start time for $H$ call it $T_s$.
4. Start at top of fluid task list.
5. Get next fluid task $F$; call nominal execution time $\tau$.
6. If $t + \tau > T_s$, go to step 5.
7. Otherwise, schedule task, remove $F$ from fluid list.
8. Go to step 1.

With a little additional bookkeeping it is easy to provide a method for integrating new fluid tasks at arbitrary times. This allows rapid response to pop-up events.

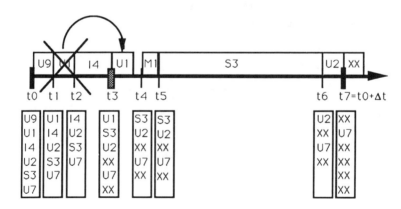

**Figure 10.7** Best first time line with failed task.

In terms of our example, the algorithm functions as follows. The fluid queue at time $t_0$ consists of six fluid tasks. Some time after $t_2$ we recognized that U1 failed and a new queue of tasks was integrated. We recognized that no task could be executed after the rescheduled U1 without violating the latest start time of our hard deadline task M1. At time $t_7 = t_0 + \Delta t$ new fluid and hard task queues are generated and the process continues.

In summary, we do not recommend the brick-packing approach for $M$-level sensor tasking. The brick-packing approach, however, still may be useful for $\mu$-level tasking where time constraints may be more prevalent and arise naturally as a consequence of trying to service the $M$-level requests.

### 10.3.4 Decision-Making Techniques

This section gets to the fundamental part of the question, *How* do we perform sensor management? How does an automated system make decisions about which sensor tasks are most important to schedule? To be more concrete, we reference our discussion to $M$-level management of an ESA.

Because this section is so lengthy, it is useful to summarize our goals up front. We begin by establishing a formal problem statement for $M$-level decision making for an ESA. We then discuss two major philosophies for decision making: the *descriptive* and *normative* approaches. We then survey each of these major approaches and select one specific approach from each, *fuzzy decision trees* (descriptive) and *utility theory* (normative). We will provide a description of each of these specific techniques and discuss how they can be applied to our problem statement. Finally, we provide a general comparison of these two specific approaches.

### *10.3.4.1 Formal Problem Statement*

In developing a formal problem statement, the first element to establish is the *action space*. The idea is to define a set of configurations of the ESA that, as a set, can accomplish all desired ESA activities. Thus, the problem of choosing all the parameters of the ESA at a given instant can be reduced to the selection of one of a finite set of configurations (at least from an $M$-level point of view). This set is called the action set $A$. The algorithm's objective is to select a member from this action set in accordance with a selection criteria. For this chapter, the following explicit action set is considered. If ownship currently holds $N$ tracks then the following action set consisting of $2N + 1$ potential actions is to be considered:

$$A = \left\{ \begin{array}{l} \text{illuminate any of } N \text{ tracks for update,} \\ \text{illuminate any of } N \text{ tracks for ID,} \\ \text{initiate a search scan of the next bar} \end{array} \right\} \tag{10.1}$$

This action space could be expanded by allowing for other parameter variations, such as different sensor modes, by simply defining additional actions. The fundamental concept is that a finite discrete set of actions (i.e., modes) can be defined to encompass all desired ESA activity. Because the relative length in time of each of these actions is of the same order of magnitude, we assume that once an action has been selected, it cannot be terminated until completion.

The algorithm's functioning is by best first scheduling: wait until the current action is completed, then select the next action in a manner consistent with the preceding guidelines and the current inferred state of the world. This discussion allows the precise posing of the allocation problem as follows: construct a decision rule that, at any time and subject to the given and inferred state of the world, can linearly rank the actions of set *A* in accordance with some criterion.

The term *some criterion* is purposefully vague. The choice of this criterion determines the actual technique used for problem solution. With this problem statement as a backdrop, we next try to map out the myriad of approaches available for its solution.

### 10.3.4.2  *Classifying the Various Approaches*

It is important to understand the distinction between normative and descriptive decision-making techniques. A normative technique produces decisions based on some axiomatic description of general human decision making and specific *a priori* data relevant to the decision at hand. A descriptive technique tries to produce decisions that match what a human would have decided based on available information. In short, a normative approach gives answers that a human *should* give in a similar situation whereas a descriptive approach gives answers a human *would* give in a similar situation. The approaches differ primarily in their definition of how a problem should be solved rather than in the information used to solve it. The thrust of normative approaches is to establish a formal decision-making criterion and remain faithful to it; the thrust of descriptive approaches is to provide a system by which any human decision-making behavior (whether or not it is formally consistent) can be easily codified. Even though, in principle, the same problem domain information could be used as the starting point for either approach, quite often the type of available problem domain knowledge will help drive the decision as to whether to use a normative or a descriptive approach. As we discuss, descriptive approaches can be constructed on a weaker problem domain description than is required by a normative approach.

*Descriptive or Knowledge Based.* The major advantage of the descriptive approaches is that they are amenable to situations for which either no objectively verifiable information is available or situations for which there is a strong motive to make use of information that clearly is subjective. Descriptive approaches include fuzzy reasoning, evidential reasoning (perhaps as discussed later), Mycin, knowledge-based approaches, and most other nonclassical approaches proposed by various academic and industrial researchers. Descriptive techniques are most amenable to applications typically addressed by expert systems (although there have been examples of expert systems using normative approaches; see [23] for a discussion). The goal of these systems generally is to mimic expert human behavior for a particular problem domain. This is the essence of the descriptive paradigm. The descriptive paradigm allows systems to be constructed for problem domains for which no clear models for how the problem should be solved can be constructed. We simply hope to capture the behavior of a human faced with the same problem.

*Normative or Decision Theoretic.* The major advantage of normative approaches is that they lead to systems for which performance criteria can be analyzed. The performance of a normative system can be guaranteed with respect to a defensible criteria (related to the axiomatic bases used for decision). Normative approaches include probability theoretic reasoning, utility theoretic reasoning, and evidential reasoning. Normative techniques are useful in applications where a strong structure can be imposed on the decision-making process. These tend to be application areas where given sufficient information, everyone would agree on the correct answer. Thus, applications suitable for a normative approach are those that tend to lend themselves to an objective analysis.

### 10.3.4.3  *Selecting a Descriptive Approach*

Several criteria that should be kept under consideration when selecting a descriptive approach include theoretic maturity, capability for reasoning under uncertainty, maintainability, extensibility, and execution speed.

Descriptive approaches have previously been reported on by [19, 30]. The approach taken by [30] amounts to assigning each type of task to a fixed category (or priority) and exhausting all tasks in a given category before considering lower-priority tasks. The advantage of this approach is its simplicity (although the author admits [30] that there may be some difficulties in getting to low-priority tasks under heavy sensor loading). Perhaps at the other end of the complexity spectrum is the system described in [19], which is based on the use of special purpose LISP machines and a standardized expert system inference engine. We seek to explore an intermediate ground. We seek a method that provides the flexibility of advanced reasoning techniques while minimizing computational and coding expense.

In terms of theoretic maturity and the capability to reason under uncertainty, we immediately are motivated to consider some approach based on fuzzy set theory. Fuzzy set theory enjoys a theoretical maturity not shared by any other descriptive technique. Of the various descriptive techniques described in the literature, fuzzy reasoning is by far the most formally developed. For example (an example of extreme mathematical depth only for those not mathematically faint of heart), it has been argued on the basis of a category theoretic argument [14] that the conceptual codification capabilities of fuzzy sets may in principle be unsurpassable. For the less mathematically inclined, mathematical research in fuzzy sets varies from simple extensions of high school mathematics to studies in the generalization of measure theory.

In terms of maintainability and extensibility, we immediately are motivated to consider some sort of knowledge-based system. We next show how we can adapt a standard *artificial intelligence* (AI) technique (decision trees) to achieve a rule-based system. This approach will have the advantages that it operates with inexact reasoning and is compatible with fast execution and low computational burden requirements. Before discussing our approach, however, we first provide a fuzzy set primer. This primer will help establish the fundamentals we will need to define our approach.

*A Fuzzy Set Primer*

Consider a normal "crisp" subset $A$ of the universe of discourse $X$. Denote by $x$ an element of $X$. Then the set $A \subset X$ may be defined by identifying the elements $x \in A$. One way to do this is to specify a condition by which $x$ comes to be a member of $A$. Thus, $A$ can be defined as

$$A = \{x \,|\, x \text{ meets some condition}\} \tag{10.2}$$

For example, let $X$ be the universe of discourse composed of all people. Let the set $A$ be the set of all females. Thus,

$$A = \{x \,|\, x \text{ is a female}\} \tag{10.3}$$

An equivalent way of specifying $A$ is through its membership function.

$$A \rightleftharpoons \mu_A(x) = \begin{cases} 1 & \text{if } x \in A \\ 0 & \text{if } x \notin A \end{cases} \tag{10.4}$$

We say that $A$ is mathematically equivalent to its membership function $\mu_A(x)$ in the sense that knowing $\mu_A(x)$ is the same as knowing $A$ itself.

Next, consider the "fuzzy" set $B \subset X$. Again, $B$ can be defined by a condition any $x$ must meet to be in $B$; except, now the condition can be vague:

$$B = \{x \,|\, x \text{ meets some vague condition}\} \tag{10.5}$$

For example, let $B$ be the set of all *tall* people. The problem is that tall is not a crisp notion. Certainly if man $x$ has height 5.0′, he is not *tall;* whereas, if man $x$ has height 6.5′, he is a member of the set $B$. But, what if he has height 5.7′? The idea behind a fuzzy set is to assign to each $x \in X$ a number in the range $[0, 1]$ that represents the degree of agreement between the nature of $x$ and the defining concept of the set. Thus, we say that $B$ is mathematically equivalent with its membership function:

$$B \rightleftharpoons \mu_B : X \mapsto [0, 1] \qquad (10.6)$$

Note that a normal crisp set is indeed a special case of a fuzzy set. The exact definition of this membership function represents the subjective notion of the concept *tall*. For example, a suitable membership function for the concept of *tall people* represented by the set $B$ may be defined in terms of person $x$'s height as shown in Figure 10.8.

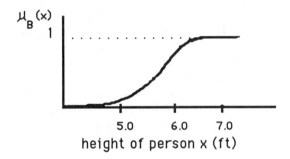

**Figure 10.8** Membership function expressing the notion of a tall person.

An important observation is that the notion of *tall* has been encoded by the subset $B$. Thus, we can think of the set $B$ as being the subjective concept *tall*.

Finally, we can define fuzzy set logical connectives, **and, or,** and **not** as

$$\cap : A \cap B \rightleftharpoons \mu_{A \cap B}(x) = \min[\mu_A(x), \mu_B(x)]$$
$$\cup : A \cup B \rightleftharpoons \mu_{A \cup B}(x) = \max[\mu_A(x), \mu_B(x)] \qquad (10.7)$$
$$^{-} : \overline{B} \rightleftharpoons \mu_{\overline{B}}(x) = 1 - \mu_B(x)$$

The appropriateness and usefulness of these definitions is supported by the following observations. Note that the definitions correspond to the normal notions of intersection, union, and complement when applied to crisp sets (i.e., sets with membership functions that take on only values of 1 and 0). Note that the following properties usually associated with binary logic hold: commutativity, associativity, idempotence, distributivity, De Morgan's law, and absorption. Note, however, that the normal notion of the excluded middle does not hold, in that

$$\overline{B} \cup B \neq X \quad \text{and} \quad \overline{B} \cap B \neq \emptyset \qquad (10.8)$$

These logical connectives can be used to define concepts that are composites of already defined concepts. For example, the concept of a *tall woman* can be defined by $A \cap B$. The fact that most of the normal structure of binary logic still holds provides a large amount of structure for the development of such composite concepts.

*Expert System and the Fuzzy Decision Tree Approach*

We motivate the development of our fuzzy decision tree approach with a discussion of the background and advantages of expert systems and inexact reasoning. At the simplest level, an expert system can be described as consisting of two parts: a knowledge base and a reasoning scheme (or inference engine). The knowledge base is a codification of the expert's domain-specific knowledge (typically in the form of "if–then" rules of thumb). The inference engine operates on the knowledge base to draw conclusions.

Many expert systems employ "inexact" reasoning schemes. Such reasoning schemes operate on rules as follows: the degree to which the premise of a rule is true leads to a degree of truth that the conclusion is true. This conclusion then can be used as part of the premise of succeeding rules. Thus, rules can be chained together by propagating the confidences of each rule element to establish the confidence in the conclusion of more general or composite inferences.

*The Importance of Inexact Reasoning.* There are several motivations for focusing on inexact reasoning schemes:

- *Manipulation of Conceptual Meaning versus Manipulation of Symbols.* An important theoretical issue that should be understood is that inexact reasoning (particularly in the case of fuzzy logic) enables us to build a system that manipulates conceptual entities rather than simple symbols [29]. For example, both an exact reasoning system and an inexact reasoning system may have an assertion of the form: John is tall. Note that in an exact reasoning system tall is simply a symbol with no further meaning attached. In a fuzzy logic system, however, tall would be a linguistic variable described by a distribution over a domain of discourse of heights. This approach allows knowledge about John's height to relate to any other piece of knowledge that in turn also could be related to this same domain of discourse, whereas an exact approach would be able only to match other occurrences of the exact symbol tall. The result is that inexact reasoning schemes are a much more expressive tool for the codification of knowledge.
- *Smaller Subsets.* In general, inexact reasoning systems will require fewer rules than exact reasoning schemes. This primarily is an outgrowth of the fact that inexact reasoning allows the manipulation of conceptual meaning as discussed earlier. Fewer rules need to be written because the knowledge base need not have an exact premise for all possible eventualities. Partial matching of prem-

ises allows a smaller rule set to avoid no-match conditions that otherwise would lead to deadlock [29].

- *Dealing with Uncertainty.* For our particular application, the decisions that must be made are predicated on data that may be inherently uncertain. For example, the true intent of an enemy target. Inexact reasoning systems can accommodate naturally these uncertainties.

*Implementing Inexact Reasoning.* There is no general agreement within the AI community as to the "correct" way to perform inexact reasoning and several different schemes have been successfully implemented [23, 7, 33, 15]. Our proposed approach can be interpreted in either of two ways: as an implementation of an inexact reasoning expert system or as the fuzzification of the standard [32] AI technique of decision trees. An example of a standard decision tree is shown in Figure 10.9. The standard decision tree diagram is read as follows. Each box represents an assertion about reality and may be either true or false. The truth of any assertion is dependent on the truths of any assertion connected to it from below. Thus, for example, the truth of *Important* relies on the truth of the assertions *Bearing In* and *Maneuvering.* Lines from an assertion with no arc indicate the logical connective **or.** Lines with an arc represent the logical connective **and.** The operation **not** is represented by a circle with a tilde in it. Thus, for example, truth of the assertion *Important* relies on the truth of *Attacking* ∪ *Bearing In* ∪ *Maneuvering.* Note that if we interpret this tree as a statement about a target we could have represented the same knowledge equally well by a small rule base:

r1. IF target is *Attacking* or *Bearing In* or *Maneuvering,* THEN the target is *Important.*

r2. IF target is *Close* and not *Friend,* THEN the target is *Attacking.*

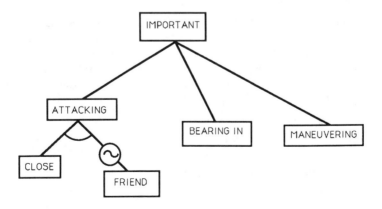

**Figure 10.9** Sample tree for target importance.

Thus we see that exact Boolean rule bases are intimately tied to decision trees. It is straightforward to extend the standard crisp decision tree to the concept of a fuzzy decision tree. Truth no longer has only the crisp states of true and false but rather is represented by a number ranging from zero to one. This number represents the degree of truth of the assertion. Each assertion then is a fuzzy set that represents a concept. Therefore we see that the fuzzy decision tree is tied intimately to the notion of an inexact rule base and inferencing scheme. The knowledge still is codified by the two rules (or tree given in Figure 10.9). The goal of the algorithm is to use these rules of thumb to determine the degree of belief it can assign to the assertion that a target is *Important*. The procedure used is as follows. First, the system determines the degree of truth of the bottom assertions *Close* and *Friend, Bearing In* and *Maneuvering*. Truth of these root concepts are evaluated by applying what is known about the environment to fuzzy set membership functions that represent these root concepts. Examples of such membership functions are shown in Figure 10.10.

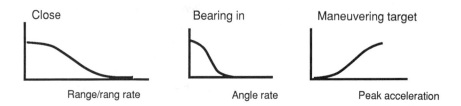

**Figure 10.10** Sample membership functions.

For example the system computes $r/\dot{r}$ (note that this is a measure of the time it would take to intercept) and applies this to the membership function that codifies the concept of close. The less time to go the more truth is assigned to *Close*.

In summary, the approach encodes basic or root concepts as membership functions of fuzzy sets. Composite or higher-order concepts are built by using the standard definitions of the fuzzy set operations $\cap$, $\cup$, $^-$ as logical connectives. The highest-order concepts are decisions about which sensor operations would be most appropriate for the current situation. A detailed application of this technique will be given in Section 10.4.

*Approach Advantages*

This approach maintains all the standard advantages of expert systems: encoding of human decision making, modular knowledge-based design, maintainability, and extensibility. In particular, the use of min-max assures that the truth of an assertion is not influenced by the number of contributing factors, but only the degree of truth of the dominant term. Thus, rules can be added without concern about rescaling the contributions of other rules. Other well-known inexact reasoning schemes such as Mycin [26] cannot make this claim. Therefore, this approach has improved extensibility and maintainability.

Additionally, this approach requires only modest computational burden. All root functions calculations can be accomplished via lookup tables and the rest of operations are primarily min and max operations, which are very inexpensive. Other inexact reasoning approaches that use probability models or evidential reasoning require significantly more computation.

### 10.3.4.4 Selecting a Normative Approach

Several criteria should be kept under consideration when selecting a normative approach: flexibility, the nature of the required *a priori* information, and the computational burden.

- Probabilistic Reasoning. Of the techniques we have been discussing, probabilistic reasoning is formulated in terms of the most restrictive axiomatic base and therefore most restrictive in the type of information that can be used. All information must have a proper probabilistic interpretation, and a large amount of data is required to keep and maintain consistency. Note that some authors (e.g., Pearl [21]) would argue that subjectivity and reduced data can be employed, but whether they actually are abandoning probability in doing so is clearly debatable. Note that the use of subjective priors in a probabilistic reasoning also brings its normative status into question (this pokes at the age old debate between Bayesians and statisticians, and we will consider it no further). The result is that the probabilistic approach requires a great deal of data that may not be attainable for sensor management problems.
- Utility Theoretic Reasoning. Utility theory develops an axiomatic base for consistent decision making. The approach allows construction of utility functions that codify human subjective criteria with respect to decision making. Decisions then are made to maximize the expected (in a strict probability sense) utility outcomes. In a way, utility theory is a way to allow subjective knowledge (encoded by a utility function) to be combined with objective knowledge (encoded by probabilistic models). Most of the comments relative to the probability approach apply here as well, except that an axiomatic method for the inclusion of some subjectivity is provided.
- Evidential Reasoning. This technique is based on a weaker axiomatic base than probability (in fact, evidential reasoning results from a direct weakening of one of the axioms of probability). The technique is amenable to a normative interpretation and also may allow for a subjective interpretation. The caveat with the classification of evidential reasoning depends on the nature of the infor-

mation used to create the *a priori* data base. If, as is normally done, the data can be interpreted as objectively deduced (e.g., something on which anyone would have to agree based on basic evidence), then the technique is normative. If, however, the *a priori* data is purely subjective (i.e., no attempt has been made to objectify it), then the technique is more properly classified as descriptive. The amenability to expert system use has been demonstrated [28], and its suitability for classification applications is well documented.

*The Utility Theoretic Approach.* If it has been decided that a normative approach must be used, then we would recommend the utility theory because it offers the greatest flexibility while maintaining a normative stature. Several systems with a normative emphasis have been reported [11, 16, 24, 31]. These systems relied on models of various aspects of system performance and attempted to manage sensor behavior consistent with these models. In essence, we recommend the same thing here. The only difference is that through utility theory we attempt to make all decisions based on a common framework rather than through a collection of independent models of system behavior.

## Utility Theory Primer

Presented here are those concepts from utility theory necessary to understand the results presented in Section 10.4. As the theory is being developed, reference will be made to the allocation problem in general so that the reader can immediately begin to see the motivation. The material that follows draws heavily on [18]. The value of repeating it here is that the exemplary material will be cast directly in allocation terms, and only that material essential to the understanding of the algorithm will be included. Finally, note that the pertinent fundamental results will be stated but not proved.

Utility theory is a technique that allows for consistent decision making over multiple objectives under uncertainty. Assume that a single entity will make all the decisions. This entity will be appropriately referred to as the *decision maker.* Thus, the decision maker is the entity whose preferences we wish to represent algorithmically. The fundamental construct of the theory is that the decision maker is faced with several alternative actions denoted $\{a_1, a_2, \ldots, a_m\}$. Associated with each action is a probabilistic set of outcomes denoted $\{\omega_1, \omega_2, \ldots, \omega_n\}$. Note that this set of outcomes need not be discrete. All that matters is that each $a_i$ can be associated with a probability distribution over the set of outcomes. Finally, it is essential that the decision maker can order these outcomes according to his or her preference for their realization. Thus, assuming that the outcomes have been ordered according to preference, write

$$\omega_1 < \omega_2 < \ldots < \omega_n \tag{10.9}$$

where the symbol $\prec$ is read "less preferable to." Note that, as stated so far, this preferential ordering is without regard to the probability distribution over these outcomes. The heart of utility theory, however, is dealing with the decision maker's preference to these outcomes with regard to their probability distribution.

The concept of a lottery is the final construct we will need before we can develop the tools of utility theory. We have indicated that each action leads to a probabilistic outcome. Now assume that the outcomes $\{\omega_i\}$ have been mapped to a random variable $\tilde{x}$ or set of random variables $\{\tilde{x}_i\}$. The notation $\tilde{x}$ will be used to refer to the random variable itself; whereas $x$ will be used to reference a particular realization of $\tilde{x}$. These random variables will be called *attributes*. The attributes for a particular decision problem are chosen so that they serve as indicators for the possible outcomes of the choices that are to be made. Consider a generic attribute $\tilde{x}$. The lottery is simply the probability density

$$l_i(x) \triangleq p(x \mid a_i) \tag{10.10}$$

over the attribute $\tilde{x}$ conditioned on the choice of action $a_i$. The comparison of these lotteries will give us access to the decision maker's behavioral attitudes and encode them in a utility-based algorithm.

Before we proceed with the development of utility theory, we identify the elements discussed in the ESA allocation problem. The set of actions from which one is to be selected correspond to the allocation actions, such as (1) scan a volume of space and attempt to find new targets, (2) revisit a previously detected target and attempt to update its track file, (3) use a specialized waveform and longer dwell time on a previously detected target in an attempt to identify the target type.

The careful reader probably has caught the operative phrase *attempt to*. This is because deciding to perform one of these operations does not guarantee the results that will be achieved. The algorithm, then, must consider the probabilistic nature of the outcomes when selecting actions. Once accurately defined, these probabilistic results will form the set $\{\omega_i\}$ of possible outcomes and the likelihood of their occurrence. The enumeration of the outcomes of a particular choice of action requires careful thought. The decision maker must be able to clearly define all the positive and negative repercussions of each particular action. For example, in terms of our allocation problem, we might develop the following list of the repercussions of an update attempt on track $k$. The *Update track k* decision will lead to

- A $P_d$ chance at improving the error covariance of track $k$.
- The extrapolation of all other currently held tracks (corresponding to degradation in the error covariances for each track's states).
- No chance to detect any new targets.
- No improvement in target identification for any held tracks.

These outcomes then are associated with the set of random variables called the *attributes*.

Consider, for example, the attribute associated primarily with update actions. If an update is successful, (which occurs with probability $P_d$, the probability of detection) then the entries of the Kalman filter error covariance indicate the merit of the result. Similarly, if the update is unsuccessful (which occurs with probability $(1 - P_d)$), then the entries of the Kalman predictor error covariance indicate the degradation of the result. Thus it is reasonable to define one of the attributes based on the Kalman error statistics. This anticipated gain in this attribute would then help to measure the merit of selecting an update action.

The lottery is simply that action $a_i$ leads to consequences $\{x_i\}$ with probabilities $\{p_i\}$, or equivalently, that action $a_i$ is associated with the random variable $\tilde{x}$ having probability density $l_i(x)$. In our example, action *update attempt* leads to {*filtered error covariance, predicted error covariance*} with probabilities $\{P_d, (1 - P_d)\}$.

It is important to realize that the final algorithm starts to take shape as soon as the action set and the attribute set are specified. These specifications are not unique for a particular problem. The decision maker already is indicating what is important to him as soon as he establishes these sets. Finally, it is important that the attributes are defined in a way that allows a probability density to be prescribed over them for each possible action.

## The Goal of Utility Theory

The goal of utility theory now can be stated in terms of the preceding constructs. Utility theory provides a systematic way of expressing the decision maker's attitude toward uncertainty so as to embody these attitudes in a decision-making algorithm by virtue of a utility function. A utility function $u(\tilde{x})$ is nothing more than a scalar functional of the attributes. These utility functions are constructed so that more preferred lotteries result in larger expected utility values than less preferred lotteries. Thus, if the decision maker considers probability density $l_1(x)$ over attribute $\tilde{x}$ to be preferable to a $l_2(x)$, then the utility function $u(x)$ will be constructed such that

$$\int u(x)l_1(x)\,dx > \int u(x)l_2(x)\,dx \tag{10.11}$$

or, in terms of actions, if action $A$ leads to density $l_1(x)$ and action $B$ leads to density $l_2(x)$, the utility is such that

$$E[u(\tilde{x})|A] > E[u(\tilde{x})|B] \tag{10.12}$$

Thus, by performing that action which maximizes the expected utility, the algorithm will act in accordance with the decision maker's preference structure.

To get an intuitive feel for the usefulness of utility functions, consider the following monetary example. The use of a money amount as the random variable is common practice in utility theory discussions. Somehow attaching money to the example gives most people an immediate sense about the underlying implications. An example of this classic type is a decision maker faced with the following choices [18]:

1. Act A ≡ earn $100,000 for sure.
2. Act B ≡ earn $200,000 or $0, each with probability 0.5.
3. Act C ≡ earn $1,000,000 with probability 0.1 or $0 with probability 0.9.
4. Act D ≡ earn $200,000 with probability 0.9 or lose $800,000 with probability 0.1.

The expected monetary return of a lottery denoted and defined as

$$\bar{x} \triangleq E[\tilde{x}] \tag{10.13}$$

Note, that although the expected outcome in each case is $100,000, the decision maker may have quite different preferences for these lotteries. Thus, it is clear that we cannot merely select the action that maximizes the expected monetary return. Utility theory provides the means to systematically describe the decision maker's preference structure so that the utility function could be used to order any given set of lotteries in the same order of preference as the decision maker. We will come back to this example once we have presented the tools to allow a deeper investigation of exactly how the utility function represents a particular preference structure.

The skeptical reader may question whether it is theoretically possible to prove that a scalar functional can order all possible lotteries according to a decision maker's preference structure. The answer is a qualified yes. The proof and the necessary assumptions about the decision maker's preference structure are provided in [10].

## Risk Aversion

The preceding foundation is sufficient to allow us to investigate the behavior of an algorithm based on the characteristics of its utility functions. The behavior we wish to explore is termed *risk aversion*. Informally, a decision maker who tends to act conservatively is said to be risk averse; otherwise, risk prone. Because a utility function represents the decision maker's preferences, a utility function is risk averse if for all lotteries (pdfs of $\tilde{x}$)

$$u(E[\tilde{x}]) > E[u(\tilde{x})] \tag{10.14}$$

To get an intuitive feel for risk aversion, consider the previous monetary example. In talking about simple lotteries, where the random variable outcome assumes only two values

$$\tilde{x} = a \text{ with probability } p \tag{10.15}$$

$$\tilde{x} = b \text{ with probability } (1 - p) \tag{10.16}$$

we use the triplet notation $\langle a, b, p \rangle$ as a shorthand description. Thus, for example, lottery $B$ would be described by $\langle 2, 0, .5 \rangle$, where we have taken the liberty to scale the outcomes by a factor of \$100,000. For this monetary example, it is reasonable to assume that the utility function will increase monotonically (i.e., when it comes to money, more is always better). Now, intuitively, we would expect that a risk averse decision maker would prefer act $A$ to $B$ and would prefer $B$ to $C$. In symbols,

$$A > B > C \tag{10.17}$$

The definition given by eq. (3.1) is really a pointwise test for risk aversion. To investigate a utility function's preference for general lotteries, as we would like to do in the preceding example, we need to know when a utility function is risk averse over a region of lotteries.

*Fundamental Result: 1 A decision maker is risk averse over a range of $\tilde{x}$ if and only if his or her utility function is convex $\cap$ over that region.* This theorem will enable us to show that a risk averse utility function will pick the same ordering as the decision maker in the monetary example. Given that $u$ is strictly convex $\cap$ implies, by use of Jensen's inequality, that

$$u[px_1 + (1 - p)x_2] > pu(x_1) + (1 - p)u(x_2) \qquad \forall p \in (0, 1) \tag{10.18}$$

That is, the function at an interpolated point exceeds the interpolation of the function. Note that the utility of the lottery associated with action $A$ actually is just

$$E[u(\tilde{x}_A)] = u(\bar{x}) \tag{10.19}$$

Remember that for the current example

$$E[\tilde{x}_A] = E[\tilde{x}_B] = E[\tilde{x}_C] = \bar{x} \tag{10.20}$$

Thus, by direct application of Jensen's inequality, any convex $\cap$ utility function would rank

$$A > B \quad \text{and} \quad A > C \tag{10.21}$$

It is a little more difficult to show any convex $\cap$ function will pick lottery $B$ as preferable to lottery $C$. To see that this indeed is the case, we find a parametric equation of the expected utility for lotteries $B$ and $C$ and then show that convexity $\cap$ is all that is required of the utility function to guarantee that

$$E[u(\tilde{x}_B)] > E[u(\tilde{x}_C)] \tag{10.22}$$

and, hence, any convex $\cap$ utility function will provide the correct ordering.

A geometric argument can be used to show that if lottery $i$ is described by the triplet $\langle a_i, b_i, p_i \rangle$, then the expected value of its utility function is

$$E[u(\tilde{x}_i)] = [u(a_i) - u(b_i)] \frac{(\bar{x}_i - b_i)}{a_i - b_i} + u(b_i) \qquad (10.23)$$

Thus, for lottery $B \equiv \langle 2, 0, .5 \rangle$ (again for convenience, we have scaled the outcome by $100,000), we have

$$E[u(\tilde{x}_B)] = [u(2) - u(0)] \frac{\bar{x}}{2} + u(0) \qquad (10.24)$$

Similarly, for lottery $C \equiv (10, 0, .1)$,

$$E[u(\tilde{x}_C)] = [u(10) - u(0)] \frac{\bar{x}}{10} + u(0) \qquad (10.25)$$

It follows from Jensen's inequality for strictly convex $\cap$ functions that

$$u(2) > .2u(10) + .8u(0) \qquad (10.26)$$

Substituting the right side of the inequality into eq. (3.2) yields

$$E[u(\tilde{x}_B)] > \frac{.2u(10) + .8u(0) - u(0)}{2} \bar{x} + u(0) \qquad (10.27)$$

But, the right side of inequality (3.4) equals the right side of eq. (3.3). Thus,

$$E[u(\tilde{x}_B)] > E[u(\tilde{x}_C)] \qquad (10.28)$$

for all $u$ strictly convex $\cap$.

The notion of a risk-prone decision maker is the obvious counterpart to the previous discussion of a risk averse one.

*Fundamental Result 2: A decision maker is risk prone over a range of $\tilde{x}$ if and only if his or her utility function is convex $\cup$ over that region (note that convex $\cup$ is defined by eq. (10.18) with the inequality reversed).*

Similarly, the notion of risk neutrality is straightforward.

*Fundamental Result 3: A decision maker is risk neutral over a range of $\tilde{x}$ if and only if his or her utility function is linear over that region.*

We hope that this example has served two purposes. First, it should encourage the reader to believe that preference structure can be encapsulated in a utility function. Second, risk aversion or, equivalently, the convexity is an important qualitative feature of a utility function.

*Applying Utility Theory*

To develop a utility-theoretic solution to the sensor management problem requires the following steps:

- Specify the action set.
- Select a set of attributes.
- Develop expressions for the distribution on attributes given action choice. Note that this may be the toughest part. If the required probability densities cannot be derived then we cannot proceed. It cannot be overemphasized that this required *a priori* information can be extremely difficult to attain legitimately.
- Develop the appropriate utility functions. This, too, is a far from trivial task, particularly for multiattribute problems. We recommend selecting the regions of the attributes over which you want to be risk averse, risk neutral, and risk prone, and then rough in functions with the appropriate convexities. Although not discussed in our primer, the degree of risk aversion is related to the degree of curvature. This fact may also be employed when roughing in the utility functions.

Once this set-up work is complete then the utility approach is simply to rank actions based on their expected utilities.

Although this presentation of utility theory admittedly has been brief, all the necessary tools have been presented to allow us to pursue a discussion of the proposed ESA algorithm. A realization of the proposed algorithm has been simulated and the results are presented in Section 10.4 to help demonstrate the approach in a concrete way.

### 10.3.4.5 *Comments on Picking a Decision-Making Approach*

We described various approaches to decision making. We attempt to provide some guidelines for selecting among these alternatives. Although selecting an approach for sensor management is not clear-cut, we argue in favor of the descriptive techniques and in particular for descriptive techniques based on fuzzy set theory. Figure 10.11 is a brief "summary at a glance" of trade-offs between utility theoretic and fuzzy decision tree approaches.

*Recommendations for Maintainability and Extensibility.* Two main factors help determine the maintainability and extensibility of a knowledge-based system: (1) the cleavage between the knowledge base and the inferencing mechanism (the essence of the expert system paradigm) and (2) the format and ease of the codification of the

| Evaluation Criteria | Utility theory (Normative) | | Fuzzy Trees (Descriptives) | |
|---|---|---|---|---|
| Maintainability | NO | Mods to utility Functions not obvious | YES | Traceable |
| Extensibilty | NO | Not modular | YES | Very modular |
| Processor loading | HIGH | Burden of probability calcs can be high | LOW | Only simple operations |
| Apriori data required | SEVERE | Probabilistic model for all outcomes required | SIMPLE | No formal probability models required |

**Figure 10.11** The advantages of the fuzzy tree approach.

domain knowledge stored in the knowledge base. Therefore we argue in favor of fuzzy logic on these grounds.

*Recommendations Based on Computational Burden.* In general, the fuzzy decision tree approach will require only min and max operations, which a computer can execute very quickly. Root function evaluation generally can be performed via look-up table. Thus the fuzzy decision tree approach has very low computational burden compared with the probability calculations required by the utility approach.

*Recommendations Based on Required* A Priori *Information.* In general, if well-founded normative information is available for an application, the normative approach should be strongly considered because the normative approach leads to more defensible systems. For many problems, however, it is unrealistic to assume objective *a priori* probabilities can be gathered. In these cases, descriptive approaches must be utilized. We argue that all but the most basic $M$-level systems will require descriptive approaches because their goal is to trade off decisions for which no firm probability models exist. For $\mu$-level systems, the choice would have to be made based on the available *a priori* information for the given application.

## 10.4 DEMONSTRATIONS OF SENSOR MANAGEMENT

In this section, we offer simulation results that demonstrate examples of the imperatives marked * in Section 10.2. The importance of these results is twofold:

- The results demonstrate the impact of some of the sensor management imperatives on a tracking system.
- The results demonstrate the validity of the techniques for sensor management discussed in Section 10.3.

Demonstrating sensor management activity is somewhat of a challenge because it serves as a feedback link in a complex sensor-tracking system. It is difficult to isolate which effects are directly the result of the feedback. A "before and after" demonstration is not possible because, as we depicted in Figure 10.2, without sensor management a human operator formed the feedback path. It is always difficult to develop a demonstrative figure of merit for a system that in effect (or to some extent) replaces a human operator. The best we can do here is show some simple test cases and verify that at least the systems seem to do what is intended. It would be beyond the scope of this chapter to develop and demonstrate any true tactical measures of performance. We have broken down our sensor management results into five separate demonstrations. Doing so allows us to demonstrate various behaviors independently and thus, we hope, more clearly. The five demonstrations are described in terms of the feedback paths (as shown in Figure 10.2) that they implement and the imperatives they demonstrate:

1. Demonstrates a *descriptive* approach that implements the feedback paths from *situation assessment* and *data fusion* (actually the situation assessment function also is implemented as part of the *M* manager). The results demonstrate the following sensor management imperatives: *management of agile aperture resources, response to assessed situation, track maintenance, reduction in pilot workload,* and *collection of missing tactical information.* This single-sensor system is the most complete of all those demonstrated. It illustrates many of the advantages we hope to gain from sensor management. Some discussion of extending this system to a more general system is provided.

2. Demonstrates a *descriptive* approach that implements the feedback path from *data fusion.* The results demonstrate the following sensor management imperatives: *cooperative reinforcement, intersensor cueing,* and *emission control.* The purpose of this demonstration is to call attention to the role sensor management can play in a multisensor system.

3. Demonstrates a *descriptive* approach that implements the feedback path from *data association.* The results demonstrate the following sensor management imperative: *maintenance of tracks in dense environments.* The limited nature of this demonstration allows us to draw attention to what otherwise would be a very salient feature. The intent was to demonstrate only how a specific data association criterion could be fed back to improve tracking.

4. Demonstrates a *normative* approach that implements the feedback path from *data fusion.* The results demonstrate the following sensor management imperatives: *management of agile aperture resources, track maintenance,* and *reduction in pilot workload.* This system is very much the normative counterpart of the system of Demonstration 1. The *a priori* information requirements of utility theory, however, restrict the versatility of the system that can be constructed. Thus this system is not capable of responding as well to the tactical behavior of the targets as the system of Demonstration 1.

5. This is not really a demonstration at all. Rather, it is a discussion of some of the issues one might address in the design of a $\mu$ manager for an ESA radar.

Because a $\mu$-manager design is highly sensor dependent, a detailed demonstration of specific results would be of less general interest. This discussion is included for completeness as we have paid little direct attention to $\mu$-manager issues up to this point. The discussion addresses one sensor management imperative: *control of agile multimode resources.*

### 10.4.1 Demonstration 1

A sensor management system based on the fuzzy decision tree approach described in Section 10.3 was designed to manage the agile sensor aperture of an ESA radar. The goal of the system was to demonstrate the ability to dynamically direct the ESA radar among the $M$-level tasks of *search, target update,* and *target identification.* We take significant effort here to explain exactly how the results we present were attained. We do this to help concretize the definition of the fuzzy decision tree approach described in Section 10.3. Because this is an algorithm of the descriptive type, the first step in its construction is to establish the heuristic criteria by which it is to perform its decision making.

*Heuristic* ESA *Allocation*

The following set of heuristic guidelines or rules of thumb is a first-cut subset of a knowledge base for $M$-level ESA allocation. The rule base for an actual allocation ESA system of course would include other guidelines.

H1.  Search is important because an average flux of new targets must be detected.
H2.  In general, kinematic updates must be performed on tracks that may be lost due to insufficient attention.
H3.  It is important to keep tight tracks (in the sense of the Kalman filter error covariances) on targets that may want to engage ownship (our craft).
H4.  Identification of tracks with generally poor ID is important.
H5.  It is important to be sure of the *Friend or Foe* ID of a target close to ownship.

The heuristic truth of these statements should be clear. Exactly how these general rules of thumb may be encoded into a decision-making rule base is the focus of this demonstration.

As described in Section 10.3 the rules by which we would like to govern sensor activity can be represented in terms of a rule base that, in turn, can be codified by a fuzzy decision tree. We next establish a simple rule base that expresses three types of knowledge:

- Knowledge about how tracking performance should govern sensor behavior (i.e., the criteria that should be used to close the loop between the tracking system and the sensors).

- Knowledge about how the tactical situation should govern sensor behavior (i.e., the criteria that should be used to close the loop between the situation assessment and the sensors).
- Knowledge about how the tracking information should be used to form an assessment of the situation (i.e., the method by which situation assessment can be developed from basic track data).

The following rule base contains a few representative rules for each of these three types of knowledge. A real system of course would have a far more extensive set of rules. Note that in an actual system, it would be a good idea to partition the overall rule-based system into two rule-based systems. The rules involved with *situation assessment* generally can be evaluated at a less frequent rate than the *sensor tasking* rules, which must have an overall throughput commensurate with the rate at which fluid data queues must be sent to the $\mu$ manager.

r1. IF: track is *lethal* **and** track is *close,* THEN: track is *dangerous.*

r2. IF: track has *uncertain ID,* THEN: track is *dangerous.*

r3. IF: track is *dangerous* under r1 **or** r2, THEN: track is *dangerous.*

r4. IF: track is *close* **and** *dangerous* then track is *attacking.*

r5. IF: track is *bearing in* **and** (track is **not** *friend* **or** track has *marginal ID*), THEN: track is *attacking.*

r6. IF: track is *attacking* under r4 **or** r5, THEN: track is *attacking.*

r7. IF: track is *loose,* THEN: *update track.*

r8. IF: track is *attacking* **and** tracking variance *exceeds kill variance,* THEN: *update track.*

r9. IF: track requires update under r7 **or** r8, THEN: *update track.*

r10. IF: track has *uncertain ID,* THEN: *identify track.*

r11. IF: track has *marginal ID* **and** track is *close,* THEN: *identify track.*

r12. IF: track identification is indicated under r10 **or** r11, THEN: *identify track.*

r13. IF: undetected targets are *large flux,* THEN: *search.*

r14. IF: *update track, identify track, search,* THEN: select the *best action.*

As explained in Section 10.3 this decision process can be graphically represented as a fuzzy decision tree. The tree shown in Figure 10.12 graphically represents those parts of the rule base that have to do with the decision to update a track.

This tree has been extended slightly to include hooks for incorporating knowledge about emission control and the sensor capability to perform the requested action. The hooks are provided by the inclusion of two concepts that constrain our desire for update. Specifically, the tree shows the addition of two constraint concepts: (1) the consistency of employing the sensor, given tactical requirements governing the overtness allowed to ownship *(update allowed under radiation policy);* and (2) the ability of the sensor to perform the desired update *(update possible).* Each of these concepts itself could be generated by complex trees that are not shown in the figure.

The rule base includes simple rules for search and ID activity. The system similarly can evaluate the need to perform these activities and select those activities from

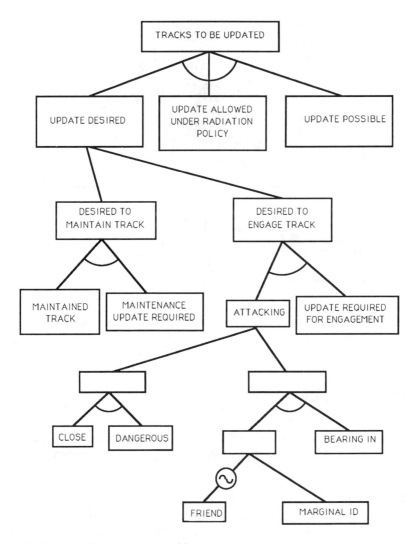

**Figure 10.12** Fuzzy tree for track update decision.

each category that are most desired. Of course, a real ESA may have many more modes than just track update, track ID, and simple search. Figure 10.13 shows a decision tree with hooks for several typical ESA modes. Thus, we see how the fuzzy decision tree approach allows this system to be readily extended to more and more complicated systems. This extensibility is a very important, desirable feature of the fuzzy decision tree approach.

Note that when adding any new system functionality the designer need only be concerned with the part being added. He or she need not revisit those parts of the

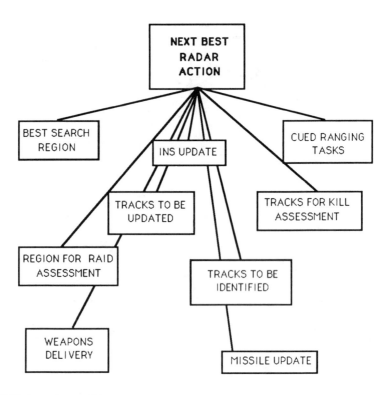

**Figure 10.13** A tree for a multimode sensor.

system already in place. This demonstrates the maintainability of the fuzzy decision tree approach. Having codified, via the fuzzy trees, the expert reasoning to take place, the next step is to establish how the system is to use these trees to emulate the expert's behavior.

The first step is to define how the root concepts are to be evaluated. We therefore need to establish the subjective definitions used to define the root concepts of *close, lethal, friend, uncertain ID, marginal ID, bearing in, loose, exceeds kill variance,* and *large flux.*

Consider the fuzzy set *close* with the interpretation being the set of all targets that are close (i.e., in a time-to-go sense) to ownship. The universe of discourse is the set of all tracks, and each track *i* has a membership to the fuzzy set *close* based on its current range $R$ (nmi) and range rate $\dot{R}$ (ft/s). An appropriate membership function would be

$$\mu_{\text{close}}(i) = \frac{1}{1 - \alpha |R_i - R_{\min}|/\max(-\dot{R}_i, \dot{R}_{\min})} \tag{10.29}$$

where $\alpha$, $R_{\min}$, and $\dot{R}_{\min}$ are chosen subjectively (our simulation used $\alpha = .025(\text{ft/s} \cdot \text{nmi})$, $R_{\min} = 10(\text{nmi})$, and $\dot{R}_{\min} = 100(\text{ft/s})$.

The set *lethal* is the set of tracks $i$ currently considered lethal. This membership function is defined in terms of the ID probability density over target type. Our simulation considered only Friend or Foe or Neutral typing. The membership function used was

$$\mu_{\text{lethal}}(i) = \Pr\{\text{track } i \text{ is foe type}\} \tag{10.30}$$

The set *uncertain ID* was defined in terms of the entropy of the ID probability density as

$$\mu_{\text{uncertain ID}}(i) = K \sum_j p_{ij} \log[p_{ij}] \tag{10.31}$$

where $p_{ij} = \Pr\{\text{track } i \text{ is of type } j\}$, and $K$ scales maximum entropy to 1.

In a similar manner, the other root concepts were defined as follows : *friend* in terms of ID density; *marginal ID* in terms of ID density; *bearing in* in terms of angle-rate and heading; *loose* in terms of Kalman filter error covariances; *exceeds kill variance* in terms of Kalman filter error covariances; and *large flux* in terms of integrated predicted average new target flux.

By applying the logical connectives and their properties to the rule base, the composite concepts *dangerous, attacking, update track, identify track, search,* and *best action* all can be defined. For example, rules r4, r5, and r6 allow us to infer

$$\mu_{\text{attacking}}(i) = \max\{\min(\mu_{\text{close}}(i), \mu_{\text{dangerous}}(i)), \tag{10.32}$$
$$\min[\mu_{\text{bearing in}}(i), \max(1 - \mu_{\text{friend}}(i), \mu_{\text{marginal ID}}(i))]\}$$

Finally, the fuzzy set *best-action* is constructed as follows. The universe of discourse here is not the set of all tracks but rather the set of all possible actions (i.e., the action set $A$ defined earlier). The membership of action $a$ in the set *best-action* is given by

$$\mu_{\text{best-action}}(a) = \begin{cases} \mu_{\text{update track}}(i) & \text{if } a = \text{update } i \\ \mu_{\text{identify track}}(i) & \text{if } a = \text{ID } i \\ \mu_{\text{search}} & \text{if } a = \text{search} \end{cases} \tag{10.33}$$

The rule base starts with the concepts *close, lethal, friend, uncertain ID, marginal ID, exceeds kill variance, bearing in, loose,* and *large flux* and, through the use of the logical connectives and their properties, generates the concepts of tracks to be updated *(update track)*, tracks to be identified *(identify track)*, and importance of search *(search)*. Finally, the concept of the best action to perform next *(best action)* is constructed by assigning a value to each action equal to the desire to perform the action on the task.

Thus, the rule base can be used to delineate a fuzzy subset (in a way, a fuzzy answer) of the universe of all possible actions *A*. The set *best-action* is in a sense a fuzzy answer to the question, Which action should the radar attempt next? We may consider the element *a* with the highest grade of membership as the crisp answer to this question, or we may choose to take an $\alpha$-cut (all elements with membership above the value $\alpha$) to assemble a queue of tasks to send to the radar.

The system just described was simulated and applied to the scenario shown in Figure 10.14. The scenario is plotted with respect to ownship that remains fixed at $(x, y) = (0, 0)$. The scenario has one friendly aircraft that is flying in formation with ownship and therefore remains fixed relative to it. The other three enemy aircraft start at the boundaries of the plot and have the relative paths as plotted.

The algorithm must initiate tracks by discovering targets through search. It must infer target type by allocating an identification process. And finally, it must strive to maintain tracks by update illuminations, paying particular attention to targets inferred to be important. Figure 10.14 also shows the allocator's update and ID requests during the simulation run. A plus has been placed along tracks each time they were updated and an $\times$ was placed each time they were IDed. Notice that the rule base recommends IDs on tracks that are just picked up as initial ID is *uncertain ID*. Note that the rule base detects the more potentially threatening geometry that occurs when target 3 turns toward ownship. Target 3 received more IDs at this point because its time-to-go was greatly reduced (hence, an increase in membership to *close* due to its new velocity heading). The rule base also notes the potentially less threatening geometry that occurs when target 2 turns away from ownship. The update rate drops off because target 2's membership to *bearing in* drops off (*bearing in* was a function of angle-rate and heading) and thus its overall *attacking* status drops.

These results show the power of the descriptive decision-making approach in the emulation of human decision-making behavior. Empowered by the inexact reasoning approach, this system, even with its very few rules, is capable of responding to various target behaviors as the scenario evolves.

Finally, we comment on the obvious extensions of this system to an *M* manager for a multisensor system. Just as a tree was developed for the ESA, trees could be generated for each of the other sensors (such as an IRST and a RWR). Each tree then could generate a queue to send to each sensor. This approach, however, is not sufficient as it achieves sensor coordination only minimally, one of our prime imperatives for a multisensor system. (Minimal coordination is achieved because, due to the feedback nature of sensor tasking, if a track is not supported by one sensor, the *M* manager, in an effort to maintain central-level track quality, will direct the other sensors to take up the slack.)

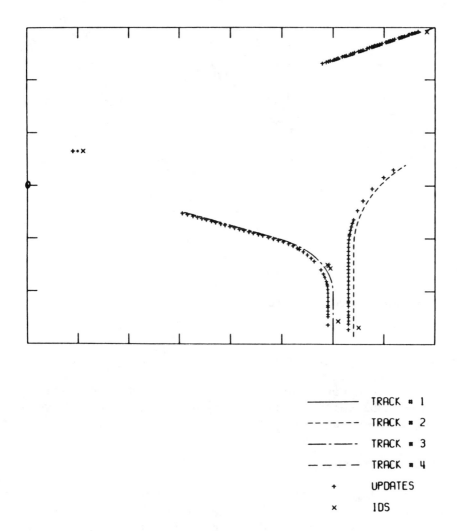

|  | TRACK = 1 |
| ------- | --------- |
| ------- | TRACK = 2 |
| --·--- | TRACK = 3 |
| ---- | TRACK = 4 |
| + | UPDATES |
| × | IDS |

**Figure 10.14** Scenario and results.

To achieve stronger coordination of sensor behavior, we recommend the following. These trees should be combined to form a tentative multisensor queue in accordance with the tree shown in Figure 10.15.

A rule base then can be constructed that operates on this multisensor queue to (1) arbitrate requests to multiple sensors for the same information; (2) redirect tasks among sensors to respond to the current inability of a particular sensor to respond to a task; (3) redirect tasks among sensors to respond to the emission control require-

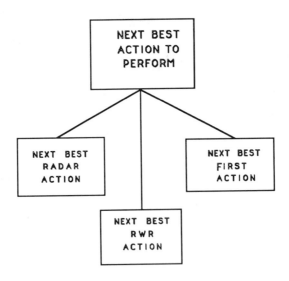

**Figure 10.15** Extending approach to multiple sensors.

ments; and (4) generate request for special services as required by rules of intersensor cueing. Once the multisensor queue has been processed in this way it can be resplit into individual sensor queues for distribution to the individual sensor $\mu$ managers. An example of this type of intersensor queuing for improved track quality and emission control is the subject of our next demonstration.

## 10.4.2  Demonstration 2

The purpose of this demonstration is to show the significance of the sensor management imperatives related to multisensor fusion: coordination of multiple sensor resources for improved tracking and coordination of multiple sensor resources for emission control. This section focuses on the results of sensor management rather than the details of the approach. The technique used to achieve these results was similar to that of Demonstration 1 and will not be repeated here. Therefore, this demonstration serves less as a *how to* and more as a motivation for the importance of our multisensor management imperatives. We consider two examples of multisensor management. The first case shows how sensor management can coordinate an IRST and a radar to improve track stability and reduce active illumination. The second case shows how sensor management can coordinate a radar and an IRST to improve tracking range. The results of this demonstration follow those of [8].

Consider the case of a radar attempting to track the closely spaced targets shown in Figure 10.16. The true target paths are depicted by the thin lines and the sensor level tracks formed on these targets are represented by the thicker lines. As is typical, when targets are closely spaced the radar has trouble keeping the data associated correctly and hence the tracks tend to wander between the two targets finally resulting in lost tracks.

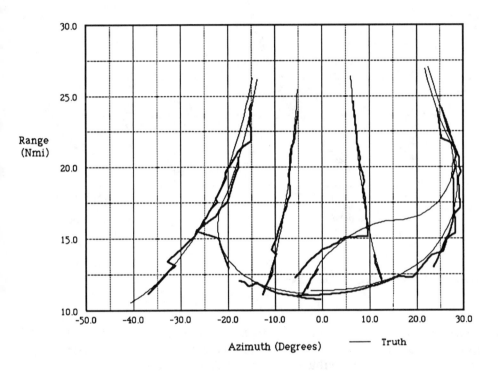

**Figure 10.16** Uncoordinated radar tracking of closely spaced targets.

We might think that if IRST data were available, fusing it with the radar data should lead to a central tracking file that more accurately represents reality. The hope would be that the superior angular resolution of the IRST would enable it to form IRST sensor level tracks that do not suffer from track switching (i.e., what is a closely spaced target scenario for a radar is easily resolved by an IRST). Figure 10.17 shows the results of sensor fusion without any coordination of sensor tasking.

By *uncoordinated* we mean that the sensor tracks from the IRST and the radar were fused, but no sensor management effort was made to coordinate the way in

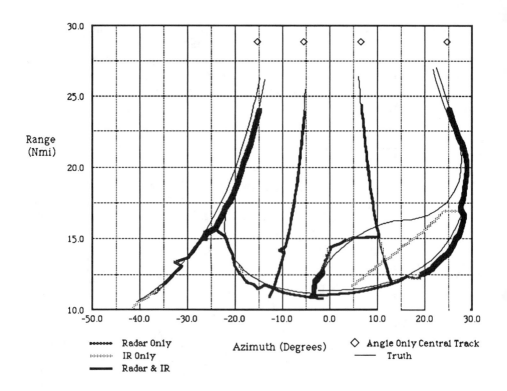

**Figure 10.17** Central tracking without coordination.

which the sensors collected their information. The symbology on the plot is as follows. The true target paths are still shown with the thinnest lines. The system groups closely spaced tracks into groups. The thickness of the tracks is proportional to the number of objects the system believes are in a group. As shown in the key, the tracks are plotted in either black, dark gray, or light gray depending on whether they were the result of fusing both radar and IRST tracks, only radar tracks, or only IRST tracks. We see that without coordination, although the fused central tracks are more stable than the unfused radar tracks, there still are undesired anomalies due to the poor radar information.

However, if we provide sensor management functionality that monitors range degradations of the central tracks and utilizes only the radar when range is required, then we achieve two important goals, as shown in results of Figure 10.18. First, overall tracking performance is improved because the radar sensor is being cued to make sure it can provide vital data on targets the radar otherwise would not have collected

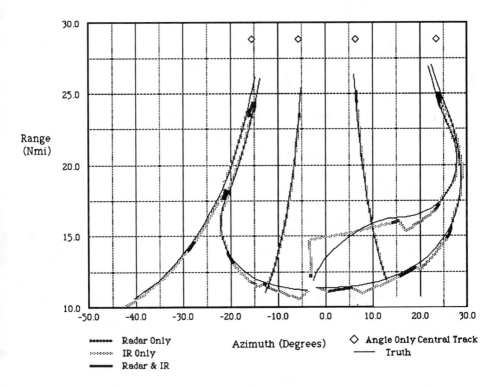

**Figure 10.18** Central tracking with coordination.

due to its relatively poor association capabilities. Second, note that for this case the radar was instructed to collect data for only very limited lengths of time as evidenced by the shortness of the black parts of the central tracks. Thus, not only did sensor management coordination of multiple sensors improve the overall tracking quality, it did so under a more restrictive emission control policy.

For our second example, consider a target whose range and radar cross section are such that the probability of detection by the radar is low. Figure 10.19 illustrates the radar tracking in such a case. Tracking is unstable because consistent observations cannot be made.

Now assume that angle-only information were available from another sensor, such as an IRST. Because an IRST relies on a target signature that is independent of the radar signature, the IRST might have a consistently higher probability of detection. Sensor management can utilize bearing data from the IRST as a cue to the radar. Directing the radar's attention along the cued angle allows for a higher cumu-

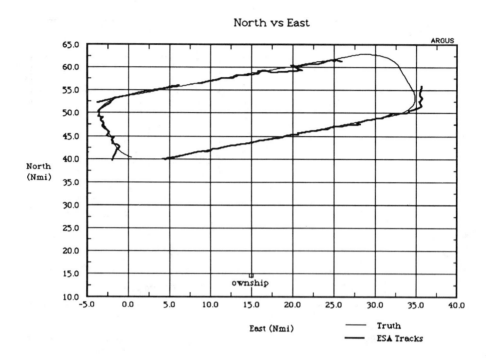

**Figure 10.19** Tracking a target with low SNR leads to unstable tracking.

lative probability of radar detection than would be possible with the unaided radar. Figure 10.20 demonstrates this effect. Note how few active detections are required to maintain a stable fused track.

### 10.4.3 Demonstration 3

Our next set of results directly pertains to our ability to adapt sensor behavior in direct response to tracking performance. This corresponds to representative implementation of the feedback loop shown in Figure 10.2 between the data association algorithm and the sensors. This section focuses on the results of sensor management rather than the details of the approach. The technique used to achieve these results was similar to that of Demonstration 1 and will not be repeated here. Therefore, this demonstration serves less as a *how to* and more as a motivation for the importance of one of our sensor management imperatives. The results of this demonstration follow those of [8].

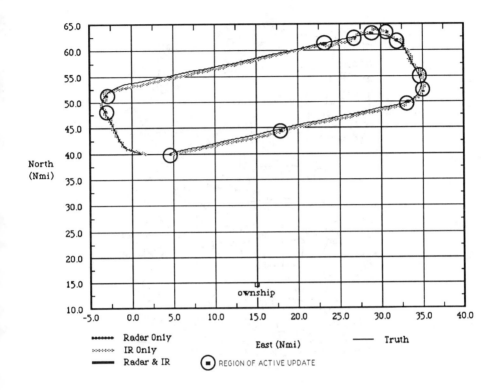

**Figure 10.20** Coordination with a longer range angle-only sensor extends the tracking range.

The problem we wish to address here is similar to that in the previous demonstration. We would like to show that, even in a single-sensor radar system, sensor management can help alleviate data association problems related to the tracking of closely spaced targets. Figure 10.21 shows the radar tracks for a closely spaced target scenario (note only the tracks are shown, not the paths of the actual targets). This scenario is slightly different from that of the previous demonstration in that the targets to the left are more closely spaced than the targets to the right. The figure shows the track switching and loss common in such cases. Also plotted on the figure are dots where radar observations had occurred. Figure 10.22 shows how the results change when sensor management is used to direct the sensor to collect more information when data association begins to fail.

Note that the greatest amount of sensor resource was allocated to the tracks on the left as evidenced by the higher density of observations taken on the targets generating these tracks. Note the more modest increase in resources allocated toward

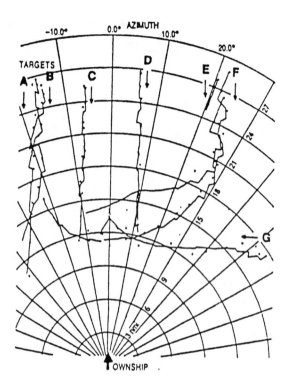

**Figure 10.21** Radar tracking without management.

the tracks on the right. Also note the additional sensor activity in regions where targets crossed. The additional sensor activity improves the track quality, as evidenced by less track switching and drop.

The results of this and the previous demonstration show how the same problem of tracking closely spaced targets via radar can be addressed by sensor management in both single- and multiple sensor systems. As the results indicate, more improvement can be achieved in multiple sensor systems.

### 10.4.4  Demonstration 4

This demonstration illustrates the utility theory counterpart of Demonstration 1. The reader will note that the described utility system deals only with a limited subset of the decision making with which the fuzzy system dealt. This reflects the difficulty encountered in trying to assemble and support the probability distributions required by the utility theoretic approach. Therefore, when using the utility approach, we were able to design a system which dealt only with decisions about the most basic

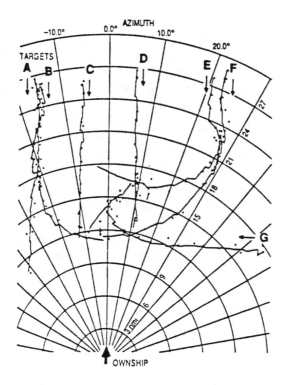

**Figure 10.22** Radar tracking with management.

consequences of sensor tasking. The results of this demonstration follow those of [6, 5].

As with Demonstration 1, we present a more detailed description of the approach than the two previous examples. This discussion will help to concretize the utility theoretic approach defined in Section 10.3. The description of the exact utility theoretic solution is not quite as complete as that provided for the fuzzy decision tree solution for two reasons. First, we do not fully recommend the utility theory approach because complete probability measures are very difficult to construct. Second, although the required measures were easily constructed for this simple case, their detailed presentation is very tedious.

In setting up the utility theoretic solution, we follow the steps for applying utility theory outlined in Section 10.3. The action set $A$ is

$$A = \left\{ \begin{array}{c} \text{illuminate any of } N \text{ tracks for update,} \\ \text{illuminate any of } N \text{ tracks for ID,} \\ \text{initiate a search scan of the next bar} \end{array} \right\} \tag{10.34}$$

The next step is to select a set of attributes $\tilde{x}$ that are to be considered the indicators of the system's performance. Note, we will need to establish probability distributions, $p(\tilde{x} \mid a)$   $\forall a \in A$, for each of the attribute random variables conditioned on action selection. Therefore we are free to select only attributes for which legitimate distribution can be constructed and maintained. The following set of attributes was chosen:

$Q$   The set of all Kalman filter error variances of all currently held tracks. This set represents the general quality of the currently held tracks and indicates the possible improvements in quality achievable for an attempted update of any track.

$\mathcal{P}$   This is the set of probability distributions over the possible target types. It represents the current uncertainty of the target type of each track as well as its most probable identity. It indicates the need and possible gains from attempting an identification illumination.

$\mathcal{N}$   This is the number of targets that possibly could be detected on search. The probability distribution over $\mathcal{N}$ indicates the expected flux of as yet undetected targets.

$\mathcal{T}$   This is the amount of time that must be committed to perform a selected action.

As in Demonstration 1, we focus more of our attention on the part of the algorithm that has to do with track update. This will allow us to provide details of the algorithm at some depth without becoming overly tedious.

Each of these attributes itself may be a complicated expression. For example, $Q$ represents the overall quality of all of the currently held tracks. $Q$ is really just a vector of vectors $\vec{Q}_n$.

$$Q = (\vec{Q}_1 \ \vec{Q}_2 \cdots \vec{Q}_N) \tag{10.35}$$

where $N$ is the number of currently held tracks, and where $\vec{Q}_n$ is a quality vector for the $n$th track. Each vector $\vec{Q}_n$ is composed of four components $Q_{x_n}$, which represent the kinematic quality of $x$, where $x$ takes on range, range-rate, angle, or angle-rate. (Note, a simplified two-dimensional geometry is assumed throughout.)

$$\vec{Q}_n = \begin{pmatrix} Q_{r_n} \\ Q_{\dot{r}_n} \\ Q_{\gamma_n} \\ Q_{\dot{\gamma}_n} \end{pmatrix} \tag{10.36}$$

where these kinematic quality figures are based on the error covariances of the Kalman estimator.

Next, consider the range of the attribute $Q$. If the algorithm chooses not to update any of the currently held tracks, then the Kalman filter for each track necessarily will have to be extrapolated without data. Therefore, each $\vec{Q}$ will reflect the degradation calculated by the Kalman predictor. If, on the other hand, the algorithm chooses to update the $n$th track, then depending on whether a detection occurs, the $n$th track will be updated with data; and the remaining tracks will be extrapolated without data. Thus, the quality factor $\vec{Q}_n$ for the $n$th track may (again depending on detection) reflect the improvement in quality calculated by the Kalman filter; and the values of $\vec{Q}$ corresponding to the other tracks will degrade as if no attempt at update had been made.

Therefore, at any time point, the components $Q_{x_n}$ of $\vec{Q}_n$ can take on only one of two values, denoted $Q_{ex_n}$ or $Q_{ux_n}$, which represents the kinematic quality of an extrapolated track (no new data taken, hence Kalman predictor error covariance) or an updated track (a new data sample taken, hence Kalman filter error covariance), respectively.

The probability distribution over $Q$ for any given action is as follows. The distribution when the attempted action is update of track $n$ is

$$Q = (\vec{Q}_1 \, \vec{Q}_2 \cdots \vec{Q}_N) \qquad (10.37)$$

where

$$\vec{Q}_n = \begin{cases} \vec{Q}_{u_n}, & \text{with Prob. } P_{du_n} \\ \vec{Q}_{e_n}, & \text{with Prob. } (1 - P_{du_n}) \end{cases} \qquad (10.38)$$

where $P_{du_n}$ is probability of detection of the $n$th track during update, and

$$\vec{Q}_j = \vec{Q}_{e_j} \text{ with Prob. } 1 \qquad \forall_j \neq n \qquad (10.39)$$

The distribution over $Q$ for the other actions can be derived correspondingly. As for the other attributes $\mathcal{N}$, $\mathcal{P}$, and $\mathcal{T}$, we omit all details in the interest of being terse.

Having selected the attributes and derived their probability distributions conditioned on the actions, the final step is to establish a utility function to encode the preference structure. As we discussed in Section 10.3, this is a matter of deciding on regions and degrees of risk aversion over the attributes and roughing in a utility function with regions of the appropriate degrees of curvature. A presentation of this process would be far too lengthy for inclusion here. Suffice it to say that a utility function of the following form was constructed.

$$U(Q, \mathcal{N}, \mathcal{P}, \mathcal{T}) = f_T(\mathcal{T})\{K_U U_{\text{update}}(Q)$$

$$+ K_S U_{\text{search}}(\mathcal{N}, Q) + K_I U_{ID}(\mathcal{P})\} \qquad (10.40)$$

or, more explicitly,

$$U(Q, N, P, T) = f_T(T)K_U\left[\sum_{j=1}^{N} I_j(\vec{P})U_{utrack}(\vec{Q})\right]$$

$$+ f_T(T)K_S f(Q)U_s(N) + f_T(T)K_I\left[\sum_{j=1}^{N} I_{G_j}U_{itrack}(\vec{P})\right] \tag{10.41}$$

where the interdependence of the attributes is more apparent.

The complexity of (10.41) and our inability to be terse in its discussion, brings up an interesting point: the lack of maintainability of the utility theoretic approach. It should be apparent that documenting the rationale behind a complex multiattribute utility function and subsequently adjusting it to handle design changes in other parts of the system represents a formidable maintainability problem. Furthermore, if the need should arise to increase the functionality of a utility theoretic sensor manager, the selection of more attributes and the derivation of their probability densities could severely limit the systems extensibility. Thus, we would caution the use of this approach for the design of sensor managers of high complexity.

The foregoing discussion allows the precise posing of the allocation problem as follows: *Construct a decision rule that, subject to the current situation, selects an action from the action set A that is optimal with respect to the anticipated gain in attributes* $(Q, P, N, T)$. The utility theoretic decision rule is simply this: *Choose, from set A, the action that, subject to the current situation, maximizes* $E[U(Q, P, N, T)]$, *the expected utility.* The following simulation results were produced to verify the validity of this approach. The simulation was run on the scenario depicted in Figure 10.23.

The resulting update, ID, and search behavior are as shown in Figure 10.24. The graphics are to be interpreted according to the following key. Specific examples of the use of the key follow immediately.

- S: Search in progress. A number occurring after S indicates detected target.
- I: Identification in progress. After the third I, $y : z$ indicates target $y$ was being IDed and that the algorithm deduced its relative importance (on a scale of 0 to 10) as $z$.
- M: A missed identification attempt is indicated by M in place of the third I of the ID sequence.
- U: Update illumination in progress. The indication $y : z$ has the same interpretation as for ID.
- X: A missed update illumination is indicated by X.

- The column of numbers at the left indicates elapsed time in seconds since start of scenario.

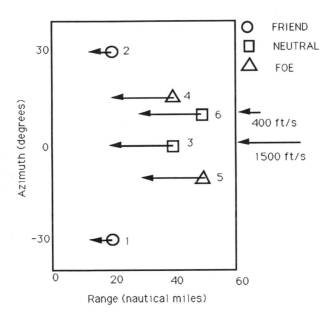

**Figure 10.23** Evaluation scenario.

- The next field depicts search activity. Search is carried out one bar at a time. A bar is a search volume one beamwidth in elevation and $-30°$ to $+30°$ in azimuth. The entire search volume is considered to be covered by four search bars (bar indication is in the heading). A bar takes 1 s to complete. Once a scan is started it runs to completion. For example, referring to the figure we see that at $T = 17.8$ a search bar was initiated on the second bar. The search continued uneventfully until somewhere in the last 12° where target 2 was detected.
- The next field depicts both update and identification activity. An update is considered to take 0.2 s and once initiated cannot be terminated. For example, at $T = 18.6$ an update of target 1 was attempted and achieved. Also indicated is that the relative importance of this target is currently 0.5. An identification is considered to take 0.6 s and once started cannot be terminated. For example, at $T = 22.8$ an ID cycle was attempted and achieved on target 2. Also denoted is that this target currently has a relative importance with respect to other currently held tracks of 0.2.
- The last field indicates the current kinematic quality of all currently held tracks. At the heading is a numeric scale with the following interpretation. A value of 1 indicates that a composite of the error variances is as desired (i.e., the ratio of the error standard deviation to a desired standard deviation equals 1). A value

```
        BAR NUMBER          TRACK NUMBER        COMPOSITE TK ERROR, SIGMAS

        1   2   3   4       1  2  3  4  5  6  7   0                   1

■■■■■■■■■■■■■■■■■■:■■■■■■■■■■■■■■■■■■■■■■■■■■■■■:■■■■:■■■■:■■■■+■■■■:■■■■:■■

17.8        S           :                    ■   :   :   :    +3 1 :    :
18.0        S           :                    ■   :   :   :    + 3 1:    :
18.2        S           :                    ■   :   :   :    + 321:    :
18.4        S2          :                    ■   :   :   :   2 +   3 1
18.6                    :  U1:5               ■   :   :   :   2+   3 :
18.8                    :         U3:4        ■   :   :   : 321       :
19.0            S       :                     ■   :   :   :  321      :
19.2            S       :                     ■   :   :   :  32 1     :
19.4            S3      :                     ■   :   :   :3    +2 1 :
19.6            S       :                     ■   :   :   : 3   +2  1:
19.8            S       :                     ■   :   :   : 3  + 2  1
20.0                    :  U1:5               ■   :   :   :  31+   2 :
20.2                S   :                     ■   :   :   :  3 1   2 :
20.4                S   :                     ■   :   :   :  3+1   2:
20.6                S   :                     ■   :   :   :  3+1   2
20.8                S   :                     ■   :   :   :   3  1  2
21.0                S   :                     ■   :   :   :   3  1 :2
21.2                    :  U1:5               ■   :   :   :  1 +3    :  2  .:
21.4                    :      U2:2           ■   :   :   :  123       :    :
21.6        S1          :                     ■   :   :   :1    2 3   :    :
21.8        S           :                     ■   :   :   : 1  +23   :    :
22.0        S           :                     ■   :   :   : 1 + 23  :    :
22.2        S           :                     ■   :   :   : 1 + 2 3:    :
22.4        S           :                     ■   :   :   :  1+   23:    :
22.6                    :         U3:4        ■   :   :   :  31   2:    :
22.8                    :  I                  ■   :   :   :  3+1   2:    :
23.0                    :  I                  ■   :   :   :   3  1  2    :
23.2                    :  I2:2               ■   :   :   :  23   1 :    :
23.4                    :  U1:5               ■   :   :   :  1 23     :    :
23.6            S       :                     ■   :   :   :  123      :    :
23.8            S       :                     ■   :   :   :   123     :    :
24.0            S       :                     ■   :   :   :   +2 3   :    :
24.2            S       :                     ■   :   :   :   + 23  :    :
24.4            S2      :                     ■   :   :   :  2 + 1 3:    .
24.6                    :         U3:4        ■   :   :   :  23+  1 :    .
24.8                    :  U1:5               ■   :   :   :  3+        :    .
25.0            S       :                     ■   :   :   :  23        :    .
25.2            S       :                     ■   :   :   :  23        :    .
25.4            S3      :                     ■   :   :   :   3        :    .
25.6            S       :                     ■   :   :   : 3   21    :    .
25.8            S       :                     ■   :   :   : 3   +21   :    .
26.0                    :  U1:5               ■   :   :   :  3 + 21  :    :
26.2                S   :                     ■   :   :   :  3 + 2   :    :
26.4                S   :                     ■   :   :   :   3+  2 :    :
26.6                S   :                     ■   :   :   :   31   2:    :
26.8                S   :                     ■   :   :   :   31   2:    :
27.0                S   :                     ■   :   :   :   31   2    :
27.2                    :      U2:2           ■   :   :   :   +31  :2
                                                                 23 1 :    :
```

**Figure 10.24** Simulation results of the utility theory approach.

greater than 1 indicates tracking performance is less than desired. For example, notice that immediately after target 2 was discovered during search at $T = 18.4$, its track quality is displayed $< 1$. This quality immediately starts to degrade until an *update* was completed at $T = 21.4$. At this point, target 2's quality improves from roughly 1.3 to 1.0. Note that a successful identification implies certain attainment of update, and that a missed identification leads to a probabilistic chance of update. Finally, be aware that if two tracks have the same quality one target number may obscure the other.

*Comparison with Demonstration 1*

First, note that this utility system is capable of far less adaptation to threat behavior than the system of Demonstration 1. Furthermore, adding additional behavior to the fuzzy system is a simple matter of defining more trees and, perhaps, some root membership functions. Adding behavior to the utility theoretic system, on the other hand, may lead to a substantial amount of work.

### 10.4.5 Demonstration 5

This demonstration is not really a demonstration at all. Rather, it is an example of some of the thinking that should go into a top-level design of a $\mu$ manager for an ESA system. Most of the sensor management literature to date deals with $\mu$-manager issues (of particular interest in this respect are [11,16,30]). We draw from these works in our development of a top level ESA $\mu$-manager design.

The basic design problem explored here is as follows. Assume an ESA with a highly agile suite of sensor modes (i.e., a variety of waveforms and signal processing techniques that can be selected rapidly). Given such a radar, we have an opportunity to vary radar behavior adaptively according to the various facets of the target environment. We would hope that by adaptively optimizing the amount and nature of sensing resources for each facet of the target environment, the overall target detection and tracking capability of the radar would be improved. The design procedure, then, is to follow these steps:

1. Understand the ways in which the target environment can vary. This background study requires a full understanding of the sensor system's functional role and the environment in which it will be operated.
2. Identify a subset of these target environment variations that have an impact on critical sensor resources. Identify mode design degrees of freedom that can be tuned to account for the identified target environment variations.
3. Design a finite set (although perhaps continuously parametrized) of sensor modes that span the identified target environment variation.

4. Develop a decision methodology for dynamically selecting among these modes.
5. Choose a scheduling procedure for making a time line of prioritized sensor commands.

In the following paragraphs, we follow this design recipe. We cover each step only at a very cursory level. Our design will assume a generic air-to-air fighter mission. A complete design of course would require detailed mission and hardware specifications. Also, keep in mind that in this example we are focusing only on the control of agile multimodes. A complete design also would address some of the other sensor management imperatives we have been discussing.

*Step 1.* The target environment may be nonhomogeneous in a variety of ways, not all of which are listed here:

- Some subvolumes of the search space may tactically require longer detection range than other subvolumes.
- Some regions of the search space may have higher false alarm rates than other regions.
- Targets vary in range.
- Targets vary in radar cross section.
- Target spacing varies.
- Target revisit times vary (assuming some higher-order sensor management function chooses to update targets at varying rates).
- Weapon support tracking requirements may vary.

*Step 2.* In deciding to provide adaptation for a subset of the variations listed in Step 1, we must identify mode design degrees of freedom that might lead to useful conservation of resource. On a fighter, for example, prime power and cooling often are a primary design parameter. Therefore, we might attempt to establish modes of operation that employ power management to maintain a low average-power consumption while allowing sufficient energy for targets at longer range or with lower radar cross section. Power management can be made part of the agility of both search and target update modes. For example, tracks that have had consistently high SNR returns could be updated in the future with less power.

For a multiple-target track fire-control radar, time on target is another critical resource. By conserving the radar time line, various improvements in system performance can be achieved. The saved time line might be devoted to extend search range detection, to track more targets, or to provide more coherent integration for targets with low SNR. The sensor time line can be conserved during search in several ways. Faster scan rates (hence, less time on target) can be employed outside the primary long-range search sector. Sequential detection [5, 9, 11] can be employed to dynamically alter the amount of time line resources required to detect targets. The time line can be conserved during track update by providing alternate integration lengths depending on the tracks SNR history.

If radar processing resources can be conserved, we might be able to apply burdensome waveform-processing schemes to a limited number of difficult tracks. For example, maintenance-only tracks (i.e., those having low priority as determined by another part of the sensor manager or user) might be updated with a simple frequency modulated ranging waveform, whereas high-priority fire-control tracks might be updated with a more processing-intensive range-gated waveform. As another example, high-priority groups of interacting tracks may be illuminated with a more costly raid assessment mode in an attempt to break out the target whereas an unimportant group may be updated with a less computationally burdensome process. Therefore, assume that as a first cut, we have identified sequential detection, search scan rate, coherent integration time, and group illumination processing as mode design degrees of freedom.

*Step 3.* Having completed Steps 1 and 2, the next step is to develop a finite set of sensor modes that exploit the identified design degrees of freedom and span the environmental variations and the sensor's functional roles. The details of these modes of course are very sensor dependent. Any detailed discussion of such mode design therefore is beyond the scope of this chapter. For our purposes, we simply identify a candidate set of modes by their functions.

- Sequential Detection Search. A set of waveforms designed to sequentially detect targets. This is the search mode for the primary search volume.
- Fast Scan Search. A faster scan, short coherent integration, and posssibly power-managed waveform used to search out shorter range volumes.
- Fire Control Tracking Update. An update waveform (possibly power-managed) providing accurate angle and range information suitable for fire-control solutions.
- Maintenance Track Update. A shorter time line, lower computational burden update (consequently having less measurement performance) used for maintaining lower-priority tracks.
- Raid Assessment. A high range and velocity resolution waveform used to help break out targets that are closely spaced.
- Group Update. A simpler group illumination and processing scheme that does not attempt to break out the targets.

*Step 4.* The next step is to establish the decision-making criteria by which we will rate the relative merits of transitioning among these agile modes. The exact criteria will depend on the specifics of the sensor mode design as well as the mission. In addition to simply selecting among these waveforms, sensor management may need to dynamically tailor the implementation of some of these modes. Examples of some of the decision-making criteria that might be considered follow:

- Sequential Detection Search. Sensor management may need to get involved in the sequence of these waveforms. For example, in a full sequential probability ratio test implementation, sensor management may monitor a stopping criterion to control waveform deployment.

- Fast Scan Search. Choice between regions for sequential detection search and fast scan search would probably be specified by the operator. The operator probably would establish the primary search volume with the implicit assumption that as time permits a fast scan would be utilized outside this primary search volume. Although the system may employ only one fixed fast scan rate, criteria could be constructed for altering scan rate dynamically. Criteria could include considerations of range to ground (in down look), angle off aircraft heading, coordination with other aircraft, and so forth.

- Fire Control Tracking Update. Sensor management should monitor the quality on all tracks designated for engagement. The sensor manager also could attempt to anticipate which tracks might be designated for attack and attempt to firm up these tracks in anticipation of weapon assignment. General criteria for the fire control update might include designation by operator, weapon assignment, high closure rate, intercept heading, short range, high relative potential energy, *et cetera.* Dynamic adaptation of the update waveform might include consideration of SNR history, kinematic relation to other tracks, eclipsing, *et cetera.*

- Maintenance Track Update. Tracks that are not designated by the operator and appear to be benign relative to some criterion may be updated by a poorer quality update waveform. General criteria for maintenance tracks might include closure rate, heading, range, or relative potential energy. Dynamic adaptation of the maintenance update waveform might include ownship observability (power management).

- Raid Assessment. Criteria for employment of the raid assessment mode may include designation by operator, range closure of a current group track, track initiation on ambiguous search detections, or update of a designated track close to other held tracks.

- Group Update. Group updates would be applied to current group tracks that meet none of the raid assessment criteria.

*Step 5.* Decisions concerning the scheduling procedure should include the general comments made in Section 10.3 as well as the following specific sensor concerns.

- Mode Agility. How much time line is wasted by switching between modes? Mose radars, for example, employ pipe line data processing. Switching modes inherently may invalidate several pipeline cycles of data and, hence, front-end resources. It may be more costly to switch among some modes than others.

- Scheduling System. The choice of scheduling system may depend on mission requirements to handle pop-up events and other changes in target environment.

- Sensor Manager Cycle Time. How often should the sensor manager decision making be undertaken? Should parts of the sensor manager decision making be run at different rates? Answers to these questions should consider the computational burden of the decision making itself as well as mission response-time requirements to unexpected changes in the environment.

- System Timing and Data Management. Higher degrees of sensor mode agility comes with added complexities in computer and data management. Compromises may have to be made to fit a sensor-managed version into available sensor computer resources. The reader is directed to [31] for a discussion of system timing and data management issues.

We close by iterating that the purpose of this example was to suggest the type of planning that should go into the design of sensor management for an agile-mode sensor. Any specific design of course would be highly mission and sensor specific.

## 10.5  CONCLUSION

At this point, we take some time to review what we have done and offer some self-critical comments. We hope to point out some of the chapter's high points and some of its limitations.

The battle effectiveness of the next generation fighter aircraft relies on the efficient deployment of its sensor suite. Sensors such as the modern RWR and ESA radar are extremely flexible in the tasks they can perform. The complexity of modern sensors and the complexity of today's dense-target environments conspire to make detailed manual sensor control almost infeasible.

We claim that the various aspects of tactical environment and sensor complexity taken together form an imperative for the use of automated sensor-management techniques. We formally established such a sensor management imperative, which, in effect, is a catalog of the functions a sensor management algorithm should provide. Thus, our motive for the presentation of the imperative is twofold. First, we argue that sensor management is an essential ingredient in modern sensor systems. Second, we provide a catalog of sensor management responsibilities and functions, in effect a specification for the development of a sensor manager. With regard to the first motive, we feel that we have met our objective. The imperative indicates a range of sensor behaviors that would be difficult or impossible to achieve via manual human operation. With respect to our second objective, our success is more limited. It is impossible, of course, to claim that any such catalog of sensor management requirements could be complete for all types of sensor suites or for all applications. Our catalog, however, at least is a strawman specification for a typical fighter sensor suite for a generic fighter mission. For any *particular* fighter application, our catalog would need to be reviewed in light of the exact nature of the sensors to be used and, perhaps more important, the specific tactical role the fighter is to play.

We followed our definition of the sensor management imperative with a discussion of architectures and algorithms for its implementation. Our goal was to give a system designer insight into the choices that he or she would face, as well as some insights from our own experience designing such systems. In particular, we addressed basic architecture, scheduling issues, and decision-making techniques.

In the architectural area, we argued in favor of a hierarchical partitioning of sensor management functionality. We presented various arguments for the advantage of such an approach. We did not formally address the computer and operating system impacts of such a partitioning, however. Exactly how this architecture (i.e., partitioning of sensor management functionality) maps to processors and operating system support is not a trivial problem that must be considered early in the design phase.

In the area of scheduling, we provided some alternatives and recommendations. We, however, glossed over a very important issue. Dynamic sensor management requires two forms of tasking: front-end tasking and data processing and support tasking. By *front-end tasking* we refer to the scheduling of tasks that the sensor aperture will perform to collect data. We wrote the tasking section as though front-end tasking was the whole story; however, data collection by the front end necessitates data processing and other support tasks (such as timing and control). Many other issues come into play when considering the best scheduling scheme for these other tasks; for example, minimization of software context switching. If we assume that computer resources have been sized to generally support the raw data collecting capabilities of the sensors then for scheduling of data processing tasks, brick packing approaches may be preferable to the best first approach, which we had recommended for front-end scheduling.

In the area of decision-making approaches, we reviewed a broad range of algorithmic approaches. We offered a detailed discussion of two philosophically distinct approaches: one normative and one descriptive. We discussed the advantages of using modern descriptive decision-making techniques over the more classical normative approaches. We recommend descriptive approaches based on fuzzy set theory. The specific fuzzy set approach we described admittedly is overly simplistic. Significantly more sophistication can be achieved by using standard results available in the fuzzy set literature. The presented approach, however, should be sufficient to encourage designers to explore the use of fuzzy set based approaches. Furthermore, the presented approach, although lacking sophistication, is computationally very efficient and would require no special-purpose hardware. Therefore, it may be a viable candidate for any near-term implementation of albeit limited sensor management systems.

Finally, we demonstrated our approaches and gave concrete examples of the benefits sensor management can provide. Through these examples we support the conclusion that descriptive approaches simply are better suited for sensor management than the more classical normative approaches. We demonstrated that sensor management, in effect, implements a feedback path that monitors the subjective quality of tracking system performance (in light of the current tactical situation) and modifies the measurement process to achieve tactical goals.

Our work represents a first step in the development of future systems that will utilize the complementary nature of MTT and AI techniques. Additionally, we have shown (in an admittedly limited way) how data from an MTT system can be used to perform situation assessment for allocation. This methodology clearly could be extended to provide situation assessment for other functions, such as fire control. Furthermore, we have shown how situation assessment can be used to direct the sensor observation process to achieve overall system goals.

## REFERENCES

[1] Y. Bar-Shalom and T.E. Fortman, *Tracking and Data Association,* Academic Press, San Diego, CA, 1988.

[2] D. Barton, *Modern Radar System Analysis,* Artech House, Norwood, MA, 1988.

[3] D.R. Billetter, *Multifunction Array Radar,* Artech House, Norwood, MA, 1989.

[4] S.S. Blackman, *Multiple-Target Tracking with Radar Applications,* Artech House, Dedham, MA, 1986.

[5] S.S. Blackman; the author wishes to acknowledge the research contributions of Sam Blackman.

[6] T. Broida; the author wishes to acknowledge the research contributions of Ted Broida.

[7] B.G. Buchanan *et al.,* "Constructing an Expert System," F. Hayes-Roth, D. Waterman, and D. Lenat (eds.), *Building Expert Systems,* Addison-Wesley, Reading, MA, 1983.

[8] R. Darrah; the author wishes to acknowledge the research contributions of Becky Darrah.

[9] J. DiFranco and W. Rubin, *Radar Detection,* Artech House, Dedham, MA, 1980.

[10] T.S. Ferguson, *Mathematical Statistics, a Decision Theoretic Approach,* Academic Press, New York, 1967.

[11] W. Fleskes and G. Van Keuk, "Adaptive Control and Tracking with the ELRA Phased Array Radar Experimental System," *IEEE Radar-80 Conf. Rec.,* June 1980.

[12] S. French, *Sequencing and Scheduling: An Introduction to the Mathematics of the Job-Shop,* John Wiley & Sons, New York, 1982.

[13] A. Gelb *et al., Applied Optimal Estimation,* M.I.T. Press, Cambridge, MA, 1974.

[14] J. Goguen, Jr., "Concept Representation in Natural and Artificial Languages: Axioms, Extensions and Applications for Fuzzy Sets," *Fuzzy Reasoning and Its Applications,* Academic Press, London, 1981.

[15] T.H. Greer, "Artificial Intelligence: A New Dimension in EW," *Defence Electronics,* October 1985.

[16] E. Hanle, "Control of a Phased Array Radar for Position Finding of Targets," *IEEE Radar-75 Conf. Rec.,* 1975.

[17] S.A. Hovanessian, *Radar Detection and Tracking Systems,* Artech House, Dedham, MA, 1973.

[18] R. Kenney and H. Raiffa, *Decisions with Multiple Objectives: Preferences and Value Tradeoffs,* John Wiley & Sons, New York, 1976.

[19] R.J. McKenzie and D.G. Mullens, "Expert System Control for Airborne Radar Surveillance," *American Institute of Aeronautics and Astronautics,* 87-2854, 1987.

[20] F. Nathanson, *Radar Design Principles,* McGraw-Hill, New York, 1969.

[21] J. Pearl, "How to Do with Probabilities What People Say You Can't," Proc. IEEE Conf. on Artificial Intelligence Applications, 1985.

[22] R.F. Popoli and S.S. Blackman, "Expert System Allocation of the Electronically Scanned Antenna Radar," Proc. American Control Conf., Minneapolis, June 10–12, 1987.

[23] E. Rich, *Artificial Intelligence,* McGraw-Hill, New York, 1983.

[24] S.N. Salinger and D. Wangsness, "Target-Handling Capacity of a Phased-Array Tracking Radar," *IEEE Trans. on Aerospace and Electronic Systems,* Vol. AES-8, No. 1, January 1972.

[25]  B.H. Scheff and D.G. Hammel, "Real-Time Computer Control of Phased Array Radars," IEEE Eastcon 1967, *IEEE Trans. on Aerospace and Electronic Systems,* Vol. AES-3, No. 6, November 1967.

[26]  E. Shortliffe and B. Buchanan, "A Model of Inexact Reasoning in Medicine," *Mathematical Biosciences,* Vol. 23, 1975, pp. 351–379.

[27]  M. Skolnik, *Introduction to Radar Systems,* McGraw-Hill, New York, 1980.

[28]  K. Fu and J. Yao, "Speril: An Expert System for Safety Evaluation of Structures," Proc. IEEE Conf. on Computation, 1984.

[29]  M. Togai and H. Watanabe, "Expert System on a Chip: An Engine for Real-Time Approximate Reasoning," *IEEE Expert,* Fall 1986.

[30]  L. Weinberg, "Scheduling Multifunction Radar Systems," *IEEE Eastcon 77 Record,* 1977.

[31]  W. Weinstock, "Computer Control of a Multifunction Radar," *RCA Engineer,* Vol. 18, No. 1, June–July 1972. 1967.

[32]  P. Winston, *Artificial Intelligence,* Addison-Wesley, Philippines, 1977.

[33]  L.A. Zadeh, "Making Computers Think Like People," *IEEE Spectrum,* August 1984.

# Chapter 11
# ATTRIBUTE FUSION AND SITUATION ASSESSMENT WITH A MANY-VALUED LOGIC APPROACH

**Ronald M. Yannone**

**GE Aerospace**

**Piero P. Bonissone**

**GE Corporate Research and Development**

## 11.1 INTRODUCTION

The aggregation of uncertain information (facts) is a recurrent need in the reasoning process of an expert system. Facts must be aggregated to determine the degree to which the premise of a given rule has been satisfied; to verify the extent to which external constraints have been met; to propagate the amount of uncertainty through triggering a given rule; to summarize the findings provided by various rules, knowledge sources, or experts; to detect possible inconsistencies among the various sources; and to rank different alternatives or different goals.

In a survey of reasoning with uncertainty [6, 7, 9], the presence of uncertainty in reasoning systems is noted to be due to a variety of sources: the *reliability* of the information, the inherent *imprecision* of the representation language in which the information is conveyed, the *incompleteness* of the information, and the *aggregation* or summarization of information from multiple sources.

The existing approaches surveyed in that study are divided into two classes: numerical and symbolic representations. The numerical approaches generally tend to impose some restrictions on the type and structure of the information (e.g., mutual exclusiveness of hypotheses, conditional independence of evidence). These approaches represent uncertainty as a precise quantity (scalar or interval) on a given scale. They require the user or expert to provide a *precise* yet *consistent* numerical assessment of the uncertainty of the atomic data and their relations. The output produced by these systems is the result of laborious computations, guided by well-defined calculi, and *appears* to be equally precise. However, given the difficulty in consistently eliciting such numerical values from the user, it is clear that these models of uncertainty require an unrealistic level of precision that does not actually represent a realistic assessment of the uncertainty.

Models based on symbolic representations, on the other hand, are designed mostly to handle the aspect of uncertainty derived from the *incompleteness* of the information. However, they generally are inadequate to handle the case of *imprecise* information, because they lack any measure to quantify confidence levels.

The objective of Sections 11.1 through 11.5 is to examine the various calculi of uncertainty and to define a rationale for their selection. The number of calculi to be considered will be a function of the uncertainty granularity (i.e., the finest level of distinction among different quantifications of uncertainty that adequately represents the user's discriminating perception). To accomplish this objective, we establish the theoretical framework for defining the syntax of a small subset of calculi of uncertainty operating on a given term set of linguistic statements of likelihood.

In Section 11.2, the negation, conjunction, and disjunction operators that form the various calculi of uncertainty are described in terms of their most generic representation: families of functions (triangular norms and conorms) satisfying the basic axioms expected of set operations such as intersection and union.

In Section 11.3, linguistic variables defined on the [0, 1] interval are interpreted as verbal probabilities and their semantics are represented by fuzzy numbers. The term set of linguistic variables defines the granularity of the confidence assessment values that can be consistently expressed by users or experts. A nine-element term set is given as an example.

Section 11.4 describes two experiments, consisting of evaluating 9 and 11 different *T*-norms with the elements of three different term sets containing 5, 9, and 13 elements, respectively. A review of the techniques required to implement the experiment also is provided. The review covers the implementation of the extension principle (a formalism that enables crisply defined functions to be evaluated with fuzzy-valued arguments) and describes linguistic approximation (a process required to map the result of the aggregation of two elements of the term set back into the term set).

Section 11.5 illustrates the conclusions of theory discussion (Sections 11.2–11.5). Section 11.6 summarizes the GE-developed *reasoning with uncertainty module* (RUM) and its run-time counterpart, RUMrunner, which codifies the results of the theory. Section 11.7 applies the theory using RUM to tactical and surveillance platform threat and target ID fusion, respectively.

## 11.2 AGGREGATION OPERATORS

According to their characteristics, there are three basic classes of aggregation: *conjunctions, trade-offs,* and *disjunctions*. Dubois and Prade [11] have shown that triangular norms (*T*-norms), averaging operators, and triangular conorms (*T*-conorms) are the most general families of binary functions that, respectively, satisfy the requirements of the conjunction, trade-off, and disjunction operators. *T*-norms and *T*-conorms are two-place functions from $[0, 1] \times [0, 1]$ to $[0, 1]$ that are monotonic, commutative, and associative. Their corresponding boundary conditions satisfy the truth tables of the logical AND and OR operators. Averaging operators are symmetric and idempotent but are not associative. They do not have a corresponding logical operator because, in the $[0, 1]$ interval, they are *located* between the conjunctions and disjunctions.

The generalizations of conjunctions and disjunctions play a vital role in the management of uncertainty in expert systems: they are used in evaluating the satisfaction of premises, in propagating uncertainty through rule chaining, and in consolidating the same conclusion derived from different rules. More specifically, they provide the answers to the following questions:

- When the premise is composed of multiple clauses, how can we aggregate the degree of certainty $x_i$ of the facts matching the clauses of the premise? (That is, what is the function $T(x_1, \ldots, x_n)$ that determines $x_p$, the degree of certainty of the premise?)
- When a rule does not represent a logical implication, but rather an empirical association between premise and conclusion, how can we aggregate the degree of satisfaction of the premise $x_p$ with the strength of the association $s_r$? (That is, what is the function $G(x_p, s_r)$ that propagates the uncertainty through the rule?)
- When the same conclusion is established by multiple rules with various degrees of certainty $y_1, \ldots, y_m$, how can we aggregate these contributions into a final degree of certainty? (That is, what is the function $S(y_1, \ldots, y_m)$ that consolidates the certainty of that conclusion?)

The following three subsections describe the axiomatic definitions of the conjunction, disjunction, and negation operators.

### 11.2.1 Conjunction and Propagation Using Triangular Norms

The function $T(a, b)$ aggregates the degree of certainty of two clauses in the same premise. This function performs an *intersection* operation and satisfies the conditions of a *T*-norm:

$$T(0, 0) = 0 \qquad \text{(boundary)} \qquad (11.1)$$

$$T(a, 1) = T(1, a) = a \qquad \text{(boundary} \qquad (11.2)$$
$$T(a, b) \leqslant T(c, d) \text{ if } a \leqslant c \text{ and } b \leqslant d \quad \text{(monotonicity)} \qquad (11.3)$$
$$T(a, b) = T(b, a) \qquad \text{(commutativity)} \qquad (11.4)$$
$$T[a, T(b, c)] = T[T(a, b), c] \qquad \text{(associativity)} \qquad (11.5)$$

Although defined as two-place functions, the $T$-norms can be used to represent the intersection of a larger number of clauses in a premise. Because of the associativity of the $T$-norms, we can recursively define

$$T(x_1, \ldots, x_n, x_{n+1}), \text{ for } x_1, \ldots, x_{n+1} \in [0, 1], \text{ as}$$
$$T(x_1, \ldots, x_n, x_{n+1}) = T[T(x_1, \ldots, x_n), x_{n+1}] \qquad (11.6)$$

A special case of the conjunction is the *detachment* function $G(x_p, s_r)$, which attaches a certainty measure to the conclusion of a rule. This measure represents the aggregation of the certainty value of the premise of the rule $x_p$ (indicating the degree of fulfillment of the premise) with the strength of the rule $s_r$ (indicating the degree of causal implication or empirical association of the rule). This function satisfies the same conditions of the $T$-norm (although it does not need to be commutative.)

## 11.2.2  Disjunction Using Triangular Conorms

The function $S(a, b)$ aggregates the degree of certainty of the (same) conclusions derived from two rules. This function performs a *union* operation and satisfies the conditions of a $T$-conorm:

$$S(1, 1) = 1 \qquad \text{(boundary)} \qquad (11.7)$$
$$S(0, a) = S(a, 0) = a \qquad \text{(boundary)} \qquad (11.8)$$
$$S(a, b) \leqslant S(c, d) \text{ if } a \leqslant c \text{ and } b \leqslant d \quad \text{(monotonicity)} \qquad (11.9)$$
$$S(a, b) = S(b, a) \qquad \text{(commutativity)} \qquad (11.10)$$
$$S[a, S(b, c)] = S[S(a, b), c] \qquad \text{(associativity)} \qquad (11.11)$$

A $T$-conorm can be extended to operate on more than two arguments in a manner similar to the extension for the $T$-norms. By using a recursive definition, based on the associativity of the $T$-conorms, we can define

$$S(y_1, \ldots, y_m, y_{m+1}) = S[S(y_1, \ldots, y_m), y_{m+1}] \qquad (11.12)$$

### 11.2.3  Relationships Between T-Norms and T-Conorms

For suitable negation operations $N(x)$, such as $N(x) = 1 - x$, T-norms $T$ and T-conorms $S$ are duals in the sense of the following generalization of DeMorgan's law:

$$S(a, b) = N\{T[N(a), N(b)]\} \qquad T(a, b) = N\{S[N(a), N(b)]\} \qquad (11.13)$$

This duality implies that the extensions of the intersection and union operators cannot be defined independently, and they, therefore, should be analyzed as DeMorgan triples $(T(\cdot, \cdot), S(\cdot, \cdot), N(\cdot))$ or, for a common negation-operator like $N(a) = 1 - a$, as DeMorgan pairs $(T(\cdot, \cdot), S(\cdot, \cdot))$.[1] Some typical pairs of T-norms $T(a, b)$ and their dual T-conorms $S(a, b)$ are the following:

$$T_0(a, b) = \min (a, b) \qquad\qquad S_0(a, b) = \max (a, b) \qquad (11.14)$$
$$\qquad\quad \text{if } \max (a, b) = 1 \qquad\qquad\qquad \text{if } \min (a, b) = 0$$
$$\qquad\quad = 0 \text{ otherwise} \qquad\qquad\qquad\quad = 1 \text{ otherwise}$$

$$T_1(a, b) = \max (0, a + b - 1) \qquad S_1(a, b) = \min (1, a + b) \qquad (11.15)$$

$$T_{1.5}(a, b) = \frac{ab}{2 - (a + b - ab)} \qquad S_{1.5}(a, b) = \frac{a + b}{1 + ab} \qquad (11.16)$$

$$T_2(a, b) = ab \qquad\qquad\qquad\qquad S_2(a, b) = a + b - ab \qquad (11.17)$$

$$T_{2.5}(a, b) = \frac{ab}{a + b - ab} \qquad\qquad S_{2.5}(a, b) = \frac{a + b - 2ab}{1 - ab} \qquad (11.18)$$

$$T_3(a, b) = \min (a, b) \qquad\qquad S_3(a, b) = \max (a, b) \qquad (11.19)$$

These operators are ordered as follows:

$$T \leqslant T_1 \leqslant T_{1.5} \leqslant T_2 \leqslant T_{2.5} \leqslant T_3 \qquad (11.20)$$
$$S_3 \leqslant S_{2.5} \leqslant S_2 \leqslant S_{1.5} \leqslant S_1 \leqslant S_0$$

An analysis of their properties can be found elsewhere [5]. The appendix to this chapter provides a summary of such properties.

---

[1]Quinlan [20] raised a criticism regarding the use of the min operator, considered an *optimistic* intersection operator, and the max operator, considered a pessimistic union operator. The use of this pair of operators actually is not a contradiction, as they are their respective DeMorgan duals.

Note that any *T*-norm $T(a, b)$ and any *T*-conorm $S(a, b)$ are bounded by

$$T_0(a, b) \leqslant T(a, b) \leqslant T_3(a, b)$$
$$S_3(a, b) \leqslant S(a, b) \leqslant S_0(a, b)$$
(11.21)

This set of boundaries implies that the averaging operators, used to represent trade-offs, are located between the min operator $T_3$ (upper bound of *T*-norms) and the max operator $S_3$ (lower bound of *T*-conorms). These limits have a very intuitive explanation because, if compensation is allowed in the presence of conflicting goals, the resulting trade-off should lie between the most optimistic lower bound and the most pessimistic upper bound (i.e., the worst and best local estimates). Averaging operators are symmetric and idempotent, but, unlike, *T*-norms and *T*-conorms, not associative. A detailed description of averaging operators can be found elsewhere [11].

### 11.2.4 Negation Operators and Calculi of Uncertainty

The selection of a *T*-norm, negation operator, and *T*-conorm defines a particular *calculus* of uncertainty. The axioms for a negation operator have been discussed by several researchers [1, 18, 26]. The axioms are

| | | |
|---|---|---|
| $N(0) = 1$ | (boundary) | (11.22) |
| $N(1) = 0$ | (boundary) | (11.23) |
| $N(x) > N(y)$ if $x < y$ | (strictly monotonic decreasing) | (11.24) |
| $N(a) = \lim_{x \to a} N(x)$ | (continuity) | (11.25) |
| $N[N(x)] = x$ | (involution) | (11.26) |

Bellman and Giertz [1] have shown that these axioms do not uniquely determine a negation operator. In addition to the above axioms they imposed a highly constraining *symmetry* condition: "A certain change in the truth value of $\mu(S)$ of $S$ (i.e., $x$) should have the same effect on the acceptance of 'not $S$' (i.e., $N(x)$) regardless of the value of $\mu(S)$ (i.e., $x$)." Only with this (sometimes questionable) axiom is it possible to determine uniquely $N(x) = 1 - x$. Klement [16] provided an excellent summary of equivalences among the various sets of axiomatic definitions of conjunction, disjunction, and negation operators.

It is important to note that, like intuitionistic logic, most[2] multiple-valued logic defined by selecting the three operators ($T(\cdot, \cdot)$, $S(\cdot, \cdot)$, $N(\cdot)$)) disregard the *excluded middle* law and its DeMorgan's dual *law of noncontradiction*. The historic reason for this departure from classical logic goes back to Godel's proof of incompleteness: if it might not be possible to derive a true theorem from a given set of axioms (i.e., if it is possible for a theorem to be logically uncertain), then it would be necessary to consider at least three logic values: *true, false,* and *unknown*. Therefore, a statement could be something other than *true* or *false* and the excluded middle law does not apply.

The requirements of distributivity (or idempotency) *uniquely* determine the conjunction and disjunction operators to be the min ($T_3$) and max ($S_3$) operators [1, 14]. This DeMorgan triple ($T_3$, $S_3$, $1 - ()$) first was used in Lukasiewicz *Aleph-1* multiple-valued logic and has been widely adopted in fuzzy logic [28, 29]. Dubois and Prade [12] have shown that the DeMorgan triple ($T_1$, $S_1$, $1 - ()$) satisfies[3] the excluded middle but is not distributive. They also have demonstrated that the distributivity property is mutually exclusive[4] with the axiom of the excluded middle.

---

[2]The only multiple-valued logic that satisfies the excluded middle are those defined by ($T(\cdot, \cdot)$, $S(\cdot, \cdot)$, $N(\cdot)$)), where the three operators were derived from the *same* generator. The additive generator of a $T$-norm is a function $f$ that is continuous, strictly decreasing on [0, 1], and satisfies the boundary conditions: $f(0) = b_0 \leq \infty$ and $f(1) = 0$. Then any continuous Archimedean $T$-norm [10] $T(a, b)$ can be defined by

$$T(a, b) = f^*[f(a) + f(b)]$$

where $f^*$ is a function defined on [0, $\infty$] by

$$f^*(x) = f^{-1}(x) \text{ for } x \in [0, b_0, \infty]$$
$$= 0 \text{ for } x \in [b_0, \infty]$$

and $f^{-1}$ is the inverse function of $f$. The generator of a negation operator is a function $t$ that is continuous, increasing and satisfies the boundaries conditions: $t(0) = 0$ and $t(1) < \infty$. Then any negation operator $N(x)$ can be defined by

$$N(x) = t^{-1}[t(1) - t(x)]$$

The $T$-norm will have the same generator if $f(x) = t(1) - t(x)$. The $T$-conorm will have the same generator if derived from the $T$-norm by using the DeMorgan duality condition [10, 26].
[3]For this triple, the common generator is $t(x) = x$.
[4]The *min* and *max* operators, which form the only pair satisfying distributivity, *cannot* be defined by any additive generator. Therefore, there is no DeMorgan triple, based on these two operators and a negation operator, in which all three operators have a common generator.

In most expert systems, a common selection of functions is

$$\text{CONJUNCTION} = T(a, b) = T_3(a, b) = \min(a, b) \tag{11.27}$$

$$\text{WEIGHTING} = G(a, b) = T_2(a, b) = ab \tag{11.28}$$

$$\text{DISJUNCTION} = S(a, b) = S_3(a, b) = \max(a, b) \tag{11.29}$$

$$\text{NEGATION} = N(a) = 1 - a \tag{11.30}$$

### 11.2.5 Families of *T*-Norms and *T*-Conorms

Sometimes it is desirable to blend some of the previously described *T*-norm operators to smooth some of their effects. Although it always is possible to generate a linear combination of two operators, in most cases this would imply giving up the associativity property. However, associativity is the most crucial property of the *T*-norms [17, 22] as it allows the decomposition of multiple-place functions in terms of two-place functions. The correct solution is to find a family of *T*-norms that ranges over the desired operators. The proper selection of a parameter then will define the intermediate operator with the desired effect while still preserving associativity.

There are at least six families of *T*-norms $T_x(a, b, p)$ with their dual[5] *T*-conorms $S_x(a, b, p)$. The value of the subscript $x$ will denote the family of norms; $p$, the third argument of each norm, will denote the parameter used by the corresponding family.

Yager: $T_Y(a, b, q)$

$$= 1 - \min \{1, [(1 - a)^q + (1 - b)^q]^{1/q}\} \qquad \text{for } q > 0 \tag{11.31}$$

Yager: $S_Y(a, b, q)$

$$= \min \{1, (a^q + b^q)^{1/q}\} \qquad \text{for } q > 0 \tag{11.32}$$

Dubois: $T_D(a, b, \alpha)$

$$= (ab)/\max\{a, b, \alpha\} \qquad \text{for } \alpha \in [0, 1] \tag{11.33}$$

Dubois: $S_D(a, b, \alpha)$

$$= [a + b - ab - \tag{11.34}$$

$$\min \{a, b, (1 - \alpha)\}]/\max\{(1 - a), (1 - b), \alpha\} \qquad \text{for } \alpha \in [0, 1]$$

Hamacher: $T_H(a, b, \gamma)$ $\tag{11.35}$

$$= (ab)/[\gamma + (1 - \gamma)(a + b - ab)] \qquad \text{for } \gamma \geq 0$$

---

[5]The dual *T*-conorms are obtained from the *T*-norm by using the generalized DeMorgan's law with negation defined by $N(x) = 1 - x$. This negation operator, however, is not unique, as illustrated by Lowen [18].

Hamacher: $S_H(a, b, \gamma)$     (11.36)

$= (a + b + (\gamma - 2)ab]/[1 + (\gamma - 1)ab]$     for $\gamma \geqslant 0$

Schweizer: $T_{Sc}(a, b, p)$     (11.37)

$= \max\{0, (a^{-p} + b^{-p} - 1)\}^{-1/p}$     for $p \in [-\infty, \infty]$

Schweizer: $S_{Sc}(a, b, p)$     (11.38)

$= 1 - \max\{0, [(1 - a)^{-p} + (1 - b)^{-p} - 1]\}^{-1/p}$ for $p \in [-\infty, \infty]$

Frank: $T_F(a, b, s)$     (11.39)

$= \log_s[1 + (S^a - 1)(S^b - 1)/(s - 1)]$     for $s > 0$

Frank: $S_F(a, b, s)$     (11.40)

$= 1 - \log_s\{1 + [S^{(1-a)} - 1][S^{(1-b)} - 1]/(s - 1)\}$ for $s > 0$

Sugeno: $T_{Su}(a, b, \lambda)$     (11.41)

$= \max\{0, (\lambda + 1)(a + b - 1) - \lambda ab\}$     for $\lambda \geqslant -1$

Sugeno: $S_{Su}(a, b, \lambda)$     (11.42)

$= \min\{1, a + b - \lambda ab\}$     for $\lambda \geqslant -1$

These families of $T$-norms and $T$-conorms are individually described in the literature [10, 13, 15, 22, 23, 24, 27]. Table 11.1 indicates the value of the parameter for which these families of norms reproduce the most common $T$-norms $\{T_0, \ldots, T_3\}$.

**Table 11.1**
Ranges of the Six Parameterized Families of $T$-Norms

| $T_Y(a, b, q)$ q | $T_D(a, b, \alpha)$ α | $T_H(a, b, \gamma)$ γ | $T_{Sc}(a, b, p)$ p | $T_F(a, b, s)$ s | $T_{Su}(a, b, \lambda)$ λ | $T$-Norm |
|---|---|---|---|---|---|---|
| →0$^+$ | · | →∞ | →−∞ | · | →∞ | $T_0$ |
| 1 | · | · | −1 | →∞ | 0 | $T_1$ |
| · | · | 2 | · | · | · | $T_{1.5}$ |
| · | 1 | 1 | →0 | →1 | −1 | $T_2$ |
| · | · | 0 | · | · | · | $T_{2.5}$ |
| →∞ | 0 | · | →∞ | →0$^+$ | · | $T_3$ |

The vertical bars in Table 11.1 indicate the legal ranges of each parameter. The table for the $T$-conorms is identical to the preceding except for the header, where the families of $T$-norms are replaced by the corresponding families of $T$-conorms, and the last column, where the $T$-norms are replaced by their respective dual $T$-conorms (i.e., $T_0$ by $S_0$, *et cetera*).

## 11.3  LINGUISTIC VARIABLES DEFINED ON THE INTERVAL [0, 1]

These families of norms can specify an infinite number of calculi that operate on arguments taking *real number* values on the [0, 1] interval. This *fine-tuning* capability would be useful if we needed to compute, with a high degree of precision, the results of aggregating information characterized by very precise measures of its uncertainty. However, when users or experts must provide these measures, an assumption of *fake precision* usually must be made to satisfy the requirements of the selected calculus.

Szolovits and Pauker [25] noted that "while people seem quite prepared to give qualitative estimates of likelihood, they are often notoriously unwilling to give precise numerical estimates to outcomes." This seems to indicate that any scheme that relies on the user providing *consistent* and *precise numerical* quantifications of the confidence level of his or her conditional or unconditional statements is bound to fail.

Instead it is reasonable to expect the user to provide *linguistic* estimates of the likelihood of given statements. The experts and users would be presented with a verbal scale of certainty expressions that they could then use to describe their degree of certainty in a given rule or piece of evidence. Recent psychological studies have shown the feasibility of such an approach: "A verbal scale of probability expressions is a compromise between people's resistance to the use of numbers and the necessity to have a common numerical scale" [2].

Linguistic probabilities offer another advantage. When dealing with subjective assessment of probability, it has been observed [20] that conservatism consistently is present among the suppliers of such assessments. The subjects of various experiments seem to stick to the original *(a priori)* assessments regardless of new evidence that should cause a revision in their belief. In an experiment [31], linguistic probabilities have been compared with numerical probabilities to determine if the observed conservatism in the belief revision was a phenomenon intrinsic to the perception of the events or due to the type of representation (i.e., numerical rather than verbal expressions). The results indicate that people are much closer to the optimal Bayesian revision when they are allowed to use linguistic probabilities.

Each linguistic likelihood assessment is internally represented by fuzzy intervals (i.e., fuzzy numbers). A *fuzzy number* is a fuzzy set defined on the real line. In this case, the membership function of a fuzzy set defined on a truth space (i.e., the interval [0, 1]) could be interpreted as the *meaning* of a label describing the degree of certainty in a linguistic manner [3, 30]. During the aggregation process, these fuzzy numbers will be modified according to given combination rules and will generate another membership distribution that could be mapped back into a linguistic term for the user's convenience or to maintain closure. This process, referred to as *linguistic approximation,* has been studied extensively [4, 5] and will be briefly reviewed in Section 11.4.2.

## 11.3.1 Example of a Term Set of Linguistic Probabilities

Let us consider the following term set $L_2$: {*impossible extremely_unlikely very_low_chance small_chance it_may meaningful_chance most_likely extremely_likely certain*}

Each element $E_i$ in this term set represents a statement of linguistic probability or likelihood. The semantics of each element $E_i$ are provided by a fuzzy number $N_i$ defined on the [0, 1] interval. A fuzzy number $N_i$ can be described by its continuous membership function $\mu_{N_i}(x)$, for $x \in [0, 1]$.

A computationally more efficient way to characterize a fuzzy number is to use a parametric representation of its membership function. This parametric representation [3] is achieved by the fourtuple $(a_i, b_i, \alpha_i, \beta_i)$. The first two parameters indicate the interval in which the membership value is 1.0; the third and fourth parameters indicate the left and right *widths* of the distribution. Linear functions are used to define the slopes. Therefore, the membership function $\mu_{N_i}(x)$, of the fuzzy number $N_i = (a_i, b_i, \alpha_i, \beta_i)$ is defined as follows:

$$\mu_{N_i}(x) = 0 \qquad \text{for } x < (a_i - \alpha_i) \qquad (11.43)$$

$$= (1/\alpha_i)(x - a_i + \alpha_i) \qquad \text{for } x \in [(a_i - \alpha_i), a_i] \qquad (11.44)$$

$$= 1 \qquad \text{for } x \in [a_i, b_i] \qquad (11.45)$$

$$= (1/\beta_i)(b_i + \beta_i - x) \qquad \text{for } x \in [b_i, (b_i + \beta_i)] \qquad (11.46)$$

$$= 0 \qquad \text{for } x > (b_i + \beta_i) \qquad (11.47)$$

Figure 11.1 shows the membership distribution of the fuzzy number $N_i = (a_i, b_i, \alpha_i, \beta_i)$. Table 11.2 indicates the semantics of the proposed term set $L_2$.

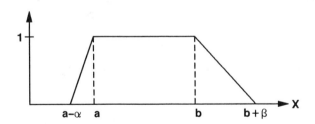

**Figure 11.1** Membership distributions of $N_i = (a_i, b_i, \alpha_i, \beta_i)$.

The membership distributions of the term set elements are illustrated in Figure 11.2. The values of the fuzzy interval associated with each element in the proposed term set were derived from an adaptation of the results of psychological experiments

**Table 11.2**
The Nine-Element Term Set $L_2$

| | |
|---|---|
| Impossible | (0 0 0 0) |
| Extremely_unlikely | (.01 .02 .01 .05) |
| Very_low_chance | (.1 .18 .06 .05) |
| Small_chance | (.22 .36 .05 .06) |
| It_may | (.41 .58 .09 .07) |
| Meaningful_chance | (.63 .80 .05 .06) |
| Most_likely | (.78 .92 .06 .05) |
| Extremely_likely | (.98 .99 .05 .01) |
| Certain | (1 1 0 0) |

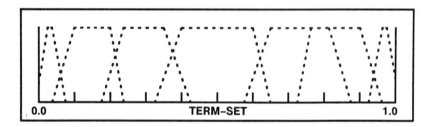

**Figure 11.2** Membership distributions of elements in $L_2$.

on the use of linguistic probabilities [20]. For most of the elements in the term set, the two measures of dispersions used by Beyth-Marom (e.g., the interquartile range ($C_{25}$–$C_{75}$) and the 80% range ($C_{10}$–$C_{90}$)), were used to define, respectively, the intervals $[a_i, b_i]$ and $[(a_i - \alpha_i), (b_i - \beta_i)]$ of each fuzzy number $N_i$.

## 11.4 DESCRIPTION OF THE EXPERIMENTS AND REQUIRED TECHNIQUES

### 11.4.1 The First Experiment

The first experiment consists of selecting nine different $T$-norms that, in combination with their DeMorgan dual $T$-conorms and a negation operator, define nine different calculi of uncertainty. Three different term sets, containing 5, 9, and 13 elements, provide three different levels of granularity for quantifying the uncertainty. For each of the three term sets, the $T$-norms will be evaluated on the cross product of the term set elements, thus generating the closure of each *T*-norm. Each closure will be compared with the closure of the *adjacent T*-norm and the number of differences will be computed. If there are no significant differences, the *T*-norms will be considered similar enough to be equivalent for any practical purpose. A threshold value will determine the maximum percentage of differences allowed among members of the same equivalence class. This concept is analogous to the hierarchical clustering technique typical of pattern recognition problems.

### 11.4.1.1   Selecting the Term Sets

The term sets used to provide the different levels of granularity in both experiments are $L_1$, $L_2$, and $L_3$. $L_2$ contains seven elements and was defined in Table 11.2. $L_1$ and $L_3$ contain 5 and 13 elements, respectively. Their labels and semantics are defined in Tables 11.3 and 11.4

**Table 11.3**
The Five Element Term Set $L_1$

| | |
|---|---|
| Impossible | (0 0 0 0) |
| Unlikely | (.01 .25 .01 .1) |
| Maybe | (.4 .6 .1 .1) |
| Likely | (.75 .99 .1 .01) |
| Certain | (1 1 0 0) |

**Table 11.4**
The 13-Element Term Set $L_3$

| | |
|---|---|
| Impossible | (0 0 0 0) |
| Extremely_unlikely | (.01 .02 .01 .05) |
| Not_likely | (.05 .15 .03 .03) |
| Very_low_chance | (.1 .18 .06 .05) |
| Small_chance | (.22 .36 .05 .06) |
| It_may | (.41 .58 .09 .07) |
| Likely | (.53 .69 .09 .12) |
| Meaningful_chance | (.63 .80 .05 .06) |
| High_chance | (.75 .87 .04 .04) |
| Most_likely | (.78 .92 .06 .05) |
| Very_high_chance | (.87 .96 .04 .03) |
| Extremely_likely | (.98 .99 .05 .01) |
| Certain | (1 1 0 0) |

## 11.4.1.2 Selecting the T-Norms

To select the $T$-norms for the experiment, we first took the three most important $T$-norms[6] (i.e., $T_1$, $T_2$, $T_3$, which provide the lower bound of the copulas,[7] an intermediate value, and the upper bound of the $T$-norms). We then used a parameterized family of $T$-norms capable of covering the entire spectrum between $T_1$ and $T_3$. Our choice fell on the family of $T$-norms proposed by Schweizer and Sklar (i.e., $T_{Sc}(a, b, p)$), described in Section 11.2.5). The selection of this particular family of $T$-norms was due to its full coverage of the spectrum and its numerical stability in the neighborhood of the origin. We then selected six values of the parameter $p$ to probe the space between $T_1$ and $T_2$ ($p \in [-1, 0]$), and between $T_2$ and $T_3$ ($p \in [0, \infty]$). The six $T$-norms instantiated from this family were $T_{Sc}(a, b, -0.8)$, $T_{Sc}(a, b, -0.5)$, $T_{Sc}(a, b, -0.3)$, $T_{Sc}(a, b, 0.5)$, $T_{Sc}(a, b, 1)$, $T_{Sc}(a, b, 2)$.

The selection of the parameter values was guided by the relative location of the six $T$-norms within the $T$-norm space bounded by $T_1$ and $T_3$. Figure 11.3 describes the space of $T$-norms $T_i(a, b) = K$ in the $[0, 1] \times [0, 1]$ universe of $a \times b$ for $K = 0.25, 0.50$, and $0.75$. From this figure we can observe that, for small and medium values of $K$, the six $T$-norms instantiated from the parametric family proposed by Schweizer and Sklar (i.e., $T_{Sc}(a, b, p)$), provide a well-distributed coverage[8] of the space between $T_1$, $T_2$, and $T_3$.

---

[6] $T_0$, the lower bound of the $T$-norms, is rather uninteresting as its discontinuous and extreme behavior limits its applicability.

[7] A *copula* is a continuous two-place function $T: [0, 1] \times [0, 1] \rightarrow [0, 1]$ that satisfies the boundary and monotonicity conditions of the $T$-norms plus the following condition:

$$T(a, d) + T(c, b) \leqslant T(a, b) + T(c, d) \text{ when } a \leqslant c, b \leqslant d$$

Schweizer and Sklar [22] have shown that if a $T$-norm has an additive generator, the $T$-norm is a copula if and only if the additive generator is a *convex* function. With this more restrictive condition, we have that any copula $T(a, b)$ is bounded by

$$T_1(a, b) \leqslant T(a, b) \leqslant T_3(a, b)$$

This is the more familiar set of boundaries used for the probability (and for the belief function) of the intersection of events.

[8] The nine $T$-norms considered in this experiment (six instances of the Schweizer and Sklar family in addition to $T_1$, $T_2$, and $T_3$) are maximally separated at the point $a = b$. The coordinates of the points in which the line $a = b$ intersects the six $T$-norms $T_{Sc}(a, b, p) = 0.25$ can be obtained from the expression

$$a = [0.5(1 + (K)^{-p})]^{-1/p}$$

The values of the coordinate $a$ for the intersection points of the nine $T$-norms ($T_1(a, b)$, $T_{Sc}(a, b, -0.8)$, $T_{Sc}(a, b, -0.5)$, $T_{Sc}(a, b, -0.3)$, $T_2(a, b)$, $T_{Sc}(a, b, 0.5)$, $T_{Sc}(a, b, 1)$, $T_{Sc}(a, b, 2)$, $T_3(a, b)$) with the line $a = b$ are

0.250 0.342 0.400 0.444 0.500 0.573 0.562 0.600 0.625

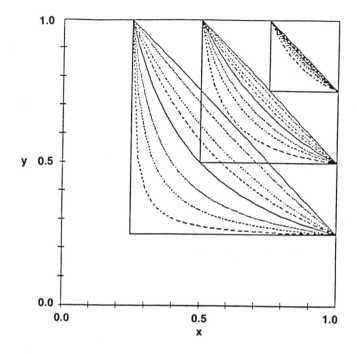

**Figure 11.3** Space of $T$-norms $T_i(a, b) = K$, for $K = 0.25, 0.50,$ and $0.75$.

### 11.4.2 The Second Experiment

The second experiment was motivated by the behavior of the triangular conorms for high values of $K$, as illustrated in Figure 11.3. It was noted that the area of the triangular spaces corresponding to the various values of $K$ decreases as $K$ increases in value (i.e., area $= (1 - K)^2/2$). This can be explained by the saturation effect that most $T$-norms have for low values of $K$ (and $T$-conorms for high values of $K$). However, it was also noted that for large values of $K$, most $T$-norms (all but $T_3$) seemed to converge toward $T_1$; therefore, the space between $T_{Sc}(a, b, 2)$ and $T_3$ was much larger than the space between any other $T$-norm. Figure 11.4 shows a plot of the nine $T$-norms $T_i(a, b)$, evaluated on the plane $a = b$. The figure illustrates both the saturation effect for small values of $K$ and the convergency effect for high values of $K$.

For the sake of completeness, a second experiment was designed to provide a better sample of the space between $T_{Sc}(a, b, 2)$ and $T_3$. Two more $T$-norms were instantiated from the same family of $T$-norms, $T_{Sc}(a, b, 5)$ and $T_{Sc}(a, b, 8)$, and added to the original 9, for a total of 11 $T$-norms. The same three-term sets used in the first experiment also were used in this second experiment to define the input granularity. The objective of the second experiment was to verify if the first experiment had overlooked any relevant calculus requiring its own equivalence class.

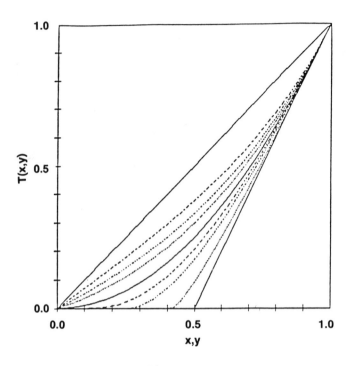

**Figure 11.4** Space of $T$-norms $T_i(x, y)$ plotted for $x = y$.

### 11.4.3 Computational Techniques

The preceding experiments can be performed only if some particular computational techniques are used. It is necessary to evaluate the selected $T$-norms (crisply defined functions) with the elements of the term sets (linguistic variables with fuzzy-valued semantics). Furthermore, the results of this evaluation must be another element of the term set. This implies that closure must be maintained under the application of each $T$-norm. The following subsections describe the techniques necessary to satisfy these requirements.

#### 11.4.3.1 The Extension Principle

The extension principle [3] allows any nonfuzzy function to be fuzzified in the sense that if the function arguments are made fuzzy sets, then the function value is also a fuzzy set whose membership function is uniquely specified. The extension principle states that if the scalar function, $f$, takes $n$ arguments $(x_1, x_2, \ldots, x_n)$, denoted by $X$, and if the membership functions of these arguments are denoted by $\mu_1(x_1)$, $\mu_2(x_2)$,

$$\mu_{f(x)}(y) = \mathop{\mathrm{SUP}}_{\substack{X \\ \mathrm{s.t.}f(X) = y}} \mathop{[\mathrm{INF}\mu_i(x_i)]}_{i=1}^{n} \tag{11.48}$$

where SUP and INF denote the *Supremum* and *Infimum* operators.

The use of this formal definition entails various types of computational difficulties [3]. The solution to these difficulties is based on the parametric representation of the membership distribution of a fuzzy number[9] (i.e., $N_i = (a_i, b_i, \alpha_i, \beta_i)$) described in Section 11.3.1. Such a representation allows us to describe uniformly a *crisp number* $(a_i, a_i, 0, 0)$; a *crisp interval* $(a_i, b_i, 0, 0)$; a *fuzzy number* $(a_i, a_i, \alpha_i, \beta_i)$; and a *fuzzy interval* $(a_i, b_i, \alpha_i \beta_i)$.

The adopted solution consists of deriving the *closed-form* parametric representation of the result. This solution is a very good approximation of the result obtained from using the extension principle to evaluate arithmetic functions with fuzzy numbers and with a much more limited computational overhead. Table 11.5 shows the formulas providing the closed form solution for inverse, logarithm, addition, subtraction, multiplication, division, and power. The scope of each formula is defined by its attached condition[10] on the third column of Table 11.5. Table 11.6 shows the formulas for evaluating the minimum and maximum of two normal convex fuzzy numbers. All of these formulas were used in the implementation of the experiments described in Sections 11.4.1 and 11.4.2.

### 11.4.3.2  Linguistic Approximation

The process of *linguistic approximation* consists of finding a *label* whose meaning is the same or the closest (according to some metric) to the meaning of an unlabeled

---

[9]Two restrictions are imposed on the shape of the membership function of the fuzzy number represented by this parametric representation: *normality* and *convexity*. All the fuzzy numbers used to define the semantics of the proposed term sets satisfy this condition. Furthermore, except for *impossible*, the first element of each term set $L_1, L_2, L_3$, corresponding to a *crisp zero*, all the other elements are *positive normal convex* fuzzy numbers. They are the *only* type of fuzzy numbers that form a *commutative semigroup* [20]. They do not form a group as they lack the inverse elements for addition and multiplication. All other fuzzy numbers either do not satisfy the closure condition under some operation or do not satisfy the distributivity law.

[10]The conditions described in the third column of Table 11.5 refer to the sign of a fuzzy number. A fuzzy number $N_i = (a_i, b_i, \alpha_i, \beta_i)$ is positive (i.e., $N_i > 0$) if its support is positive (i.e., $a - \alpha \geqslant 0$ if $\alpha \neq 0$ or $a - \alpha > 0$ if $\alpha = 0$). Analogously, $N_i < 0$ implies that its support is negative (i.e., $b + \beta \leqslant 0$ if $\beta \neq 0$ or $b + \beta < 0$ if $\beta = 0$).

**Table 11.5**

Formulas for Arithmetic Operations with Fuzzy Numbers

| Operation | Result | Conditions | Formula No. |
|---|---|---|---|
| $-\tilde{n}$ | $(-d, -c, \delta, \gamma)$ | all $\tilde{n}$ | (1) |
| $1/\tilde{n}$ | $\left[\dfrac{1}{d}, \dfrac{1}{c}, \dfrac{\delta}{d(d+\delta)}, \dfrac{\gamma}{c(c-\gamma)}\right]$ | $\tilde{n} > 0, \quad \tilde{n} < 0$ | (2) |
| $e^{\tilde{n}}$ | $[e^c, e^d, e^c(1 - e^{-\gamma}), e^d(e^\delta - 1)]$ | $\tilde{n} > 0$ | (3) |
| $\log \tilde{n}$ | $\left[\log c, \log d, \log \dfrac{c}{(c-\gamma)}, \log \dfrac{(d+\delta)}{d}\right]$ | $\tilde{n} > 0$ | (4) |
| $\tilde{m} + \tilde{n}$ | $(a + c, b + d, \alpha + \gamma, \beta + \delta)$ | all $\tilde{m}, \tilde{n}$ | (5) |
| $\tilde{m} - \tilde{n}$ | $(a - d, b - c, \alpha + \delta, \beta + \gamma)$ | all $\tilde{m}, \tilde{n}$ | (6) |
| $\tilde{m} \times \tilde{n}$ | $(ac, bd, a\gamma + c\alpha - \alpha\gamma, b\delta + d\beta + \beta\delta)$ | $\tilde{m} > 0, \quad \tilde{n} > 0$ | (7) |
| | $(ad, bc, d\alpha - a\delta + \alpha\delta, -b\gamma + c\beta - \beta\gamma)$ | $\tilde{m} < 0, \quad \tilde{n} > 0$ | (8) |
| | $(bc, ad, b\gamma - c\beta + \beta\gamma, -d\alpha + a\delta - \alpha\delta)$ | $\tilde{m} > 0, \quad \tilde{n} < 0$ | (9) |
| | $(bd, ac, -b\delta - d\beta - \beta\delta, -a\gamma - c\alpha + \alpha\gamma)$ | $\tilde{m} < 0, \quad \tilde{n} < 0$ | (10) |
| $\tilde{m} \div \tilde{n}$ | $\left[\dfrac{a}{d}, \dfrac{b}{c}, \dfrac{a\delta + d\alpha}{d(d+\delta)}, \dfrac{b\gamma + c\beta}{c(c-\gamma}\right]$ | $\tilde{m} > 0, \quad \tilde{n} > 0$ | (11) |
| | $\left[\dfrac{a}{d}, \dfrac{b}{c}, \dfrac{c\alpha - a\gamma}{c(c-\gamma)}, \dfrac{d\beta - b\delta}{d(d+\delta)}\right]$ | $\tilde{m} < 0, \quad \tilde{n} > 0$ | (12) |
| | $\left[\dfrac{b}{d}, \dfrac{a}{c}, \dfrac{b\delta - d\beta}{d(d+\delta)}, \dfrac{a\gamma - c\alpha}{c(c-\gamma)}\right]$ | $\tilde{m} > 0, \quad \tilde{n} < 0$ | (13) |
| | $\left[\dfrac{b}{c}, \dfrac{a}{d}, \dfrac{-b\gamma - c\beta}{c(c-\gamma)}, \dfrac{-a\delta - d\alpha}{d(d+\delta)}\right]$ | $\tilde{m} < 0, \quad \tilde{n} < 0$ | (14) |
| $\tilde{m}^{\tilde{n}}$ | $[a^c, b^d, a^c - (a - \alpha)^{c-\gamma}, (b + \beta)^{d+\delta} - b^d]$ | $\tilde{m} \in [1, \infty)\, \tilde{n} > 0$ | (15) |
| | $[b^c, a^d, b^c - (b + \beta)^{c-\gamma}, (a - \alpha)^{d+\delta} - a^d]$ | $\tilde{m} \in [1, \infty)\, \tilde{n} < 0$ | (16) |
| | $[a^d, b^c, a^d - (a - \alpha)^{d+\delta}, (b + \beta)^{c-\gamma} - b^c]$ | $\tilde{m} \in [0, 1]\, \tilde{n} > 0$ | (17) |
| | $[b^d, a^c, b^d - (b - \beta)^{d+\delta}, (a - \alpha)^{c-\gamma} - a^c]$ | $\tilde{m} \in [0, 1)\, \tilde{n} < 0$ | (18) |

Note: $\tilde{m} \triangleq (a, b, \alpha, \beta)$ and $\tilde{n} \triangleq (c, d, \gamma, \delta)$.

membership function generated by some computational model. Bonissone [4, 5] has discussed the general solution to this problem.

For our experiments, this process was simplified by the small cardinality of the term sets. Therefore, a simplified solution was adopted. From each element of the term set and from the unlabeled membership function representing the result of some arithmetic operation, two features were extracted: the first moment of the distribution and the area under the curve. A weighted Euclidean distance, where the weights reflected the relevance of the two parameters in determining semantic similarity, provided the metric required to select the element of the term set that more closely represented the result.

This process was used in the experiments described in Sections 11.4.1 and 11.4.2 to provide *closure* under the application of the various *T*-norms. The closure requirement is required by any calculus of uncertainty to maintain the form and

**Table 11.6**
Formulas for Minimum and Maximum Operators with Fuzzy Numbers

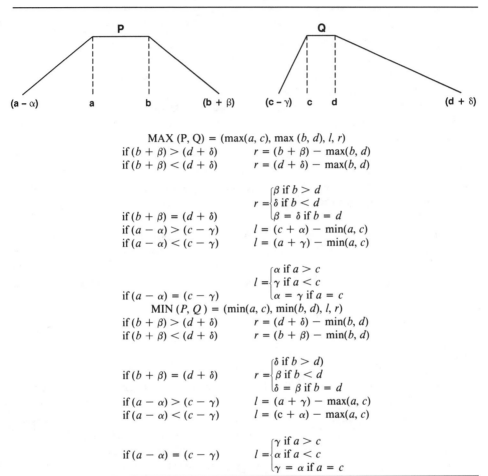

$$\text{MAX } (P, Q) = (\max(a, c), \max (b, d), l, r)$$

if $(b + \beta) > (d + \delta)$     $r = (b + \beta) - \max(b, d)$

if $(b + \beta) < (d + \delta)$     $r = (d + \delta) - \max(b, d)$

if $(b + \beta) = (d + \delta)$     $r = \begin{cases} \beta \text{ if } b > d \\ \delta \text{ if } b < d \\ \beta = \delta \text{ if } b = d \end{cases}$

if $(a - \alpha) > (c - \gamma)$     $l = (c + \alpha) - \min(a, c)$

if $(a - \alpha) < (c - \gamma)$     $l = (a + \gamma) - \min(a, c)$

if $(a - \alpha) = (c - \gamma)$     $l = \begin{cases} \alpha \text{ if } a > c \\ \gamma \text{ if } a < c \\ \alpha = \gamma \text{ if } a = c \end{cases}$

$$\text{MIN } (P, Q) = (\min(a, c), \min(b, d), l, r)$$

if $(b + \beta) > (d + \delta)$     $r = (d + \delta) - \min(b, d)$

if $(b + \beta) < (d + \delta)$     $r = (b + \beta) - \min(b, d)$

if $(b + \beta) = (d + \delta)$     $r = \begin{cases} \delta \text{ if } b > d) \\ \beta \text{ if } b < d \\ \delta = \beta \text{ if } b = d \end{cases}$

if $(a - \alpha) > (c - \gamma)$     $l = (a + \gamma) - \max(a, c)$

if $(a - \alpha) < (c - \gamma)$     $l = (c + \alpha) - \max(a, c)$

if $(a - \alpha) = (c - \gamma)$     $l = \begin{cases} \gamma \text{ if } a > c \\ \alpha \text{ if } a < c \\ \gamma = \alpha \text{ if } a = c \end{cases}$

meaning of the linguistic confidence measures throughout the rule chaining and aggregation process.

## 11.5 CONCLUSIONS ON THE THEORY SECTION

### 11.5.1 Summary of the Results

In Sections 11.2 through 11.4 we presented a formalism to represent any truth functional calculus of uncertainty in terms of a selection of a negation operator and two elements from families of *T*-norms and *T*-conorms. Because of our skepticism regarding the realism of a *fake precision* assumption required by most existing numerical approaches, we proposed using a term set that determines the finest level of specificity (i.e., the *granularity*) of the measure of certainty that the user or expert could *consistently* provide. The suggested semantics for the elements of the term set are given by fuzzy numbers on the [0, 1] interval. The values of the fuzzy numbers were determined on the basis of the results of a psychological experiment aimed at the consistent use of linguistic probabilities.

We then proceeded to perform two experiments to test the required level of discrimination among the various calculi, given a fixed uncertainty granularity. We reviewed the techniques required to implement the experiments, such as the extension principle (that permits the evaluation of crisply defined function with fuzzy arguments), a parametric representation of fuzzy numbers (that allows closed-form solutions for arithmetical operations), and the process of *linguistic approximation* of a fuzzy number (that guarantees *closure* of the term set under the various calculi of uncertainty).

In [8], the closure of 9 and 11 *T*-norm operators applied to three different term sets was computed. In analyzing the sensitivity of each operator with respect to the granularity of the elements in the term set, it was determined that only three *T*-norms, $T_1$, $T_2$, and $T_3$, generated sufficiently distinct results for those term sets that contain no more than nine elements.

### 11.5.2   Impact of the Results on Expert System Technology

In our final conclusions, we would like to establish an explicit link between the results of this chapter and the problem of reasoning with uncertainty in expert systems. In building expert systems architectures, three distinct layers must be defined: *representation, inference,* and *control* layers. The treatment of uncertainty in expert systems must address each of these layers. The characterization of uncertainty measures as linguistic variables with fuzzy-valued semantics and the use of a given uncertainty calculus addresses the representation and inference layers, respectively. The selection of the most appropriate calculus to be used must be addressed by the control layer.

However, in most expert systems, the control layer has been procedurally embedded in the inference engine, thus preventing any opportunistic and dynamic change in ordering inferences and in aggregating uncertainty. Usually, the same type of aggregation operators (i.e., the same uncertainty calculus) is selected *a priori* and used uniformly for any inference made by the expert system. The most recent trend in building expert systems is moving toward having a declarative representation for the control layer.

As an integral part of this layer, we suggest to define a set of context-dependent rules that will select the most appropriate calculus for any given situation. Such a rule will be relatively small because it must describe the selection policies for only a small number of calculi. The reduced number of calculi is the result of the analyzed trade-off between complexity and precision. These rules will rely on contextual information such as the nature, reliability, and characteristics of the evidence sources, as well as on the meanings of the three or five analyzed calculi that will be used in the inference layer.

## 11.6   REASONING WITH UNCERTAINTY—RUM AND RUMrunner

### 11.6.1   Introduction

The *reasoning with uncertainty module* (RUM), a development environment for reasoning with uncertainty, and RUMrunner, RUM's run-time counterpart, are GE-proprietary reasoning systems that have been under development over the last four years by the Artificial Intelligence Program of GE-CRD. The reasoning with uncertainty module is a proven tool that permits the knowledge engineer to build complex applications in a user-friendly, error-tolerant, powerful programming environment. This environment also makes available many artificial intelligence techniques, such as a belief revision system and reasoning with uncertainty. The RUMrunner tool provides a small, fast, streamlined run-time system along with a virtually transparent transition path from the development environment to the deployment environment. These two tools combine to allow the knowledge engineer to build the prototype and deploy the final application in the most desirable environments.

#### *11.6.1.1   RUM*

RUM is based on Bonissone's theory of plausible reasoning, which provides a representation of uncertain information, uncertainty calculi for inferencing, and selection of calculi for inference control. Uncertainty is represented in both facts and rules. A fact represents the assignment of a value to a variable. A rule represents the deduction of a new fact (conclusion) from a set of given facts (premises). Facts are qualified by a degree of *confirmation* and a degree of *refutation*. Rules are discounted by *sufficiency,* indicating the strength with which the premise implies the conclusion, and *necessity,* indicating the degree to which a failed premise implies a negated conclusion. The uncertainty in this deductive process leads to considering several possible values for the same variable.

RUM's rule-based system integrates both procedural and declarative knowledge in its representation. The rule-based approach captures expertise gained from experience or "rules of thumb," thereby codifying heuristic knowledge without any underlying model. In addition, natural expression of procedural knowledge can be integrated smoothly through user-defined predicates in RUM rules. The integration of both techniques is essential to solve situation assessment problems, which involve both heuristic and procedural knowledge.

The expressiveness of RUM is further enhanced by two other functionalities: the *context mechanism* and *belief revision.* The context represents the set of preconditions determining the rule's applicability to a given situation. This mechanism efficiently screens the knowledge base by focusing the inference process on small rule subsets. For instance, in *situation assessment* (SA), selected rules describe the behavior of friendly planes, whereas others should be applied only to unfriendly or unidentified ones. The rule's context provides this filtering mechanism.

RUM's belief revision is essential to the dynamic aspect of the classification problem. The belief revision mechanism detects changes in the input, keeps track of the dependency of intermediate and final conclusions on these inputs, and maintains the validity of these inferences. For any conclusion made by a rule, the mechanism monitors the changes in the certainty measures that constitute the conclusion's support. Validity flags are used to reflect the state of the certainty. For example, a flag can indicate that the uncertainty measure is valid, unreliable (because of a change in the support), too ignorant to be useful, or inconsistent with respect to the other evidence.

RUM offers both backward and forward processing. A *lazy evaluation,* running in the backward mode, recomputes the certainty measures of the minimal set of facts required to answer a given query. This mode is used when the system or the user decides that the tasks are time critical. Breadth-first, forward-mode processing recomputes the certainty measures, attempting to restore the integrity of the rule deduction graph. This mode is used by the system when time is not critical.

These artificial intelligence capabilities are used to develop a knowledge base, in conjunction with RUM's software engineering facilities, such as flexible editing, error checking, and debugging. Some of these features, however, are no longer necessary once the development cycle is complete. At run-time, applications do not create new knowledge (facts or rules), as their basic structure has been determined at compile time. The only run-time requirement is the ability to instantiate rules and facts from their predetermined definitions. By eliminating the development features which are unnecessary at run-time, a real-time AI system can improve upon the algorithms and methodologies used in RUM. RUM is available on the Sun and Symbolics Lisp Machines and requires KEE to build the knowledge base.

### 11.6.1.2  RUMrunner

The objective of RUMrunner is to provide a software tool that transforms the customized knowledge base generated by the development phase into fast and efficient real-time application. RUMrunner provides both the functionality to reason about a broad set of problems and the speed to properly use the results of the reasoning process. Performance improvements are obtained by implementing all of RUM's functionalities with leaner data structures, using Flavors (for the Symbolics version) or *defstructs* (for the Sun version). Furthermore, RUMrunner no longer requires the use of the KEE software; thus, it can be run at any Symbolics or Sun work station with much smaller memory configurations and without a KEE software license. RUMrunner's inference engine also provides a scheduling mechanism, a planning algorithm for reasoning under time pressure, and other functionalities needed in real-time application. RUMrunner has four major qualities: it provides a meaningful subset of AI techniques; it runs fast; it has the functionality of a real-time system; and it does not require the software engineer to reprogram the application in the target environment.

To increase speed, RUMrunner takes advantage of the fact that the application has been completely developed and debugged. It provides a minimum of error checking because the application is assumed either to be debugged already or robust enough to handle errors. RUMrunner's time performance in reasoning tasks is partially due to the compilation of the knowledge base. As a result of this compilation, new or different rules or units cannot be created in the knowledge base after the translation.

RUMrunner provides additional functionality for applications that must satisfy real-time requirements. A RUMrunner application is able to carry out and control a set of activities to rapidly respond to its environment. To meet these goals, the interface of RUMrunner with the application program is designed to be asynchronous, allowing the application to avoid unnecessary delays. In addition, the application is able to handle externally or internally driven interrupts. It also can set tasks priorities by using an agenda mechanism so that RUMrunner handles the most important ones first. RUMrunner is performance-conscious by ensuring that tasks execute within a specified amount of time. Finally, RUMrunner is implemented in Common LISP; thus, it can be ported to many machines without requiring any proprietary software. None of this additional functionality takes an unreasonable amount of time, and if not desired, most of it can remain unused with no great time penalty. A C-version of RUMrunner is presently under development and will be available during the year.

## 11.6.2   Applications of the RUM Technology

RUM and RUMrunner are being used in a number of GE components for a variety of problems ranging from situation assessment problems to diagnostic problems. One major application of RUM and RUMrunner has been DARPA's *Pilot's Associate* (PA) Program, where the RUM technology is being used in the SA module. Pilot's Associate aims to improve the combat effectiveness of post-1995 aircraft through the application of mature AI technologies. The situation assessment module is one of six modules within the overall PA system. SA is concerned with analyzing the external environment, such as determining enemy threats to ownship. RUM has been used to develop two modules within SA. One module determines the class and type of enemy aircraft; the second module determines the target value of an aircraft. Target value is composed of target importance, target opportunity, target capability, and the intent (to engage, evade, influence) of the bogey.

As part of DARPA's Submarine Operational Automation System, the RUM-RUMrunner technology is being used to develop two modules of situation assessment: the contact assessor and the intent projector. In this program, RUM has been used to perform temporal reasoning (i.e., has the contact *recently* been in active sonar?) and hypothetical reasoning to determine the intent, location, and heading of a contact following acoustic blackout. One GE component has been using RUM in a classified problem involving the identification of objects.

Another GE component is using RUM in the advanced crew station contracts. They will be using RUM-RUMrunner in their *air land battle management* (ALBM) contract as well as in the Platoon Leader Advisor Program.

RUM has also been used on an IR&D Mars Roving Vehicle Project. LOTTA, an object-based simulator, will simulate the Martian environment (terrain and related features). RUM will be used to implement navigational decisions that then will be communicated to the vehicle control.

Another GE component has been using RUM in diagnosing aircraft engine faults. They have also used RUM for a diagnostic module in the *integrated electronic warfare system* (INEWS) sensor fusion system.

## 11.7  TACTICAL AND SURVEILLANCE PLATFORM APPLICATIONS

This section deals with *identification* (ID) fusion for airborne fighter and surveillance platform scenarios. Basic scenario situations are described in which "rules" are written to form the input to GE's RUM tool. The $T$-norm, $T_3$, and $T$-conorm, $S_3$, were used in the algorithm.

### 11.7.1  The Airborne Fighter Problem

In the airborne fighter arena, two potential situations must be considered simultaneously: the defensive and offensive phases. Tomorrow's *electronic warfare* (EW) system must operate across the entire electromagnetic spectrum: infrared, *electro-optic* (EO), RF, and laser.

In the defensive phase of the mission, the fighter is concerned with *threats*. A *threat* is an entity around the fighter that can do harm to the fighter in the near or short term. The threat may be at high or low altitude. It may be an *antiaircraft artil-*

*lery* (AAA) site or *surface-to-air missile* (SAM) installation. It may be a missile in flight, be it an *air-to-air missile* (AAM) or SAM, or salvos, consisting of two or more ripple fired missiles (AAMs, SAMs).

In the airborne scenarios, the requirement to shoot an air-to-air missile, to apply some kind of countermeasure, or to maneuver the platform is to know something about the target or threat's identification and classification (ID/CLASS). The identification of the entity may be a threat platform (e.g., MiG-31 Foxhound), threat missile (e.g., AA-10C Alamo), or threat radar (e.g., Gundish ground AAA radar). CLASS is more ambiguous than the ID declaration. For example, for the three ID examples just given, fighter, AAM, and fire-control radar are the target's classifications, respectively.

The source of information relating to the threat can be one of the following measurables: threat radar RF emissions analyzed by an electronic support measures sensor, IR signature information processed by an infrared search and track sensor, or the radar returns off a threat's engine inlets processed by the *jet engine modulation* (JEM) mode of the ownship fire-control radar.

The connection between the preceding sections and what follows here is the use of rules to capture levels of knowledge of threat or target ID, using the sensor processed IR, EO, RF, and or laser information. The amount of uncertainty of knowledge is operated on to adjust accordingly the aggregate confidence of ID/CLASS. Rules are written with sufficiency and necessity values assigned to them. $T$-norms ($T_3$) and $T$-conorms ($S_3$) are selected based on the amount of correlation among the premise components. The goal is to achieve a certain mean and sigma for ID/CLASS, from which "responses" can be made. Each "sensor" provides different data from which to build on the latest aggregate threat or target ID.

In the defensive mission, the better we know the threat ID/CLASS, the better suited will be the countermeasure. Identification is the least ambiguous declaration. The "more ambiguous" declaration, threat CLASS, has several levels of ambiguity. Figure 11.5 depicts an abbreviated ID/CLASS tree. The entities boxed are IDs, and the others are CLASS nodes.

Referring back to Figure 11.1, the "mean" ID/CLASS and variance are computed as

$$\text{Mean} = [2\alpha + 2\beta + (a - \alpha)]/4 \tag{11.49}$$
$$\text{Variance} = b - a + (1/2)\alpha + (1/2)\beta \tag{11.50}$$

A representative set of rules developed for the tactical fighter is summarized in Table 11.7, with the corresponding sufficiency ($s$)/necessity ($n$) given in Table 11.8. The sufficiency denotes the degree to which the premises imply the conclusion, and the necessity denotes the degree to which the conclusion implies the premises. Figure

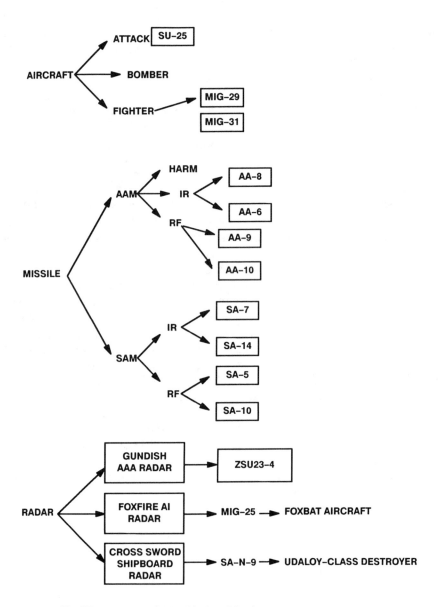

**Figure 11.5** ID/CLASS tree representing ambiguity of the threat.

11.6 summarizes "lower" and "upper" bound properties of fuzzy numbers used. The algorithm used to aggregate rules using $s$, $n$ is given in Figure 11.7.

For a silent attack against the friendly fighter, data measured regarding threat ID/CLASS are processed and the conclusions, based on the nine-element linguistic term set, using RUM, are given in Table 11.9. Tables 11.10 and 11.11 give additional cases for the tactical fighter. The two numbers given within double parentheses in each case are the "mean" and "variance," of the ID/CLASS, as extracted from the conclusions LB and UB.

### 11.7.2 The Surveillance Mission Problem

The surveillance mission problem is such that an E-2C or AWACS-type platform is observing thousands of targets in a specific sector or 360° about the aircraft. The platform's charter might be to hand off target state vector data to an interceptor to intercept an attacking bomber, for instance. To assign assets, ID/CLASS information will be required, as in the fighter arena. To illustrate an example of this problem, we wrote 26 rules and their corresponding rule strengths. The rule set is illustrated in Table 11.12. The rule strengths are described in Table 11.13. Tables 11.14 through 11.16 summarize three surveillance platform cases. Different cases were run, using $T_2$ and $S_3$ for detachment and aggregation, respectively. These results, too, are illustrated in Tables 11.14 through 11.16, summarizing the probability of ID with the associated confidence of ID.

### 11.8 SUMMARY AND CONCLUSIONS

In this chapter we discussed three things:

- The theoretical basis for defining the syntax and semantics of a small subset of calculi of uncertainty operating on a given term set of linguistic statements of likelihood.
- The GE-developed environment for reasoning with uncertainty module and RUM's run-time counterpart RUMrunner, which embed the theory developed.
- Fighter and surveillance applications of RUM to attribute (ID/CLASS) fusion problems.

We can readily conclude that the GE-developed RUM and RUMrunner offers powerful tools with which to develop attribute fusion algorithms based on the use of triangular norms and conorms.

Table 11.7

Identification/Classification Rules— Tactical Fighter

| | |
|---|---|
| RULE 1 | If ESM-report is ground radar then bogey is SAM-id1, SAM-id2. |
| RULE 2 | If ESM-report is ground radar then bogey is AAA-id1, AAA-id2. |
| RULE 3 | If missile-ir-report is yes and boost time is t-boost and sustain-time is t-sustain then bogey is missile-id1, missile-id2. |
| RULE 4 | If missile-launch-range is greater than z miles and missile-ir-report is yes then bogey missile seeker is RF. |
| RULE 5 | If missile-launch-range is less than z miles and missile-ir-report is yes then bogey missile seeker is IR. |
| RULE 6 | If atmosphere-report is cloudy then bogey missile-seeker is RF. |
| RULE 7 | If atmosphere-report is clear then bogey missile-seeker is IR. |
| RULE 8 | If IR-laser report is AI IRST, then bogey is Mig-id1, Mig-id2. |
| RULE 9 | If laser-report is LRF and altitude-report is airborne then bogey is Mig-id1, Mig-id2. |
| RULE 10 | If laser-report is LRF and altitude report is surface-based then bogey is AAA-id1, AAA-id2. |
| RULE 11 | If laser report is laser-target-designator and altitude report is surface-based, then bogey is AAA-id1, AAA-id2. |
| RULE 12 | If IR-laser-report is caged-ir-AAM, then bogey is IR-AAM-launch. |
| RULE 13 | If IR-laser-report-id is yes and aircraft-based-report is yes then bogey is IR-AAM-id. |
| RULE 14 | If altitude-report is airborne and ESM-report is yes and aircraft-based is yes then bogey is Mig-id1, Mig-id2. |
| RULE 15 | If altitude-report is airborne and ESM-mode is guidance and missile-ir-report is yes then bogey is RF-AAM-id1, RF-AAM-id2. |
| RULE 16 | If ESM-mcde is guidance and missile-ir-report is yes then bogey is IR-AAM-id1, IR-AAM-id2. |
| RULE 17 | If ESM-report is yes and altitude-report is airborne then bogey is Mig-id1, Mig-id2. |

| RULE 18 | If warning–missile–radar is yes, then missile is t–seconds away. |
|---|---|
| RULE 19 | If eo–laser–report is IDVO or DVO, then bogey is AAA or SAM. |
| RULE 20 | If laser–report is LRF and altitude–report is airborne then bogey class is aircraft. |
| RULE 21 | If laser–report is LRF and altitude–report is airborne then bogey is IR–AAM. |
| RULE 22 | If FCR–JEM–Mode–Response is yes, then bogey is Mig–id1, Mig–id2. |
| RULE 23 | If AAM–attack–angle is rear and ESM–report is no, then bogey is IR–SAM–id1, SAM–id2, IR–AAM–id1, AAM–id2. |
| RULE 24 | If C3–report is GCI, then bogey–danger is yes. |
| RULE 25 | If C3–report is ACI, then bogey–danger is yes. |
| RULE 26 | If C3–report is SAM–link, then bogey–danger is yes. |
| RULE 27 | If mission–type is enemy–territory–attack and C3–report is GCI, then bogey is Mig–id1, Mig–id2. |
| RULE 28 | If mission–type is enemy–territory–attack and C3–report is SAM–link, then bogey is SAM–id1, SAM–id2. |
| RULE 29 | If AWACS–report is yes and mission type is enemy–territory–attack, then bogey class is fighter. |
| RULE 30 | If AWACS–report is yes, and mission–type is friendly–territory–defend, then bogey class is bomber. |
| RULE 31 | If IRST–report is yes and bogey is above ownship then bogey class is aircraft. |
| RULE 32 | If JTIDS–report is unknown then bogey is friend, foe, or unknown. |
| RULE 33 | If laser report is LRF and altitude report is airborne then bogey id is IR–AAM–id1. |
| RULE 34 | If bogey class is IR–SAM and IR–laser–report–id is yes then bogey id is IR–AAM–id1. |
| RULE 35 | If bogey missile–ir–report is no and ownship altitude is less than x then bogey class is IR–SAM or AAA. |
| RULE 36 | If bogey missile–ir–report is yes and ownship altitude is less than x then bogey class is IR–SAM. |

**Table 11.8**
Sufficiency-Necessity Values for the 36 Rules in Table 11.7 (Tactical Fighter)

| Rule | Sufficiency | Necessity |
|------|-------------|-----------|
| 1 | Extremely_likely | It_may |
| 2 | Extremely_likely | It_may |
| 3 | Meaningful_chance | It_may |
| 4 | Most_likely | Very_low_chance |
| 5 | Most_likely | Very_low_chance |
| 6 | Most_likely | Impossible |
| 7 | Most_likely | Impossible |
| 8 | Extremely_likely | Small_chance |
| 9 | Extremely_likely | Small_chance |
| 10 | Extremely_likely | Small_chance |
| 11 | Extremely_likely | Small_chance |
| 12 | Extremely_likely | It_may |
| 13 | Certain | Small_chance |
| 14 | Most_likely | Meaningful_chance |
| 15 | Most_likely | Meaningful_chance |
| 16 | Most_likely | Extremely_likely |
| 17 | It_may | It_may |
| 18 | It_may | It_may |
| 19 | Extremely_likely | Meaningful_chance |
| 20 | Extremely_likely | Meaningful_chance |
| 21 | Extremely_likely | It_may |
| 22 | Extremely_likely | Meaningful_chance |
| 23 | Most_likely | Most_likely |
| 24 | Certain | Extremely_likely |
| 25 | Certain | Extremely_likely |
| 26 | Certain | Extremely_likely |
| 27 | It_may | It_may |
| 28 | It_may | It_may |
| 29 | Meaningful_chance | Small_chance |
| 30 | Meaningful_chance | Small_chance |
| 31 | Certain | It_may |
| 32 | Extremely_likely | It_may |
| 33 | Extremely_likely | Small_chance |
| 34 | Certain | Small_chance |
| 35 | Most_likely | It_may |
| 36 | Most_likely | It_may |

- A MEASURE OF IGNORANCE ABOUT A PROPOSITION IS THE DIFFERENCE BETWEEN THE UB AND LB (I.E., UB–LB)
- IF LB > UB THEN WE HAVE A CONFLICT
- A LB - UB PAIR WILL BE DENOTED BY [LB, UB]
- TRUE WILL NOW BE REPRESENTED AS [1, 1]
- FALSE WILL BE [0, 0]
- COMPLETE IGNORANCE IS [0, 1]
- (LB–0) REPRESENTS TH EAMOUNT OF POSITIVE EVIDENCE
- (1–UB) REPRESENTS THE AMOUNT OF NEGATIVE EVIDENCE

**Figure 11.6** "Lower" and "upper" bound properties.

- COMPUTE THE CONFIDENCE REGION FOR CONCLUSION IN EACH RULE
  - FOR EACH RULE COMPUTE LB AND UB OF PREMISE

    $LB_p = T_i\ (LB_1, LB_2, \ldots, LB_{\text{nth PREMISE}})$

    $UB_p = T_i\ (UB_1, UB_2, \ldots, UB_{\text{nth PREMISE}})$

  - FOR EACH RULE, PERFORM DETACHMENT, COMPUTING (LB, UB) OF CONCLUSION

    $LB_{\text{CONCLUSION}} = T_K\ (LBp, S)$

    $UB_{\text{CONCLUSION}} = 1 - T_K\ ((1-UBp), n)$

- COMPUTE THE AGGREGATE LB, UB FOR THE CONCLUSION USING (LB, UB)'s FROM EACH CORRELATED RULE
  - $LB = S_{ii}\ (LB_1, LB_2)$, $UB = S_{ii}\ (UB_1, UB_2)$ } $(LB, UB)_{1,2}$
  - $LB = S_{ii}\ (LB, LB_3)$, $UB = S_{ii}\ (UB, UB_3)$ } $(LB, UB)_{1,2/3}$

    .
    .
    .

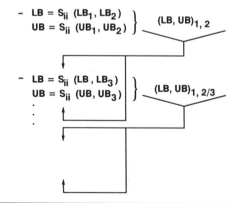

**Figure 11.7** Algorithm for aggregating rules.

**Table 11.9**
Passive AAM Engagement: Scenario

```
"Case 1"
"mission-type enemy-territory-attack"
((:IGNORANT 500 1000))
((:IGNORANT 500 1000))
"c3-report gci"
((AIRCRAFT 1000 0))
((MIG-ID2 682 635) (MIG-ID1 682 635))
"ir-laser-report ir-missile-seeker-caged"
((AIRCRAFT 1000 0))
((IR-AAM-LAUNCH 978 45) (MIG-ID2 682 635) (MIG-ID1 682-635))
"irst yes"
"bogey above ownship"
((AIRCRAFT 1000 0))
((IR-AAM-LAUNCH 978 45) (MIG-ID2 682 635) (MIG-ID1 682-635))
"laser-report lrf"
((AIRCRAFT 1000 0))
((IR-AAM-LAUNCH 978 45) (MIG-ID2 682 635) (MIG-ID1 682-635))
"altitude-report airborne"
((AIRCRAFT 1000 0))
((IR-AAM-LAUNCH 978 45) (MIG-ID2 978 45) (MIG-ID1 978 45) (IR-AAM-ID1 978 45))
"missile-ir-report yes"
((AIRCRAFT 1000 0))
((IR-AAM 978 45) (IR-AAM-LAUNCH 978 45) (MIG-ID2 978 45) (MIG-ID1 978 45)
(IR-AAM-ID1 978 45)
"ir-laser-report-id yes"
((AIRCRAFT 1000 0))
((IR-AAM 978 45) (IR-AAM-LAUNCH 978 45) (MIG-ID2 978 45) (MIG-ID1 978 45)
(IR-AAM-ID1 978 45)
"aircraft-based-report yes"
((AIRCRAFT 1000 0))
((IR-AAM-ID1 1000 0) (IR-AAM 978 45) (IR-AAM-LAUNCH 978 45) (MIG-ID2 978 45)
(MIG-ID1 978 45)
"warning-missile-radar yes"
((AIRCRAFT 1000 0))
((IR-AAM-ID1 1000 0) (IR-AAM 978 45) (IR-AAM-LAUNCH 978 45) (MIG-ID2 978 45)
(MIG-ID1 978 45)
```

**Table 11.10**
Tactical Fighter Case (Cases 2 and 3)

```
"Case 2"
"ownship altitude"
":MISSILE-LAUNCH-RANGE less-z"
((:IGNORANT 500 1000))
((AAA 875 200) (IR-SAM 875 250))
((:IGNORANT 500 1000))
"laser-report laser-target-designator"
"altitude-report surface-based"
((:IGNORANT 500 1000))
(AAA 875 250) (IR-SAM 875 250))
((SAM-ID2 682 635) (SAM-ID1 682 635) (AAA-ID2 682 635) (AAA-ID1 682 635)
"missile-ir-report yes"
((IR 875 250))
(IR-SAM 875 250))
((:IGNORANT 500 1000))
"altitude-report surface based"
((IR 875 250))
((IR-SAM 875 250))
((:IGNORANT 500 1000))
"ir-laser-report-id yes"
((IR 875 250))
(IR-SAM 875 250))
((IR-AAM-ID1 1000 0))

"Case 3"
":LASER-REPORT lrf :ALTITUDE-REPORT airborne"
((:IGNORANT 500 1000))
((AIRCRAFT 978 45))
((MIG-ID2 978 45)) (MIG-ID1 978 45) (IR-AAM-ID1 978 45))
"missile-ir-report yes"
((:IGNORANT 500 1000))
((AIRCRAFT 978 45))
((IR-AAM 978 45) (MIG-ID2 978 45) (MIG-ID1 978 45) (IR-AAM-ID1 978 45))
"missile-attack-angle rear"
((:IGNORANT 500 1000))
((AIRCRAFT 978 45))
((IR-AAM 978 45) (MIG-ID2 978 45) (MIG-ID1 978 45) (IR-AAM-ID1 978 45))
```

**Table 11.11**
Tactical Fighter Case (Case 4)

```
"Case 4"
":MISSION-TYPE enemy-territory-attack"
((:IGNORANT 500 1000))
((:IGNORANT 500 1000))
"eo-laser-report idvo"
((SAM 978 45) (AAA 978 45))
((:IGNORANT 500 1000))
"esm-report ground-based"
((SAM 978 45) (AAA 978 45))
((SAM-ID2 978 45) (SAM-ID1 978 45) (AAA-ID2 978 45) (AAA-ID1 978 45))
"altitude-report surface-based"
((SAM 978 45) (AAA 978 45))
((SAM-ID2 978 45) (SAM-ID1 978 45) (AAA-ID2 978 45) (AAA-ID1 978 45))
"esm-mode search"
((SAM 978 45) (AAA 978 45))
((SAM-ID2 978 45) (SAM-ID1 978 45) (AAA-ID2 978 45) (AAA-ID1 978 45))
"atmosphere-report clear"
((SAM 978 45) (AAA 978 45))
((SAM-ID2 978 45) (SAM-ID1 978 45) (AAA-ID2 978 45) (AAA-ID1 978 45))
"bogey-danger yes"
((SAM 978 45) (AAA 978 45))
((SAM-ID2 978 45) (SAM-ID1 978 45) (AAA-ID2 978 45) (AAA-ID1 978 45))
"c3-report"
((SAM 978 45) (AAA 978 45))
((SAM-ID1 1000 0) (AAA-ID2 978 45) (AAA-ID1 978 45) (SAM-ID2 978 45))
"esm-mode guidance"
((SAM 978 45) (AAA 978 45))
((SAM-ID1 1000 0) (AAA-ID2 978 45) (AAA-ID1 978 45) (SAM-ID2 978 45))
"boost-time t-boost"
((SAM 978 45) (AAA 978 45))
((SAM-ID1 1000 0) (AAA-ID2 978 45) (AAA-ID1 978 45) (SAM-ID2 978 45))
"sustain-time t-sustain"
((SAM 978 45) (AAA 978 45))
((SAM-ID1 1000 0) (AAA-ID2 978 45) (AAA-ID1 978 45) (SAM-ID2 978 45))
"ir-laser-report-id yes"
((SAM 978 45) (AAA 978 45))
((SAM-ID1 1000 0) (AAA-ID2 978 45) (AAA-ID1 978 45) (SAM-ID2 978 45))
"warning-missile-radar yes"
((SAM 978 45) (AAA 978 45))
((SAM-ID1 1000 0) (AAA-ID2 978 45) (AAA-ID1 978 45) (SAM-ID2 978 45))
```

**Table 11.12**

Surveillance Mission Problem Rule Set

| | |
|---|---|
| RULE 1 | If bogey has jammers then surveillance class is bomber. |
| RULE 2 | If bogey has no targets and sidelobe jamming is cancelled then jammer class is self–screening or escort. |
| RULE 3 | If bogey has no targets and sidelobe jamming is cancelled then surveillance class is bomber. |
| RULE 4 | If bogey's jammers are nulled and bogey has targets then jammer class is standoff or standoff–and–escort. |
| RULE 5 | If bogey has no targets and sidelobe jamming is cancelled then sensor cue is irst. |
| RULE 6 | If bogey's r–dot is greater than 1.5 and target altitude is greater than 60 then surveillance class is scm. |
| RULE 7 | If bogey's radar signal is x then surveillance class is bomber. |
| RULE 8 | If bogey's target altitude is less than 20 then surveillance class is bomber. |
| RULE 9 | If bogey's target altitude is less than 20 then altitude accuracy is poor. |
| RULE 10 | If bogey's dsa–report–range is greater than x then surveillance class is bomber. |
| RULE 11 | If esm report then surveillance is id y–id. |
| RULE 12 | If radar report is yes then surveillance class is aircraft. |
| RULE 13 | If military–iff is yes and no iff response then interrogator is off and surveillance class is not–military. |
| RULE 14 | If military–iff is yes and iff response then surveillance class is friendly. |
| RULE 15 | If bogey irst report then surveillance class is aircraft. |
| RULE 16 | If range of the jammer decreases then jammer class is soj. |
| RULE 17 | If range of the jammer decreases then jammer class is self–screening or escort. |
| RULE 18 | If strength of the jammer increases then jammer class is self–screening or escort. |
| RULE 19 | If range of the jamemr is greater than 250 then surveillance id is bear. |
| RULE 20 | If surveillance id is bear then surveillance class is cm. |
| RULE 21 | If surveillance id is blackjack then surveillance class is scm. |
| RULE 22 | If surveillance id is blackjack then surveillance class is bomber. |
| RULE 23 | If surveillance id is blackjack then surveillance class is aircraft. |
| RULE 24 | If bogey's irst-report is above and ownship's altitude is between 25 and 35 then surveillance class is scm. |
| RULE 25 | If bogey's irst-report is below and ownship's altitude is between 25 and 35 then surveillance class is cm. |
| RULE 26 | If bogey's irst-report is above and ownship's altitude is between 25 and 35 and bogey's los is high then surveillance class is scm. |

**Table 11.13**
Rule Strength Parameters for the 26 Rules of Table 11.9

| Rule | Sufficiency | Necessity |
|------|-------------|-----------|
| 1 | Extremely_likely | Meaningful_chance |
| 2 | Most_likely | Most_likely |
| 3 | Certain | It_may |
| 4 | Certain | It_may |
| 5 | It_may | It_may |
| 6 | Extremely_likely | Extremely_likely |
| 7 | Most_likely | Most_likely |
| 8 | Extremely_unlikely | Extremely_unlikely |
| 9 | Extremely_unlikely | Extremely_unlikely |
| 10 | Certain | Extremely_likely |
| 11 | Extremely_likely | Most_likely |
| 12 | Most_likely | Most_likely |
| 13 | Certain | Very_low_chance |
| 14 | Certain | Meaningful_chance |
| 15 | Most_likely | It_may |
| 16 | Extremely_unlikely | Extremely_likely |
| 17 | Most_likely | Extremely_likely |
| 18 | Most_likely | Extremely_likely |
| 19 | Most_likely | Extremely_likely |
| 20 | Extremely_likely | Extremely_likely |
| 21 | Extremely_likely | Extremely_likely |
| 22 | Certain | Meaningful_chance |
| 23 | Certain | Meaningful_chance |
| 24 | Most_likely | It_may |
| 25 | Most_likely | It_may |
| 26 | Most_likely | It_may |

**Table 11.14**
Case 1—Surveillance Platform

"Case 1—surveillance-class, surveillance-id"
"jammers-present yes"
((BOMBERS 978 45))
((:IGNORANT 500 1000))
"no targets detected"
"sidelobe jamming cancelled"
((BOMBERS 1000 0))
((:IGNORANT 500 1000))
"irst-report yes"
((BOMBERS 1000 0) (AIRCRAFT 875 250))
((:IGNORANT 500 1000))
"esm yes"
((BOMBERS 1000 0) (AIRCRAFT 875 250))
((Y-ID 978 45))

**Table 11.15**
Case 2—Surveillance Platform

"Case 2—surveillance-class, surveillance-id"
"dsa-report yes"
((BOMBERS 1000 0))
((:IGNORANT 500 1000))
"esm yes"
((BOMBERS 1000 0))
((Y-ID 978 45))
"radar-signal-strength x"
((BOMBERS 1000 0))
((Y-ID 978 45))
"military-iff: yes and no iff response"
((BOMBERS 1000 0) (NOT-MILITARY 1000 0))
((Y-ID 978 45))

**Table 11.16**
Case 3—Surveillance Platform

"Case 3—surveillance-class, surveillance-id"
"dsa-report yes"
((BOMBERS 1000 0))
((:IGNORANT 500 1000))
"esm yes"
((BOMBERS 1000 0))
((Y-ID 978 45))
"irst above and los high"
((BOMBERS 1000 0) (SCM 875 250))
((Y-ID 978 45))
"radial velocity > M1.5 and target altitude > 60 kft"
((BOMBERS 1000 0) (SCM 875 250))
((Y-ID 978 45))

## APPENDIX 11.A: PROPERTIES OF *T*-NORM OPERATORS

The subset of properties satisfied by a given *T*-norm operator succinctly defines its behavior. The properties that capture the most salient features of such an operator are

Continuous: An infinitesimal change in one of the arguments cannot cause a noticeable change in the result.

Archimedean: Continuous and satisfying the following conditions:
$$T(x, x) < x \qquad S(x, x) > x \qquad \text{for all } x \in [0, 1]$$

Idempotent: $T(x, x) = x$   $S(x, x) = x$   for all $x \in [0, 1]$

Strict: Continuous and strictly increasing in both places; that is, satisfying the following conditions:

$T(x, y) < T(x, y')$ and $T(y, x) < T(y', x)$   for $x > 0, y < y'$   (11.A1)

$T(a, b) = \lim_{c \to a} T(c, b) = \lim_{d \to b} T(a, d)$

Nilpotent: Given a sequence $\{x_1, \ldots, x_n\}$ of numbers in $[0, 1]$, there is a finite number $n$ for which

$$T(x_1, \ldots, x_n) = 0 \text{ and } \sum_{i=1}^{n} f(x_i) > f(0) \qquad (11.A2)$$

where $f(x)$ is the additive generator of the $T$-norm [17, 20].

The $T$-norm operators used in the last column of Table 11.1 satisfy the following properties:

|  | $T_0$ | $T_1$ | $T_{1.5}$ | $T_2$ | $T_{2.5}$ | $T_3$ |
|---|---|---|---|---|---|---|
| Continuous | No | Yes | Yes | Yes | Yes | Yes |
| Archimedean | No | Yes | Yes | Yes | Yes | No |
| Idempotent | No | No | No | No | No | Yes |
| Strict | No | No | Yes | Yes | Yes | No |
| Nilpotent | 12 | Yes | No | No | No | 12 |

Any continuous Archimedean $T$-norm is either *strict* or *nilpotent*. Its classification can be obtained by analyzing the $T$-norm's additive generator. Continuous Archimedean *Strict* $T$-norms have an additive generator $f(x)$ such that

$f(0) = \infty$ and $f(1) = 0$   (11.A3)

Continuous Archimedean *Nilpotent* $T$- norms have an additive generator $f'(x)$ such that

$f(0) < \infty$ and $f(1) = 0$   (11.A4)

It is worth noting that the three $T$-norms analyzed in the conclusions ($T_1$, $T_2$, and $T_3$) are nilpotent, strict, and idempotent, respectively.

## LIST OF SYMBOLS

| 1$A$ | negation of $A$ |
|---|---|
| AAA | anti-aircraft artillery |

| | |
|---|---|
| AAM | air-to-air missile |
| ACI | air controlled intercept |
| ACQ | acquisition |
| AI | airborne interceptor; artificial intelligence |
| AWACS | airborne warning and control system |
| BVR | beyond visual range |
| C3 | command, control, communications |
| CLASS | classification |
| CM | countermeasure; cruise missile |
| DVO | direct view optics |
| E-2C | Hawkeye surveillance platform |
| ELINT | electronic intelligence |
| EMCON | emissions control |
| EO | electro-optics |
| EOB | electronic order of battle |
| ESM | electronic support measures |
| EW | electrical warfare |
| EWS | electronic warfare subsystem |
| FEBA | forward edge of the battle area |
| FOV | field of view |
| $G(a, b)$ | weighting $T$-norm |
| GCI | ground controlled intercept |
| HARM | high-speed antiradiation missile |
| ID | Identification |
| IFF | identification friend or foe |
| ILL | illuminator |
| INS | inertial navigation system |
| IR | infrared |
| IRST | infrared search and track |
| JTIDS | joint tactical identification distribution system |
| KB | knowledge based |
| kft | kilofeet |
| L(A) | lower bound of $A$ |
| LB | lower bound |
| $L_i$ | $i$th linguistic term set |
| LOS | line of sight |
| LRF | laser range finder |
| LTD | laser target designation |
| max | maximum |
| min | minimum |
| MEL | medium energy laser |
| N | necessity |

| $N(x)$ | negation operator |
|---|---|
| PK | probability of kill |
| Ps | probability of survival |
| $\dot{r}$ | range rate |
| $R$ | range |
| RF | radio frequency |
| RM | response management |
| RRM | resource/response management |
| RUM | reasoning with uncertainty module; GE-developed reasoning with uncertainty tool |
| $S$ | sufficiency |
| SA | situation assessment |
| $S(a, b)$ | triangular conorm ($T$-conorm) |
| SAM | surface-to-air missile |
| SCM | supersonic cruise missile |
| $S_i$ | $i$th conorm |
| SOJ | standoff jammer |
| $t$ | time |
| $T(a, b)$ | triangular norm ($T$-norm) |
| $TBD_{1,2}$ | to-be-determined constants |
| $T_i$ | $i$th $T$-norm |
| $t_n$ | $n$th time point |
| $t_0$ | initial time point |
| TP | tactical planner |
| $U(A)$ | upper bound of $A$ |
| UB | upper bound |
| $y$-id | arbitrary ID |
| $\mu$ | mean |
| $\sigma$ | standard deviation |
| $\mu_{N_i}(x)$ | membership function of fuzzy number |

## REFERENCES

[1]   R. Bellman and M. Giertz, "On the Analytic Formalism of the Theory of Fuzzy Sets," *Information Sciences,* Vol. 5, 1973, pp. 149–156.

[2]   R. Beyth-Marom, "How Probable Is Probable? A Numerical Taxonomy Translation of Verbal Probability Expressions," *J. Forecasting,* Vol. 1, 1982, pp. 257–269.

[3]   P.P. Bonissone, "A Fuzzy Sets Based Linguistic Approach: Theory and Applications," T.I. Oren, C.M. Shub, and P.F. Roth (eds.), *Proc. 1980 Winter Simulation Conf.,* Orlando, FL, December 1980, pp. 99–111. Also in M.M. Gupta and E. Sanchez (eds.), *Approximate Reasoning in Decision Analysis,* North Holland Publishing Co., New York, 1982, pp. 329–339.

[4]   P.P. Bonissone, "A Pattern Recognition Approach to the Problem of Linguistic Approximation in Sytem Analysis," Proc. IEEE Int. Conf. on Cybernetics and Society, Denver, October 1979, pp. 793–798.

[5]     P.P. Bonissone, "The Problem of Linguistic Approximation in System Analysis," Ph.D. dissertation, University of California, Berkeley, 1979. Also in University Microfilms International Publications No. 80-14,618, Ann Arbor, MI.

[6]     P.P. Bonissone, "Reasoning with Uncertainty in Expert Systems: Past, Present, and Future," KBS Working Paper presented at the International Fuzzy Systems Association (IFSA), Mallorca, Spain, July 1–5, 1985.

[7]     P.P. Bonissone and A.L. Brown, "Expanding the Horizons of Expert Systems," Proc. Second Int. Conf. on Artificial Intelligence Techologies, Expert Systems and Knowledge Engineering, Ruschlikon, Switzerland, April 25–26, 1985.

[8]     P.P. Bonissone and K.S. Decker. "Selecting Uncertainty Calculi and Granularity: An Experiment in Trading off Precision and Complexity," CRD Rep. 85CRD171, December 1985.

[9]     P.P. Bonissone and R.M. Tong, "Editorial: Reasoning with Uncertainty in Expert Systems," *Int. J. of Man-Machine Studies,* Vol. 22, No. 3, March 1985.

[10]    D. Dubois and H. Prade, "A Class of Fuzzy Measures Based on Triangular Norms," *Int. J. of General Systems,* Vol. 8, No. 1, 1982.

[11]    D. Dubois and H. Prade, "Criteria Aggregation and Ranking of Alternatives in the Framework of Fuzzy Set Theory," H.J. Zimmerman, L.A. Zadeh, and B.R. Gaines (eds.), *TIMS/Studies in the Management Science,* Vol. 20, Elsevier Science Publishers, New York, 1984, pp. 209–240.

[12]    D. Dubois and H. Prade, "New Results about Properties and Semantics of Fuzzy Set-Theoretic Operators," in P.P. Wang and S.K. Chang (eds.), *Fuzzy Sets: Theory and Applications to Policy Analysis and Information Systems,* Plenum Press, New York, 1980, pp. 59–75.

[13]    M.J. Frank, (1979). On the simultaneous associativity of $F(x,y)$ and $x + y - F(x,y)$, *Aequationes Mathematicae,* Vol. 19, pp. 194–226.

[14]    L.W. Fung and K.S. Fu, "An Axiomatic Approach to Rational Decision-Making in Fuzzy Environment," L.A. Zadeh, K.S. Fu, K. Tanaka, and M. Shimura (eds.), *Fuzzy Sets and Their Applications to Cognitive and Decision Processes,* Academic Press, New York, 1975, pp. 227–256.

[15]    Hamacher, H., (1975). Uber logische Verknupfungen unscharfer Aussagen und deren zugehorige Bewertungs-funktionen, in *Progress in Cybernetics and Systems Research, Vol. II,* R. Trappl and F. de P. Hanica (eds.), Hemisphere Pub. Corp., New York, pp. 276–287.

[16]    E.P. Klement, "Operations of Fuzzy Sets and Fuzzy Numbers Related to Triangular Norms," *Proc. 11th Int. Symp. on Multiple-Valued Logic,* IEEE Computer Society Press, Oklahoma City, OK, May 27–29, 1981, pp. 218–225.

[17]    C-H Ling, (1965). Representation of Associative Functions, *Publicationes Mathematicae Debrecen,* Vol. 12, pp. 189–212.

[18]    R. Lowen, "On Fuzzy Complements," *Information Science,* Vol. 14, 1978, pp. 107–113.

[19]    M. Mizomoto, and K. Tanaka, (1979). Some Properties of Fuzzy Numbers, in *Advances in Fuzzy Set Theory and Application,* M.M. Gupta, R.K. Ragade, R.R. Yager (eds.), pp. 153–164, North-Holland Publishing Co.

[20]    L. Phillips and W. Edwards, "Conservatism in a Simple Probability Inference Task," *J. Experimental Psychology,* Vol. 72, 1966, pp. 346–354.

[21]    J.R. Quinlan, (1983). INFERNO: A Cautious Approach to Uncertain Inference, *Computer Journal,* Vol. 26.

[22]    B. Schweizer and A. Sklar, "Associative Functions and Abstract Semi-Groups," *Publicationes Mathematicae Debrecen,* Vol. 10, 1963, pp. 69–81.

[23]    M. Sugeno, (1977). Fuzzy Measures and Fuzzy Integrals: a Survey, in *Fuzzy Automata and Decision Processes,* M.M. Gupta, G.N. Saridis and B.R. Gaines (eds.), pp. 89–102, North Holland, New York.

[24]    M. Sugeno, (1974). Theory of Fuzzy Integrals and its Applications, Ph.D. dissertation, Tokyo Institute of Technology.

[25]    P. Szolovits and S.G. Pauker, "Categorical and Probabilistic Reasoning in Medical Diagnosis," *Artificial Intelligence J.,* Vol. 11, 1978, pp. 115–144.

[26]    E. Trillas, "Sobre funciones de negacion en la teoria de conjuntos difusos," *Stochastica* [Polytechnic University of Barcelona, Spain], Vol. 3, No. 1, 1979, pp. 47–60.

[27]    R. Yager, (1980). On a General Class of Fuzzy Connectives, *Fuzzy Sets and Systems,* Vol. 4, pp. 235–242.

[28]    L.A. Zadeh, "Fuzzy Logic and Approximate Reasoning (in Memory of Grigor Moisil)," *Synthese,* Vol. 30, 1975, pp. 407–428.

[29]    L.A. Zadeh, "Fuzzy Sets," *Information and Control,* Vol. 8, 1965, pp. 338–353.

[30]    L.A. Zadeh, "The Concept of a Linguistic Variable and Its Application to Approximate Reasoning, Part I," *Information Sciences,* Vol. 8, 1975, pp. 199–249; Part II, Vol. 8, pp. 301–357; Part III, Vol. 9, pp. 43–80.

[31]    A.C. Zimmer, "The Estimation of Subjective Probabilities via Categorical Judgments of Uncertainty," *Proc. Workshop on Uncertainty and Probability in Artificial Intelligence,* Los Angeles, August 14–16, 1985, pp. 217–224.

# INDEX

## The Artech House Radar Library

David K. Barton, *Series Editor*

*Monopulse Principles and Techniques* by Samuel M. Sherman

*Monopulse Radar* by A.I. Leonov and K.I. Fomichev

*MTI and Pulsed Doppler Radar* by D. Curtis Schleher

*Multifunction Array Radar Design* by Dale R. Billetter

*Multisensor Data Fusion* by Edward L. Waltz and James Llinas

*Multiple-Target Tracking with Radar Applications* by Samuel S. Blackman

*Multitarget-Multisensor Tracking: Advanced Applications,* Yaakov Bar-Shalom, ed.

*Over-The-Horizon Radar* by A.A. Kolosov, et al.

*Principles and Applications of Millimeter-Wave Radar,* Charles E. Brown and Nicholas C. Currie, eds.

*Principles of Modern Radar Systems* by Michel H. Carpentier

*Pulse Train Analysis Using Personal Computers* by Richard G. Wiley and Michael B. Szymanski

*Radar and the Atmosphere* by Alfred J. Bogush, Jr.

*Radar Anti-Jamming Techniques* by M.V. Maksimov, *et al.*

*Radar Cross Section Analysis and Control* by A.K. Bhattacharyya and D.L. Sengupta

*Radar Cross Section* by Eugene F. Knott, *et al.*

*Radar Detection* by J.V. DiFranco and W.L. Rubin

*Radar Electronic Countermeasures System Design* by Richard J. Wiegand

*Radar Evaluation Handbook* by David K. Barton, *et al.*

*Radar Evaluation Software* by David K. Barton and William F. Barton

*Radar Propagation at Low Altitudes* by M.L. Meeks

*Radar Range-Performance Analysis* by Lamont V. Blake

*Radar Reflectivity Measurement: Techniques and Applications,* Nicholas C. Currie, ed.

*Radar Reflectivity of Land and Sea* by Maurice W. Long

*Radar System Design and Analysis* by S.A. Hovanessian

*Radar Technology,* Eli Brookner, ed.

*Receiving Systems Design* by Stephen J. Erst

*Radar Vulnerability to Jamming* by Robert N. Lothes, Michael B. Szymanski, and Richard G. Wiley

*RGCALC: Radar Range Detection Software and User's Manual* by John E. Fielding and Gary D. Reynolds

*SACALC: Signal Analysis Software and User's Guide* by William T. Hardy

*Secondary Surveillance Radar* by Michael C. Stevens

*SIGCLUT: Surface and Volumetric Clutter-to-Noise, Jammer and Target Signal-to-Noise Radar Calculation Software and User's Manual* by William A. Skillman

*Signal Theory and Random Processes* by Harry Urkowitz

*Solid-State Radar Transmitters* by Edward D. Ostroff, *et al.*

*Space-Based Radar Handbook,* Leopold J. Cantafio, ed.

*Spaceborne Weather Radar* by Robert M. Meneghini and Toshiaki Kozu

*Statistical Theory of Extended Radar Targets* by R.V. Ostrovityanov and F.A. Basalov

*The Scattering of Electromagnetic Waves from Rough Surfaces* by Peter Beckmann and Andre Spizzichino

*VCCALC: Vertical Coverage Plotting Software and User's Manual* by John E. Fielding and Gary D. Reynolds